INTRODUCTION TO
PHYSIOLOGICAL CHEMISTRY

BY MEYER BODANSKY

AND

MARION S. FAY

ASSOCIATE PROFESSOR OF BIOLOGICAL CHEMISTRY
SCHOOL OF MEDICINE, UNIVERSITY OF TEXAS

Laboratory Manual of Physiological Chemistry. Third Edition, Revised. Cloth. 6 x 9 inches. 274 pages. 9 figures.

PUBLISHED BY

JOHN WILEY & SONS, INC.

INTRODUCTION TO
PHYSIOLOGICAL CHEMISTRY

BY

MEYER BODANSKY, Ph.D.

Director of Laboratories, John Sealy Hospital, Galveston, and Professor of Pathological Chemistry, University of Texas

THIRD EDITION

Rewritten and Reset

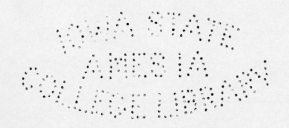

NEW YORK

JOHN WILEY & SONS, Inc.

London: CHAPMAN & HALL, Limited

1934

4/35

PRESS OF
BRAUNWORTH & CO., INC.
BOOK MANUFACTURERS
BROOKLYN, NEW YORK

PREFACE TO THE THIRD EDITION

THE last few years have witnessed unprecedented research activity and progress affecting practically every branch of biochemistry. A rapid succession of important achievements has greatly extended the boundaries of our knowledge in many directions. It has therefore been somewhat of a problem to determine how best to treat the prodigious accumulation of new data without losing the historical perspective or enlarging the book beyond reasonable bounds. It is evident that a new edition of a textbook of this type must be more than a digest of recent advances. At the same time it cannot be permitted to grow by accretion. These considerations have made it necessary to rewrite many sections of the book and to revise extensively much of the remainder. Such enlargement as the book has undergone in the process has resulted either from the necessity of including adequate accounts of some of the newer developments in physiological chemistry, or from the deliberate extension of the scope of the book in certain particulars. Thus the discussions of the chemistry of enzymes, the regulation of gastric acidity, muscle metabolism, the mineral requirements in nutrition, the vitamins, hormones, and many other topics have each required a small amount of additional space. It also seemed desirable to treat in greater detail than formerly the composition of the blood and other body fluids. However, the aim of the book has remained essentially the same.

To Professor William C. Rose, Professor Vincent du Vigneaud, and the editors of the *Journal of Biological Chemistry* the author is indebted for their permission to reproduce Figs. 37, 38, and 39 (pages 556, 559, and 560). The task of reading the proof has been shared by Miss Elizabeth D. Runge, librarian of the Medical School of the University of Texas, Dr. Geo. M. Decherd, Jr., Mr. M. M. Greenberg, and Dr. J. J. Westra. To them the author is deeply indebted, as he is to his other associates at the University of Texas and to his colleagues and friends in other institutions for their valuable suggestions and advice. He would also express his appreciation to his publishers for their constant interest and the care which they have exercised in printing this book.

THE AUTHOR

March 26, 1934

v

PREFACE TO THE SECOND EDITION

THE privilege of revising this textbook is one which the author has sincerely appreciated, as it has given him the opportunity of incorporating many of the more recent contributions in physiological chemistry. In reviewing these contributions he has abstained from conveying an impression of finality and has attempted to show the changing aspects of the subject. The experience of the last few years has proven that even long cherished conceptions and apparently well established facts may at any time undergo drastic revision. The same may be expected of the future. With this subject in such a state of flux and rapid development it is not likely that even a frequently rewritten textbook will quite keep abreast of the times and it is therefore especially desirable that the student of biochemistry should be introduced to the literature as early as possible. For this reason, the author has continued the practice of referring directly to specific investigations and has included as abundant a bibliography as is consistent with moderate brevity.

In preparing this, the second edition, it seemed appropriate to add two chapters, one dealing with the composition of foodstuffs and the other devoted to a brief consideration of the composition of milk and of certain tissues, including bone, cartilage and muscle. Otherwise, the scope of the book, though somewhat extended, has not been changed materially.

The author takes this opportunity to thank Professor John J. Abel for the micro-photograph of insulin crystals, reproduced on page 296, and Dr. W. Robson for permission to use the diagram on page 335. Acknowledgment is also due to Dr. John Pryde and Messrs. J. and A. Churchill for permission to reproduce, with slight modifications, the diagram on page 207 from Pryde's "Recent Advances in Biochemistry," second edition.

To his colleagues and many friends in other institutions the author is deeply indebted for the warm reception accorded the first edition and for much valuable advice and criticism. It is also a pleasure to acknowledge his obligations to his associates at the University of Texas for their suggestions and to his publishers for the care which they have exercised in printing this work.

MEYER BODANSKY.

GALVESTON, TEXAS,
    April, 1930.

PREFACE TO FIRST EDITION

In aiding the student to correlate physiological chemistry with allied sciences and to define its scope, a textbook fulfils a very useful purpose. A small book, if it is sufficiently coherent and comprehensive, is likely to serve this purpose better than a large one, valuable as the latter may be as a source of reference. It was this idea that stimulated the author to write the present book. He has aimed to make it brief enough for use as an introductory volume and yet to give it sufficient scope to cover the field comprehensively. Laboratory methods and the description of tests have been omitted intentionally, since they are to be found in laboratory manuals devoted to the subject. The main aspects of physiological chemistry have been developed in relation to recent advances in the science. It is hoped that in this way the student will be afforded not only a knowledge of fundamental principles but also a realization of the developmental state of the subject.

It is obvious that a certain amount of condensation has been necessary, but the author hopes that he has not condensed the material at the expense of vital information. Wherever he has felt that collateral reading would be desirable, he has referred the student to easily accessible sources, such as journal articles, reviews, monographs, and other works. The student who enters upon the study of physiological chemistry is, strictly speaking, not a beginner. He is not unfamiliar with the principles of inorganic and organic chemistry, and in many cases he has received some training in physico-chemical concepts. He has therefore attained sufficient maturity to profit by collateral reading.

For a considerable amount of the material the author was dependent upon various books and journal articles. To the authors of these he takes this opportunity to acknowledge his debt of gratitude. *Physiological Reviews*, edited for the American Physiological Society and published by the Williams and Wilkins Co., Baltimore, Md., and the "Monographs on Biochemistry," edited by R. H. A. Plimmer and F. G. Hopkins and published by Messrs. Longmans, Green and Co., have been of especial value to the author in helping him to correlate and synthesize the vast literature on the subject of physiological chemistry. He also takes this opportunity to express his gratitude to Dr. Graham Lusk and

Dr. D. D. Van Slyke for their kind permission to reproduce certain material from their works.   The author also wishes to thank P. Blakiston's Son and Co., for their kindness in permitting him to reproduce, from Hawk's "Practical Physiological Chemistry," the absorption spectra given on page 157 of this book.

In the preparation of the book, much discerning advice and criticism was received from Dr. C. L. Alsberg, director of the Carnegie Food Research Institute at Stanford University.   The author takes this occasion to express his sincere gratitude for Dr. Alsberg's unfailing interest and almost daily encouragement.

Some of the points of view developed in the present volume the author has derived from his teacher and friend, Dr. William C. Rose of the University of Illinois.   He wishes to acknowledge at this time his debt to Dr. Rose, as well as a similar debt to Dr. Byron M. Hendrix of the University of Texas.

Important suggestions were also received from the author's colleagues at Stanford University, among whom are included Professors L. B. Becking, George S. Parks, and Robert E. Swain.

For reading the proof and for valuable criticism, the author is indebted to Dr. B. M. Hendrix and Dr. Marion Fay of the University of Texas.   He also wishes to thank Miss Elizabeth D. Runge, librarian of the University of Texas School of Medicine, for her assistance in verifying the references.

The author will at all times welcome suggestions and criticism.

MEYER BODANSKY.

University of Texas,
School of Medicine,
Galveston, Texas,
December 8, 1926.

CONTENTS

INTRODUCTION TO
PHYSIOLOGICAL CHEMISTRY

CHAPTER I

INTRODUCTION

THE subject of physiological chemistry, or biochemistry, is primarily concerned with the chemical aspects of life. Its rapid growth as a science has been intimately related to the development of theoretical chemistry, particularly in the fields designated as organic and physical. While biochemistry has drawn largely from these sources, it has in turn contributed fundamentally to every phase of biological science. We may illustrate this, for example, by the volume of experimental research summarized in such works as Czapek's "Biochemie der Pflanzen," [1] or the more recent "Plant Physiological Chemistry" by Harvey.[2] Or we may consider in this light von Fürth's "Vergleichende chemische Physiologie der niederen Tiere," [3] a classic prepared a generation ago, embodying the then accumulated data of the chemistry of digestion, respiration, nutrition, metabolism, excretions, secretions, tissue pigments, poisons, etc., of the lower forms of animal life—knowledge to which much has been added in the intervening years. And again there is the recently published monumental work of Joseph Needham, "Chemical Embryology," [4] which further testifies to the all-embracing influence that biochemical research has exercised in extending and amplifying biological science.

A considerable proportion of present-day research in bacteriology, immunology, and pathology either has a chemical basis or depends upon biochemical methods of study. But significant as have been the contributions of chemistry to these fields of investigation, their influence

[1] F. Czapek, "Biochemie der Pflanzen," Jena, 2d edition, 1913.

[2] R. B. Harvey, "Plant Physiological Chemistry," Century Co., New York, 1930.

[3] O. von Fürth, "Vergleichende chemische Physiologie der niederen Tiere," Jena, 1903.

[4] J. Needham, "Chemical Embryology," The Cambridge University Press, 1931.

in illuminating many obscure problems in clinical medicine has been even more conspicuous. Select at random a journal devoted to clinical investigation to ascertain the prevailing trend. Many of the contributions are concerned with such problems as calcium and phosphorus metabolism, normal and pathological calcification, the colloid osmotic pressure of the blood, serum protein in relation to disease of the kidney, the relation of the thyroid to the sodium and potassium content of heart muscle, the normal and pathological variations of the concentration of lactic acid in the blood, the relation of protein intake to the course of renal disease, the composition of gastric juice and the factors which may alter it, etc. Examples like these may be multiplied many times by referring to the numerous journals, published in English and other languages and representing internal medicine, pediatrics, obstetrics, and even gynecology, surgery, and ophthalmology.

No boundaries actually separate physiology from biochemistry, or these from biophysics. The three subjects, at the present stage of development, are so closely interrelated, so mutually dependent on each other, that their classification as separate sciences is purely arbitrary. To a more limited degree, this interrelationship extends to pharmacology and pathology. Much space and emphasis, for example, are given in modern textbooks of physiology to chemical and physical concepts, and an even greater assimilation of this type of fundamental knowledge characterizes an ever-increasing proportion of the work published from physiological, pharmacological, and pathological laboratories.

In short, the biochemist is close kin to the physiologist, pharmacologist, and pathologist, and in order that he may work in cooperation with them, should learn something of their methods and viewpoints.

The student of biochemistry should be equipped with a knowledge of fundamental chemical principles, as he must learn to apply these principles to the study of physiological processes. He also requires technique in quantitative chemical analysis. With this scientific equipment as a minimum, he may proceed to study the composition of tissues, the chemical constitution of foodstuffs, the fate of these in digestion and metabolism, the data of animal calorimetry, and similar problems. It should always be borne in mind, however, that in the nature of things he will be limited in certain respects. A tissue subjected to chemical manipulation is no longer a living tissue; the process of analysis involves its alteration or destruction. One of the student's tasks, therefore, is to learn to correlate analytical data with function. As biochemists, we are especially interested in the numerous changes or reactions that occur in every living cell of the living organism.

That the cell is the unit structure of the living organism is a fundamental concept in biology. The cell is largely composed of protoplasm, a complex and heterogeneous mixture of substances, viscid in consistency, which was early recognized as the active living part of the organism and which Huxley characterized as the "physical basis of life."

It is customary to describe protoplasm as composed of water, protein, fats, carbohydrates, inorganic salts, enzymes, and other substances. But even if our knowledge of the organic constitution of protoplasm were complete, it would still afford us no clear insight into its extraordinary properties. L. J. Henderson[5] has asserted that a sufficiently clear and intelligible definition of the term protoplasm is at present impossible. Conspicuous, however, is the interdependence of the various components of protoplasm and their apparent organization into coordinated physicochemical systems which underlie its manifold activities and properties. Significant also is the fact that in the same cell a number of reactions may occur simultaneously and in an orderly fashion and without interfering with one another, reactions of oxidation and reduction, hydrolysis and synthesis, upon which depend the irritability, nutrition, respiration, metabolism, growth, and self-perpetuation of protoplasm—properties which are conventionally cited by the biologist as the criteria that distinguish the living from the lifeless.[6]

Elementary Composition of Tissues. Water constitutes from 70 to 90 per cent of most tissues.[7] Accordingly, in a consideration of the elementary composition of protoplasm and tissues, it is obvious that both oxygen and hydrogen are quantitatively important. Indeed, the human body is more than 60 per cent oxygen and nearly 10 per cent hydrogen. Together with carbon, these elements enter into the constitution of carbohydrates, and with carbon, nitrogen, and sulfur into the composition of proteins. Phosphorus occurs in certain proteins

[5] L. J. Henderson, "Blood," New Haven, 1928, p. 5.

[6] For a comprehensive view of the subject the student is referred to E. B. Wilson's "The Cell in Development and Heredity," Macmillan, New York, 1928, Chap. I, as well as to his review "The Physical Basis of Life," in "Colloid Chemistry," edited by J. Alexander, Chemical Catalog Co., New York, Vol. II, 1928, pp. 515–524. Consult also in the same volume: W. Seifriz, "The Physical Properties of Protoplasm," pp. 403–450; L. V. Heilbrunn, "Protoplasm," pp. 451–459; R. S. Lillie, "The Colloid Structure of Protoplasm and Protoplasmic Action," pp. 461–466; R. Chambers, "The Nature of the Living Cell as Revealed by Micro-manipulation," pp. 467–486. It may also be added that a journal entitled *Protoplasma* is devoted almost exclusively to problems pertaining to the cell and to protoplasm, and that a series of monographs ("Protoplasma-Monographien") have appeared in recent years which afford authoritative reviews of the various aspects of the subject.

[7] Muscle contains about 75 per cent of water, bone about 40 per cent, and the enamel of the teeth, the hardest tissue of the body, approximately 5 per cent.

and lipids and in inorganic combination with sodium, potassium, and calcium. The order of abundance in the human body of the four last-named elements is as follows: C, 20.2 per cent; N, 2.5 per cent; P, 1.14 per cent; S, 0.14 per cent.

Sodium and potassium are widely distributed in plants and animals and are very important physiologically. Potassium is more abundant than sodium in plants. Human blood plasma contains more sodium than potassium, whereas the reverse holds in the red corpuscles. The human body has been estimated to contain 0.10 per cent sodium and 0.11 per cent potassium.

Calcium is an essential cell constituent and is especially abundant in the skeletal structures of vertebrates. Magnesium is likewise a widely distributed constituent of tissues. It is a component of the chlorophyll molecule, chlorophyll being the green pigment of plants and a very important factor in plant economy. Marine algae contain both elements in large amount. The calcium content of the human body has been estimated to be 2.5 per cent; the amount of magnesium is about 0.07 per cent.

Iron is an essential constituent of plant and animal protoplasm. It is a constituent of hemoglobin, the respiratory pigment contained in the red blood corpuscles, as well as of certain tissue pigments that are even more widely distributed in nature than hemoglobin. The content of iron in the human body is estimated to be 0.01 per cent.

In certain of the lower animals, the Mollusca and Crustacea, copper-protein compounds (hemocyanins) are present and are said to play a rôle similar to that of hemoglobin in other forms of animal life. It has also been shown that copper, zinc, manganese, aluminum, and even nickel and cobalt are normal constituents of plant and animal organisms.

Certain marine organisms (corals, sponges) contain an iodine derivative of tyrosine, 3,5-diiodo-tyrosine. This compound is also present in the thyroid gland, which contains in addition the important iodine-containing substance thyroxin. Brain, liver, and other animal tissues are known to contain iodine, as well as small amounts of bromine. These elements likewise occur in many plants. Chlorine is the most abundant of the halogens, occurring largely in inorganic combination with sodium and potassium. The human body contains 0.16 per cent of chlorine. In small amounts, fluorine is widely distributed in nature, particularly in bones, teeth, and the shells of molluscs.

Silicon is found in plants and in many marine organisms, such as diatoms and sponges. In the higher animals, it has been found in hair, skin, lung, liver, kidney, muscle, thymus, and other tissues.

Among the more uncommon elements may be mentioned arsenic (found in minute quantities in the thyroid, brain, liver, hair, etc.), boron, lead (present in certain corals), and vanadium (found in the blood of *Ascidia*). Still other elements, including lithium, cerium, rubidium, barium, radium, strontium, and even gold, have been reported as present in living tissues, but whether these are normal constituents of protoplasm or whether their occurrence is merely adventitious, it is impossible to say.[8,9]

The earthly origin of man is not a mere figure of speech, for all the elementary constituents of plant and animal organisms are to be found in the earth. But it is interesting to observe that although there is an apparent abundance of plant life, the carbon content of the earth's crust is only about 0.18 per cent. In the human body, however, it is about 20.2 per cent. Next to oxygen, silicon is the most abundant element in nature; yet in our bodies it is present in an almost negligible amount. Aluminum is likewise plentiful in the earth, but is present in exceedingly small amounts in the human body.[10]

Relation to Composition of Sea Water. Comparative studies of the mineral constituents of tissue fluids have brought out the highly interesting fact that there is a remarkable uniformity of composition in different animals. A particularly extensive study has been made with respect to the elements sodium, potassium, calcium, and magnesium. In the following table are given the results obtained by Macallum with the blood sera of various animals, the results being calculated on the basis of 100 for the percentage concentration of sodium in any given species. In the table are also included analyses of ocean water. What is the significance of these observations? In the first place, it is to be

[8] In this connection the student is referred to a review by M. Swartz Rose, "Nutritional Significance of Some Mineral Elements Occurring in Traces in the Animal Body," *Yale J. Biol. and Med.*, **4**, 499 (1932). See also J. H. Sheldon and H. Ramage, "A Spectrographic Analysis of Human Tissues," *Biochem. J.*, **25**, 1608 (1931).

[9] Improved methods for the detection and estimation as well as for the localization of inorganic constituents in cells and tissues have been developed in recent years. One procedure depends on heating mounted tissue specimens in a red-hot furnace so as to burn away all the organic matter, leaving the mineral part of the tissue presumably in the position it occupied in the living cells. As a further development in technique, the organic material in a given area is incinerated by an electric spark and the emission spectrum photographed in order to reveal the inorganic constituents present. For details the reader is referred to A. Policard's paper, "Some New Methods in Histochemistry," Harvey Lectures, Series **27**, p. 204, 1931–32.

[10] A comparison of the composition of the human body with that of the earth's crust is given by A. J. Lotka, "Elements of Physical Biology," Williams & Wilkins, Baltimore, 1925, p. 192.

TABLE I

COMPOSITION OF SERA OF ANIMALS AS RELATED TO THAT OF SEA WATER*

Species	Na	K	Ca	Mg
Dogfish (*Acanthias vulgaris*)	100	4.6	2.7	2.5
Cod (*Gadus callarias*)	100	9.5	3.9	1.4
Pollock (*Pallachinus virens*)	100	4.3	3.1	1.5
Dog	100	6.9	2.5	0.8
Man	100	6.1	2.7	0.9
Lobster (*Homarus americanus*)	100	3.7	4.9	1.7
Horseshoe crab (*Limulus polyphemus*)	100	5.6	4.1	11.2
Jellyfish (*Aurelia*)—tissue fluid	100	5.2	4.1	11.4
Ocean water	100	3.6	3.9	12.1

* After Macallum, *Trans. Coll. Phys. of Philadelphia*, **39**, 289, 1917.

noted that the proportion of calcium to sodium in sea water and in sera is nearly the same. The correspondence is not so close with potassium, but nearly so. On the other hand, there is considerable variation in the case of magnesium. Macallum and, somewhat earlier, the German physiologist, Bunge, have suggested that the high content of sodium chloride in the blood of vertebrates may be an inheritance from our remote ancestors who lived in the sea. Supposing that these animals took to the land after the development of a closed circulatory system, it might follow that the composition of the sea, as it was at that time, has persisted in their blood to the present day. How, then, are we to account for the divergences in potassium and magnesium? It has been suggested that since the Cambrian period less potassium has been supplied to the sea than prior to that time, because so much of this element has been required by plant life, which has been more profuse since the Cambrian era. However, the magnesium content of the ocean and the proportion of magnesium to sodium have been steadily increasing since pre-Cambrian time, the concentration found at present in the higher animals corresponding presumably to the low magnesium content of the sea at the time the animals in question acquired a terrestrial habitat. The calcium content has been increasing but slowly, owing perhaps to the utilization of calcium in the building of corals and the bones and shells of other marine organisms. To sum up, it may be stated that the blood serum of mammals resembles, except for the difference in its magnesium content, diluted sea water of our own day.[11]

[11] For further details the student is referred to A. B. Macallum, "The Paleochemistry of the Body Fluids and Tissues," *Physiol. Rev.*, **6**, 316 (1926); see also F. W. Clarke, "The Data of Geochemistry," 4th edition, *U. S. Geol. Survey*, *Bull.* 695.

Properties of Solutions, Relation to Gas Laws. The behavior of substances in solution occupies a dominant position in biochemical and physiological thought and discussion. Nor can it be otherwise when we consider that water and the dissolved substances which it contains constitute the "internal environment" of the animal organism. It is a curious fact, and one with which the student is doubtless familiar, that substances in solution behave very much like gases. For this reason, a brief review of the gas laws is appropriate in this connection.[12]

Gas Laws. The relations governing the behavior of gases were first discovered empirically and, as later found, only approximately. *Boyle's law* (1662) states that, when the temperature of a gas is held constant, the volume varies inversely as the pressure:

$$v \propto \frac{1}{p} \text{ (temperature constant)} \tag{1}$$

Gay-Lussac's law (1801) states that, when the pressure is held constant, the volume varies directly as the absolute temperature:

$$v \propto T \text{ (pressure constant)} \tag{2}$$

A corollary of the first two laws is that, at constant volume, the pressure of a gas is directly proportional to its absolute temperature.

$$p \propto T \text{ (volume constant)} \tag{3}$$

The expressions (1) and (2) may be combined to give (4):[13]

$$v \propto \frac{T}{p} \tag{4}$$

[12] The scope of this book does not permit a detailed consideration of physicochemical principles. All that can be attempted here is a brief résumé of a few salient facts and the definition of certain terms commonly encountered in biochemical discussions. The need for a more comprehensive understanding and appreciation of the fundamental facts of physical chemistry by the student of biology and medicine has been so generally recognized that several splendid books have been written with this specific purpose in mind, and these books the student is urged to consult. D. I. Hitchcock, "Physical Chemistry for Students of Biology and Medicine," C. Thomas, Springfield, Ill., 1932. A. Findlay, "Physical Chemistry for Students of Medicine," Longmans, Green & Co., London, 1927. M. Steel, "Physical Chemistry and Biophysics for Students of Biology and Medicine," John Wiley & Sons, Inc., New York, 1928.

[13] The mathematical principle underlying this derivation is stated by Hall and Knight, as follows: "If A varies as B when C is constant, and A varies as C when B is constant, then will A vary as BC when both B and C vary." This proposition "can easily be extended to the case in which the variation of A depends upon that of more than two variables. Further, the variation may be either direct or inverse." (For details, see H. S. Hall and S. R. Knight, "Higher Algebra," Macmillan, 4th edition, 1929, pp. 23–25.)

and, introducing a proportionality factor,

$$v = k\frac{T}{p} \tag{5}$$

or

$$pv = kT \tag{6}$$

The value of k may be found by substituting for p the standard pressure of 1 atmosphere; for v, the volume of the molecular weight of the gas in grams; and for T, the standard temperature, $0°$ C., or $273°$ Absolute. Using the proper units, k, which we will call the *molecular gas constant* and designate by R, becomes 0.08204 liter-atmosphere per degree, or 8.31×10^7 ergs per degree.[14] Since, by *Avogadro's law*, the molecular weight of all gases occupies the same volume at a given temperature and pressure, the relation $pv = RT$ will hold for all gases. The equation naturally applies to quantities of a mol when the proper factor is introduced. Hence, dropping subscripts and introducing this factor, we obtain the general formulation of the three gas laws:

$$pv = nRT$$

when n denotes the number of mols of gas present.

The above relation, $pv = nRT$, is approximate, holding for certain gases only within certain temperature and pressure ranges. When it is attempted to give this relation a theoretical background, as in the kinetic molecular theory, it is necessary to assume (1) that the molecules of a gas are so far apart that they exert no attraction upon one another and (2) that the space which they themselves occupy is negligibly small in comparison with the volume of the containing vessel. These are conditions attained by no real gas and hence may be taken as properties of the ideal or perfect gas. In chemical thermodynamics, compliance (1) with the relation $pv = nRT$ and (2) with the relation that the energy is a function of the temperature alone is taken as the definition of a perfect gas.

---

[14] $R = \dfrac{(1 \text{ atmosphere})(22.4 \text{ liters})}{273} = 0.08204$ liter-atmosphere, per degree.

In the c.g.s. system of units, $R = \dfrac{(76 \text{ cm. Hg pressure}) (22{,}400 \text{ cc.})}{273°}$. A pressure of 76 cm. Hg is equal to a force of $76 \times 13.6 \times 980$, or 1.013×10^6 dynes per $\overline{\text{cm.}}^2$ Therefore,

$$R = \frac{\left(\dfrac{1.013 \times 10^6 \text{ dynes}}{\overline{\text{cm.}}^2}\right)(22{,}400 \overline{\text{cm.}}^3)}{273°} = 8.31 \times 10^7 \text{ ergs, per degree.}$$

Osmotic Pressure. Of the many properties which substances in solution exhibit, one of the most interesting is that of osmotic pressure. The classical experiments of Pfeffer may be used to illustrate the phenomenon. The accompanying sketch (Fig. 1) shows the form of Pfeffer's apparatus. A precipitate of copper ferrocyanide is deposited in the walls of a porous cup *A*. *B* is a mercury manometer. The cup is filled with the solution to be tested, the surface of the latter being made even with the surface of the mercury in *C*. Tube *D* is then sealed off and the whole apparatus immersed in a bath of distilled water kept at constant temperature. The water at first passes through the membrane, increasing the pressure inside the apparatus and forcing the mercury up the manometer tube. This continues until a point is reached when there is no further increase in pressure in the cup. The reading of the manometer is then taken as the osmotic pressure of the solution.

Before considering the mechanism of this phenomenon, let us see what relation it bears to the concentration of the solute and the tem-

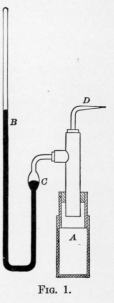

Fig. 1.

perature of the solution. The following data from Pfeffer show that the osmotic pressure is directly proportional to the concentration.

TABLE II

RELATION OF OSMOTIC PRESSURE TO CONCENTRATION

C Per Cent of Cane Sugar	P cm. Hg	$\dfrac{P}{C}$
1	53.5	53.5
2	101.6	50.8
4	208.2	52.1
6	307.5	51.3

This relation, the importance of which was first pointed out by van't Hoff, may be put into a slightly different form. In making up solutions of a definite amount of material, the concentration of the solution varies inversely as the volume of the solution. For instance,

2 grams dissolved in 100 cc. gives twice as strong a solution as the same amount dissolved in a volume twice as great, 200 cc. Hence, if the osmotic pressure of a solution is directly proportional to the concentration of the solute, it is inversely proportional to the volume.

$$\text{Volume} = k_1 \frac{1}{\text{pressure}}$$

This relation is analogous to Boyle's law for gases.

Similarly, as the following table indicates, the relation between osmotic pressure and temperature is analogous to Gay-Lussac's law, the pressure varying directly with the temperature.

TABLE III

VARIATION OF OSMOTIC PRESSURE WITH TEMPERATURE

Temperature °C.	T Absolute Temperature 273° + °C.	Osmotic Pressure in cm. Hg	$\dfrac{\text{Osmotic Pressure}}{T} = k_2$
6.8	279.8	50.5	0.181
13.2	286.2	52.1	0.182
14.2	287.2	53.1	0.185
22.0	295.0	54.8	0.186
36.0	309.0	56.7	0.183

The question that next presents itself is whether Avogadro's hypothesis applies to solutions. The significance of Pfeffer's work was not appreciated until van't Hoff recalculated the data in order to bring out the existing relations between pressure, volume, and temperature. In studying the effect of temperature on osmotic pressure, Pfeffer used a 1 per cent solution of cane sugar (1 gram in 100.6 cc. of solution) or one containing 0.02906 mol of sucrose per liter. From the gas laws, van't Hoff calculated the gas pressure of 0.02906 mol of hydrogen at 0° C. and found it to be 0.649 atmosphere. Since, according to the formula, $P = k_3 T$, the pressure of the gas would increase $\frac{1}{273}$, or 0.00367 for each degree above 0° C., or 273° A., then for any other temperature, the pressure would be

$$0.649 (1 + 0.00367t)$$

where t is the temperature in Centigrade. Van't Hoff now recalculated Pfeffer's data on this basis, comparing the observed results of osmotic pressure with the values computed for the various temperatures from the gas laws. These data are tabulated below:

TABLE IV

Temperature, °C.	Observed Pressure in Atmospheres	Calculated Gas Pressure in Atmospheres
6.8	0.664	0.665
13.7	0.691	0.681
15.5	0.684	0.686
22.0	0.721	0.701
32.0	0.716	0.725
36.0	0.746	0.735

In the case of gases, R, the molecular (or molar) gas constant, in the equation $PV = RT$ is equivalent to 0.08204 liter-atmosphere. Taking 0.649 as the osmotic pressure of 1.0 per cent sucrose at 0° C. and 760 mm. Hg pressure, and 34.2 liters as the volume occupied by one mol of the solute, van't Hoff obtained 0.0813 as the value for R when the gas equations were applied to the solution. These results led him to the important conclusion that *the osmotic pressure exerted by any substance in solution is the same as it would exert if it were a gas in the same volume as that occupied by the solution.* All this holds in dilute solutions where the volume of the solute is small as compared with the volume of the solvent.[15]

[15] The laws of dilute solution which we have been outlining above are not detached pieces of information. They can be shown to follow rigorously, i.e., mathematically, from the First and Second Laws of Thermodynamics. The First Law is familiar to us as the *Law of Conservation of Energy.* Whenever a system undergoes a change in energy, the change is evidenced in the heat absorbed from or given off to its environment and the work done by or on the system. The Second Law, known as the *Law of Entropy*, is more difficult to understand. Ordinary observation shows us that every system, left to itself, changes in such a way as to approach a definite final state of equilibrium. Substances diffuse from concentrated solutions to dilute ones, heat passes from hot bodies to cold, clocks run down. In short, systems lose their capacity for spontaneous change. And they can lose this capacity without losing any energy. For instance, let us conceive of a system in which there is a hot body and a cold one. The heat passes from the former to the latter, until finally the two are at the same temperature. No energy has been lost, but the capacity for spontaneous change has vanished. The more a system lacks the capacity for spontaneous change, the more *entropy* it is said to have. For a detailed discussion the student is referred to G. N. Lewis and M. Randall, "Thermodynamics," McGraw-Hill Book Co., New York.

The formula $PV = nRT$, known as the van't Hoff equation, applies only to certain substances, such as urea, glucose, sucrose. Van't Hoff pointed out that the osmotic pressure of salts of strong acids and strong bases was greater than would be expected from this formula. How was this to be explained? In 1887 Arrhenius advanced the hypothesis that the molecules of certain substances when brought into solution dissociate into electrically charged particles or ions. This is known as the *theory of electrolytic dissociation.* It will be recalled that, many years before, Faraday classified substances as electrolytes and non-electrolytes; the former, he believed, were broken up by the passage of the electric current. What really happens, however, is that the molecules dissociate spontaneously and the ions carry the electric charge. The osmotic effect of a salt that dissociates almost completely is nearly twice as great as that produced by an equimolecular quantity of a non-electrolyte like urea or cane sugar. This is so because each molecule of NaCl, for example, may yield two particles or ions.

To illustrate further the meaning of the laws of dilute solutions and of van't Hoff's equation, in the case of osmotic pressure, suppose that

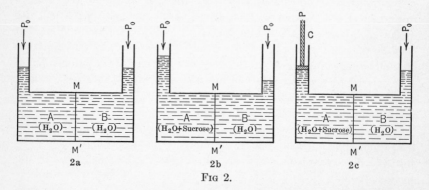

2a   2b   2c

Fig 2.

we have a cell with two compartments, each containing distilled water and separated by a membrane MM' through which the water can pass (Fig. 2a). In this case the tendency of the water molecules to escape from A into B will be equal to the tendency for them to pass from B into A. As a result, no water passes either way. Suppose, now, that some soluble substance such as sodium chloride or sucrose which does not pass through the membrane is added to A. The addition of a solute lowers the escaping tendency of the solvent. Hence the escaping tendency of the water in A is now lowered whereas that in B, remaining the same, exceeds it. Water, therefore, tends to pass into compartment A and the level in A tends to rise. However, a sufficient pressure, P, exerted on the solution in A by means of piston C will prevent an actual passage of water. This pressure, P, *minus* the original (usually atmospheric) pressure, P_0, on the pure solvent is known as the osmotic pressure. The equation relating the osmotic pressure to other variables is:

$$\frac{d(P - P_0)}{dN_2} = \frac{RT}{\overline{v}_1}$$

where N_2 is the mol fraction of the solute; $\overline{v}_1$, the partial mol volume of solvent; R, T, P, P_0, the meanings we have already assigned. In very dilute solutions this equation reduces to van't Hoff's familiar $(P - P_0)V = nRT$, or $PV = nRT$ (p. 8).

Elevation of the Boiling-point. The vapor pressure of a liquid increases with temperature. When the vapor pressure of the liquid equals the pressure of the atmosphere above it, the liquid boils. If a non-volatile substance is added, the vapor pressure is decreased. Hence it takes a higher temperature to produce a vapor pressure equal to the atmospheric pressure, that is, to make the liquid boil. The elevation in boiling-point produced by dissolving one mol (the molecular weight in grams) of a substance in 1000 grams of solvent may be termed the molar elevation of the boiling-point. It follows, therefore, that the osmotic pressure of a solution is directly proportional to the elevation of the boiling-point above that of the pure solvent. The osmotic pressure exerted by a molar solution of a non-electrolyte (molecular weight of a substance dissolved in a liter of water) is 22.4 atmospheres. Such a solution exhibits a boiling-point elevation of 0.54° C.

Depression of the Freezing-point. Biological fluids do not ordinarily lend themselves to boiling-point methods for determining osmotic pressure.[16] Since a substance in solution lowers the freezing-point of the solvent, freezing-point or cryoscopic methods have found wide application. Water freezes at 0° C. A molar solution of a non-electrolyte in water lowers the freezing-point of the water to $-1.86°$ C. The freezing-point of mammalian blood serum is about $-0.56°$, corresponding to a 0.3 molar solution of a non-electrolyte, or about 0.16 molar $NaCl$, and equivalent to an osmotic pressure of 6.6 atmospheres. The freezing-point depression (Δ) of urine is much greater, being frequently in excess

---

[16] A. V. Hill has recently described a thermal method for measuring vapor pressure (*Proc. Roy. Soc.* (*London*), *A.*, **127**, 9 (1930); also described by R. Margaria, *J. Physiol.*, **70**, 417 (1930) and by A. V. Hill in "Adventures in Biophysics," University of Pennsylvania Press, Philadelphia, 1931, Chap. 1). The method is applicable to biological problems and has been found to have a high degree of sensitivity and accuracy.

of 2.0°. Sea water freezes at about −2.30. The Δ of the body fluids of coelenterates, echinoderms, worms, and crustaceans is about the same as that of the ocean water in which they live, namely 2.2–2.3. This is also true for body fluids of the elasmobranchs, but not for the fluids of marine teleosts, which have a lower osmotic pressure.

Osmotic Pressure Phenomena in the Organism. DeVries made the first attempts to measure osmotic pressure in living cells using the epidermal cells of certain plants for this purpose. The outer wall of most plant cells consists of a framework or skeleton of cellulose. In the normal state, the protoplasm within the cells presses closely against this framework. Placing a plant cell in solutions of higher osmotic pressure than that of the cell sap results in loss of water from the cell; the protoplasm contracts and draws away from the outer membrane. Owing to its rigidity, the cellulose wall can withstand considerable changes of internal pressure. The phenomenon described is called *plasmolysis*. The degree of plasmolysis is determined by the concentration of the outer fluid. If the plasmolyzed cells are placed in solutions of lower osmotic pressure than that of the cells themselves (*i.e.*, *in hypotonic solutions*), they will regain their former appearance and turgor. In a solution of equivalent osmotic pressure to the cell contents (*isotonic solution*), plasmolysis does not occur. The osmotic pressure of cells of unknown tonicity can be determined by suspending them in a series of solutions of known concentration and observing the concentration of the solution that just fails to cause plasmolysis. Conversely, cells of known tonicity may be employed in determining the osmotic pressure of unknown solutions.

The membrane surrounding red blood corpuscles cannot withstand great changes of internal pressure. For this reason, when red corpuscles which are approximately isotonic with 0.95 per cent NaCl are immersed in hypotonic solutions, they swell, and, if the swelling is sufficient, the cells may burst. The process is called *hemolysis* and consists in the liberation from the corpuscles of hemoglobin, the red coloring matter of the blood. On the other hand, red corpuscles contract when placed in solutions of higher osmotic pressure (hypertonic solutions), the membrane acquiring a characteristic irregular or *crenated* appearance. The behavior of red corpuscles toward solutions of varying concentration has been made the basis of a method for determining indirectly the osmotic pressure of solutions. It involves the use of the hematocrit, which is a graduated capillary tube of small diameter into which blood may be drawn. On centrifuging at high speed, the corpuscles separate from the serum and collect at one end of the tube, the volume occupied by the corpuscles being read off from the graduations on the tube.

When immersed in an isotonic solution, the corpuscles do not change in volume; but when suspended in hypotonic or hypertonic solutions, they increase or diminish in volume, as the case may be.

Osmotic changes in red blood cells may be determined by various other methods. It has been generally assumed that the red corpuscle takes in water without losing any osmotically active substances to the surrounding medium and that it thus acts as a "perfect osmometer." Actually the cells do not swell in hypotonic solutions as much as would be expected if this were true.[17]

Reference has been made elsewhere (p. 13) to the method developed in A. V. Hill's laboratory for measuring vapor pressure. Employing this procedure Margaria[18] has determined the osmotic pressure of the blood of 18 men at rest and obtained an average value corresponding to 0.9447 per cent NaCl. The range of variation was 0.9318 to 0.9622. In women (16 subjects) the values varied between 0.9065 and 0.9401, the average being 0.9269. This difference between men and women has been related to the somewhat lower concentration in women of certain of the blood constituents, viz., urea. uric acid, bicarbonate, hemoglobin.

Muscle tissue is probably in osmotic equilibrium with the blood. During exercise, largely as a result of the increased formation of various metabolites, the osmotic pressure of the blood is elevated. This has been clearly demonstrated by the work of Margaria. A runner after a steeplechase of 2 miles, which was covered in 11 min. 15 sec., had a specimen of blood taken $1\frac{1}{2}$ min. after the run. The osmotic pressure was found to be equivalent to $1.0482 \pm .0026$ per cent NaCl, an increase of about 10 per cent above the normal value. In another subject, after a standing run of $1\frac{1}{2}$ min., the osmotic pressure of blood was equivalent to 1.033 per cent NaCl.

The osmotic pressure of the blood is lowered by water drinking. In one subject, Margaria observed it to diminish from an initial value of 0.9341 to a minimum of 0.8819, attained $1\frac{1}{2}$ hours after drinking 1500 cc. of tap water.

The freezing-point of egg yolk is $-0.58°$ C., whereas that of the white is $-0.46°$ C. There is accordingly a difference in osmotic pressure of about 1.5 atmospheres. This difference tends to diminish and disappear as the egg ages.

Marine organisms differ in their ability to adjust themselves to changes in the osmotic pressure of the external environment. The blood of the dogfish, an elasmobranch, has an osmotic pressure equivalent

[17] J. Macleod and E. Ponder, *J. Physiol.*, **77**, 181 (1933).

[18] *J. Physiol.*, **70**, 417 (1930).

to that of the sea water in which it lives. If the environment is changed
to diluted water (not below 75 per cent of the initial concentration), the
osmotic pressure of the blood changes correspondingly, the adjustment
being due to the diffusion of water into the animal, as may be shown by
the increase of its weight. If the concentration of the sea water is still
further diminished, the dogfish dies. Obviously, it does not possess the
mechanism for maintaining its own internal environment, independently
of the external environment. Other organisms possess this ability to a
varying degree. The conger eel, for example, can tolerate a 1 : 10
dilution of the sea water which is its natural habitat, with only a moderate change in the osmotic pressure of the blood. The shore crab,
though normally in osmotic equilibrium with sea water, is capable of
withstanding marked changes in the concentration of its environment
with correspondingly smaller changes in the osmotic pressure of its
body fluids. So far as we know, the osmotic pressure of the blood of
mammals is practically independent of the external environment.[19]

In the animal organism one of the most important membranes is the
capillary endothelium. Under normal conditions, it will allow everything but proteins to pass from the circulatory system to the tissue
spaces. The proteins, then, depress the escaping tendency of the water
on the circulatory side of the capillary endothelium and offer resistance
to the capillary blood pressure. Where the other side contains no
protein, as is the case in Bowman's space in the glomeruli of the kidney,
this depression of the escaping tendency will amount to about 30 to
40 mm. Hg, as was first shown by Starling,[20] and the filtration of water
through the capillaries of the glomeruli will encounter that much resistance. The fluid of the tissue spaces, on the other hand, has about half
the protein content of the blood. Hence the resistance which water will
encounter in filtering from capillary to tissue space should amount to
only 15 to 20 mm. Hg.

The protein content of the blood is lowered in certain pathological
conditions, or else changes so that it is not as effective as normally in
depressing the escaping tendency of water. Filtration into the tissue
spaces becomes easier and edema results. This topic will be considered
again in other connections.

---

[19] The student is referred to A. V. Hill, "Adventures in Biophysics," Lecture
III, "The Conception of the Steady State," and also to the following articles: R.
Margaria, "The Osmotic Changes in Some Marine Animals," Proc. Roy. Soc. (Lon-
don), B, 107, 606 (1931); M. Duval, Ann. Inst. oceanogr. Monaco, N. S., 2, 233
(1925); C. Schlieper, Z. vergl. Physiol., 9, 478 (1929); C. F. A. Pantin, J. Expt.
Biol., 8, 63, 73, 82 (1931).

[20] J. Physiol., 19, 312 (1896).

Electrolytic Dissociation. Measurement of the degree of dissociation of electrolytes in solution is made by determining the electrical conductivity of the solution. For description of methods, the student is referred to modern textbooks on physical chemistry. Acids, bases, and salts are electrolytes and in water dissociate into *cations* (positively charged ions) and *anions* (negatively charged ions).

Dissociation of Acids. An acid, HA, will dissociate as follows:

$$HA \rightleftarrows H^+ + A^-$$

Applying the mass-law equation,

$$\frac{[H^+] \times [A^-]}{[HA]} = K_a$$

K_a is the dissociation constant of the acid in question; $[H^+]$, the concentration of hydrogen ions; $[A^-]$, the concentration of the negative ions, and $[HA]$, the concentration of the undissociated acid.

Dibasic acids dissociate in two steps; for each step there is a different constant, as follows:

$$H_2A \rightleftarrows H^+ + HA^-$$

$$HA^- \rightleftarrows H^+ + A^=$$

Applying the mass law to this acid,

$$\frac{[H^+] \times [HA^-]}{[H_2A]} = K_1; \quad \frac{[H^+] \times [A^=]}{[HA^-]} = K_2$$

For oxalic acid, $K_1 = 3.8 \times 10^{-2}$, $K_2 = 4.9 \times 10^{-5}$; for tartaric acid, $K_1 = 9.7 \times 10^{-4}$, $K_2 = 4.5 \times 10^{-5}$.

Phosphoric acid is tribasic and ionizes in three steps:

$$H_3PO_4 \rightleftarrows H^+ + H_2PO_4^-$$
$$\Updownarrow$$
$$H^+ + HPO_4^=$$
$$\Updownarrow$$
$$H^+ + PO_4^\equiv$$

The three constants are:

$$K_1 = 9 \times 10^{-3}; \quad K_2 = 8.8 \times 10^{-8}; \quad K_3 = 3.6 \times 10^{-13}.$$

Acids that are highly dissociated (strong acids) will give, according to the mass-law equation, a high value for the dissociation constant K. Weakly dissociated acids will give low values. Acid solutions of equivalent normality have the same amount of replaceable hydrogen, but the concentration of hydrogen ions in an acid solution depends on the degree of dissociation of the acid. Thus, 0.1 N hydrochloric acid contains the same amount of replaceable hydrogen as 0.1 N acetic acid, but the concentration of hydrogen ions in the former is approximately 70 times greater than in the latter, inasmuch as the hydrochloric acid (0.1 N) is 92 per cent dissociated and the acetic acid (0.1 N) only 1.3 per cent. Physiologically, the effect of acids frequently depends on the concentration of hydrogen ions.

Dissociation of Bases. Bases ionize according to the equation:

$$BOH \rightleftarrows B^+ + OH^-$$

where B is any basic radical. The dissociation constant is derived from the relation:

$$\frac{[B^+] \times [OH^-]}{[BOH]} = K_b$$

Ionization of Water. In view of the preceding discussion it is natural to inquire regarding the behavior of water. Water dissociates according to the equation:

$$HOH \rightleftarrows H^+ + OH^-$$

From the mass law, it follows that

$$\frac{[H^+] \times [OH^-]}{[H_2O]} = K_W$$

However, the degree of dissociation is so slight that the concentration of the undissociated portion is very nearly the same as the total concentration. Accordingly, it is permissible to simplify the equation to

$$[H] \times [OH] = K_W$$

The dissociation constant for water has been measured by many investigators, the value generally accepted being $K_W = 1.012 \times 10^{-14}$ at 25° C. Since on dissociation a molecule of water yields one hydrogen ion and one hydroxyl ion,

$$[H] = [OH] = \sqrt{K_W} = 1.006 \times 10^{-7}$$

or approximately 1×10^{-7}. This means that 1 liter of water contains one ten-millionth of a gram of hydrogen ions, or that there is 1 gram of hydrogen ions in 10 million liters of water. A tenth-normal solution of hydrochloric acid contains 1 gram of hydrogen ions in 10 liters of water.

*p*H. For several reasons it is usually more convenient to express hydrogen-ion concentration in simplified form. In 1909, Sørensen pointed out that there were advantages in designating hydrogen-ion concentration in terms of the logarithm (to the base 10) of its reciprocal. This suggestion has since been accepted universally. Sørensen gave to $\log \frac{1}{[H]}$ the symbol P_H, but for typographical reasons it has been found more convenient to use the form *p*H. Thus, a neutral solution has a hydrogen-ion concentration (C_H) or [H^+] value of 1×10^{-7}. The *p*H value of such a solution is therefore $\log \frac{1}{1 \times 10^{-7}}$, or $\log 10^7$, or 7.

If the hydrogen-ion concentration is given, the corresponding *p*H may be calculated as follows:

$$[H^+] = 2 \times 10^{-6}$$

$$p\mathrm{H} = \log \frac{1}{[H]}; \quad \therefore \; p\mathrm{H} = \log \frac{1}{2 \times 10^{-6}}$$

$$= \log 1 - \log (2 \times 10^{-6})$$

Since

$$\log 1 = 0, \; p\mathrm{H} = - \log (2 \times 10^{-6})$$

$$= - \log 2 - \log 10^{-6}$$

$$= - 0.301 + 6$$

$$p\mathrm{H} = 5.699, \text{ or approximately } 5.7.$$

*p*H values may be converted into hydrogen-ion concentration as follows:

$$p\mathrm{H} = 2.3$$

$$= 3 - .7$$

$$= 3 - \log 5.01$$

$$= \log \frac{1}{5.01 \times 10^{-3}}$$

$$[H^+] = 5.01 \times 10^{-3}.$$

Acid solutions have a *p*H range below 7, whereas the range of alkaline solutions is above 7. The following table of figures, showing approximately the relation of normality of HCl and NaOH solutions to *p*H, will make this point clear. For this purpose the assumption is made that the acid and alkali are completely ionized.

TABLE V

Normality	Concentration of H Ions	Concentration of OH Ions	pH	pOH
N HCl................	1	10^{-14}	0	14
0.1HCl...............	10^{-1}	10^{-13}	1	13
0.01HCl..............	10^{-2}	10^{-12}	2	12
0.001HCl.............	10^{-3}	10^{-11}	3	11
0.0001HCl............	10^{-4}	10^{-10}	4	10
0.00001HCl...........	10^{-5}	10^{-9}	5	9
0.000001HCl..........	10^{-6}	10^{-8}	6	8
0.0000001HCl.........	10^{-7}	10^{-7}	7	7
Neutrality.............	10^{-7}	10^{-7}	7	7
0.0000001NaOH.......	10^{-7}	10^{-7}	7	7
0.000001NaOH........	10^{-8}	10^{-6}	8	6
0.00001NaOH.........	10^{-9}	10^{-5}	9	5
0.0001NaOH..........	10^{-10}	10^{-4}	10	4
0.001NaOH...........	10^{-11}	10^{-3}	11	3
0.01NaOH............	10^{-12}	10^{-2}	12	2
0.1NaOH.............	10^{-13}	10^{-1}	13	1
N NaOH..............	10^{-14}	1	14	0

As stated, these values are approximate, since neither HCl nor NaOH is 100 per cent ionized.

The Determination of Hydrogen Ions. In the present volume it is possible only to refer to the two methods that are in common use for the determination of hydrogen ions. The first is an electrometric method; the second involves the use of indicators. Valuable treatises on this subject have been prepared by W. M. Clark,[21] Michaelis,[22] Kolthoff and Furman, and Kolthoff.[23]

Of the two methods, the one based on the use of indicators lends itself more readily to a brief description. Organic indicators are dyes which are essentially weak acids or weak bases and give rise to color changes in varying degrees of acidity and alkalinity. A familiar example of an acid indicator is phenolphthalein. This compound exists in two tautomeric forms; in acid solution it is in the colorless form, whereas when

[21] W. M. Clark, "The Determination of Hydrogen Ions," 3d edition, Williams & Wilkins, Baltimore, 1928.

[22] L. Michaelis, "Hydrogen Ion Concentration," translated by W. A. Perlzweig, Williams & Wilkins, Baltimore, 1926.

[23] I. M. Kolthoff and N. H. Furman, "Potentiometric Titrations," John Wiley & Sons, Inc., New York, 1926.

I. M. Kolthoff, "The Colorimetric and Potentiometric Determination of pH," John Wiley & Sons, Inc., New York, 1931.

added to an alkaline solution it acquires a magenta color. Methyl orange is a weak base which in acid solution is pink and in basic solution yellow. A number of indicators exhibit gradations in color within certain ranges of hydrogen-ion concentration and have therefore found extensive application in biochemistry.

The color that develops when a given indicator is added to a solution of unknown pH may be compared with the color given by the same indicator in solutions of known hydrogen-ion concentration. These standard solutions are usually prepared from mixtures of highly purified electrolytes which act as buffers, a buffer solution being one that does not readily change its hydrogen-ion concentration upon the addition of small amounts of acid or alkali. The buffer solutions used frequently as standards contain the following constituents.

TABLE VI

Constituents	For pH Range
KCl—HCl	1.2– 2.2
KH Phthalate—HCl	2.2– 3.8
KH Phthalate—NaOH	4.0– 6.2
KH_2PO_4—NaOH	5.8– 8.0
KCl—NaOH	7.8–10.0

Buffer standards may be prepared for a wide range of pH values. A large number of dyes are now also available for the determination of hydrogen-ion concentration. Among these are the following indicators:

TABLE VII

Indicator	pH Range	Indicator	pH Range
Thymol blue	1.2–2.8	Bromthymol blue	6.0–7.6
Bromphenol blue	3.0–4.6	Phenol red	6.6–8.2
Methyl red	4.4–6.0	Cresol red	7.2–8.8
Bromcresol purple	5.4–7.0	Thymol blue	8.2–9.8

As we proceed from one phase of biochemistry to another, we shall see the important bearing of hydrogen ions upon physiological phenomena.

The Colloidal State of Matter. The student is no doubt familiar with the observations of Thomas Graham,[24] who, in 1861, found that

[24] *Liebig's Ann. Chem.*, **121**, 1 (1862).

certain substances—urea, sodium chloride, sucrose, etc.—readily diffused through parchment membranes, but that other substances—gelatin, egg albumin, starch, etc.—failed to do so.   To distinguish the two classes of substances, Graham called the first group crystalloids, and the non-diffusible substances, because of their glue-like character, colloids. Aqueous colloidal solutions Graham called hydrosols.   When sufficiently concentrated, these set to a gel, hence the name hydrogel.

A substance may, however, exhibit, under one set of conditions, the properties of a crystalloid, whereas, under different conditions, it may behave as a colloid.   For example, sodium chloride dissolved in water is a crystalloid; in benzene it forms a colloidal solution.   It is more correct, therefore, to speak of a substance as being either in the colloid or the crystalloid state.

Colloids are usually, though not always, amorphous, and in water frequently form viscous solutions.   However, the real criterion of the colloidal state is that the particles are so much larger than molecules that they possess surface, and yet are not so large as to settle out easily by the action of gravity.   In true solution, a substance exists either as ions, molecules, or small aggregates of molecules.   The individual particles cannot be distinguished even with the aid of the ultramicroscope.   Solutions of this type are said to be *homogeneous*; there is but one "phase," a term first employed in this sense by the distinguished American scientist, J. Willard Gibbs.   Colloidal systems, on the other hand, are made up of more than one phase, and are therefore *heterogeneous*.   Suppose a solid mass, such as a bar of gold, were placed in water. This would constitute a two-phase system, the solid mass being one phase; the water, the other.   There would still be two phases even though the gold bar were subdivided into smaller and smaller particles until particles of colloidal dimension were obtained.   In a colloidal system, the suspended particles constitute the *dispersed* or *internal phase* (also dispersoid); the other phase is the *dispersion medium* or *external phase* (also continuous phase).

Surface.   One of the characteristics of a dispersed system is the development of the surface of contact between the phases.   A 1-cm. cube has a surface of 6 sq. cm.   Subdivision of this into exceedingly small cubes, having 0.1 micron as the side dimension, would result in the development of the surface to 60 sq. m.   The question of surface is of much importance in physiological phenomena in which surface forces play a part, as in enzyme action.   Many substances tend to become concentrated at a surface, this phenomenon of surface condensation being known as *adsorption*.   Adsorption is an important property of colloids for the reason that these have a large surface as compared with their mass.   Adsorption is thought to be a factor in the staining reactions of tissues, the action of drugs, and many other phenomena.

Suspensoids and Emulsoids.   The division of colloids into two classes is based on the ability of some colloids to take up water.   Kaolin, platinum, gold, arsenious sulfide, etc., when in the colloidal state consist of pure solid and are hence classified as *suspensoids* (also lyophobic, or hydrophobic, literally "water-hating," colloids).   Other colloids in aqueous solution have so marked an attraction for water that the dispersoid may contain large quantities of water.   These are the *emulsoids* (also hydrophilic or lyophilic, literally "water-loving," colloids).   The latter group is of primary importance physiologically, protoplasm being essentially an emulsoid type of colloid.   Other familiar examples are starch, soap, egg white, and gelatin.   No confusion should arise due to the fact that colloidal systems in which both phases are liquid are usually classified as emulsions.   The name emulsoid is properly confined to those cases in which the internal phase contains more or less water, although it may sometimes more closely approximate a solid.   It would be impossible to give an acceptable classification of colloids without bringing into the discussion a considerable amount of detail and the conflicting points of view of several authorities.   This information belongs more properly to works devoted to colloid chemistry.[25]

Viscosity.   Viscosity is due to the internal friction of the molecules of a liquid.   Solutions are almost always more viscous than the pure solvents.   The viscosity of suspensoids in water is not much greater than that of the water, but in the case of emulsoids the viscosity is very markedly increased.   Thus, the viscosity of 1 per cent agar is several thousand times that of water.   Increasing the concentration of the dispersed phase, particularly in the case of emulsoids, increases the viscosity of colloidal systems.

Size of Colloidal Particles.   The limit of vision with the aid of the microscope is about 0.0001 mm. or 0.1 μ.[26]   Colloidal particles range in diameter between 1 mμ and 100 mμ (1 μ = 0.001 mm.; 1 mμ = 0.001 μ) and therefore are below the range of microscopic visibility. It is possible, however, to detect particles of colloidal dimension by their diffraction images.   Faraday, and later Tyndall, observed that when a beam of light is sent through a clear solution of finely divided

[25] For a comprehensive survey of the theoretical aspects of colloid chemistry, as well as of its applications in biology and medicine, the student is referred to "Colloid Chemistry—Theoretical and Applied," edited by J. Alexander, Chemical Catalog Co., New York, Vol. I (1926); Vol. II (1928); Vol. III (1930); Vol. IV (1932).

[26] μ = micron; mμ = millimicron.

gold, some of the light is diffracted by the solid particles. The effect is the same when a beam of sunlight passes into a darkened room through a small opening. The light is made visible because of the scattering of a portion of it by the particles of dust in its path. In turn, the motion of these particles is made visible in the diffused light. Even distilled water may contain particles which exhibit a similar effect, but the phenomenon is much more apparent in colloidal suspensions. This is known as the Tyndall or Faraday–Tyndall phenomenon and is of importance because upon this principle is based the use of the " dark field " or ultramicroscope.

Electric Charge. Colloidal particles usually carry either a positive or a negative electric charge and are attracted to poles of opposite sign. The neutralization of the charge of colloidal particles causes them to be precipitated. The movement of electrically charged particles toward an oppositely charged electrode is known as *cataphoresis.* Hemoglobin, ferric hydroxide, and aluminum hydroxide are electropositive; gold, silver, platinum, arsenious sulfide, kaolin, and charcoal are examples of electronegative colloids.

Donnan's Theory of Membrane Equilibria. The application of Donnan's theory[27] of membrane equilibria to physiological problems has received much attention during the past few years. Briefly stated, the theory defines the relations which will exist between the ions of a solution of electrolytes separated by a membrane which is impermeable to one of the ions. Let us consider, as an illustration, two electrolytes, NaR and NaCl, on opposite sides of a membrane represented below by a vertical line.

(1)	(2)
Na^+	Na^+
R^-	Cl^-

Of these ions R^- cannot diffuse through the membrane. At equilibrium therefore, the following condition will exist.

(1)	(2)
Na^+	Na^+
R^-	
Cl^-	Cl^-

---

[27] Donnan, *Chem. Rev.* **1**, 73 (1924). For a recent discussion consult the monograph of T. L. Bolam, "The Donnan Equilibria," G. Bell and Sons, Ltd., London, 1932.

From the principles of thermodynamics it has been deduced that *at equilibrium the products of the concentrations of the diffusible ions on each side of the membrane are equal.* Remembering that on one side of the membrane there is a non-diffusible ion, R^-, the very fact that the product of the concentrations of the diffusible Na^+ and Cl^- ions on one side of the membrane is equal to their product on the other shows that the concentration of either ion on one side is different from its concentration on the other. On the same side containing the non-diffusible ion R^-, the concentration of the cation Na^+ is the sum of the cations combined with the non-diffusible anion, R^-, plus the cations in combination with Cl^-. But on the other side of the membrane the concentration of the Na^+ ions is only that of Na^+ combined with Cl^- and equal to the concentration of Cl^-. Therefore to fulfill Donnan's equation which is

$$[Na^+]_1 \times [Cl^-]_1 = [Na^+]_2 \times [Cl^-]_2$$

the following conditions must exist:

$$[Na]_1 > [Na]_2$$

and

$$[Cl]_1 < [Cl]_2$$

The above is a simple illustration of Donnan's theory. The situation is more complex in dealing with a large number of ions.

This inequality of distribution of ions on the opposite sides of a membrane is frequently encountered in biological systems. On the basis of this relation, Loeb also accounted for the influence of electrolytes on many of the properties of colloids, such as viscosity, swelling, and osmotic pressure.

The Concept of "Free" and "Bound" Water. Certain observations have prompted the view that a part of the water in solutions of lyophilic colloids, tissues, and biological fluids exists in a different state from the familiar form. Rubner noted that in tissues only a portion of the total water, as determined by drying to constant weight, was converted into ice when the tissues were cooled to $-20°$ C. He contended that the water which did not freeze was "bound" to the tissues. The idea of "bound" water, though not so clearly defined, had been previously expressed by others.

Rubner's[28] technique which depends essentially on measuring the heat of fusion of ice has been elaborated by Thoenes[29] and by Robin-

[28] *Abhandl. Preuss. Akad. Wiss.*, No. 1 (1923).
[29] *Biochem. Z.*, **157**, 174 (1925).

son.[30] It has also been modified on the principle that the conversion of water into ice is associated with an increase in volume (dilatometer method).

Either by definition or implication, the doctrine of "free" and "bound" water assumes that only in the former are added substances dissolved, while in the latter the dissolving power is presumed to be zero. Hence, the so-called "colligative" properties of solutions (depression of freezing-point, elevation of boiling-point, osmotic pressure) should show deviations from the values expected on the basis of total water, when a part of it exists in an associated or "bound" form. The study of these properties in plant saps, wheat kernels, colloidal solutions, blood, animal tissues, etc., has convinced certain workers of the existence of "bound" water.

According to adherents of the theory, the "bound" water constitutes a considerable proportion of the total. Values of 20–25 per cent, and even higher, have been recorded for muscle. In *Laminaria*, from 34 to 38 per cent of the water is bound, according to Thoenes. In solutions of gelatin, about 25 per cent is in this form, corresponding to about 2 grams of "bound" water for each gram of dry gelatin. The data for blood are somewhat variable, but in a few instances the amounts exceed 25 per cent.

The following quotation from Gortner[31] defines, in general, the point of view of those supporting the concept under consideration:

... more and more it is becoming evident that the water in living tissues and even in inanimate colloidal systems does not exist wholly as "free" water such as characterizes water in bulk, but that a greater or smaller fraction of water in such systems is intimately "bound" to the organic structures and becomes an essential part of the disperse phase as contrasted with the "free" water of the dispersion medium.

This theory, which as stated is based on alleged differences in the colligative properties of "free" and "bound" water, has been strongly challenged by Hill,[32] Grollman,[33] Sunderman,[34] Greenberg,[35] and others. From vapor-pressure studies on frog's muscle, Hill has been led to conclude that if any "bound" water exists in this tissue, the amount

[30] *J. Biol. Chem.*, **92**, 699 (1931).

[31] R. A. Gortner, *Ann. Rev. Biochem.*, **1**, 21 (1932); see also Gortner's "Outlines of Biochemistry," John Wiley & Sons, Inc., New York, 1929, pp. 229, etc.

[32] *Proc. Roy. Soc. (London)*, B, **107**, 115 (1930); also A. V. Hill's "Adventures in Biophysics," Lecture II.

[33] *J. Gen. Physiol.*, **14**, 661 (1930–31).

[34] *J. Biol. Chem.*, **96**, 271 (1932).

[35] D. M. and M. M. Greenberg, *J. Gen. Physiol.*, **16**, 559 (1933).

is less than 2 per cent. Grollman has measured the lowering of the vapor pressure of colloidal solutions (gelatin, gum acacia) caused by adding NaCl, KCl, and other substances. His results show that the degree of hydration is relatively small in gelatin and undetectable in gum acacia. Consequently, the assumption that hydrophilic colloids are strongly hydrated or that part of the water is "bound" is untenable. Sunderman investigated the osmotic pressure of the blood by the freezing-point method and found all the water to be "free," a conclusion in harmony with Hill's observations. Even more convincing are the data of Greenberg and Greenberg, who studied the problem by the ultrafiltration method. They added various substances (glucose, urea, NaCl, KCl) to colloidal solutions (casein, gelatin, starch, pectin, glycogen, blood serum). A crystalloidal substance, according to the theory, should dissolve only in the "free" water. If the solution is filtered through a membrane which permits only the passage of the solvent and other crystalloids, holding back the colloidal constituents, the concentration of the substance in the ultrafiltrate becomes a measure of the "free" water in the colloidal solution. It was found that the concentration of the substance in the colloidal solution (based on the amount of total water) was equivalent to the concentration in the filtrate. This seemed to justify the conclusion that at most only a very small fraction of the water can be associated with the colloid in "bound" form.

In short, many of the available data fail to support the concept of "free" and "bound" water. Nevertheless, the subject cannot be dismissed lightly as it will probably continue to receive considerable attention, partly because of the nature of the problems that have been brought into the discussion. Aside from the physiological and pathological aspects of the subject, there are such problems as the relation of the state of water to the winter hardiness of wheat, the resistance of wheat to drought, the resistance of fruits and insects to cold—problems whose economic importance is self-evident.

CHAPTER II

THE CARBOHYDRATES [1]

Concerning the mode of formation of carbohydrates in the plant, there is much difference of opinion, although it has been recognized for many years that chlorophyll, the green coloring matter of plants, is in some way concerned with the synthesis and that the carbon is derived from carbon dioxide. The theory which first gained wide acceptance was proposed by Baeyer[2] in 1870. According to Baeyer's hypothesis, the first step in carbohydrate synthesis in the plant is a reduction of carbon dioxide to carbon monoxide, which is then further reduced to formaldehyde. This is followed, according to the theory, by condensation of the formaldehyde, yielding sugars and polysaccharides.

The conception that formaldehyde is the first stage in the photosynthetic process in the green leaf is based partly on indirect experimental evidence. Butlerow[3] treated trioxymethylene, a polymer of formaldehyde, with lime and obtained a sweetish syrup. Loew[4] later demonstrated the conversion of formaldehyde, *in vitro*, in the presence of bases, into a mixture of sugars. From this mixture, a fermentable sugar was isolated. Baly[5] and his students have described the reduction by ultraviolet light of carbon dioxide into formaldehyde and the condensation of the latter, which is assumed to be produced in an

$$\text{``activated'' form } (H-\overset{\mid}{\underset{\mid}{C}}-OH),$$

"activated" form (H—C—OH), into reducing sugars. Other investigators, however, have been unable to confirm Baly's results.

More direct evidence in support of the formaldehyde hypothesis would be a demonstration of its existence in the plant. Klein and

---

[1] The International Union of Pure and Applied Chemistry has proposed the term "glucides" to embrace the carbohydrates and glucosides.

[2] *Ber.*, **3**, 63 (1870).

[3] *Ann. Chem. Pharm.*, **120**, 295 (1861).

[4] *J. prakt. Chem.*, N. F., **33**, 321 (1886); *Ber.*, **22**, 482 (1889).

[5] *J. Chem. Soc.*, **119**, 1025 (1921); **121**, 1078 (1922); *Proc. Roy. Soc.* (*London*), A, **116**, 197, 212 (1927); *Science*, **68**, 364 (1928).

Werner[6] claim to have detected formaldehyde in various plants by means of dimethyl-resorcinol, with which it reacts to form an insoluble condensation product. These observations have been challenged, however, by Barton–Wright and Pratt.[7] In short, there is as yet no definite proof for the view that formaldehyde is the first product of photosynthesis.[8]

In summarizing the subject, Harvey[9] states that six definite stages can be recognized in the photosynthetic process. First is the physical process of diffusion of carbon dioxide into the leaf. After absorption it forms H_2CO_3, which may react in part with the basic groups of amino acids, or protein (2). The resulting compounds, which are described by Harvey as carbaminates, as well as free H_2CO_3, form addition compounds with chlorophyll (3). Through the absorption of light energy, these compounds undergo isomerization, with the formation of a peroxide linkage (4). The isomerized chlorophyll-peroxide then decomposes; formaldehyde and oxygen are liberated, and the chlorophyll is regenerated (5). This reaction can proceed in the dark and is referred to as the *Blackman reaction*, Blackman having originally shown that one stage of the photosynthetic process occurs in the absence of light. The final stage (6) is the polymerization of the activated formaldehyde.

It is considered that the primary process in photosynthesis consists in the absorption of energy quanta by chlorophyll, a property which endows this pigment with unique importance in nature. Chlorophyll exists in two forms, designated chlorophyll a and chlorophyll b, to which the following formulas have been ascribed by Willstätter and Stoll:[10]

$$\text{Chlorophyll a} \quad C_{55}H_{72}O_5N_4Mg$$

$$\text{Chlorophyll b} \quad C_{55}H_{70}O_6N_4Mg$$

These investigators have developed the conception that chlorophyll combines with carbonic acid and that by a series of changes the latter is

[6] *Biochem. Z.*, **168**, 361 (1926).

[7] *Biochem. J.*, **24**, 1210 (1930).

[8] For a general survey of the subject the student is referred to H. A. Spoehr's monograph, "Photosynthesis," Chemical Catalog Company, New York, 1926. See also Spoehr's "Chemical Aspects of Photosynthesis," *Ann. Rev. Biochem.*, **2**, 453 (1933).

[9] R. B. Harvey, "Plant Physiological Chemistry," Century Co., New York, 1930, p. 308.

[10] R. Willstätter and A. Stoll, "Untersuchungen über die Assimilation der Kohlensäure," Berlin, 1918.

reduced to formaldehyde, in which form it is liberated from its union with the chlorophyll.[11]

Chlorophyll readily loses two atoms of hydrogen by dehydrogenation, yielding dehydrochlorophyll. This fact is considered to be very significant by Conant[12] and his associates, who have suggested that the hydrogen thus rendered available is utilized in the reduction of carbon dioxide. This is the first stage of the photosynthetic reaction; it occurs in the dark and apparently depends on the intervention of an enzyme. Designating chlorophyll by Ch and dehydrochlorophyll by Ch(—2H), the first stage may be represented thus:

(1) Dark reaction:

$$12Ch + 6CO_2 \xrightarrow{\text{enzyme}} 12Ch(-2H) + \underset{\text{(glucose)}}{C_6H_{12}O_6} + 6H_2O$$

In the second stage, radiant energy is required for the regeneration of the chlorophyll.

(2) Light reaction:

$$12Ch(-2H) + light + 12H_2O \rightarrow 12Ch + 6O_2$$

The light reaction is not affected by temperature and proceeds at a much greater speed than the dark reaction, which is dependent on temperature, being slower at low than at high temperatures.[13]

The exact nature of the first sugar formed in photosynthesis is not known definitely, but most of the experimental evidence indicates that it is probably a hexose.[14]

[11] E. Q. Adams [*J. Am. Chem. Soc.*, **48**, 292 (1926)] has suggested that the formula of chlorophyll a is $C_{55}H_{72}O_5N_4Mg$ and of chlorophyll b $C_{56}H_{72}O_6N_4Mg$. He has pictured the chlorophyll as going through a cycle of four reactions, two of them associated with the absorption of two quanta each of radiation, and two follow-reactions requiring water and carbon dioxide but not light:

[ ] represents $C_{55}H_{72}O_4N_4Mg$

[ ]—O is a-chlorophyll   and   [ ]—CO₂ is b-chlorophyll.

(1) [ ]—O + H₂O + 2 quanta λ666 mμ   → [ ] + H₂O₂
(2) [ ] + CO₂   → [ ]—CO₂
(3) [ ]—CO₂ + H₂O + 2 quanta λ640 mμ   → [ ]—CO + H₂O₂
(4) [ ]—CO + H₂O   → [ ]—O + HCHO

[12] J. B. Conant, J. F. Hyde, W. W. Moyer and E. M. Dietz, *J. Am. Chem. Soc.*, **53**, 359 (1931); Conant, Dietz, and S. E. Kamerling, *Science*, **73**, 268 (1931). Compare with R. B. Gordon, *Biol. Abstracts*, **6**, 683 (1932); cited by Spoehr, *Ann. Rev. Biochem.*, **2**, 453 (1933).

[13] R. Emerson and W. Arnold, *J. Gen. Physiol.*, **15**, 391 (1932); **16**, 191 (1932); see also Emerson, *ibid.*, **12**, 609 (1929); Arnold, *ibid.*, **17**, 135, 145 (1933).

[14] E. C. Barton-Wright and M. C. Pratt, *Biochem. J.*, **24**, 1217 (1930); H. F. Clements, *Plant Physiol.*, **7**, 547 (1932).

In summary it may be stated that much evidence points to the participation of carbon monoxide and formaldehyde in photosynthesis; however, certain phases of the mechanism of the reaction and the nature of the intermediate products remain to be clarified. Essentially the process of photosynthesis consists in the transformation of radiant energy into chemical energy, which is stored in the plant in the form of carbohydrate, protein, and fat. This stored energy is the basis for practically all plant and animal life.

CLASSIFICATION OF THE CARBOHYDRATES

Glycolic aldehyde, containing one aldehyde and one primary alcohol group ($CH_2OH \cdot CHO$), is the simplest aldehyde having the properties commonly associated with the sugars. It is sweet to the taste, crystalline, and readily soluble in water. The following compounds are usually grouped with the simple carbohydrates:

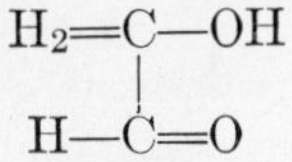

$$H_2=C-OH \qquad\qquad H_2=C-OH \qquad\qquad H_2=C-OH$$

$$H-C=O \qquad\qquad H-C-OH \qquad\qquad H-C-OH$$

Glycolic aldehyde (a diose)

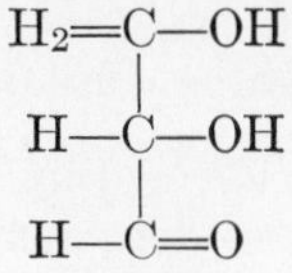

$$H-C=O \qquad\qquad H-C-OH$$

Glycerose (a triose)

$$H-C=O$$

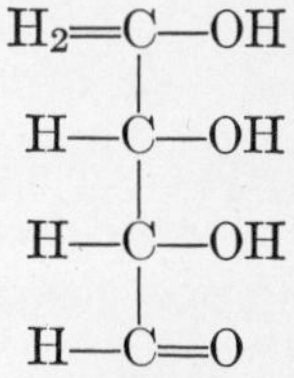

Erythrose (a tetrose)

Sugars having an aldehyde group are termed aldoses; those with a ketone ($C=O$) group are classified as ketoses. Of the latter, the lowest member is dioxyacetone ($CH_2OH \cdot CO \cdot CH_2OH$).

THE MONOSACCHARIDES [15]

$$(C_m(H_2O)_m)$$

Except for the methyl pentoses, the general formula $C_m(H_2O)_m$ may be applied to the *simple sugars, or monosaccharides.* These may be classified as follows:

Biose (diose)—($C_2H_4O_2$)—glycolaldehyde (glycolose).
Trioses ($C_3H_6O_3$) —Aldose—glycerose.
  Ketose—dioxyacetone.

[15] The classification given here is based on that of Sherman in "Chemistry of Foods and Nutrition," Macmillan, 1928 edition, p. 10.

Tetroses ($C_4H_8O_4$)	—Aldoses—erythrose, threose.
	Ketose—erythrulose.
Pentoses ($C_5H_{10}O_5$)	—Aldoses—arabinose, xylose, lyxose, ribose.
	Ketose—araboketose, xyloketose.
	[Methyl pentoses ($C_6H_{10}O_5$)—rhamnose, fucose.]
Hexoses ($C_6H_{12}O_6$)	—Aldoses—glucose, galactose, mannose, gulose, idose, talose, allose, etc.
	Ketoses—fructose, sorbose, tagatose.
Heptoses ($C_7H_{14}O_7$)	—Aldoses—mannoheptose, etc.
	Ketoses—sedoheptose, etc.

Relatively few of the monosaccharides occur free in nature. Those occurring naturally are fructose, glucose, sedoheptose, and mannoheptose. Arabinose, xylose, galactose, mannose, and other monosaccharides may be obtained by fermentation or hydrolysis of naturally occurring substances. Others are merely laboratory products. Among these may be mentioned erythrose, lyxose, and gulose. Three octoses ($C_8H_{16}O_8$), two nonoses ($C_9H_{18}O_9$), and one decose ($C_{10}H_{20}O_{10}$) have been prepared in the laboratory.

THE DISACCHARIDES

($C_{12}H_{22}O_{11}$)

The monosaccharides cannot be split or hydrolyzed into simpler carbohydrates, thus differing from the disaccharides and polysaccharides which on hydrolysis yield monosaccharides. For example,

$$C_{12}H_{22}O_{11} + H_2O \rightleftarrows 2C_6H_{12}O_6$$

The disaccharides may therefore be looked upon as being made up of two molecules of the same or of different monosaccharides from which one molecule of water has been abstracted. The general formula for these compounds would therefore be $C_{2m}(H_2O)_{2m-1}$.

1. Anhydrides of fructose and glucose: the best-known example is sucrose.

2. Anhydrides of glucose and galactose: e.g., lactose.

3. Anhydrides of glucose and glucose: maltose, isomaltose, trehalose, etc.

A variety of other disaccharides have been described. These include a dipentose saccharide, diarabinose, $C_{10}H_{18}O_9$, and several pentose-hexose saccharides.

The Trisaccharides

$$(C_{18}H_{32}O_{16})$$

By the elimination of two molecules of water from three monosaccharide molecules, we obtain the empirical formula for the trisaccharides $[C_{3m}(H_2O)_{3m-2}]$, of which the following are the most familiar compounds:

1. Anhydride of fructose + glucose + galactose: raffinose. Raffinose occurs in the sugar beet, cottonseed meal, etc.

2. Anhydride of glucose + fructose + glucose: melicitose (melezitose). This is found in the twigs of the larch and of the Douglas fir, and elsewhere.

The tetrasaccharides may be regarded as resulting from the condensation of four monosaccharide molecules with the loss of three molecules of water, $C_{4m}(H_2O)_{4m-3}$. The best-known example is stachyose $(C_{24}H_{42}O_{21})$, which on hydrolysis yields two molecules of galactose and one molecule each of fructose and glucose. It occurs in peas, ash manna, and the twigs of the white jasmine.

The Polysaccharides

The polysaccharides yield on complete hydrolysis either pentoses or hexoses and are obviously the polymerides of these molecular units.

I. Pentosans

$$(C_5H_8O_4)_x$$

The pentosans are the chief constituents of gums and mucilages.

(a) Xylans (anhydrides of xylose). These are found in straw, oat hulls, corn cobs, and most woods.

(b) Arabans (anhydrides of arabinose). The arabans are found chiefly in cherry gum or gum arabic.

II. Hexosans

$$(C_6H_{10}O_5)_x$$

(a) Glucosans (anhydrides of glucose). These are the most abundant of polysaccharides. Examples: cellulose, starch, dextrin, glycogen.

(b) Mannans or mannosans (anhydrides of mannose). These are found in the ivory nut, from which buttons are made, and in various legumes.

(c) Galactans (anhydrides of galactose). Many gums, agar, algae, lichens, and mosses contain galactans. Fruit pectins likewise contain galactans. A polysaccharide has been recently described which is analogous to glycogen, but yields galactose on hydrolysis; hence the name galactogen. It occurs, together with glycogen, in snails and exclusively in the eggs of the snail.[16]

(d) Fructosans (anhydrides of fructose). Inulin, present in the tubers of the Jerusalem artichoke, is the most familiar example. It is also present in the bulbs of the onion and garlic. On hydrolysis, inulin yields fructose.

Optical Activity. A beam of light may be *polarized*, i.e., caused to vibrate in one plane, by passing through a Nicol prism. This consists of a specially constructed rhomb of Iceland spar or calcite (pure $CaCO_3$). When a beam of polarized light is passed through certain substances in solution, its plane may be turned either to the right or to the left. Such substances are said to be optically active; those that turn the plane of polarized light to the right are *dextro-rotatory*, whereas those that turn the beam to the left are *levo-rotatory*. The polarimeter is an instrument used in measuring the angle through which the plane of polarized light is turned.[17]

Pasteur[18] was among the first to appreciate that a relation existed between optical activity, chemical constitution, and biochemical behavior. In his epoch-making investigations on tartaric acid, he discovered that the so-called racemic acid, which was itself optically inactive, could be separated into two crystalline forms, one being the mirror image of the other. When separated, one form was dextro-rotatory and the other levo-rotatory.

The problem was further elucidated by the work of Le Bel[19] and van't Hoff,[20] who independently established the relationship between optical activity in organic compounds and the presence in them of asymmetric carbon atoms. An asymmetric carbon atom is one united to four different atoms or groups of atoms. Lactic acid contains one

---

[16] F. May, *Z. Biol.*, **92**, 319, 325 (1932); cited by Cori and Cori, *Ann. Rev. Biochem.*, **2**, 137 (1933).

[17] For a description of the polariscope and its uses, the student is referred to special treatises on the subject, such as Landolt's book "The Optical Rotatory Power of Organic Substances and Its Practical Applications" (trans. by Long). See also Getman's "Outlines of Theoretical Chemistry," Chap. V, and "Allen's Commercial Organic Analysis," **1**, p. 41.

[18] *Ann. chim. phys.*, **24**, 442 (1838); **28**, 56 (1850); **31**, 67 (1851).

[19] *Bull. soc. chim.*, **22**, 337 (1874).

[20] *Ibid.*, **23**, 295 (1875).

asymmetric carbon atom. The spatial arrangement of the atoms in lactic acid may be represented as follows:

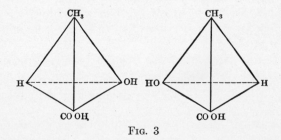

Fig. 3

Lactic acid, therefore, occurs in two optically active forms. Inactive, or racemic, lactic acid is a mixture of the two active forms, in equal proportions. It is of importance to note here that in laboratory syntheses of compounds containing asymmetric carbon atoms the products are usually optically inactive, since by the law of probabilities an equal number of molecules of the levo- and dextro-rotatory forms would be obtained. Natural syntheses result in the formation of substances which may and frequently do show optical activity.

Tartaric acid contains two asymmetric carbon atoms and exists in four forms, namely as (a) inactive racemic acid which may be separated into (b) dextro-tartaric and (c) levo-tartaric acids; and (d) mesotartaric acid which is inactive because of "internal compensation" within the molecule. These compounds may be represented structurally as follows:

Racemic Acid

COOH	COOH	COOH
H—C—OH	HO—C—H	H—C—OH
HO—C—H	H—C—OH	H—C—OH
COOH	COOH	COOH
d-Tartaric Acid	l-Tartaric Acid	Mesotartaric Acid

Stereo-isomerism and the Constitution of the Monosaccharides.
If the structural formula of glycerose is examined (p. 31), it will be seen that the middle carbon atom is asymmetric, since it is united to four different atoms or groups of atoms. Accordingly, there must exist a dextro-rotatory and a levo-rotatory form of glycerose in addition to the inactive or racemic form, which is a mixture in equal proportions of

the two optically active varieties. The optically active forms of glycerose may be represented as follows:

$$
\begin{array}{ccc}
H_2\!\!=\!\!C\!\!-\!\!OH & & H_2\!\!=\!\!C\!\!-\!\!OH \\
| & & | \\
H\!\!-\!\!C\!\!-\!\!OH & \text{and} & OH\!\!-\!\!C\!\!-\!\!H \\
| & & | \\
H\!\!-\!\!C\!\!=\!\!O & & H\!\!-\!\!C\!\!=\!\!O
\end{array}
$$

According to the Le Bel-van't Hoff hypothesis, if n represents the number of asymmetric carbon atoms in a given sugar molecule, then 2^n will be the total number of active forms of the sugar. Applying the formula to a 4-carbon-atom sugar having 2 asymmetric carbon atoms, we obtain 4 as the number of isomers. These are d- and l-erythrose and d- and l-threose. Similarly, 8 aldo-pentoses, d- and l-arabinose, d- and l-xylose, d- and l-ribose and d- and l-lyxose, are theoretically possible. In the case of the aldo-hexose sugars, the empirical formula indicates the presence of 4 asymmetric carbon atoms.

$$
\begin{array}{c}
H_2\!\!=\!\!C\!\!-\!\!OH \\
| \\
H\!\!-\!\!C\!\!-\!\!OH \\
| \\
H\!\!-\!\!C\!\!-\!\!OH \\
| \\
H\!\!-\!\!C\!\!-\!\!OH \\
| \\
H\!\!-\!\!C\!\!-\!\!OH \\
| \\
H\!\!-\!\!C\!\!=\!\!O
\end{array}
$$

On this basis, 16 stereo-isomeric modifications are theoretically possible. Except in the case of d- and l-glucose, the designations d- and l- do not necessarily imply dextro-rotation and levo-rotation. A d-sugar is a sugar which is structurally related, so far as the asymmetry of its carbon atoms is concerned, to d-glycerose. An l-sugar is similarly structurally related to l-glycerose. Of the 16 sugars, 3 are known to occur naturally either free or in combination (glucose, mannose, galactose.) All the others have been prepared artificially, chiefly by Emil Fischer. The last two to have been synthesized are l-allose and l-altrose.[20a]

[20a] W. C. Austin and F. L. Humoller, *J. Am. Chem. Soc.*, **55**, 2167 (1933); *Proc. Am. Soc., Biol. Chem.*, 1934.

THE ALDOHEXOSES [21]

```
      CHO                CHO                CHO                CHO
   H—C—OH            HO—C—H             HO—C—H             H—C—OH
   H—C—OH            HO—C—H             H—C—OH             HO—C—H
  HO—C—H             H—C—OH             HO—C—H             H—C—OH
  HO—C—H             H—C—OH             HO—C—H             H—C—OH
     CH₂OH              CH₂OH              CH₂OH              CH₂OH
   l-Mannose          d-Mannose          l-Glucose          d-Glucose


      CHO                CHO                CHO                CHO
   H—C—OH            HO—C—H             HO—C—H             H—C—OH
  HO—C—H             H—C—OH             HO—C—H             H—C—OH
   H—C—OH            HO—C—H             H—C—OH             HO—C—H
  HO—C—H             H—C—OH             HO—C—H             H—C—OH
     CH₂OH              CH₂OH              CH₂OH              CH₂OH
   l-Idose            d-Idose            l-Gulose           d-Gulose


      CHO                CHO                CHO                CHO
  HO—C—H             H—C—OH             H—C—OH             HO—C—H
   H—C—OH            HO—C—H             H—C—OH             HO—C—H
   H—C—OH            HO—C—H             H—C—OH             HO—C—H
  HO—C—H             H—C—OH             HO—C—H             H—C—OH
     CH₂OH              CH₂OH              CH₂OH              CH₂OH
   l-Galactose        d-Galactose        l-Talose           d-Talose


      CHO                CHO                CHO                CHO
  HO—C—H             H—C—OH             H—C—OH             HO—C—H
  HO—C—H             H—C—OH             HO—C—H             H—C—OH
  HO—C—H             H—C—OH             HO—C—H             H—C—OH
  HO—C—H             H—C—OH             HO—C—H             H—C—OH
     CH₂OH              CH₂OH              CH₂OH              CH₂OH
   l-Allose           d-Allose           l-Altrose          d-Altrose
   (unknown)                             (unknown)
```

The number of aldo-hexose isomerides would be limited to 16 on the assumption that the structure of the aldo-hexose molecule is that of an open-chain aldehyde. The structural formula that the organic chemist

[21] Based on table in E. F. Armstrong's "Simple Carbohydrates and Glucosides," Longmans, Green & Co., 1924, p. 34.

assigns to a given organic compound is determined by what is known concerning its physical and chemical properties. If, from this standpoint, the best known of the aldo-hexoses, namely d-glucose, is subjected to a critical examination, it is discovered that the straight-chain aldehyde formula, as given above, does not fully account for all the chemical and physical properties of this compound.

Reactions. On heating glucose with a concentrated solution of hydriodic acid, the oxygen is removed and it is converted to n-secondary-hexyliodide, $[CH_3 \cdot CH_2 \cdot CHI \cdot CH_2 \cdot CH_2 \cdot CH_3]$, which is a derivative of n-hexane, $[CH_3 \cdot CH_2 \cdot CH_2 \cdot CH_2 \cdot CH_2 \cdot CH_3]$. This proves that glucose is a straight-chain compound.

The hydroxyl groups react with metals to form compounds resembling the "alcoholates." When glucose is treated with acids, acid anhydrides, and acid chlorides, esters are formed in which 5 hydrogen atoms of the hydroxyl groups are replaced by acid radicals. An example of such an ester is glucose pentacetate $[C_6H_7O(O \cdot CO \cdot CH_3)_5]$. This is evidence that there are five hydroxyl groups, and, because of the stability of glucose, it is to be assumed that each hydroxyl group is associated with a different carbon atom.

The aldehyde group of glucose may be reduced with sodium amalgam to an alcohol group, yielding a hexahydric alcohol, sorbitol, $[CH_2OH(CHOH)_4CH_2OH]$, or it may be oxidized to give gluconic acid, $[COOH(CHOH)_4CH_2OH]$. Oxidation of the terminal primary alcohol group yields glycuronic acid, $[COOH(CHOH)_4CHO]$, then saccharic acid, $[COOH(CHOH)_4COOH]$, as the end-product. Because of the aldehyde group, glucose reduces alkaline copper solutions and other metallic hydroxides. It reacts with hydrocyanic acid to yield glucose cyanhydrin:

$$CH_2OH(CHOH)_4CHO + HCN = CH_2OH(CHOH)_4C \overset{\displaystyle H}{\underset{\displaystyle CN}{\Big\langle}} OH$$

This, on hydrolysis, gives glucoheptonic acid, which, on reduction, yields a sugar containing seven carbon atoms, namely, glucoheptose, $[CH_2OH(CHOH)_5CHO]$. Treated with hydroxylamine, glucose yields the corresponding oxime;[22] with phenylhydrazine, glucosazone is ob-

---

[22]
$$
\begin{array}{lll}
CHO & + H_2N \cdot OH & CH:N \cdot OH + H_2O \\
| & \text{Hydroxylamine} & | \\
(CHOH)_4 & = & (CHOH)_4 \\
| & & | \\
CH_2OH & & CH_2OH \\
\text{Glucose} & & \text{Glucose-oxime}
\end{array}
$$

tained.[23] Taken by themselves, these reactions would seem to afford sufficient proof for the open-chain aldehydic structure of the glucose molecule; but when the reactivity of the compound is compared with that of other hydroxy-aldehydes, it becomes apparent that glucose is not as reactive as might be expected from the simple aldehyde formula. Indeed, if the structure of glucose were as represented by the open-chain aldehyde formula, it would be impossible to explain certain of its physical properties.

Mutarotation. It has been observed that the optical rotation of a freshly prepared aqueous solution of glucose or of any other sugar containing a free aldehyde group changes on standing. The initial specific rotations of d-glucose prepared in different ways may be totally different. Thus glucose prepared by recrystallization from acetic acid gives, when freshly dissolved in water, a rotation $[\alpha]_D$ of about $+110°$ (see p. 62). Prepared by crystallization from an aqueous solution above 98° C., the d-glucose exhibits an initial rotation $[\alpha]_D$ of about $+19°$. Either solution, when allowed to stand, very slowly changes its rotation until a value of $[\alpha]_D$ of $+52.5°$ is obtained. The change occurs almost immediately if a small amount of alkali is added. This phenomenon, first observed by Dubrunfaut in 1846, is known as *mutarotation* (also birotation or multirotation) and is believed to be due to the conversion of one form of the sugar into another having a different molecular configuration and hence a different optical rotation.

Glucoside Formation. When glucose is treated with methyl alcohol in the presence of dry hydrochloric acid gas, two distinct compounds are formed, neither having an aldehyde group. Both compounds are methyl glucosides, and one may be separated from the other by fractional crystallization. The methyl glucosides do not behave as aldehydes. It has been determined that in each case a methyl group replaces a hydrogen atom belonging to an hydroxyl group attached to the carbon atom which is supposedly part of the aldehyde group of the

[23]
$$
\begin{array}{ll}
\text{CHO} & \text{CH:N·NH·C}_6\text{H}_5 \\
| & | \\
\text{CHOH} \quad + \text{C}_6\text{H}_5\text{·NH·NH}_2 = & \text{CHOH} \qquad + \text{H}_2\text{O} \\
| \qquad\qquad \text{Phenylhydrazine} & | \\
\text{(CHOH)}_3 & \text{(CHOH)}_3 \\
| & | \\
\text{CH}_2\text{OH} & \text{CH}_2\text{OH} \\
\text{Glucose} & \text{Phenylhydrazone of glucose}
\end{array}
$$

$$
\begin{array}{ll}
\text{CH:N·NH·C}_6\text{H}_5 & \text{CH:N·NH·C}_6\text{H}_5 \\
| & | \\
\text{CHOH} \qquad + 2\text{C}_6\text{H}_5\text{NH·NH}_2 = & \text{C:N·NH·C}_6\text{H}_5 \; + \text{C}_6\text{H}_5\text{NH}_2 + \text{NH}_2 \\
| & | \\
\text{(CHOH)}_3 & \text{(CHOH)}_3 \qquad\qquad + \text{H}_2\text{O} \\
| & | \\
\text{CH}_2\text{OH} & \text{CH}_2\text{OH} \\
& \text{Glucosazone}
\end{array}
$$

glucose molecule. The two methyl glucosides have been distinguished by the prefixes α and β, and for reasons to be considered presently have been represented structurally by the following formulas:

$$
\begin{array}{ll}
\text{H—C—O—CH}_3 & \text{H}_3\text{C—O—C—H} \\
| & | \\
\text{H—C—OH} & \text{H—C—OH} \\
| & | \\
\text{HO—C—H} \quad \text{O} & \text{HO—C—H} \quad \text{O} \\
| & | \\
\text{H—C—OH} & \text{H—C—OH} \\
| & | \\
\text{H—C} & \text{H—C} \\
| & | \\
\text{CH}_2\text{OH} & \text{CH}_2\text{OH} \\
\alpha\text{-Methyl glucoside} & \beta\text{-Methyl glucoside}
\end{array}
$$

The two compounds differ in solubility, melting-point, rotatory power, and crystalline form, the α-glucoside crystallizing in long needles, and the β-form in rectangular prisms.

	Melting-point	Rotatory Power
α-Methyl glucoside.....................	165°	+157°
β-Methyl glucoside.....................	104°	− 33°

The methyl glucosides also differ in their reactions toward enzymes. Maltase acts only on the α glucoside, having no effect on the β-form. The latter is acted on by the enzyme emulsin. The pure β-form may be prepared by incubating the mixture of the two glucosides with ordinary baker's yeast. The maltase contained in the yeast hydrolyzes the α-methyl glucoside, and the zymase, which is also present, ferments the resulting glucose to carbon dioxide and ethyl alcohol. The β-methyl glucoside remains unaffected.

The behavior of ordinary glucose in forming two methyl glucosides suggests the probability that an hydroxyl (OH) group is available at the terminal (aldehyde) carbon atom. It also indicates that two distinct forms of glucose are acted upon to yield the two methyl glucosides.

Lactones and Lactals. A distinguishing feature of the γ- and δ-hydroxyacids is that they are capable of forming cyclic esters, when the carboxyl group enters into reaction with the hydroxyl group. The formation of these cyclic compounds is accelerated by mineral acids, whereas cleavage of the lactone linkage may be accomplished through the agency of alkali hydroxides and carbonates. As an illustration of a γ-lactone, we have:

$$
\gamma\ \overset{H_2}{C}\text{—OH} \qquad \overset{H_2}{C} \qquad \rightleftarrows \qquad
$$

$$
\gamma\ \overset{\diagup H_2}{C}\text{—OH} \qquad\qquad \overset{\diagup H_2}{C}
$$

$$
\beta\ CH_2 \qquad\qquad CH_2
$$

$$
\rightleftarrows
$$

$$
\alpha\ CH_2 \qquad\qquad CH_2 \qquad\qquad O + H_2O.
$$

$$
C\text{—OH} \qquad\qquad C
$$

$$
\diagdown O \qquad\qquad\quad \diagdown O
$$

(γ -Hydroxybutyric   (γ -Butyrolactone)
acid)

The following is the formula of the lactone of δ-hydroxy valeric acid:

$$
\overset{\displaystyle \boxed{O}}{CH_2\text{—}CH_2\text{—}CH_2\text{—}CH_2\text{—}CO}
$$

$$
\quad\ \delta \qquad\ \gamma \qquad\ \beta \qquad\ \alpha
$$

(δ -Valerolactone)

The sugar acids, which may be formed by the oxidation of the aldehyde group to a carboxyl group, show the same tendency to form
lactones. In a careful study of the relation between the chemical constitution and the optical rotatory power of 24 different sugar-acid
lactones, Hudson[24] advanced the hypothesis, now usually referred to
as Hudson's "lactone rule," that lactones which are dextro-rotatory
have the lactone ring on one side, represented on the right side of
the structure, whereas lactones which are levo-rotatory have it on the
other side, and that the position of the ring shows the former position
of the OH group on the γ-carbon atom. Hudson concluded that the
sugar acids form γ-lactones. Although this configuration is undoubtedly
the predominant one, evidence has, however, accumulated[25] pointing to
the existence of δ-lactones of sugar acids. Thus, gluconic acid is said
to yield at least two lactones, namely a γ- and a δ-lactone:

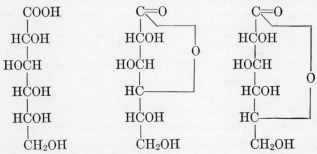

24 *J. Am. Chem. Soc.*, **32**, 338 (1910).
25 J. U. Nef, *Ann. Chem.*, **403**, 204 (1914); W. N. Haworth and V. S. Nicholson,
J. Chem. Soc., **129**, 1899 (1926).

The lactones of the sugar acids are relatively stable, and some have been prepared in crystalline form. Levene[26] is of the opinion that, in a solution of sugar acids, all theoretically possible lactones are formed. In a freshly prepared solution the unstable lactones are said to predominate, but after a short time only the stable forms are present in measurable quantities.

Analogous to the formation of lactones from the sugar acids are the intramolecular rearrangements which the sugars themselves exhibit. Here also, an oxygen bridge is introduced which may be supposed to link carbon atoms 1 and 4 (γ-linkage), 1 and 5 (δ-linkage), etc. Assuming for the present the $<1,5>$ linkage, the glucose molecule may be represented by the formula:

$$
\begin{array}{cl}
1 & \overset{\displaystyle H\diagdown \quad \diagup OH}{\underset{|}{C}} \\
2 & HCOH \\
3 & HOCH \qquad O \\
4 & HCOH \\
5 & HC \\
6 & CH_2OH
\end{array}
$$

Levene refers to compounds of this type as " lactals," a term which has been suggested by Helferich and Fries.[27]

Structure of the Glucose Molecule. We may now consider whether the lactal structure of the glucose molecule offers an adequate explanation for certain physical and chemical properties of glucose which we are unable to account for on the basis of the open-chain aldehyde structure.

It will be observed that in the lactal formula for glucose just given, in addition to the asymmetry of carbon atoms 2, 3, 4, and 5, the terminal carbon atom 1 is also asymmetric. Consequently, two isomeric modifications of d-glucose are possible, depending on the space relations of the terminal H and OH groups. In accordance with the nomenclature used in describing the methyl glucosides (p. 40), the formulas for glucose, referred to as the α- and β-amylene-oxide forms, may be written:

[26] P. A. Levene, *Chem. Rev.*, **5**, 1 (1928).
[27] *Ber.*, **58**, 1246 (1925).

H—C—OH
H—C—OH
HO—C—H   O
H—C—OH
H—C
CH$_2$OH
α-Glucose

HO—C—H
H—C—OH
HO—C—H   O
H—C—OH
H—C
CH$_2$OH
β-Glucose

The existence of two forms of d-glucose was demonstrated by Tanret[28] in 1896. He described an " α " glucose ($[\alpha]_D = + 110°$) which on standing changed its specific optical rotation to the equilibrium point ($[\alpha]_D = + 52.5°$). Another sugar of rotation ($[\alpha]_D = + 19°$) increased its rotatory power to 52.5°. These observations have been confirmed by other investigators and help to explain the phenomenon of mutarotation. Both the α- and the β-forms of glucose are present when ordinary anhydrous glucose is dissolved, and the initial optical rotation, in any given case, will depend on the relative proportions of the two isomeric modifications. The change of α-glucose to β-glucose is reversible and occurs readily, the direction of the change depending on how much of each form is present in the solution. If, on standing, the change α-glucose → β-glucose should exceed the transformation β-glucose → α-glucose, the optical rotation will diminish. If the reverse should be true, the optical rotation will steadily increase. When equilibrium is reached, i.e., when the specific optical rotation is $[\alpha]_D = + 52.5°$, it is found that approximately one-third of the glucose is present as α-glucose and two-thirds as β-glucose.

The α- and β-methyl glucosides are clearly derivatives of the α- and β-forms of glucose, respectively. It is interesting to note that the average specific optical rotation of the glucosides is +62°, and of the glucoses, +63.5°, a physical relationship that has been ascribed to their structural similarity. When α-methyl glucose is hydrolyzed it yields a sugar having a high initial optical rotation, obviously α-glucose; and when the β-methyl glucoside is hydrolyzed, it yields a sugar of low initial optical rotation, obviously β-glucose.[29]

[28] Bull. soc. chim., 15, 195, 349 (1896).

[29] The molecular rotation of a sugar is the product of its molecular weight and specific rotation (p. 62). Hudson postulated that the molecular rotation depends on two factors: (1) the optical effect of the end asymmetric carbon atom of the sugar, and (2) the optical effect of the remaining asymmetric carbon atoms. If the rotation due to the terminal asymmetric carbon atom of α-d-glucose is represented by A and

In addition to the cyclic forms of glucose, the existence of a non-cyclic form must be assumed if we are to explain its reactions as an open-chain aldehyde. The opening of the cyclic structure with the formation of the aldehydic form has for many years been associated with the change of one isomeric form of glucose to the other (α-glucose $\rightleftarrows$ β-glucose) which underlies the phenomenon of mutarotation.

α-Glucose	Intermediate phase during mutarotation	β-Glucose

the rotation of the remaining four asymmetric carbon atoms by B, the molecular rotation of the whole molecule is this $A + B$. The molecular rotation of the other isomer, β-d-glucose, will then be $-A + B$. These facts may be summarized as follows:

Molecular rotation of α-d-glucose $= 180 \times + 110° = 19,800 = A + B$

Molecular rotation of β-d-glucose $= 180 \times + 19° = 3,420 = -A + B$

Accordingly, the difference in molecular rotation $(2A) = 16,380$ and the sum $(2B) = 23,220$.

Hudson has developed the following generalizations:

(1) The difference between the molecular rotations of the α- and β-forms of all the aldehyde sugars and all their derivatives in which the added substance is not joined directly to the end asymmetric carbon atom is a nearly constant quantity (about 16,200).

(2) The α- and β-forms of those derivatives (e.g., glucosides, etc.) of any aldose sugar in which only the asymmetric carbon atom is affected have molecular rotations whose sum is equal to the sum for the α- and β-forms of the aldose (approximately 23,000 to 24,000).

(3) The names of the α- and β-forms of the sugars should be so selected that for all sugars which are genetically related to d-glucose the subtraction of the rotation of the β-form from that of the α-form gives a positive difference, and for all sugars which are genetically related to l-glucose a negative difference.

(4) The names of the α- and β-forms of the derivatives of any sugar should be so selected that the difference of their molecular rotations is equal to and of the same sign as the similar difference for the forms of that glucose (d- or l-) to which the first sugar is genetically related.

These rules have proved to be very useful in the study of the molecular configuration of the sugars and their derivatives. C. S. Hudson, *J. Am. Chem. Soc.*, **31**, 66 (1909). That the principles involved have certain limitations and may not be applied uniformly to all sugars is suggested by recent work.

The presence of the transitional aldehyde form is taken as an indication that the sugar is undergoing or has undergone mutarotation. In fact, it has been pointed out (Levene and others) that the sugars or their derivatives which show a higher velocity of mutarotation are also those in which the change to the aldehyde form proceeds with higher velocity.

It was formerly believed by Lowry that the cyclic isomers take up a molecule of water and pass through a transitory aldehydrol stage to the aldehyde form.[30] This view, however, has been challenged by Armstrong[31] on the ground that there is an increase in the conductivity of sugar solutions during mutarotation, a fact which is inconsistent with the formation of an aldehydrol. The chemical mechanism involved in the process of mutarotation has been the subject of intensive study during the last few years, and it seems not unlikely that the phenomenon is purely a tautomeric change and does not depend on the intervention of water. Some of this work has been reviewed by Lowry.[32]

Although it is to be admitted that there is, as yet, no general agreement regarding the nature of the intermediate products which accompany mutarotation, or of the mechanism of their formation, it is probably safe to assume, on the basis of available evidence, that at some stage or another the open-chain aldehyde form of glucose is present. This variety of d-glucose is in equilibrium with the α- and β-isomers of the amylene-oxide forms and possibly with other cyclic isomeric modifications. When glucose is treated with a reducing or oxidizing agent, with phenylhydrazine, hydrocyanic acid, or any reagent which acts on the free aldehyde group, the equilibrium relations are disturbed by the removal of the aldehyde form from the reacting system. As a result, the

[30] If this view were correct, the formation of the aldehyde form of glucose could be represented by the following formulas:

Glucose aldehydrol   Aldehyde form

[31] *J. Chem. Soc.*, **83**, 1305 (1903). See also E. F. Armstrong's "The Carbohydrates and the Glucosides," London, 1924 edition, p. 47.

[32] *Z. physik. Chem.*, **130**, 125 (1927); Lowry and Smith, Dixième conf. union intern. chim., p. 79 (1930).

α- and β-forms are converted to the aldehyde, and, as the reaction proceeds, more and more of the cyclic forms are changed to the aldehyde form. On the assumption that at any given moment during a reaction only a small amount of the free aldehyde is present, rests the explanation which some have urged for the fact that the sugars are more slowly reactive than are hydroxyaldehydes which do not have a cyclic configuration.

Proof of the Amylene-oxide Formula of Glucose. In describing the cyclic forms of glucose (p. 43) and the corresponding methyl glucosides (p. 40), the δ-, or amylene-oxide, structure was assumed. It remains to present some of the evidence upon which this is based.[33]

(1) 2 : 3 : 6 trimethyl glucose gives on oxidation 2 : 3 : 6 trimethylgluconic acid, which readily forms a lactone. This has been identified as a γ-lactone. If this compound is methylated, it yields 2 : 3 : 5 : 6 tetramethyl gluconolactone. This is a crystalline solid.

$$
\begin{array}{c}
\text{C} = \text{O} \\
| \\
\text{H} - \text{C} - \text{OCH}_3 \\
| \\
\text{CH}_3\text{O} - \text{C} - \text{H} \qquad \text{O} \\
| \\
\text{H} - \text{C} - \\
| \\
\text{H} - \text{C} - \text{OCH}_3 \\
| \\
\text{CH}_2\text{OCH}_3
\end{array}
$$

2:3:5:6 Tetramethyl
gluconolactone

[33] The chemical constitution of the carbohydrates has engaged the attention of numerous investigators for over a generation. Numbered among the pioneer workers in this field were Emil Fischer, J. U. Nef, and E. F. Armstrong, who laid the foundation for the more recent work of J. C. Irvine, C. S. Hudson, P. A. Levene, W. N. Haworth, J. Pryde, their associates and others, which has resulted in an almost complete revision of our knowledge of the stereochemistry of the sugars. This subject is a very difficult one, and the methods of investigation are very complex. In gaining an appreciation of the present status of the subject, the student will be aided by the following references: (1) "Progress in the Structural Study of Carbohydrates," J. C. Irvine, *Chem. Rev.* 4, 203 (1927); (2) "Active Glucose," P. A. Levene, *ibid.*, 5, 1 (1928); (3) W. Charlton, W. N. Haworth, and S. Peat, *J. Chem. Soc.*, 129, 89 (1926); W. N. Haworth and G. C. Westgarth, *ibid.*, p. 880; W. N. Haworth, "The Constitution of Sugars," London, 1929; The Chemistry of the Carbohydrates and Glucosides, P. A. Levene, and A. L. Raymond, *Ann. Rev. Biochem.*, 1, 213 (1932); 2, 31 (1933); also refer to papers by C. S. Hudson and associates, *J. Am. Chem. Soc.*, 52, (1930), etc., and by W. N. Haworth and associates in recent volumes of the *J. Chem. Soc., London.*

2 : 3 : 6 trimethyl glucose on methylation forms a tetramethyl glucose. When this is oxidized it yields a tetramethyl gluconolactone, which is a liquid and which in its physical and chemical properties differs markedly from the 2 : 3 : 5 : 6 tetramethyl gluconolactone given above. Accordingly, this can only be the 1 : 5 lactone:

$$
\begin{array}{c}
C{=}O \\
| \\
H{-}C{-}OCH_3 \\
| \\
CH_3O{-}C{-}H \qquad O \\
| \\
H{-}C{-}OCH_3 \\
| \\
H{-}C \\
| \\
CH_2OCH_3
\end{array}
$$

2:3:4:6 Tetramethyl
gluconolactone

From this it has been concluded that the normal tetramethyl glucose (and hence, glucose itself) is an amylene oxide.[34]

(2) Crystalline tetramethyl glucose is oxidized by nitric acid to xylo-trimethoxy-glutaric acid, as follows:

$$
\begin{array}{c}
H \quad OH \\
\diagdown C \diagup \\
| \\
H{-}C{-}OCH_3 \\
| \\
CH_3O{-}C{-}H \qquad O \\
| \\
H{-}C{-}OCH_3 \\
| \\
H{-}C \\
| \\
CH_2OCH_3
\end{array}
\rightarrow
\begin{array}{c}
COOH \\
| \\
H{-}C{-}OCH_3 \\
| \\
CH_3O{-}C{-}H \\
| \\
H{-}C{-}OCH_3 \\
| \\
COOH
\end{array}
$$

(3) Tetramethyl galactonolactone, derived from tetramethyl galactose, is known to have an amylene-oxide configuration. Trimethyl arabinose and trimethyl xylose are also known to give 1 : 5 lactones. These three lactones have properties which are almost identical with those of

[34] Hudson has expressed doubt of the validity of Haworth's assumption that rings never shift in the methylation of glucosides and glucoside-like derivatives (*J. Am. Chem. Soc.*, **52**, 1680, 1707 [1930]). Hudson's objections have been challenged, however, by Haworth and Hirst (*J. Chem. Soc.* 2615 [1930], *J. Am. Chem. Soc.*, **52**, 4168 [1930]), and the weight of opinion at present (see Levene and Raymond, *Ann. Rev. Biochem.*, **1**, 213 [1932]) seems to be in favor of the views of the latter school.

the lactone obtained from tetramethyl glucose. By analogy, it has therefore been inferred that the tetramethyl glucose is also an amylene-oxide.

Space Relations of the H and OH Attached to Carbon Atom 1. The positions of the H and OH, attached to carbon atom 1, in the formulas of α- and β-glucose, are not arbitrarily chosen, but are based partly on the following observations:

(1) The conductivity of α-glucose in boric acid solution diminishes during mutarotation as it is converted to β-glucose, whereas the conductivity of β-glucose is increased under similar conditions as α-glucose is formed. The change in conductivity takes place with the same velocity as the mutarotation, showing that the two phenomena are related. It has been shown that an alcohol increases the conductivity of a boric acid solution if it has two hydroxyl groups attached to two neighboring carbon atoms and situated in the same plane on the same side of the carbon chain. Accordingly, it is concluded that the OH groups attached to carbon atoms 1 and 2 are on the same side in α-glucose and on opposite sides in β-glucose.

(2) On heating α-glucose (150–155° C. under a pressure of 15 mm.),

$$
\text{α-glucosan, } \overset{\displaystyle \overbrace{}^{\textstyle O}}{CH_2OH-CH-CHOH-CHOH-CH-CH}, \text{ is obtained. This}
$$

$$\underset{\diagdown O \diagup}{}$$

has an ethylene-oxide structure and is formed by the loss of HOH from the two hydroxyl groups attached to carbon atoms 1 and 2. On the assumption that the hydroxyls are able to react with one another only when they are on the same side of the carbon chain, it is inferred that the OH group attached to carbon atom 1, in α-glucose, occupies the position as represented by the formula on p. 43. β-glucose yields β-glucosan,[35]

$$
\overset{\displaystyle \overbrace{}^{\textstyle O}}{\underset{\underbrace{}_{\textstyle O}}{CH_2-CH-CHOH-CHOH-CHOH-CH.}}
$$

Cyclic Forms of Glucose, Other than the Amylene-oxide. "Active Glucose." The stable form of glucose, as well as of mannose, galactose, fructose, xylose, arabinose, and probably other sugars, in aqueous solu-

[35] For a more complete and more critical discussion of this question, see Armstrong's "The Carbohydrates and Glucosides," p. 44. See also, P. A. Levene and H. Sobotka, *J. Biol. Chem.*, **67**, 759 (1926). Reference may also be made to the important papers of J. Böeseken and associates, *Ber.*, **46**, 2612 (1913); *Proc. Roy. Acad. Amsterdam*, **18**, 1654 (1916); *Rec. trav. chim.*, **40**, 354 (1921); and to the paper of M. Levy and E. A. Doisy, *J. Biol. Chem.*, **84**, 749 (1929).

tion, is the amylene-oxide form, but it is unlikely that this is the only cyclic structure which glucose (and the other sugars) may possess. Indeed, a considerable amount of evidence points to the existence of a so-called " active " (or reactive) glucose which is not an amylene-oxide compound. Some of the observations which have led to this belief may be pointed out.[36]

(1) Different sugars ferment at different velocities; yet the intermediate and final products are identical. This is also true of the biological oxidation of various sugars. The assumption is that the different sugars are changed to a form common to all, which then undergoes decomposition, and that this form is the so-called " active " glucose.

(2) Glycogen is more rapidly converted to lactic acid than free glucose. The conclusion drawn is that glycogen glucose is in a more labile state than are the common forms of glucose.

(3) Various derivatives of glucose have been shown to exist as several ring isomers which differ from one another in their stability.

As to the nature of the " active " glucose, there is some basis for the view that it is the γ-, or butylene-oxide form. Levene is of the opinion, however, that in aqueous sugar solutions, all theoretically possible cyclic structures may co-exist in equilibrium with one another (i.e., the α- and β-modifications of the ethylene oxide, the α- and β-modifications of the propylene-oxide, as well as the two isomers of the butylene-oxide and amylene-oxide forms of glucose). The amylene-oxide, being the most stable, predominates. The other forms may be present, usually in insignificant amounts, but are brought into existence individually by agents which act specifically or preferentially on one lactal form and none other.

In considering the nature of " active " glucose the remarkable instability exhibited by sugars in alkaline solution cannot be neglected. Sugars are weak acids, and as such form ionizable salts with base. It is to this property that Shaffer and Friedemann[37] have attributed the instability and reactivity of the sugars. That the " active " forms of the sugars may be *sugar ions* is a significant concept. The action of alkali on glucose and other sugars will be dealt with shortly.

The main conclusion to be derived from the discussion in the preceding paragraphs is that glucose in solution does not behave as though it were a compound having a fixed molecular structure. On the contrary, it is to be regarded as existing in at least five and possibly in nine different forms, one of which is represented as the open-chain aldehyde, and the other eight possessing cyclic configurations (ethylene-oxide,

[36] P. A. Levene, *Chem. Rev.*, **5**, 1 (1928).

[37] *J. Biol. Chem.*, **86**, 345 (1930).

propylene-oxide, butylene-oxide, and amylene-oxide).[38] Of these the amylene-oxide form predominates, the others being usually present in very small amounts. The various forms are in equilibrium with one another, and under appropriate conditions are convertible one into another. Nor does this concept apply only to glucose. It is very likely that what has been said with regard to this sugar applies with equal force to the other simple carbohydrates.

The Action of Alkali on Glucose and Other Monosaccharides. If d-glucose is treated with a dilute basic solution, such as 0.05 N Ca(OH)$_2$, it changes its optical rotation, which ultimately reaches an equilibrium. The equilibrium mixture contains d-glucose, d-fructose, and d-mannose, as well as small amounts of d-glutose, and d-pseudofructose.[39] This conversion, first studied by Lobry de Bruyn,[40] also occurs if d-fructose or d-mannose is treated with alkali, the final products being the same as with glucose. It seems that in these interconversions, the α- and β-carbon atoms are involved. It is believed that glucose, fructose, and mannose are capable of forming an enol which is common to all, and that from this enol the three sugars are regenerated. The relationship may be represented as follows:

$$d\text{-mannose}$$
$$\updownarrow$$
$$\text{CHOH}$$
$$\|$$
$$\text{C—OH}$$
$$|$$
$$\text{HO—C—H}$$
$$d\text{-glucose} \leftrightharpoons \qquad | \qquad \rightleftharpoons d\text{-fructose}$$
$$\text{H—C—OH}$$
$$|$$
$$\text{H—C—OH}$$
$$|$$
$$\text{CH}_2\text{OH}$$

Enol form common
to glucose, fructose
and mannose

In more concentrated alkaline solutions, the sugars are oxidized spontaneously in the presence of air, with the formation of a large num-

[38] If the α- and β- isomers of the hexylene-oxide, ϵ or $< 1 : 6 >$ form, the existence of which is questioned, were included, the total number of glucose isomerides would be eleven.

[39] Glutose, when represented in the noncyclic form, is CH_2OH—$CHOH$—CO—$CHOH$—$CHOH$—CH_2OH. Pseudofructose differs from fructose (p. 54) in the β-carbon atom configuration.

[40] *Rec. trav. chim.*, **14**, 156, 203 (1895).

ber of simpler compounds.   Nef[41] was of the opinion that from glucose
at least 93 substances are formed in this way, and possibly as many
as 116 if those compounds are included which result from the resynthesis
of the initial fragments of glucose disintegration.

The acidic property of sugars has been a subject of investigation in
Shaffer's laboratory.[42]   For glucose, fructose, and sucrose, Urban and
Shaffer have recently obtained the following values for the first two
dissociation constants, at 25° C.:

	pK_1	pK_2
Glucose....................	12.09	13.85
Fructose...................	11.68	13.24
Sucrose....................	12.60	13.52

The existence of a third acidic group has been considered, but
Urban and Williams were unsuccessful in obtaining evidence of a third
dissociation constant below pH 13.6, for any of the sugars studied, with
the possible exception of lactose.

It is thus seen that a moderate alkalinity is required to bring out
the first acidic group and a high alkalinity the second and third,
assuming the last to exist.   And, as has been stated previously, it is in
the presence of sufficient alkali to form salts that the sugars acquire
their greatest instability and reactivity.   This has been clearly brought
out in a series of remarkable experiments by Shaffer and Friedemann.[37]
These investigators determined the relation of the degree of alkalinity
to the non-oxidative transformation of various sugars into the so-called
saccharinic acids (C_3, C_4, etc., acids) and lactic acid.   They found that
a high alkalinity favored the yield of lactic acid, while low alkalinity or
a high sugar concentration and a high temperature lowered the yield.

The Structural Relationship of the Monosaccharides.   Two methods
have been especially valuable in studying the structural relationship of
the simple sugars.   The first method is the so-called cyanhydrin synthesis of Kiliani, which is based on the reaction of aldehydes and ketones
with HCN.   If a sugar, such as d-glucose, is treated with HCN, the corresponding nitrile is formed, which on hydrolysis yields an acid containing one carbon atom more than the original sugar; in this case a
seven-carbon sugar acid (glucoheptonic acid).   On reduction, the acid is

[41] *Ann. Chem.*, **357**, 214 (1907); **403**, 204 (1913).
[42] *J. Biol. Chem.*, **94**, 697 (1932); **100**, 237 (1933).

converted to the aldehyde, glucoheptose.[43] By this method it is possible to produce from d-glycerose the two four-carbon monosaccharides, d-erythrose and d-threose. From these the four d-pentoses may be synthesized and, in turn, the eight d-hexoses. Continuing the cyanhydrin synthesis, it is possible to prepare heptoses, octoses and even higher monosaccharides.

The second method is that of Wohl, which depends on the reaction of aldehydes and ketones with hydroxylamine with the formation of oximes. From glucose, glucose-oxime is formed. When this is treated with concentrated NaOH, it yields the nitrile of gluconic acid, which, on heating, decomposes to HCN and arabinose.[44] This method of degradation of sugars, together with Kiliani's method of synthesis, have been especially useful in determining the stereo-isomeric relationship of the sugars.

It may be pointed out again that the d and l nomenclature of the sugars is not based on the direction of their optical rotation, but on their relationship to d- and l-glycerose, or to d- and l-glucose. On p. 53, this relationship is shown by means of formulas, the arrangement being based on Emil Fischer's classification. The members of the l-series, derived from l-glycerose, may be represented in a similar way.

Hexose Sugars. Of the hexoses, those that are found free in nature are d-glucose and d-fructose. The former is widely distributed in fruit and plant juices (grape, sweet corn, onions, unripe potatoes). It is also referred to as grape sugar, or dextrose. Glucose is a normal constituent of the blood and is utilized by the tissues in the production of energy. It may be obtained readily by enzymic or acid hydrolysis of maltose, lactose, sucrose, dextrin, starch, glycogen, and cellulose. The products of sucrose hydrolysis are fructose and glucose. Sucrose is dextro-rotatory $[\alpha]_D = + 66.5°$. As fructose is more strongly levo-rotatory, the mixture obtained after sucrose is hydrolyzed is levo-rotatory $[\alpha]_D = - 19.84°$.

[43] $$\underset{\text{Glucose}}{C_6H_{12}O_6} + HCN = \underset{\substack{\text{Nitrile of} \\ \text{glucoheptonic acid}}}{C_6H_{13}O_6 \cdot CN};$$

$$C_6H_{13}O_6 \cdot CN + 2H_2O = \underset{\text{Glucoheptonic acid}}{C_6H_{13}O_6 \cdot COOH} + NH_3;$$

$$C_6H_{13}O_6 \cdot COOH \xrightarrow{-0} \underset{\text{Glucoheptose}}{C_7H_{14}O_7}.$$

[44] $$\underset{\text{Glucose}}{C_5H_{11}O_5 \cdot CHO} + \underset{\text{Hydroxylamine}}{NH_2OH} = \underset{\text{Glucose-oxime}}{C_5H_{11}O_5 \cdot CH : NOH} + H_2O;$$

$$C_5H_{11}O_5 \cdot CH : NOH + NaOH = \underset{\substack{\text{Nitrile of} \\ \text{gluconic acid}}}{C_5H_{11}O_5 \cdot CN} + NaOH + H_2O;$$

$$C_5H_{11}O_5 \cdot CN \xrightarrow{\text{heat}} \underset{\text{Arabinose}}{C_5H_{10}O_5} + HCN.$$

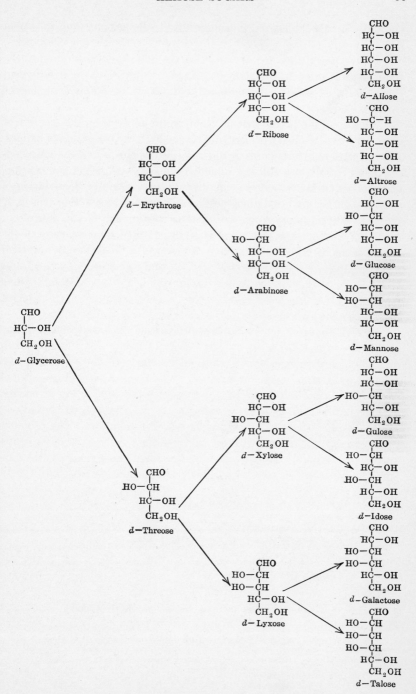

Tetrose, Pentose and Hexose Sugars Derived from *d*-Glycerose

The term " invert sugar " has therefore been applied in referring to the mixture of glucose and fructose resulting from the hydrolysis, or " inversion," of sucrose.

Fructose may be prepared readily by acid hydrolysis of inulin. Together with glucose it occurs in fruit juices and in honey. From " invert sugar," the ordinary crystalline glucose and fructose are isolated. The latter is believed to be an amylene-oxide compound (Haworth and Hirst).[45] It seems, however, that as it exists in the sucrose molecule, the fructose is in the labile or γ-form. The γ-fructose itself has not been isolated, but when heptamethyl-sucrose is hydrolyzed, the fructose component is obtained in the form of tetramethyl-γ-fructose. Accordingly, it has been assumed that, immediately on its liberation from its union with glucose, the labile variety passes into the more stable δ-variety of fructose. This may be represented as follows:

Sucrose → glucose (normal) + fructose (labile or γ)

crystalline fructose (normal)
on isolation

The normal variety of fructose, of which there is, of course, both an α- and a β-form, is represented as having an amylene-oxide configuration:

$$
\begin{array}{c}
CH_2OH \\
|\\
HO-C------\\
|\\
HO-C-H \\
|\qquad\qquad O\\
H-C-OH \\
|\\
H-C-OH \\
|\\
CH_2------
\end{array}
$$

Fructose (β-Form)

d-Galactose is the constituent sugar of the polysaccharides which are classified as galactans. These are widely distributed in plants, being especially abundant in algae, and lichens, including agar-agar and Irish moss. By hydrolytic methods, galactose may be conveniently prepared from these substances, as well as from the wood of the western larch. Galactose also occurs in saponins. It is a constituent sugar of the disaccharide lactose (milk sugar) and is likewise a component of certain fatlike substances, present in brain tissue, known as cerebrosides (p. 83).

[45] *J. Chem. Soc.*, **129**, 1858 (1926).

Snails and especially the eggs of snails are said to contain a galactogen, an analogue of glycogen.

Mannose is the constituent sugar of the mannans, a group of poly-saccharides widely distributed in plants, but especially abundant in the endosperm of the seed of the tagua palm. Levene and Mori[46] have reported mannose to be a constituent of ovomucoid, a conjugated protein (p. 88) which occurs in egg white.

Pentose Sugars. The pentoses have been detected, in small amounts, in the free form, in certain plants, but for the most part they occur in polysaccharide combination as pentosans. Cherry gum yields *l*-arabinose. Hydrolysis of straw, hay, oat hulls, corn cobs, and most woods yields *d*-xylose. *d*-Ribose is a normal constituent of the mono-nucleotides, guanylic and inosinic acids, as well as of plant nucleic acid. The sugar in animal nucleic acid (thymonucleic acid) is a desoxyaldopen-tose, namely, *d*-2-ribodesose.

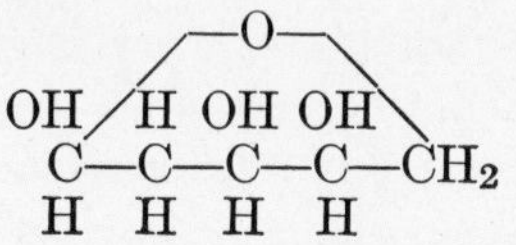

$$
\begin{array}{c}
\overbrace{}^{O} \\
\overset{OH}{\underset{H}{C}}\!\!\overset{H}{\underset{H}{-C}}\!\!\overset{OH}{\underset{H}{-C}}\!\!\overset{OH}{\underset{H}{-C}}\!\!-CH_2
\end{array}
$$

A pentose is present in the urine in the relatively rare condition known as pentosuria. Various workers have been unable to agree regarding the kind of pentose, some considering it to be arabinose, others ribose, still others xylose, etc. Greenwald[47] found *l*-xyloketose in four cases of pentosuria. It is possible that different types of pentosuria may exist.

Structurally, the aldo-pentoses, in their stable form, are believed to have the amylene-oxide configuration.

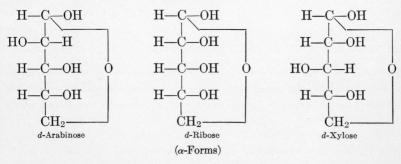

d-Arabinose   d-Ribose   d-Xylose

(α-Forms)

---

[46] *J. Biol. Chem.*, **84**, 49 (1929). The occurrence of mannose in association with proteins has also been reported by Fränkel and Jellinek (*Biochem. Z.*, **185**, 392 [1927]) and by Rimington (*Biochem. J.*, **23**, 430 [1929]); see also M. Sørensen and G. Hau-gaard, Comptes-Rendus des Trav. du Lab. Carlsberg,.**19**, No. 12 (1933).

[47] *J. Biol. Chem.*, **89**, 501 (1930).

Relation of the Sugars to Pyran, the Pyranose Series. As a further development in our conception of the molecular configuration of the normal sugars, Haworth[48] has made the generalization that they are structurally related to pyran:

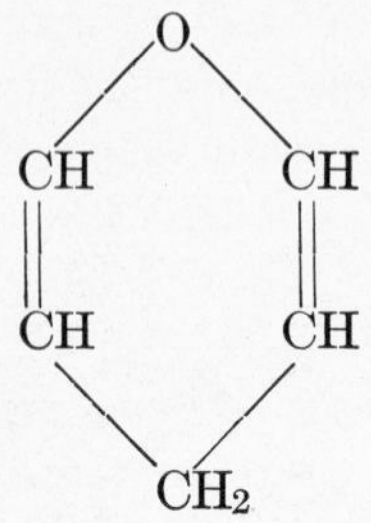

$$
\begin{array}{c}
\text{O} \\
\text{CH} \quad\quad \text{CH} \\
\text{\Vert} \quad\quad\quad \text{\Vert} \\
\text{CH} \quad\quad \text{CH} \\
\text{CH}_2
\end{array}
$$

On examining the formulas representing the stable forms of glucose (p. 43), fructose (p. 54), and the pentoses (p. 55), it will be observed that these contain a six-atom ring, five of the atoms being C, the sixth O. The six-atom ring is appropriately represented as a hexagon, and in the formulation of the normal sugars, the addenda (hydrogen atoms, hydroxyl and primary alcohol groups) may be arranged in accordance with the available knowledge of the constitution of the respective sugar. Accordingly, d-glucose (β-form) may be represented as follows:

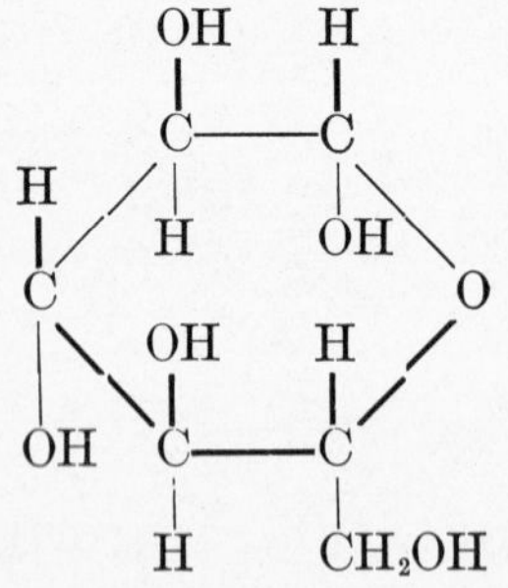

$$
\begin{array}{c}
\text{OH} \quad\quad \text{H} \\
\text{C} \text{---} \text{C} \\
\text{H} \quad \text{H} \quad\quad \text{OH} \\
\text{C} \quad\quad\quad\quad \text{O} \\
\text{OH} \quad\quad \text{H} \\
\text{OH} \quad \text{C} \text{---} \text{C} \\
\text{H} \quad\quad \text{CH}_2\text{OH}
\end{array}
$$

Indeed, Haworth has recommended the revision of the present nomenclature of the sugars and the adoption of a terminology according to which the normal sugars would be distinguished, because of their relation to pyran, as *pyranoses*. Thus arabinose, xylose, and ribose can be designated as *arabo-pyranose*, *xylo-pyranose*, and *ribo-pyranose*.

[48] W. N. Haworth, "The Constitution of Sugars," Edward Arnold Co., London, 1929.

Similarly, glucose, galactose, mannose, and fructose can be described as *gluco-pyranose, galacto-pyranose, manno-pyranose, and fructo-pyranose.*

Relation of the Labile or γ-Sugars to Furan, the Furanose Series. The γ-oxide forms of glucose, fructose, and other sugars have not been isolated, but certain of their derivatives have been prepared and studied. Sufficient evidence has accumulated to show that these have a five-atom ring structure. They, and presumably, therefore, the sugars from which they are derived, may be considered, accordingly, as being related to furan:

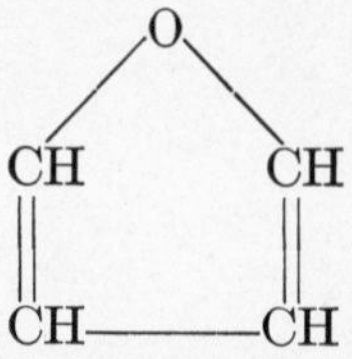

$$
\begin{array}{ccc}
& \text{O} & \\
\diagup & & \diagdown \\
\text{CH} & & \text{CH} \\
\| & & \| \\
\text{CH} & \text{—} & \text{CH}
\end{array}
$$

Analogous to the description of the normal or amylene-oxide forms of the sugars as pyranoses, the γ-oxide forms may be designated as *furanoses.*

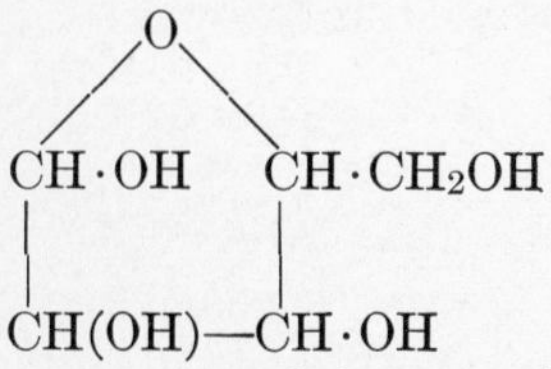

$$
\begin{array}{ccc}
& \text{O} & \\
\diagup & & \diagdown \\
\text{CH·OH} & & \text{CH·CH}_2\text{OH} \\
| & & | \\
\text{CH(OH)} & \text{—} & \text{CH·OH}
\end{array}
$$

A γ-pentose (e.g. xylo-furanose, and also arabo-, ribo-, lyxo-furanose)

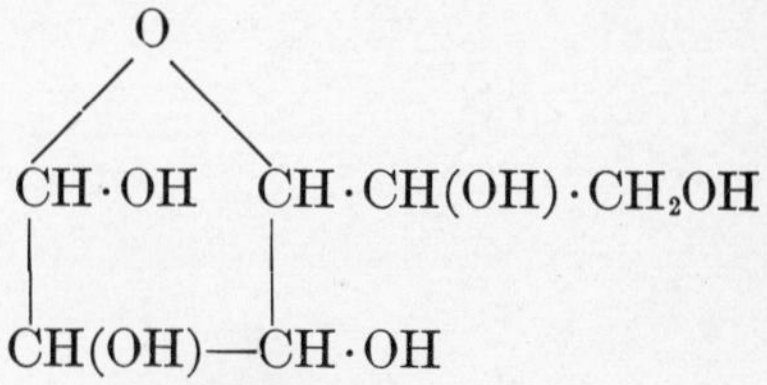

$$
\begin{array}{ccc}
& \text{O} & \\
\diagup & & \diagdown \\
\text{CH·OH} & & \text{CH·CH(OH)·CH}_2\text{OH} \\
| & & | \\
\text{CH(OH)} & \text{—} & \text{CH·OH}
\end{array}
$$

A γ-Aldo-hexose (Gluco (etc.)-furanose)

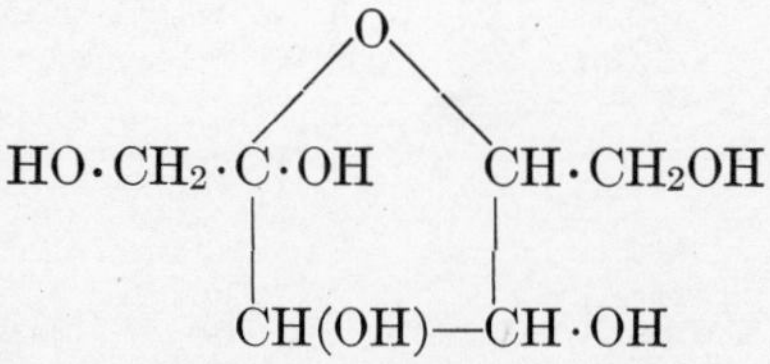

$$
\begin{array}{ccc}
& \text{O} & \\
\diagup & & \diagdown \\
\text{HO·CH}_2\text{·C·OH} & & \text{CH·CH}_2\text{OH} \\
| & & | \\
\text{CH(OH)} & \text{—} & \text{CH·OH}
\end{array}
$$

A γ-Keto-hexose (Fructo-furanose)

Occurrence and Constitution of the Disaccharides. The physiologically important dissacharides are maltose, lactose, and sucrose.

Maltose (malt sugar) may be formed from starch by incomplete hydrolysis of the latter. It is a constituent of germinating cereals and malt. The sugar crystallizes in small needles, is a reducing agent, is fermented by yeasts, forms an osazone with phenylhydrazine, and exhibits mutarotation. Maltose is α- or β-glucose α-glucoside, and, on hydrolysis by acid or the enzyme maltase, yields glucose. It is represented stereochemically by the following formula:[49]

α-Maltose (α-glucose-α-glucoside)

Two isomeric modifications, α-maltose (α-glucose-α-glucoside) and β-maltose (β-glucose-α-glucoside), are possible, depending on the arrangement of the H and OH attached to carbon atom 1 of the glucose portion of the molecule.

Lactose (milk sugar) occurs in the milk of mammals. It is hydrolyzed to glucose and galactose either by acid or by the enzyme lactase. Lactose is a reducing sugar, forms an osazone when treated with phenylhydrazine, and exhibits mutarotation. Accordingly, it must have a free or a potentially free aldehyde group and should be present in at least

[49] The molecular configuration of maltose may also be represented by the formula:

α-gluco-pyranose   α-gluco-pyranose

Maltose (α-form)

The free reducing group of the disaccharide is indicated by the asterisk.

two isomeric forms.   Lactose is believed to have the following molecular configuration:[50]

Lactose (α- or β-glucose-β-galactoside)

Sucrose (saccharose, cane sugar) occurs in the sugar beet, sorghum cane, sugar maple, pineapple, in the roots of carrots, and in many other plants.   It is fermented by yeast, the first step being the inversion of the sucrose by the enzyme invertase which is present in the yeast.   Sucrose has no reactive aldehyde group, is therefore non-reducing, does not form an osazone, and does not exhibit mutarotation.   On hydrolysis it yields fructose and glucose.   As has been pointed out previously (p. 54), the fructose in the sucrose molecule is believed to have the γ-oxide ring

[50] Lactose may also be represented by the following formula:

β-galacto-pyranose   β-gluco-pyranose

Lactose (β-form)

(fructo-furanose). Sucrose may be represented by the following structural formula:[51]

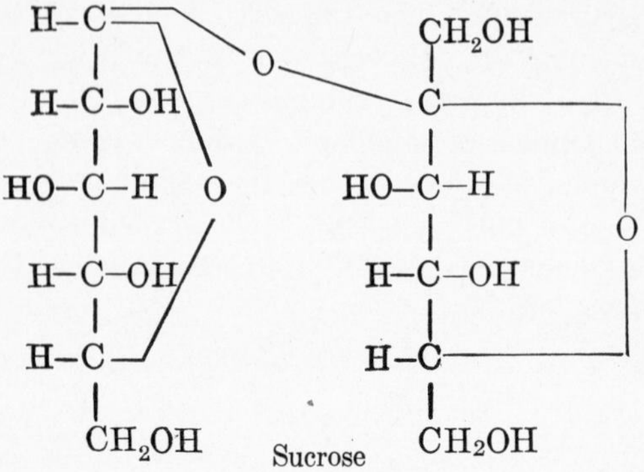

Sucrose

A number of disaccharides have been obtained from naturally occurring trisaccharides. From *gentianose*, a trisaccharide (glucose-glucose-fructose) present in the roots of the gentian, *gentiobiose* (glucose-β-glucoside) has been obtained. It is stated that in the acid hydrolysis of starch, 5.7 per cent of it is converted into gentiobiose. This disaccharide is also formed when *d*-glucose is acted on by strong hydrochloric acid. It is apparently identical with " isomaltose," which Emil Fischer obtained by the condensation of glucose. *Cellobiose*, or cellose (glucose-β-glucoside) is obtained by the partial hydrolysis of either cotton or wood cellulose.[52] *Melibiose* (glucose-β-galactoside) is formed from

[51] Sucrose may also be represented by the formula:

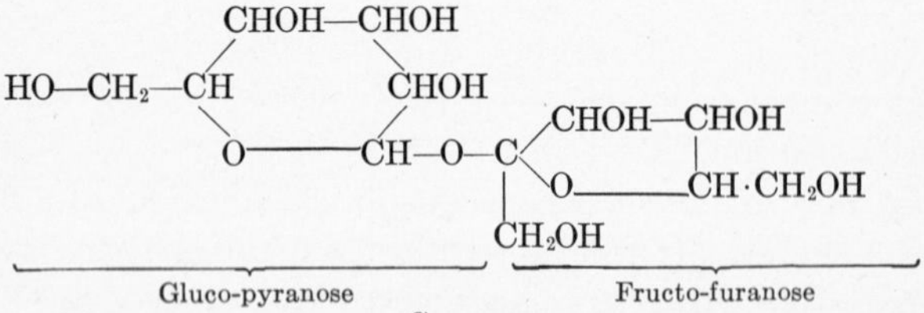

Gluco-pyranose   Fructo-furanose

Sucrose

[52] Both gentiobiose and cellobiose are glucose-β-glucose. The difference in the chemical constitution of the two sugars is indicated by the following formulas:

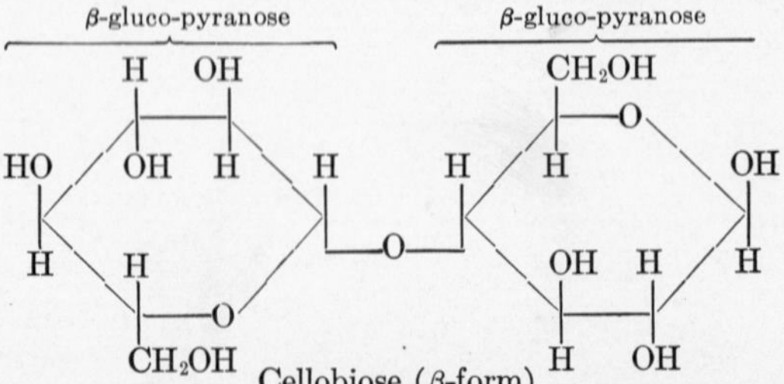

β-gluco-pyranose   β-gluco-pyranose

Cellobiose (β-form)

Footnote continued on opposite page

raffinose (fructose-glucose-galactose) by incomplete hydrolysis. Raffinose occurs in the sugar beet. *Turanose* (fructose + glucose) is obtained by hydrolyzing the trisaccharide *melezitose* or *melicitose* (glucose-glucose-fructose). Melezitose is a constituent of the sap of certain trees, such as the larch, scrub pine, and Douglas fir.

The Specific Optical Rotation of Various Sugars. Owing to the presence of asymmetric carbon atoms, the sugars have the property of rotating the plane of polarized light. The specific rotatory power, or specific rotation, determined at 20° C. in sodium light (D line) may be computed from the formula:

$$(\alpha)_{\substack{20° \\ D}} = \frac{a \times 100}{lc}$$

in which a = observed rotation, l = length of the polariscope tube in decimeters, and c = number of grams of optically active substance per 1 cc. The specific rotation (α) of a given compound is defined as the angle of rotation through which a plane of polarized light (the source of illumination is sodium light) is turned in passing through a tube 1 decimeter in length, filled with a solution containing 1 gram of the substance to 1 cc. Both the temperature, 20° C., and the source of illumination, sodium light (D line), are stated in the formula.

Determinations have been made of the specific rotation of a large variety of substances. For sucrose, the value is +66.5°. Special types of the polariscope have been designed for use in sugar analyses. These are called saccharimeters. When the specific rotation of a given compound is known, its concentration in a solution of unknown strength may be determined from the observed angle of rotation which is produced by the solution.

In Table VIII are given the specific optical rotations of a number of mutarotating sugars. It will be recalled that the shift in optical rotation which is exhibited by a sugar such as glucose, galactose, maltose,

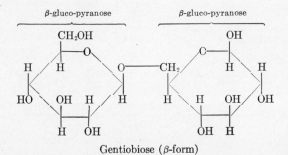

Gentiobiose (β-form)

etc., in solution, is due to the conversion of one isomeric modification to another.

TABLE VIII

SPECIFIC ROTATION IN WATER OF MUTAROTATING SUGARS

(After Abderhalden)*

Sugar	α-Form	Equilibrium	β-Form
d-Glucose....................	+113.4°	+52.2°	+19°
d-Galactose..................	+144	+80.5	+52
d-Mannose...................	+34	+14.6	-17
d-Fructose...................	-21	-92	-133.5
d-Xylose.....................	+92	+19	-20
d-Arabinose..................	-54	-105	-175
Lactose......................	+90	+55.3	+35
Maltose......................	+168	+136	+118

* Taken from data in "Biochemisches Handlexikon," vol. 10, p. 366.

The Polysaccharides: Cellulose, Starch, and Glycogen. *Cellulose* is the term applied to a class of compounds which in common with starch and glycogen may be designated by the empirical formula $(C_6H_{10}O_5)_x$ and classified as hexosans or glucosans. On complete hydrolysis, cellulose, from whatever source, yields glucose. In controlled hydrolyses, the disaccharide cellobiose may be obtained. Cellulose is the chief constituent of wood, where it occurs in combination with a substance called lignin; it is found also in the fibrous or supporting tissue of plants and the walls of plant cells. It occurs in a relatively pure form in cotton. With the exception of the covering of tunicates, cellulose is found exclusively in plants.

Cellulose is relatively resistant to the action of mild chemical reagents. Weak acids and alkalies produce very little effect. In higher concentrations, acids hydrolyze cellulose. Alkali gelatinizes and renders it translucent. Many valuable commercial products are derived from cellulose: paper, mercerized cotton, artificial silk, celluloid, collodion, cellophane, pyroxylin lacquers, varnishes, leather substitutes, motion picture films, guncotton, etc.

Herbivorous animals, particularly the ruminants, utilize a considerable proportion of the cellulose ingested. In man, this is not an important food, although it is stated that young and tender cellulose (sometimes referred to as hemicellulose), present, for example, in cabbage and lettuce, is utilized to some degree. The chief value of cellulose in the human dietary is ascribed to the fact that it provides " bulk " to the intestinal contents, thereby facilitating peristalsis and the elimination of food residues.

Our knowledge of the configuration of the cellulose molecule, as well as of the mode of linkage of the glucose units, is at present incomplete. The X-ray studies of Sponsler and Dore[53] on the constitution of ramie cellulose indicate that the glucose units of which it is composed probably exist in the amylene-oxide (pyranose) form.[54]

Starch is the principal form in which carbohydrate is stored in the plant and is especially abundant in seeds, bulbs, and tubers. In some plants (apple, banana), during the ripening process, starch is converted into glucose; in others (corn, peas, etc.), the reverse occurs, namely, conversion of sugar into starch, a process which seems to require the presence of potassium. In the plant, the starch occurs in granules which have concentric stratifications. These are characteristic for any given species of plant.

In the raw state, starch is not soluble in cold water, nor is it readily digested by starch-splitting, or amylolytic, enzymes. This is due to the resistance of the outer layer of the starch granule. Starch is a hydrophilic colloid and may take up a considerable amount of water. When it is heated in water, the granules swell but do not necessarily rupture. Prolonged heating or fine grinding may cause the disintegration of starch granules. After raw starch has been subjected to grinding in a ball mill it is found that a portion will go into solution in cold water.

When treated with iodine, most starches give an indigo-blue color. Among the first products which starch yields on hydrolysis are the dextrins. The more complex dextrins, when treated with iodine, give colors varying from purple in the case of amylodextrin to a reddish brown color given by erythrodextrin. The simpler dextrins (achroodextrin) yield no color when treated with iodine. The final product of the enzymic hydrolysis of starch by amylase is maltose. It requires the action of the enzyme maltase to complete the hydrolysis to the glucose stage. The conversion of the starch to glucose is not quantitative, however. An unfermentable residue of gentiobiose remains. Starch is one of the most important constituents of the human diet, making up 50 to 70 per cent of the solid matter of most cereal grains and about 80 per cent of the solids of the potato. It is of interest to note that a

[53] "Colloid Symposium Monograph," Vol. 4, 174 (1926), Chemical Catalog Co., New York.

[54] For a more detailed discussion of cellulose, the student is referred to Gortner's "Outlines of Biochemistry," pp. 562–569.

small amount of phosphorus exists in combination in starch; the content in potato starch has been found to be about 0.06 per cent.[55]

Glycogen is the reserve carbohydrate of the animal body and is stored principally in the liver and muscles. It is widely distributed in the animal kingdom and is especially abundant in molluscs, echinoderms, and other invertebrates. Certain fungi and yeasts likewise contain glycogen. In these plants, chlorophyll is lacking, a fact which may point to a mechanism of carbohydrate synthesis different from that in most plants. When purified, glycogen is a white amorphous powder, odorless and tasteless, having many properties in common with starch. Dissolved in water, it gives an opalescent colloidal solution. Iodine colors glycogen red-brown or deep red. Glycogen is apparently acted upon by starch-splitting enzymes.

Glycogenesis, or the synthesis of glycogen, takes place very rapidly in the animal body. The reverse process, glycogenolysis, is likewise a rapid one, especially when the tissues require carbohydrate for combustion. These transformations will be considered in greater detail elsewhere. Acid or enzyme hydrolysis of glycogen yields glucose as the final product, the intermediate products formed resembling the dextrins obtained from starch.

Not all polysaccharides are equally useful from the standpoint of nutrition. This question has been studied by Swartz and others. No enzymes capable of hydrolyzing the mannans, galactans, and levulans have been found in the digestive tract of man. Swartz,[56] nevertheless, observed that appreciable amounts of certain mannans and galactans disappeared from the alimentary tract. A similar utilization of inulin has been observed in the white rat by Bodey, Lewis, and Huber.[57] These polysaccharides may have become available for purposes of nutrition as a result of bacterial changes rather than because of enzymes secreted in the alimentary tract. On the whole, however, it seems

---

[55] For a discussion of the chemical structure of starch and glycogen the student is referred to a review by J. C. Irvine, *Chem. Rev.*, **4**, 225 (1927), as well as to the monograph by W. N. Haworth, "The Constitution of Sugars," Chap. X, London (1929). R. P. Walton's "A Comprehensive Survey of Starch Chemistry," Vol. I, Chemical Catalog Co., Inc., New York (1928), is an authoritative work of reference in the field of starch chemistry.

The microscopy of starches is comprehensively described in E. T. Reichert's "The Differentiation and Specificity of Starches in Relation to Genera, Species, etc. Stereochemistry Applied to Protoplasmic Processes and Products, and as a Strictly Scientific Basis for the Classification of Plants and Animals." Parts I and II, Carnegie Institution of Washington, Pub. 173, Washington, D. C. (1913).

[56] *Trans. Conn. Acad. Sci.*, **16**, 247 (1909).

[57] *J. Biol. Chem.*, **75**, 715 (1927).

quite certain that the polysaccharides other than starch, glycogen, and cellulose contribute little to the energy requirements in human and animal nutrition.

Immunologically Specific Polysaccharides. Soluble polysaccharides have been isolated from certain bacterial cultures which react with the antisera of the respective bacteria to form precipitates. For example, the polysaccharides obtained from fluid cultures of the various types of pneumococci, in dilutions as high as 1 : 6,000,000, have been found to be specific precipitants for the antisera of the corresponding organisms. Heidelberger and Goebel[58] hydrolyzed the polysaccharide from type III pneumococcus and obtained aldobionic acid, $C_{11}H_9O_{10} \cdot COOH$, which on further hydrolysis yielded glucose and glycuronic acid. More recently, Babers and Goebel[59] have estimated the molecular weight of the polysaccharide to be 118,000. A polysaccharide, to which the empirical formula $(C_{30}H_{44}O_{26})_x$ has been assigned by Goebel, is said to occur in type A Friedlander's bacillus. On hydrolysis, this polysaccharide yields aldobionic acid, glucose, and a disaccharide of unknown constitution.

The tubercle bacillus has also been found to contain a specific polysaccharide. On hydrolysis it yields d-mannose, d-arabinose,[60] and possibly galactose and other substances.[61] In addition, sugars seem to be associated with the various lipid fractions of the tubercle bacillus. The phosphatide fraction contains a polysaccharide which yields on hydrolysis three sugars, inosite, mannose, and a hexose that has not been identified as yet.[62] A carbohydrate complex containing d-arabinose, galactose, and mannose has been isolated from the wax fraction. The acetone-soluble fraction contains the non-reducing disaccharide, trehalose.

Hexosamines. Chitin, the outer covering of insects and Crustacea, yields on hydrolysis an amino-hexose, called chitosamine or glucosamine $[CHO \cdot CHNH_2 \cdot (CHOH)_3 \cdot CH_2OH]$. Glucosamine is also a constituent of certain mucoproteins or mucins, proteins present in mucous secre-

[58] M. Heidelberger, *Chem. Rev.*, **3**, 403 (1927); Heidelberger and W. F. Goebel, *J. Biol. Chem.*, **70**, 613 (1926); *ibid.*, **74**, 613 (1927). Goebel, *J. Biol. Chem.*, **74**, 619 (1927); **89**, 395 (1930).

[59] *J. Biol. Chem.*, **89**, 387 (1930).

[60] M. Maxim, *Biochem. Z.*, **223**, 404 (1930); A. G. Renfrew, *J. Biol. Chem.*, **89**, 619 (1930).

[61] G. A. C. Gough, *Biochem. J.*, **26**, 248 (1932).

[62] R. J. Anderson and E. G. Roberts, *J. Biol. Chem.*, **89**, 611 (1930); E. Chargaff and Anderson, *Z. Physiol. Chem.*, **191**, 172 (1930); Anderson and M. S. Newman, *J. Biol. Chem.*, **101**, 499 (1933).

tions, and it probably exists widely distributed in other combinations.[63]

The mucoproteins are classified as conjugated proteins (p. 88) and are characterized by having in combination a carbohydrate group. In certain of these, the carbohydrate group is mucoitin-sulfuric acid. This compound has been isolated from the mucin of the gastric mucosa, serum mucoid, ovomucoid, funis (umbilical cord) mucin, vitreous humor, and cornea.

The components of mucoitin-sulfuric acid are: sulfuric acid, acetic acid, a hexosamine which is probably glucosamine, and glycuronic acid.

Chondroproteins are mucoproteins which occur in connective tissue. The carbohydrate group in these is chondroitin-sulfuric acid.

On hydrolysis, chondroitin-sulfuric acid yields sulfuric acid, acetic acid, glycuronic acid, and a hexosamine which is probably galactosamine, also called chondrosamine.[64]

The Glucosides.   The glucosides are substances that on hydrolysis yield a sugar, usually glucose, and one or more additional products. The glucosides are very numerous and are widely distributed in plants. Familiar examples are *phlorhizin*, also spelled *phloridzin* (glucose + phloretin), which occurs in the bark of *Rosaceae*; *coniferin* (glucose + coniferyl alcohol), present in the bark of the fir tree; *salicin* (glucose + saligenin) in the bark of the willow tree; *amygdalin* (2 glucose + mandelonitrile), in the seeds of the bitter almond; *quercitrin* (rhamnose + quercetin), in the bark of dyer's oak; *sinigrin* (glucose + allyl thiocyanate + $KHSO_4$), in black mustard seeds; in the leaves of the foxglove occur: *digitalin* (glucose + digitalose [$C_7H_{14}O_5$] + digitaligenin), *digitonin* (2 glucose + galactose + digitogenin); *digitoxin* (2 digitoxose [$C_6H_{12}O_4$] + digitoxigenin).

In the animal body analogous compounds are found. The cerebrosides are usually classified with the lipids but may also be consid-

[63] S. Fränkel and C. Jellinek (*Biochem. Z.*, **185**, 392 [1927]), have reported the isolation from coagulated egg white and yolk proteins of a polysaccharide composed of glucosamine and mannose.   C. Rimington (*Biochem. J.*, **23**, 430 [1929]) has reported the isolation of a carbohydrate derivative from the purified proteins of horse serum. This is said to be a disaccharide composed of glucosamine and mannose.   P. A. Levene and T. Mori (*J. Biol. Chem.*, **84**, 49 [1929]) and P. A. Levene and A. Rothen (*ibid*, **85**, 63 [1929]) state that the carbohydrate groups of egg proteins are probably trisaccharides, composed of 1 molecule of glucosamine and 2 molecules of mannose.

[64] Formerly, chitosamine was thought to be either glucosamine or mannosamine. The evidence now seems to be that chitosamine is derived from glucose, being 2-amino glucose.   Epichitosamine, 2-amino-mannose, has been prepared synthetically. Chrondrosamine is 2-amino-galactose.

For further details concerning this interesting group of compounds the student is referred to the monograph by P. A. Levene, "Hexosamines and Mucoproteins," Longmans, Green & Co., New York. 1925.

ered as galactosides. The two more familiar cerebrosides are phrenosin and kerasin. When hydrolyzed, these yield fatty acids, galactose, and sphingosine, a nitrogenous base. Then there are the nucleosides which give on hydrolysis a sugar, d-ribose, and either a purine or pyrimidine.

Pectins. Pectins are carbohydrates of high molecular weight and colloidal properties which occur most abundantly in the parenchymatous tissues of fruits and vegetables, such as apples, oranges, grapefruit (in the last two, especially in the inner white rind), turnips, and beets. On hydrolysis, the pectins yield galacturonic acid, arabinose, and galactose. In the presense of suitable concentrations of acid and sucrose, the pectins form the familiar fruit jellies and jams.[65]

REACTIONS OF THE SUGARS

Sugars that have an aldehyde or ketone group are easily oxidized, thereby acting as reducing agents. Of the many tests that are known, a few will be described here. For detailed directions, the student is referred to biochemical laboratory manuals.

Fehling's Test. Two solutions are used: one contains copper sulfate, the other Rochelle salt and sodium or potassium hydroxide. Two or three cubic centimeters of each solution are mixed and heated. At this stage, heating should produce no change. Upon the addition of several drops of sugar solution and further heating, the solution at first becomes turbid and greenish in color. Later a yellow precipitate of cuprous hydroxide or a red precipitate of cuprous oxide separates. The cupric hydroxide which forms when the two solutions are mixed is held in solution by the tartrate (Rochelle salt is sodium-potassium tartrate). The reduction of the copper hydroxide by the sugar may be considered to take place as follows:

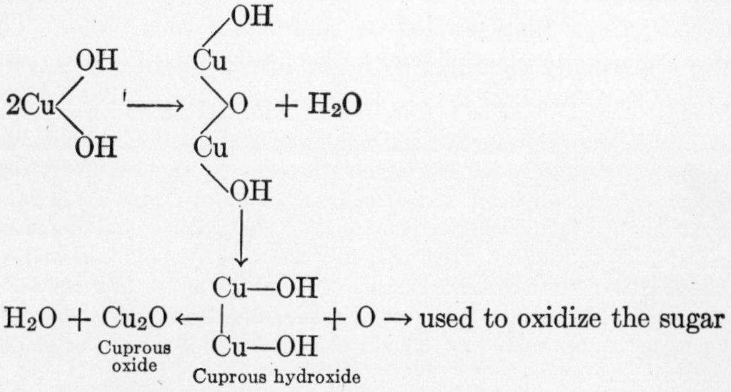

[65] The glucosides, pectins, and the related classes of substances known as gums and mucilages are more adequately described in Gortner's "Outlines of Biochemistry," John Wiley & Sons, Inc., New York, 1930, Chap. 26 (glucosides), Chap. 27 (pectins), p. 559 (mucilages), p. 560 (gums).

Fehling's method may be applied to the quantitative analysis of sugars.

Benedict's Test. This involves the use of only one solution and is more sensitive than Fehling's test. Benedict's solution contains sodium carbonate, sodium citrate, and copper sulfate. After preliminary heating of the reagent, several drops of sugar solution are added. A greenish yellow or red precipitate is produced on heating a second time. Benedict's solution and test have been modified for use in the quantitative estimation of sugar. Here, however, the end-point is indicated by the disappearance of the blue color, due to the formation of white cuprous thiocyanate (CuCNS).

Nylander-Almen Test. In this test, bismuth subnitrate is reduced by the sugar to metallic bismuth according to the following equation:

$$2Bi(OH)_2NO_3 + 2KOH \rightarrow 2Bi(OH)_3 + 2KNO_3$$

$$2Bi(OH)_3 \rightarrow Bi_2 + 3H_2O + 3O$$

Barfoed's Test. The addition of sugar solution to Barfoed's reagent (containing copper acetate in dilute acetic acid), with heating, results in the reduction of the cupric acetate to cuprous oxide. The test is given by the monosaccharides but not readily by the disaccharides; hence it is employed in distinguishing the two groups.

Reduction of Picric Acid. In alkaline solution, sugar readily reduces picric acid and its salts, supposedly to picramic acid. The reaction is only partially represented by the equation:

$$C_6H_2(NO_2)_3OH \rightarrow C_6H_2NH_2(NO_2)_2OH + O$$

Molisch Test. This is a general test for all carbohydrates as well as for other compounds containing a carbohydrate residue in their molecules. Several drops of an alcoholic solution of α-naphthol are added to the sugar solution. This is then stratified above a layer of concentrated sulfuric acid. At the zone of contact, a violet ring develops. The reaction depends on the condensation of furfural[66] or its derivatives with the α-naphthol.

Seliwanoff Reaction. This test is specific for keto-hexoses. Seliwanoff's reagent is a solution of resorcinol in hydrochloric acid. On

[66]
$$\begin{array}{c} HC\text{---}CH \\ \parallel \quad\ \ \parallel \\ HC \quad\ C\text{---}CHO \\ \diagdown\ \diagup \\ O \end{array}$$
Furfural

heating, the acid converts fructose, for example, into levulinic acid and hydroxy-methyl-furfural. The latter compound condenses with the resorcinol to form a red compound.

Orcinol-Hydrochloric Acid Test. The addition of this reagent to a solution of a pentose, with heating, results in the production of a succession of colors—violet, blue, red, and green. If the sugar solution is sufficiently concentrated, a bluish green precipitate separates.

Phloroglucinol-Hydrochloric Acid Test. The addition of phloroglucinol and hydrochloric acid to a pentose solution, with heating, results in the development of a cherry-red color. Galactose, likewise, responds to this test.

Moore's Test. Sugars are very unstable in alkaline solution. When heated with sodium hydroxide to boiling, sugar solutions develop a brown color and an odor of caramel.

Phenylhydrazine Reaction. The addition of phenylhydrazine to a solution of certain sugars (those having a free aldehyde or ketone group), with heating, results in the formation of yellow crystalline osazones, specific as to crystal form, melting point, etc. By this method it is possible to distinguish between glucose, lactose, maltose, and other sugars. Glucose, fructose, and mannose yield the same osazone. Methyl-phenylhydrazine distinguishes glucose and fructose. Sucrose does not form an osazone.

Mucic Acid Test. Oxidation of galactose with hot nitric acid yields an insoluble dicarboxylic acid, mucic acid [COOH—(CHOH)$_4$—COOH]. The corresponding dicarboxylic acid formed from glucose, namely saccharic acid, is soluble. Lactose likewise yields mucic acid, since on hydrolysis it forms both glucose and galactose.

Fermentation. Yeast ferments glucose, fructose, maltose, sucrose, and other sugars with the formation of alcohol and carbon dioxide. Ordinary brewer's yeast (*Saccharomyces cerevisiae*) does not ferment either galactose or lactose. The disaccharides are first inverted by enzymes present in yeast.

Iodine Test. Iodine yields with starch a blue or purple-blue color. With glycogen and the higher dextrins a wine-red color is produced.

CHAPTER III

THE FATS AND RELATED COMPOUNDS

Fats are the triglyceride esters of fatty acids and are closely associated in nature with the phosphatides, cerebrosides, sterols, and other substances. As regards the nomenclature applied to these compounds, there has been little uniformity. The name " lipoids " is often employed as an inclusive term, but it is also used in the more restricted sense of applying only to phosphatides and cerebrosides. Recently the term " lipides " or " lipids " has found a certain amount of usage as a general group name for the fats and fat-like substances.

The following classification has been suggested by Bloor:[1]

Lipids. Substances having the following characteristics:

a. Insolubility in water and solubility in the fat solvents, such as ether, chloroform, benzene.[2]

b. Relationship to the fatty acids as esters, either actual or potential.[3]

c. Utilization by living organisms.

Simple Lipids. Esters of the fatty acids with various alcohols.

1. Fats—esters of the fatty acids with glycerol.

2. Waxes—esters of the fatty acids with alcohols other than glycerol.

---

[1] W. R. Bloor, "Biochemistry of Fats," *Chem. Rev.*, **2**, 243 (1925–6).

[2] This property, namely solubility in fat solvents and insolubility in water, sets off the fats from the carbohydrates and proteins. Nevertheless, this property is not an absolute one; the lecithins are somewhat soluble in water and insoluble in acetone which is otherwise a good solvent for fats. The cephalins are mainly insoluble in alcohol, while sphingomyelin and the cerebrosides are difficultly soluble in ether.

[3] Bloor has wisely included this property, as well as the next one (*c*), in order to exclude organic compounds which have no biochemical relationship to the fats or fatty acids, but which from their solubilities alone would be included in the group. According to (*b*) and (*c*), the substances classified as lipids must be either ester-like combinations of the fatty acids or capable of forming such combinations, and they must be capable of performing some useful functions in living organisms.

Compound Lipids. Esters of the fatty acids containing groups in addition to an alcohol and fatty acid.

1. Phospholipids—substituted fats containing phosphoric acid and nitrogen: lecithin, cephalin (kephalin), sphingomyelin.

2. Glycolipids—compounds of the fatty acids with a carbohydrate and containing nitrogen but no phosphoric acid: phrenosin, kerasin. These are also called cerebrosides.

3. Aminolipids, sulfolipids, etc.—groups which are at present not sufficiently well characterized for classification.

Derived Lipids. Substances derived from the above groups by hydrolysis.

1. Fatty acids of various series.

2. Sterols—mostly large molecular alcohols, found in nature combined with the fatty acids and which are soluble in the fat solvents: cholesterol ($C_{27}H_{45}OH$), myricyl alcohol ($C_{30}H_{61}OH$), cetyl alcohol ($C_{16}H_{33}OH$), etc.

Fat Synthesis. In both plants and animals there is a close relationship between fats and carbohydrates, pointing to the origin of the former from the latter. For example, in the maturation of seeds, the increase in fat content is concurrent with a decrease in the amount of carbohydrate. This is shown in the following table, representing the results of analyses of almonds by Le Clerc du Sablon:[4]

TABLE IX

CONVERSION OF CARBOHYDRATE INTO FAT DURING THE MATURATION
OF THE ALMOND

Date of Gathering	Per Cent Fat	Per Cent Glucose	Per Cent Sucrose	Per Cent Starch and Dextrins
June 9	2	6	6.7	21.6
July 4	10	4.2	4.9	14.1
August 1	37	0	2.8	6.2
September 1	44	0	2.6	5.4
October 4	46	0	2.5	5.3

The reverse occurs during germination; during this process there is a decrease in the fat content of the seedlings, accompanied by an increase

[4] Cited by J. B. Leathes and H. S. Raper, "The Fats," New York and London, 2d edition, 1925, p. 103.

in the content of cellulose and other insoluble carbohydrates. This is well brought out in the following data obtained by Maquenne[5] in a study of the chemical changes occurring during the germination of *Arachis* seedlings:

TABLE X

DISAPPEARANCE OF FAT DURING GERMINATION OF ARACHIS SEEDLINGS

Age in Days	Per Cent Fat	Per Cent Carbohydrate Other than Cellulose	Cellulose and Other Insoluble Carbohydrates
0	51.39	11.55	2.51
6	49.81	8.35	3.46
10	36.19	11.09	5.01
12	29.00	12.52	5.22
18	20.45	12.34	7.29
28	12.16	9.46	9.48

Constitution of the Fat Molecule. The molecular structure of a fat may be represented by the formula:

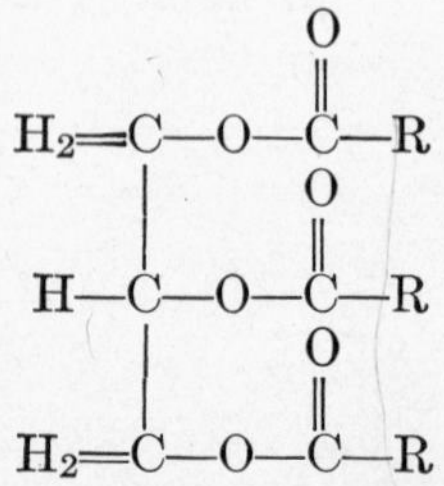

$$
\begin{array}{c}
O \\
\| \\
H_2=C-O-C-R \\
| O \\
| \| \\
H-C-O-C-R \\
| O \\
| \| \\
H_2=C-O-C-R
\end{array}
$$

in which R represents a fatty-acid radical. The following are the formulas for tripalmitin (the tripalmitic acid ester of glycerol) and triolein (the trioleic acid ester of glycerol):

$$
\begin{array}{c}
O \\
\| \\
H_2=C-O-C-(CH_2)_{14}-CH_3 \\
| O \\
| \| \\
H-C-O-C-(CH_2)_{14}-CH_3 \\
| O \\
| \| \\
H_2=C-O-C-(CH_2)_{14}-CH_3
\end{array}
$$

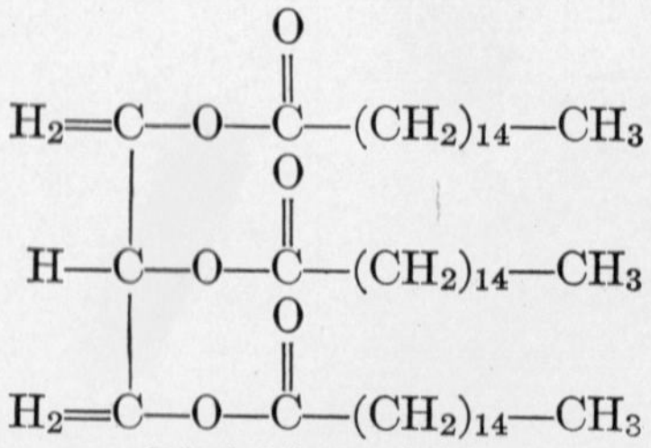

Tripalmitin or palmitin

[5] *Compt. rend.*, **127**, 625 (1898); see also the more recent results from J. R. Murlin's laboratory, *J. Gen. Physiol.*, **17**, 283, 303, 311 (1933–34).

$$H_2=C-O-\overset{O}{\overset{\|}{C}}-(CH_2)_7-\overset{H}{\overset{|}{C}}=\overset{H}{\overset{|}{C}}-(CH_2)_7-CH_3$$

$$H-\overset{|}{C}-O-\overset{O}{\overset{\|}{C}}-(CH_2)_7-\overset{H}{\overset{|}{C}}=\overset{H}{\overset{|}{C}}-(CH_2)_7-CH_3$$

$$H_2=\overset{|}{C}-O-\overset{O}{\overset{\|}{C}}-(CH_2)_7-\overset{H}{\overset{|}{C}}=\overset{H}{\overset{|}{C}}-(CH_2)_7-CH_3$$

Triolein or olein

Fats are hydrolyzed by the action of acids, alkalies, fat-splitting enzymes (lipases), and superheated steam. Three molecules of fatty acid and one of glycerol are formed as a result.

$$H_2=C-O-\overset{O}{\overset{\|}{C}}-(CH_2)_{16}-CH_3$$

$$H-\overset{|}{C}-O-\overset{O}{\overset{\|}{C}}-(CH_2)_{16}-CH_3 + 3HOH =$$

$$H_2=\overset{|}{C}-O-\overset{O}{\overset{\|}{C}}-(CH_2)_{16}-CH_3$$

Tristearin

$$H_2=C-OH$$
$$H-\overset{|}{C}-OH$$
$$H_2=\overset{|}{C}-OH$$
Glycerol
$$+$$
$$3CH_3(CH_2)_{16}-COOH$$
Stearic acid

In the presence of alkali, the fatty acid reacts to form soap. The action of alkali on fat is therefore termed saponification. Saponification, in a broader sense, is the hydrolysis of any ester with or without alkali.

Saturated Fatty Acids. Fatty acids may be divided into two general groups, the saturated and the unsaturated. With few exceptions, the fatty acids that occur in nature contain an even number of carbon atoms. However, in the blubber of porpoises is found isovaleric acid ($C_5H_{10}O_2$), and in croton oil, tiglic acid ($C_5H_8O_2$), which is an unsaturated fatty acid. The saturated fatty acids are homologues of formic acid and have the general formula $C_nH_{2n}O_2$, ($C_nH_{2n+1}COOH$).

Formic acid (HCOOH) occurs in sweat, urine, meat juice, and the bodies of ants (especially the red ant).

Acetic acid (CH_3COOH) occurs in vinegar; in smaller amounts in sweat, muscle and other tissues, feces, and urine. It occurs as a glyceride in the oil of the spindle tree.

Butyric acid, $CH_3 \cdot (CH_2)_2 \cdot COOH$, is present as a glyceride in butter, to the extent of about 6 per cent. The free fatty acid occurs in sweat.

n-Caproic acid, $CH_3 \cdot (CH_2)_4 \cdot COOH$, and n-caprylic acid, $CH_3(CH_2)_6 \cdot COOH$, occur as glycerides in butter, coconut oil, and palm-nut oil.

Capric acid, $CH_3 \cdot (CH_2)_8 \cdot COOH$, is present, in combination with glycerol, in the milk of cows and goats, as well as in coconut oil and palm-nut oil.

Lauric acid, $CH_3 \cdot (CH_2)_{10} \cdot COOH$, occurs as glyceride in milk, more abundantly in spermaceti, laurel oil, coconut oil, palm-kernel oil, etc.

Myristic acid, $CH_3 \cdot (CH_2)_{12} \cdot COOH$, is a constituent of nutmeg oil and also occurs as glyceride in milk and vegetable fats. In small amounts it has been found in lard and cod-liver oil.

Palmitic acid, $CH_3 \cdot (CH_2)_{14} \cdot COOH$, is widely distributed as glyceride in animal and vegetable fats. It occurs in cow's milk, myrtle wax, Japan wax, and palm oil. Bayberry tallow is almost pure tripalmitin. In spermaceti, a wax found in the skulls of whales and dolphins, it is present in combination as the ester of cetyl alcohol ($C_{16}H_{33}OH$); in beeswax as the ester of myricyl alcohol ($C_{30}H_{61}OH$ or $C_{31}H_{63}OH$); and in opium wax as the ester of ceryl alcohol ($C_{26}H_{53}OH$).

Stearic acid, $CH_3 \cdot (CH_2)_{16} \cdot COOH$, is contained as a glyceride in most vegetable and animal fats.

Arachidic acid, $CH_3 \cdot (CH_2)_{18} \cdot COOH$, occurs in peanut and other vegetable oils. It is also said to be present in cow's milk, and in the fat of tissues and of dermoid cysts.

There are a number of fatty acids of even greater complexity. Behenic acid, $CH_3(CH_2)_{20} \cdot COOH$, is found in the oil of ben obtained from the seeds of *Moringa pterygosperma*. Lignoceric acid, $CH_3(CH_2)_{22} \cdot COOH$, is a component of the phosphatide, sphingomyelin, and occurs also in beechwood and lignite tar. It is present as the glyceride in peanut oil. Cerotic acid ($C_{26}H_{52}O_2$) has been isolated from a variety of waxes (beeswax, carnauba wax, Chinese wax, opium wax, and wool fat). Melissic acid ($C_{30}H_{60}O_2$) occurs free in beeswax. For further details as to the distribution of the fatty acids in nature, the student is referred to Chap. I of the monograph by Leathes and Raper.

Mixed Triglycerides. The three fatty-acid radicals in a fat molecule may be all the same, as in palmitin, stearin, and olein; but it is also possible for them to differ. Thus, if the three fatty acids are all different, three combinations are possible, each representing a different mixed triglyceride. If two radicals are alike and one is different, two combinations of these radicals are possible, namely:

$$
\begin{array}{ll}
\begin{aligned}
&\quad\ \ \overset{\displaystyle O}{\overset{\|}{}} \\
H_2&=C-O-C-R_2 \\
&\ |\overset{\displaystyle O}{\overset{\|}{}} \\
H&-C-O-C-R_1 \\
&\ |\overset{\displaystyle O}{\overset{\|}{}} \\
H_2&=C-O-C-R_2
\end{aligned}
&
\begin{aligned}
&\quad\ \ \overset{\displaystyle O}{\overset{\|}{}} \\
H_2&=C-O-C-R_1 \\
&\ |\overset{\displaystyle O}{\overset{\|}{}} \\
H&-C-O-C-R_2 \\
&\ |\overset{\displaystyle O}{\overset{\|}{}} \\
H_2&=C-O-C-R_2
\end{aligned}
\end{array}
$$

Other combinations may exist. Taking into consideration the number of fatty acids occurring naturally, it is theoretically possible to have innumerable mixed triglycerides. A number of these have been isolated. Palmito-distearin occurs in lard and in beef tallow. Stearo-dipalmitin has been prepared from mutton tallow. Stearo-diolein is said to be present in the fat of the human body. Myristo-palmito-olein occurs in cacao-butter.

Unsaturated Fatty Acids. The unsaturated fatty acids contain one or more pairs of carbon atoms united by a double bond. In the oleic series of fatty acids ($C_nH_{2n-2}O_2$ or $C_nH_{2n-1}COOH$) there is one such pair. Tiglic acid, $C_5H_8O_2$, occurs in croton oil. Several isomers of the formula $C_{16}H_{30}O_2$ have been described. Hypogeic acid occurs in peanut and maize oils. Palmitoleic acid is said to be present in cod-liver oil. Physetoleic acid occurs in sperm and seal oils. The most important member of the series is oleic acid, $C_{18}H_{34}O_2$, $CH_3(CH_2)_7CH\!=\!CH(CH_2)_7COOH$, a constituent of most fats and oils, where it is present in combination with glycerol. A number of fatty acids isomeric with oleic acid have been prepared in the laboratory (elaidic and iso-oleic acids). Another isomer, rapic acid, is present as glyceride in rape or colza oil. Gadoleic acid ($C_{20}H_{38}O_2$) occurs in herring, sperm, and cod-liver oils. Erucic acid ($C_{22}H_{42}O_2$) has been found in rape-seed, mustard-seed, and cod-liver oils.

Belonging to the linoleic or linolic acid series ($C_nH_{2n-4}O_2$) and the linolenic acid series ($C_nH_{2n-6}O_2$) are fatty acids of a greater degree of unsaturation than oleic acid. Linoleic or linolic acid, $C_{18}H_{32}O_2$, $CH_3(CH_2)_6CH\!=\!CH\!-\!CH\!=\!CH(CH_2)_6COOH$, is an important constituent of cottonseed oil, and linolenic acid, $C_{18}H_{30}O_2$, $CH_3(CH_2)_5CH\!=\!CH\!-\!CH\!=\!CH\!-\!CH\!=\!CH(CH_2)_5COOH$, of linseed oil. When exposed to the air, the highly unsaturated triglycerides of linolenic acid combine readily with oxygen to form solid compounds. To this are due the useful properties of linseed and other drying oils. Clupanodonic acid ($C_{22}H_{34}O_2$) has been prepared from cod-liver and sunfish-liver oils and from herring, sardine, and whale oils. Castor oil contains a monohydroxy fatty acid, ricinoleic acid ($C_{18}H_{34}O_3$), and a dihydroxy acid, dihydroxystearic acid ($C_{18}H_{36}O_4$). Arachidonic acid ($C_{20}H_{32}O_2$) has been isolated from liver tissue of pigs and is reported to be the only highly unsaturated fatty acid occurring in thyroid, suprarenal and spleen. Arachidonic acid, and possibly tetracosapentenoic acid, $C_{24}H_{38}O_2$, are said to occur in the brain, where the highly unsaturated fatty acids seem to be present in greater proportion than in other tissues (Brown).[6] Bosworth and Brown have recently reported the

---

[6] *J. Biol. Chem.*, **83**, 777, 783 (1929); **89**, 167 (1930); A. W. Bosworth and J. B. Brown, *ibid.*, **103**, 115 (1933).

presence in butter fat of the following unsaturated fatty acids: decenoic ($C_{10}H_{18}O_2$), tetradecenoic ($C_{14}H_{26}O_2$), and a C_{22} acid of the arachidonic type. A mixture of saturated acids of high molecular weight was also found; this consisted principally of tetracosanoic (lignoceric) acid, along with small amounts of behenic and cerotic acids.

Two cyclic unsaturated fatty acids are of importance because of their therapeutic value in the treatment of leprosy. Both are found in chaulmoogra oil. They are hydnocarpic acid ($C_{16}H_{28}O_2$) and chaulmoogric acid ($C_{18}H_{32}O_2$).

CH
CH CH—CH_2—$(CH_2)_9$—COOH
CH_2–CH_2
Hydnocarpic acid

CH
CH CH—CH_2—$(CH_2)_{11}$—COOH
CH_2–CH_2
Chaulmoogric acid

Properties of Fats and Fatty Acids. *Solubility.* Mention has been made of the solubility of fats in the so-called fat solvents, ether, chloroform, and benzene, and their insolubility in water. This applies more especially to the glycerides of the higher fatty acids, for those of the lower fatty acids, such as tributyrin and tricaproin are somewhat soluble in water. In ethyl and methyl alcohol and in acetone, the fats dissolve readily in the hot, but only slightly in the cold.

All fatty acids are soluble in ether, chloroform, benzene, and hot alcohol. The fatty acids, lower than palmitic acid, are also soluble in cold alcohol. In water only the lowest members are readily soluble.

Hydroxy-fatty acids, as well as their glycerides, are insoluble in petroleum ether, a property which distinguishes them from other fatty acids and fats.

The fats themselves are very good solvents for other fats and fatty acids.

Consistency. The temperature at which a fat melts is higher than the temperature at which it solidifies. Thus, the melting-point of tristearin is 71.5° C., whereas the soldifying-point is 52.5° C. This peculiarity of having widely differing solidifying- and melting-points is not exhibited by the fatty acids. The melting-point of a fat depends upon the component fatty acids. The glycerides of the higher saturated fatty acids have higher melting-points than the glycerides of the lower fatty acids. The glycerides of the unsaturated fatty acids have even lower melting-points. Glycerides which are fluid at ordinary temperatures are commonly called oils, whereas those which are solid are called fats. This distinction, which is essentially one of convenience in industrial and culinary uses, is not ordinarily adhered to in chemical discussions, the term fat being used indiscriminately for a liquid as well as a solid fat.

Specific Gravity. The specific gravity of most solid fats (mutton tallow, lard, beef tallow, coconut oil, etc.) is very uniform, being approximately 0.86. Somewhat greater variation is found with different liquid fats, as is shown by the following data: olive oil, 0.915–0.918; peanut oil, 0.917–0.926; cottonseed oil, 0.921–0.926; maize oil, 0.921–0.927; linseed oil, 0.931–0.941.

Saponification Value. When treated with basic hydroxides, fats yield glycerol and the basic salts of fatty acids. The latter are termed soaps, and the process by which they are formed is called saponification. The soaps of commerce are usually those of sodium and potassium. Calcium and magnesium soaps are very insoluble in water.

$$C_3H_5(C_{18}H_{35}O_2)_3 + 3KOH = C_3H_5(OH)_3 + 3CH_3(CH_2)_{16}COOK$$

| Stearin | Glycerol | Potassium stearate (a soap) |

Applying the law of chemical combination to the above equation, we see that the molecular weight of fat is to three times the molecular weight of alkali as the actual weight of fat is to the actual weight of alkali. If the last three terms are known, the first can be determined. The amount of potassium or sodium hydroxide that will react with a given amount of fat in the process of saponification will depend on the average length of the constituent fatty-acid chains, for the smaller the fatty-acid molecules, the greater would be their number in a given amount of fat. Upon this principle is based a method for determining the character of different fats. The determination is made by heating a definite amount of fat (usually 1–2 grams) with a known volume of a standardized alcoholic solution of potassium hydroxide (usually 25 cc. 0.5 normal alkali) until saponification is complete. The unused alkali is determined by titration with standard acid. From the data obtained may be calculated the amount of alkali that was used in the saponification of the fat, and in turn its saponification value. *The saponification value is defined as the number of milligrams of potassium hydroxide neutralized by the saponification of one gram of fat.* Accordingly, it serves as a measure of the mean molecular weight of the fatty acids that are present in the fat. A large proportion of butter consists of the lower fatty acids; hence, butter has a relatively high saponification value (about 220–230). Similarly, coconut oil contains such large amounts of caproic, caprylic, capric, and lauric acid that it has an even higher saponification number (about 250). On the contrary, lard, mutton tallow, and cod-liver oil are composed of the higher fatty acids to a greater extent. Consequently, these have relatively low saponification values.   Another factor that may influence this constant is the presence in the fat of unsaponifiable constituents.   Fats containing appreciable amounts of such substances may have low saponification values.

Hydrogenation.   The unsaturated fats, such as those contained in vegetable oils, may be saturated by hydrogen, a reaction which is catalyzed by certain finely divided metals, including nickel.   By the introduction of two hydrogen atoms at the unsaturated bond in oleic acid, stearic acid is formed, and similarly linoleic acid may be converted by hydrogenation, first to oleic and finally to stearic acid.   This process is of great commercial and economic importance, as it makes possible the production of valuable articles of diet from comparatively inedible oils, such as cottonseed oil.   The process of hydrogenation is not carried to completion, however, as this would produce a brittle form of tallow.   The various lard substitutes of commerce are the products of partial hydrogen absorption and contain approximately 20 to 25 per cent of saturated fats (stearin), 65 to 75 per cent of olein, and 5 to 10 per cent of linolein.   The hydrogenated fats are as well utilized by the animal body as the natural fats.

Halogen Absorption; Iodine Number.   The unsaturated fatty acids react readily with the halogens, particularly with iodine, forming saturated halogen absorption derivatives.

$$
\begin{array}{ccc}
CH_3 & & CH_3 \\
| & & | \\
(CH_2)_7 & & (CH_2)_7 \\
| & & | \quad H \\
CH & +\,2I \rightarrow & C \diagdown \\
\| & & | \quad \diagdown I \\
& & | \quad H \\
CH & & C \diagdown \\
| & & | \quad \diagdown I \\
(CH_2)_7 & & (CH_2)_7 \\
| & & | \\
COOH & & COOH \\
\text{Oleic acid} & & \text{Diiodo-oleic acid}
\end{array}
$$

The more unsaturated the fatty acid, the more iodine is taken up at the double bonds, the reaction being quantitative under certain conditions. Upon this principle is based a method for determining the degree of unsaturation of fats and fatty acids.   In determining the iodine number, a weighed amount of fat is treated with a known volume (usually 25 cc.) of a solution containing iodine (Wijs or Hanus solution) and allowed to stand in the dark for one to two hours.   The unabsorbed iodine is then determined by titration with standard sodium thiosulfate. From the data thus obtained, the amount of iodine taken up by the fat may be calculated, and in turn the iodine number may be computed. *The iodine number is the number of grams of iodine that is absorbed by 100 grams of fat.* No iodine is taken up by saturated fatty acids or their corresponding glycerides. Oleic acid has one double bond and an iodine value of 90.1. Clupanodonic acid has five double bonds and an iodine number of 384. The iodine number therefore serves as an index of the degree of unsaturation of fats.

In the following table are given the melting-points,[7] iodine numbers, and saponification values of certain fats:

TABLE XI

Fat	Melting-point, °C.	Iodine Number	Saponification Value
Butter fat......................	28–33	26–38	220–230
Pork fat.......................	36–46	50–70	195–197
Beef fat.......................	40–48	36–48	193–200
Human fat.....................	17.5	57–66	193–199
Cod-liver oil..................	0–10	144–168	175–193
Cottonseed oil................	3–4	105–117	191–196
Olive oil......................	2–10	78–91	185–194
Linseed oil....................	−27	173–202	190–195

Rancidity and Oxidation of Fats. Fats are relatively unstable substances and are susceptible to deterioration, especially when exposed to light, heat, and moisture. They thus acquire characteristically disagreeable odors and flavors. At least two changes occur, one consisting in hydrolysis, with the liberation of free fatty acids. Rancid butter owes its peculiar odor partly to the formation of free butyric acid. The second change is one of oxidation and affects principally the unsaturated fatty acids, resulting in the fixing of the oxygen in the peroxide form

$$\begin{array}{ccccc}
\text{H} & \text{H} & & \text{H} & \text{H} \\
| & | & & | & | \\
-\text{C}- & \text{C}- & -- & \text{C}- & \text{C}- \\
| & | & & | & | \\
\text{H} & \text{O}- & -- & \text{O} & \text{H}
\end{array}$$

as well as in the formation of aldehydes, ketones, and acids of lower molecular weight. The two processes occur simultaneously, the presence

[7] These data are taken from a table in Robertson's "Principles of Biochemistry," Lea and Febiger, Philadelphia, 1924, p. 123.

of free acid apparently increasing greatly the susceptibility of fats to oxidation. The iodine number falls as rancidity progresses.

Certain substances, such as pyrocatechol, hydroquinone, pyrogallol, and α-naphthol, inhibit the auto-oxidation of fats. Anti-oxidants acting in a similar way are probably present in the non-saponifiable fraction of the natural fats and oils.[8]

The capacity to take up oxygen is especially marked in the highly unsaturated fats and is a property exhibited by the so-called drying oils. When thin layers of these oils are exposed to air, they absorb oxygen and are converted into tough, elastic, and waterpoof substances which adhere tightly to the painted surface and protect it from the weather. Linseed oil and tung, or Chinawood oil, are the two principal drying oils used in the manufacture of paints, varnishes, artificial rubber, linoleum, and other coverings.[9]

Phospholipids. The phospholipids (also called phospholipins and phosphatides) are present in every animal and vegetable cell and are especially abundant in the brain, heart, muscles, kidney, bone marrow, liver, and eggs. On hydrolysis these substances yield fatty acids, a nitrogenous base, phosphoric acid, and usually glycerol. Of the phospholipids that have been described, only three type substances have been studied sufficiently to establish their chemical individuality. These are the monoamino-monophosphatides, lecithin and kephalin; and the diamino-monophosphatide, sphingomyelin.

The following formula, in which R represents a fatty acid radical, suggests that more than one lecithin is possible:

$$
\begin{array}{l}
\qquad\qquad \overset{\displaystyle O}{\overset{\|}{}} \\
H_2=C-O-C-R_1 \\
\qquad\qquad \overset{\displaystyle O}{\overset{\|}{}} \\
H-C-O-C-R_2 \\
\qquad\qquad\qquad \overset{\displaystyle O}{\nearrow} \\
H_2=C-O-P{\diagup}O-CH_2 \\
\qquad\qquad OH \qquad CH_2 \\
\qquad\qquad\qquad\qquad N(CH_3)_3 \\
\qquad\quad \text{Lecithin} \quad OH
\end{array}
$$

Lecithin

[8] H. A. Mattill, *J. Biol. Chem.*, **90**, 141 (1931).

[9] For a general view of the economic importance of fats, the student is referred to the interesting and brief monograph by C. L. Alsberg and A. E. Taylor, "The Fats and Oils," Stanford University Press, 1928.

The existence of lecithins derived from β-glycerophosphoric acid is generally overlooked, although this has been clearly shown by Bailly[10] and by Karrer and Salomon.[11]

$$
\begin{array}{l}
\quad\quad\quad\quad O \\
\quad\quad\quad\quad \| \\
H_2 = C—O—C—R_1 \\
\quad | \quad\quad\quad\quad O \\
\quad\quad\quad\quad\quad // \\
H—C—O—P—O—(CH_2)_2N(CH_3)_3OH \\
\quad | \quad\quad\quad \backslash OH \\
H_2 = C—O—C—R_2 \\
\quad\quad\quad\quad \| \\
\quad\quad\quad\quad O
\end{array}
$$

β-Lecithin

Lecithins have been described in which both of the constituent fatty acids are saturated. There are others in which both acids are unsaturated, and finally those containing both a saturated and an unsaturated fatty acid. A saturated lecithin has been isolated from egg yolk. In addition, egg yolk contains lecithin in which the constituent fatty acids are oleic and arachidonic. The latter contains four double, or ethylene linkages, as shown by its conversion, on complete bromination, into octabrom-arachidic acid.

In a recent study of beef liver lecithin, Snider and Bloor[12] found the liquid (unsaturated) and solid (saturated) fatty acids to be present in the proportion of 55 : 40. Of the unsaturated acids, linoleic acid composed 45 per cent, arachidonic 31 per cent, and oleic 21 per cent. In small amounts, acids of larger molecular weight and of even greater unsaturation probably exist. Indeed, a C_{22} acid has been isolated from liver lipids which contains five ethylene bonds. It is dicosanpentenoic acid, $C_{22}H_{34}O_2$. On complete hydrogenation it is converted into behenic acid.

Brain lecithin also contains arachidonic acid. Brown[13] has reported the presence of tetracosan-pentenoic acid, $C_{24}H_{38}O_2$, in beef and sheep brains, but its absence, except for traces, in hog's brain. In some of these studies, mixtures of phosphatides were employed, and there is therefore no certainty that these acids are actually components of lecithin, although this seems probable.

[10] Ann. Chim. (9), 6, 96 (1916).

[11] Helv. Chim. Acta, 9, 1 (1926); see also Y. Shinozaki and M. Sato, J. Agr. Chem. Soc. (Japan), 9, 728 (1933). According to the latter investigators, soybean lecithin is β-lecithin to the extent of about 70 per cent.

[12] J. Biol. Chem., 99, 555 (1932–33).

[13] Ibid., 83, 783 (1929); J. B. Brown and W. C. Ault, ibid., 89, 167 (1930).

According to one concept of fat metabolism, the formation of lecithin represents an intermediate stage in the oxidation of the fatty acids. The neutral fat is believed to be converted into lecithin, and it is in this form of combination that the constituent fatty acids undergo a successive number of dehydrogenations, being thus rendered more and more unsaturated. Lecithin is doubtless essential to the life of the cell, and even in extreme emaciation its content in cellular tissues remains unchanged. Preparations of lecithin obtained from tissues do not ordinarily represent a single substance, but, as has been pointed out, are actually mixtures of lecithins and may contain as impurities other phosphatides, as well as cerebrosides.

Choline [$(CH_3)_3\equiv N(OH)—CH_2CH_2OH$], trimethyl-oxyethyl-ammonium-hydroxide, is the base obtained on hydrolysis of lecithin.

Kephalin (Cephalin). The methods in use for the separation of kephalin from lecithin and other associated substances are based principally on differences in solubility. The kephalin fraction may be precipitated by alcohol, in which it is somewhat less soluble than lecithin. Like lecithin, kephalin is widely distributed in animal tissues and may, at least theoretically, hold in combination a variety of fatty acids. Stearic, oleic, and dicosan-tetranoic acids have been isolated. The occurrence of arachidonic acid has also been reported, but if present, the amounts are very small. In lecithin, it will be recalled, arachidonic acid is an important component. In addition to the fatty acids, kephalin yields on hydrolysis glycerol, phosphoric acid, and a nitrogenous base, amino-ethyl alcohol. It is represented by the following formula, but it is to be recognized that β-kephalins probably exist:[11]

$$
\begin{array}{l}
\qquad\qquad\qquad O \\
\qquad\qquad\qquad \| \\
H_2{=}C{-}O{-}C{-}R_1 \\
\qquad\qquad\qquad O \\
\qquad\qquad\qquad \| \\
H{-}C{-}O{-}C{-}R_2 \\
\qquad\qquad\qquad\qquad O \\
\qquad\qquad\qquad\qquad \diagup\!\!\diagup \\
H_2{=}C{-}O{-}P{-}O{-}CH_2 \\
\qquad\quad\ \ OH\qquad CH_2 \\
\qquad\qquad\qquad\qquad | \\
\qquad\text{Kephalin}\qquad NH_2
\end{array}
$$

Properties of Kephalin and Lecithin. Lecithin and kephalin are miscible with water, from which they may be precipitated by acetone. Lecithin is soluble in alcohol, whereas kephalin is relatively insoluble. Both are soluble in ether, chloroform, benzene, and the other common fat solvents, with the exception of acetone, in which they are insoluble. They oxidize readily in air, turning brown and acquiring a disagreeable odor.

Sphingomyelin is a phospholipid, occurring in brain, kidney, liver, and egg yolk, which yields on hydrolysis phosphoric acid, two nitrogenous bases, choline and sphingosine, $[CH_3 \cdot (CH_2)_{12} \cdot CH{=}CH \cdot CH(NH)_2 \cdot CH(OH) \cdot CH_2OH]$,[14] and a fatty acid. Three fatty acids have been associated with sphingomyelin, namely, lignoceric acid $(CH_3 \cdot (CH_2)_{22} \cdot COOH$, stearic acid, and nervonic acid $[CH_3 \cdot (CH_2)_7 \cdot CH{=}CH \cdot (CH_2)_{13} \cdot COOH]$.[15] Accordingly, there are at least three sphingomyelins, all of which may and apparently do occur in the same sphingomyelin fraction.

$$CH_2OH \quad \overset{H}{\underset{}{N}}{-}R \quad \text{(Fatty acid radical)}$$

$$O \cdot CH \cdot CH \cdot CH{=}CH(CH_2)_{12} \cdot CH_3 \quad \text{(Sphingosine radical)}$$

$$O{=}P{-}OH$$

$$O \cdot C_2H_4N(CH_3)_3OH$$

Choline

Sphingomyelin

Properties. Sphingomyelin is soluble in cold and hot chloroform, benzene, pyridine, glacial acetic acid, and hot alcohol, from which it separates on cooling in crystalline form. It is relatively insoluble in hot and cold ether. It is somewhat soluble in hot acetone, but not in cold acetone, which may be used in precipitating it from water, in which it forms an opalescent suspension. Sphingomyelin is dextro-rotatory. As compared with lecithin and kephalin, it is a relatively stable compound, undergoing no change on exposure to air or light.

The Cerebrosides. Associated with the phosphatides in the tissues, particularly in the brain, are the cerebrosides which on hydrolysis yield the sugar galactose, the nitrogenous base sphingosine, and a fatty acid. The cerebrosides are glycolipids, and because galactose is the constituent sugar, they are also called *galactolipids* (or *galactolipines*). These compounds are essentially analogous to the glucosides found in plants. Two cerebrosides have been known for some time, *kerasin* and *phrenosin.* The fatty acid in kerasin is the same as in sphingomyelin, namely, lignoceric acid. The constituent fatty acid in phrenosin has been termed phrenosinic, or cerebronic acid, $C_{25}H_{50}O_3$ (Levene). It is to be

---

[14] E. Klenk and W. Diebold, *Z. physiol. Chem.*, **198**, 25 (1931).
[15] W. Merz, *ibid.*, **193**, 59 (1930).

noted that this is one of the few recorded instances of a naturally occurring fatty acid with an odd number of carbon atoms. There has been considerable discussion in recent years concerning the cerebronic acid. According to Klenk and Härle,[16] the fatty acid in phrenosin is α-hydroxylignoceric acid. This view has not been accepted by Taylor and Levene,[17] who nevertheless admit the existence, in addition to cerebronic acid, of other fatty acids among the products derived in the hydrolysis of the phrenosin fraction. Taking this point into consideration, as well as the reported identification by Klenk and Härle of nervonic acid $CH_3 \cdot (CH_2)_7 \cdot CH : CH \cdot (CH_2)_{12}CH_2 \cdot COOH$, and α-hydroxynervonic acid, $CH_3 \cdot (CH_2)_7 \cdot CH : CH \cdot (CH_2)_{12} \cdot CHOH \cdot COOH$, it may be be assumed that the cerebrosides constitute a larger group than was formerly supposed and that, in addition to kerasin and phrenosin, there are at least two more cerebrosides, nervone, containing nervonic acid, and hydroxynervone, containing α-hydroxynervonic acid.

The cerebrosides are soluble in hot alcohol, acetone, benzene, and pyridine. Like sphingomyelin, they are almost insoluble in hot and cold ether.

Owing to the difficulty involved in isolating and purifying the various phosphatides and cerebrosides, mixtures of these substances have frequently been mistaken for individual compounds.

Waxes. The waxes are fatty-acid esters of the higher monoatomic alcohols. Spermaceti, found in the skull of certain species of whales and dolphins, contains as its chief constituent the palmitic acid ester of cetyl alcohol ($C_{16}H_{33}OH$). Among the other constituents of spermaceti are esters of lauric, myristic, and stearic acids with the following alcohols: lethol ($C_{12}H_{25}OH$), methol ($C_{14}H_{29}OH$), and stethol ($C_{18}H_{37}OH$).

The principal constituents of beeswax are the palmitic acid ester of myricyl alcohol ($C_{30}H_{61}OH$), cerotic acid ($C_{26}H_{52}O_2$), either in the free form or as an ester, and cerolein, which is probably a mixture of several substances.

Waxes are found in wool, in sperm oil, in the secretions of many animals, particularly insects, in certain bacteria, and in many forms of plant life.

Sterols. The best-known sterol is *cholesterol* ($C_{27}H_{45}OH$), first isolated in gall-stones by Conradi in 1775. It derives its name from the fact that it is a constituent of bile (Greek χόλη). In the tissues and in the blood it exists both free and in combination with fatty acids as esters. It is abundant in brain and nerve tissue, as well as in certain tumors. It occurs in lanolin, the fat of sheep's wool, in combination

[16] *Z. physiol. Chem.*, **189**, 243 (1930).   [17] *J. Biol. Chem.*, **84**, 23 (1929).

as oleate, palmitate, and stearate. Cholesterol is also found in butter. The feathers of birds are said to contain a silicic acid ester of cholesterol. It is doubtless an essential cell constituent. Being an alcohol, it is unsaponifiable, and is indeed commonly found in the " unsaponifiable residue " of fats and oils. Fish and liver oils, in particular, are rich in unsaponifiable matter, containing in some cases as much as 20 per cent. Wheat oil contains about 2.5 per cent; cottonseed oil, corn oil, and olive oil about 1 per cent, or somewhat less.

The chemical constitution of cholesterol is still under discussion. According to a recent formulation by Windaus,[16] a leading authority of the subject, cholesterol may be represented as follows:

Cholesterol

Cholesterol has several asymmetric carbon atoms, which accounts for its optical activity $[\alpha]_D = -31.6$, and for the existence of a number of isomers. It is soluble in fat solvents, fatty acids (oleic), bile acids, and bile. It crystallizes from alcohol as white, glistening, rhombic plates with one irregular or broken corner. The melting-point is 148° C. Owing to the presence of an unsaturated bond, cholesterol combines with iodine. In the attempt to determine its constitution as well as its relation to other compounds, a large number of interesting degradation products have been prepared.[18]

Coprosterol ($C_{27}H_{47}OH$), a constituent of feces, is formed by the reducing action of bacteria in the lower intestine. It has been prepared in the laboratory by the catalytic hydrogenation of cholesterol, using nickel, in an atmosphere of hydrogen.

The *phytosterols* are found in plants and resemble cholesterol very closely. *Sitosterol* ($C_{29}H_{49}OH$) is the best-known example. Corn oil contains several isomers of sitosterol, a *dihydrositosterol* ($C_{29}H_{51}OH$),

[18] See, for example, A. Windaus, Z. *physiol. Chem.*, **213**, 147 (1932–33).

and *stigmasterol*, $C_{30}H_{49}OH$, according to Windaus, $C_{29}H_{47}OH$, according to Sandquist.[19] Wheat oil contains sitosterol and dihydrosterol.

Of unusual interest and importance is *ergosterol* ($C_{27}H_{41}OH$). This sterol was first discovered by the French chemist Tanret in ergot and later found to be present also in yeast and certain mushrooms. It is now known to be widely distributed in the fats of both plants and animals, usually in association with cholesterol. Not many years ago it was shown that on irradiation, ergosterol acquires the property of vitamin D, that is of curing or preventing rickets (p. 590). It is now known that, when irradiated, ergosterol is transformed successively into a series of isomers:[20] ergosterol → lumisterol → tachysterol → vitamin D → suprasterol I and II. To these another compound has been added,[21] *toxisterol*, so named because of its marked toxicity. It is formed as a result of prolonged irradiation. Further reference to these interesting compounds, and particularly to vitamin D, will be made in a later chapter.

It may be mentioned at this point that cholesterol is chemically related to the bile acids (p. 189). There are strong indications that the four-ring structure which characterizes the sterols is also characteristic of the formulas that have been recently proposed to represent the molecular configuration of the male and female sex hormones (pp. 493, 494).

[19] *Ber.*, **63**, 1935 (1930); **64**, 2167 (1931).

[20] A. Windaus, F. von Werder, and A. Lütringhaus, *Ann. Chem.*, **499**, 188 (1932); P. Setz, *Z. physiol. Chem.*, **215**, 183 (1933).

[21] F. Laquer and O. Linsert, *Klin. Wochschr.*, **12**, 753 (1933).

CHAPTER IV

THE PROTEINS

The resemblance between plant and animal proteins was clearly stated in 1839 by the Dutch chemist, Mulder,[1] who pointed out the importance of these substances in the constitution of cell protoplasm. The protein foodstuffs not only play an extremely important part in the regeneration of worn-out tissue and in the building of new tissue, but are also used by the body in the production of energy. Most proteins contain at least the elements carbon, hydrogen, oxygen, nitrogen, and sulfur, and, as far as can be determined by chemical analysis, seem to be closely related. However, there is nothing more characteristic of the proteins as a group than their physiological specificity. No two proteins seem to be exactly alike as far as their physiological behavior is concerned. The circulating and tissue proteins of one animal differ from those of all other animals, and the same is true of most plant proteins.

Proteins cannot be identified by the usual chemical methods. Accordingly, the classifications of these substances are based largely on physical properties such as solubility. The classification most frequently employed is that recommended jointly by the American Physiological Society and the American Society of Biological Chemists.[2] This classification is given below:

THE PROTEINS

I. Simple Proteins. Protein substances that yield, on hydrolysis, only amino acids or their derivatives.[3]

---

[1] G. J. Mulder, *J. prakt. Chem.*, **16**, 129 (1839).

[2] *J. Biol. Chem.*, **4**, p. xlviii (1908).

[3] In the light of recent studies, this classification is not strictly correct. For example, egg albumin, serum albumin, and globulin are said to contain carbohydrate groups. By definition, these should be classified as glycoproteins, a subgroup of the conjugated proteins, and not as simple proteins.

In a recent contribution, M. Sørensen and G. Haugaard (*Compt. rend. trav. lab. Carlsberg*, **19**, No. 12 [1933]) report the presence of 1.71 per cent mannose in egg albumin recrystallized many times. An easily soluble serum albumin, recrystallized several times, contained 0.47 per cent carbohydrate, consisting of equal amounts of

The various simple proteins may be designated as follows:

a. Albumins. Simple proteins soluble in pure water and coagulable by heat. (Examples: egg albumin, serum albumin, legumelin of the pea, and leucosin of wheat.)

b. Globulins. Simple proteins insoluble in pure water but soluble in neutral solutions of salts of strong bases with strong acids. (Examples: serum globulin, fibrinogen, myosinogen of muscle, edestin of hemp seed, legumin of peas, excelsin in Brazil nuts, concanavalin in the jack bean.)

c. Glutelins. Simple proteins insoluble in all neutral solvents but readily soluble in very dilute acids and alkalies. (Examples: glutenin of wheat, oryzenin in rice.)

d. Alcohol-soluble proteins—Prolamins or Gliadins. Simple proteins soluble in relatively strong alcohol (70 to 80 per cent), but insoluble in water, absolute alcohol, and other neutral solvents. (Examples: gliadin from wheat or rye, hordein from barley, zein from maize or wheat.)

e. Albuminoids. Simple proteins that possess essentially the same chemical structure as the other proteins, but are characterized by great insolubility in all neutral solvents. These substances form the principal organic constituents of the skeletal structure of animals and also of their external covering and its appendages. The albuminoids are also called scleroproteins. (Examples: keratin from hair, horns, hoofs, nails, etc.; elastin in elastic tissue, ligaments, and the walls of arteries; collagen in bones and cartilage; spongin found in the skeletal structure of the sponge; reticulin present in lung, kidney, spleen, liver, and lymphatic gland tissue; fibroin and sericin from silk.)

f. Histones. Soluble in water and insoluble in very dilute ammonia; in the absence of ammonium salts, insoluble even in an excess of ammonia. They yield precipitates with solutions of other proteins, and, on heating, a coagulum which is easily soluble in very dilute acids. On hydrolysis they yield a number of amino acids among which the basic ones predominate. (The histones are found in the red corpuscles of the blood and in spermatozoa. Examples: scombron in mackerel spermatozoa, gadus histone from the codfish, globin from hemoglobin.)

g. Protamins. Simpler polypeptides than the proteins included in the preceding groups. They are soluble in water, uncoagulable by heat, have the property of precipitating aqueous solutions of other proteins, possess strong basic properties, and form stable salts with strong mineral acids. They yield comparatively few amino acids, among which the basic amino acids greatly predominate. (Like the histones, the protamins occur in combination with nucleic acids in spermatozoa. Examples: salmine from salmon, sturine from sturgeon, scombrine from mackerel, cyprinine from carp, clupeine from herring.)

II. Conjugated Proteins. Substances that contain the protein molecule united to some other molecule or molecules otherwise than as a salt.

---

mannose and galactose, and a sparingly soluble fraction containing 0.02 per cent carbohydrate. Horse serum globulin, several times precipitated, contained 1.82 per cent carbohydrate, likewise consisting of equal amounts of galactose and mannose. Casein contained 0.31 per cent galactose, but no lactose. Well-purified lactalbumin contained 0.44 per cent galactose, but no lactose.

a. Nucleoproteins. Compounds of one or more protein molecules with nucleic acid. (Present in the germ of grain and in glandular tissue.)

b. Glycoproteins. Compounds of the protein molecule with a substance or substances containing a carbohydrate group other than a nucleic acid. (Example: mucin.)

c. Phosphoproteins. Compounds of the protein molecule with some as yet undefined phosphorus-containing substance other than a nucleic acid or lecithin. (Examples: caseinogen of milk, vitellin of egg yolk.)[4]

d. Hemoglobins. Compounds of the protein molecule with hematin or some similar substance. (Example: Hemoglobin.) (These substances are also classified as chromoproteins and include such substances as the hemocyanins.)

e. Lecithoproteins. Compounds of the protein molecule with lecithin. (Example: tissue fibrinogen.)

III. Derived Proteins.

1. *Primary Protein Derivatives.* Derivatives of the protein molecule, apparently formed through hydrolytic changes which involve only slight alterations of the protein molecule.

a. Proteans. Insoluble products which apparently result from the incipient action of water, very dilute acids, or enzymes.

b. Metaproteins. Products of the further action of acids and alkalies, whereby the molecule is so far altered as to form products soluble in very weak acids and alkalies but insoluble in neutral fluids. (Examples: acid metaprotein, alkali metaprotein.)

c. Coagulated Proteins. Insoluble products which result from (1) the action of heat on their solutions, or (2) the action of alcohols on the protein.

2. *Secondary Protein Derivatives.* Products of the further hydrolytic cleavage of the protein molecule.

a. Proteoses. Soluble in water, uncoagulated by heat, and precipitated by saturating their solutions with ammonium sulfate or zinc sulfate.

b. Peptones. Soluble in water, uncoagulated by heat, but not precipitated by saturating their solutions with ammonium sulfate.

c. Peptides. Definitely characterized combinations of two or more amino acids, the carboxyl group of one being united with the amino group of the other, with the elimination of a molecule of water.

In the classification adopted by British biochemists, the protamins, histones, albumins, globulins, glutelins, gliadins, scleroproteins, and phosphoproteins are grouped as the simple proteins. The conjugated proteins are the glucoproteins, nucleoproteins, and chromoproteins. The metaproteins or infraproteins, proteoses, and polypeptides are grouped as products of protein hydrolysis.

Amino Acids. By the action of strong acids or protein-splitting enzymes, the proteins may be broken down into simpler and simpler compounds, the end-products being the amino acids. The first of

---

[4] The tendency now is to regard vitellin as a lecithoprotein, since it occurs together with large amounts of lecithin in the egg yolk and cannot be completely freed from lecithin except by rather drastic extraction (Gortner).

these was discovered more than a century ago. Since then many amino acids have been described as cleavage products of the protein molecule, but even now only nineteen are generally recognized as such. In a recent review dealing with the history of the discovery of the amino acids, Vickery and Schmidt [5] have suggested certain criteria as the basis for considering an amino acid as a definite product of protein hydrolysis. Before applying these criteria it is assumed that the substance in question has been liberated by hydrolysis from a protein of demonstrated purity and has been adequately characterized by analysis of salts and typical derivatives. The essential criteria imposed by Vickery and Schmidt are:

(1) The amino acid must have been isolated by some worker other than the discoverer.

(2) Its constitution must have been established by synthesis and by demonstration of identity between the synthetic product and the racemized natural product, or by actual resolution of the synthetic product and preparation of the optically active natural isomer.

CLASSIFICATION OF AMINO ACIDS

I. ALIPHATIC AMINO ACIDS.

A. Monoamino-monocarboxylic Acids.

1. Glycine, $C_2H_5NO_2$, or amino-acetic acid. (1820, Braconnot) [6]

$$CH_2—NH_2$$
$$|$$
$$COOH$$

2. d-Alanine, $C_3H_7NO_2$, or α-amino-propionic acid. (Weyl, 1888)

$$CH_3$$
$$|$$
$$\alpha \ CH—NH_2$$
$$|$$
$$COOH$$

---

[5] *Chem. Rev.*, **9**, 169 (1931).

[6] The dates of discovery of these amino acids as *products of hydrolysis of proteins* and the names of the discoverers are those given by H. B. Vickery and C. L. A. Schmidt, *Chem. Rev.*, **9**, 169–318 (1931). Wherever possible, these have been confirmed by reference to original sources. It is to be pointed out that not in all cases were the constitutions of the amino acids known to their discoverers, nor are the names now in use necessarily those originally given. To cite a recent example as an illustration, methionine was discovered by Mueller, but its constitution was determined by Barger and Coyne (*Biochem. J.*, **22**, 1417 [1928]), who suggested the name. Then, also, in at least one case, alanine, the amino acid was synthesized (Strecker, 1850) long before it was obtained as a decomposition product of protein.

3. *l*-Serine, $C_3H_7NO_3$, or β-hydroxy-α-amino-propionic acid. (1865, Cramer)

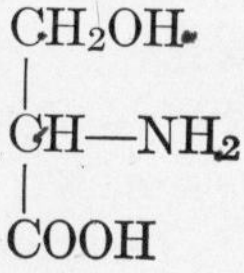

$$CH_2OH$$
$$|$$
$$CH—NH_2$$
$$|$$
$$COOH$$

4. *d*-Valine, $C_5H_{11}NO_2$, or α-amino-isovalerianic acid. (1901, Fischer)

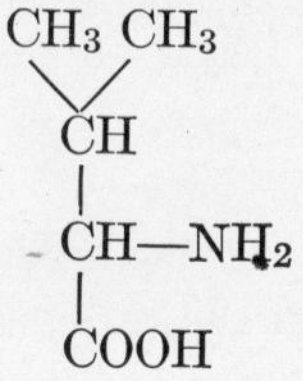

$$CH_3 \quad CH_3$$
$$\diagdown \diagup$$
$$CH$$
$$|$$
$$CH—NH_2$$
$$|$$
$$COOH$$

5. *l*-Leucine, $C_6H_{13}NO_2$, or α-amino isocaproic acid. (1820, Braconnot)

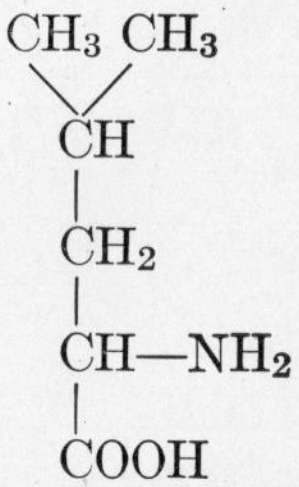

$$CH_3 \quad CH_3$$
$$\diagdown \diagup$$
$$CH$$
$$|$$
$$CH_2$$
$$|$$
$$CH—NH_2$$
$$|$$
$$COOH$$

6. *d*-Isoleucine, $C_6H_{13}NO_2$, or α-amino-β-methyl-β-ethyl-propionic acid. (1903, F. Ehrlich)

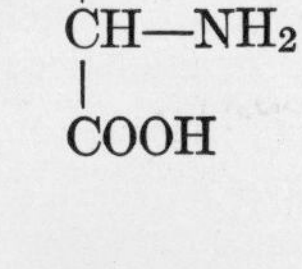

$$CH_3 \quad C_2H_5$$
$$\diagdown \diagup$$
$$CH$$
$$|$$
$$CH—NH_2$$
$$|$$
$$COOH$$

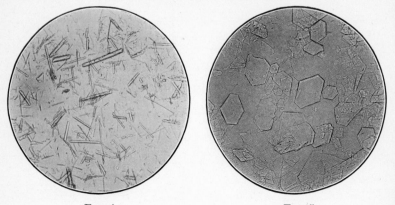

Fig. 4.   Fig. 5.

Fig. 4.—Alanine.   Magnification about 45 times.   Crystal habit—rods and needles.

Fig. 5.—Leucine.   Magnification about 45 times.   Crystal habit—colorless, thin, six-sided plates and narrow rod-like plates.

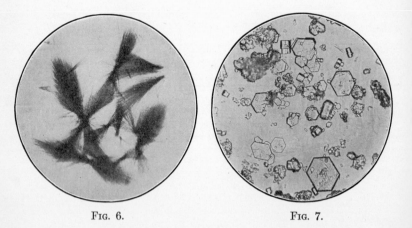

Fig. 6.   Fig. 7.

Fig. 6.—Tyrosine.   Magnification about 54 times.   Crystal habit—thin needles and rods, aggregate into tufts and sheaves.

Fig. 7.—Cystine.   Magnification about 45 times.   Crystal habit—colorless hexagonal plates and prisms.

Figures 4, 5, 6, 7, 8, and 9 are reproductions from photomicrographs which were kindly furnished to the author by G. L. Keenan of the Bureau of Chemistry, United States Department of Agriculture.   See *J. Biol. Chem.*, **62**, 163 (1924).

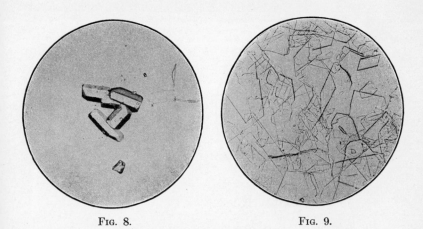

FIG. 8.   FIG. 9.

FIG. 8.—Aspartic acid.   Magnification about 36 times.   Ordinarily obtained as irregular fragments of crystals, having high refractive indices.

FIG. 9.—Tryptophane.   Magnification about 45 times.   Crystal habit—very thin plates, rhombs and irregularly six-sided crystals.

B. Monoamino-dicarboxylic Acids.

   7. l-Aspartic acid, $C_4H_7NO_4$, or amino-succinic acid.   (1868, Ritthausen)

$$COOH$$
$$|$$
$$CH_2$$
$$|$$
$$CH-NH_2$$
$$|$$
$$COOH$$

   8. d-Glutamic acid, $C_5H_9NO_4$, or α-amino-glutaric acid.   (1866, Ritthausen)

$$COOH$$
$$|$$
$$CH_2$$
$$|$$
$$CH_2$$
$$|$$
$$CH-NH_2$$
$$|$$
$$COOH$$

9. d-Hydroxyglutamic acid, $C_5H_9O_5N$, or α-amino-β-hydroxy-glutaric acid.   (1918, Dakin)

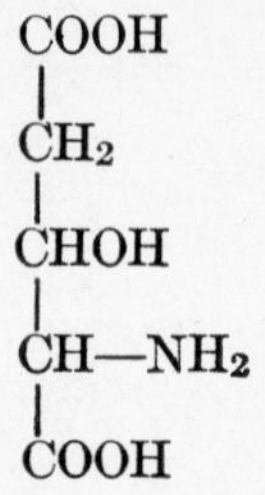

$$
\begin{array}{c}
COOH \\
| \\
CH_2 \\
| \\
CHOH \\
| \\
CH\!-\!NH_2 \\
| \\
COOH
\end{array}
$$

C. Diamino-monocarboxylic Acids.

10. d-Arginine, $C_6H_{14}N_4O_2$, or α-amino-δ-guanidine-valeric acid. (1895, Hedin)

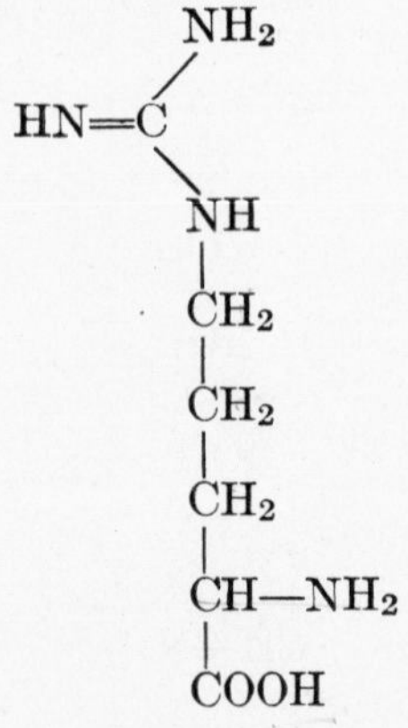

$$
\begin{array}{c}
\qquad\;\; NH_2 \\
\qquad\; \diagup \\
HN\!=\!C \\
\qquad\; \diagdown \\
\qquad\;\; NH \\
\qquad\;\; | \\
\qquad\;\; CH_2 \\
\qquad\;\; | \\
\qquad\;\; CH_2 \\
\qquad\;\; | \\
\qquad\;\; CH_2 \\
\qquad\;\; | \\
\qquad\;\; CH\!-\!NH_2 \\
\qquad\;\; | \\
\qquad\;\; COOH
\end{array}
$$

11. d-Lysine, $C_6H_{14}N_2O_2$, or α-ϵ-diamino-caproic acid. (1889, Drechsel)

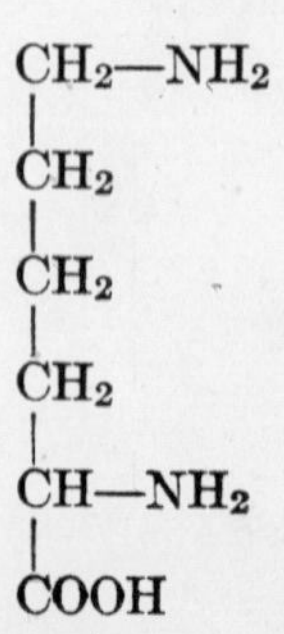

$$
\begin{array}{c}
CH_2\!-\!NH_2 \\
| \\
CH_2 \\
| \\
CH_2 \\
| \\
CH_2 \\
| \\
CH\!-\!NH_2 \\
| \\
COOH
\end{array}
$$

D. Sulfur-containing Amino Acids.

12. *l*-Cystine, $C_6H_{12}N_2O_4S_2$, or dicysteine, or di-(β-thio-α-amino-propionic acid). (1899, Mörner) [6a]

$$
\begin{array}{cc}
CH_2 & S-S & CH_2 \\
| & & | \\
CH-NH_2 & & CH-NH_2 \\
| & & | \\
COOH & & COOH
\end{array}
$$

13. *l*-Methionine, $C_5H_{11}SNO_2$, or α-amino-γ-methylthiol-*n*-butyric acid. (1922, Mueller)

$$
\begin{array}{c}
CH_2-S-CH_3 \\
| \\
CH_2 \\
| \\
CH-NH_2 \\
| \\
COOH
\end{array}
$$

II. AROMATIC AMINO ACIDS.

14. *l*-Phenylalanine, $C_9H_{11}NO_2$, or α-amino-β-phenyl-propionic acid. (1881, Schulze and Barbieri)

$$
\begin{array}{c}
CH \\
HC \quad CH \\
HC \quad CH \\
C \\
| \\
CH_2 \\
| \\
CH-NH_2 \\
| \\
COOH
\end{array}
$$

15. *l*-Tyrosine, $C_9H_{11}NO_3$, or β-parahydroxy-phenyl-α-amino-propionic acid. (1846, Liebig; 1849, Bopp)

$$
\begin{array}{c}
C-OH \\
HC \quad CH \\
HC \quad CH \\
C \\
| \\
CH_2 \\
| \\
CH-NH_2 \\
| \\
COOH
\end{array}
$$

[6a] First discovered by Wollaston in 1810.

III. HETEROCYCLIC AMINO ACIDS.

16. l-Histidine, $C_6H_9N_3O_2$, or β-imidazole-α-amino-propionic acid. (1896, Kossel, Hedin)

$$\begin{array}{l} CH\!-\!N \\ \parallel \qquad \diagdown\! CH \\ C\!-\!NH \\ | \\ CH_2 \\ | \\ CH\!-\!NH_2 \\ | \\ COOH \end{array}$$

17. l-Proline, $C_5H_9NO_2$, or α-pyrrolidine-carboxylic acid. (1901, Fischer)

$$\begin{array}{l} CH_2\!-\!\!-\!\!-\!CH_2 \\ | \qquad\quad | \\ CH_2 \quad CH\!-\!COOH \\ \diagdown \qquad \diagup \\ NH \end{array}$$

18. l-Hydroxyproline (oxyproline), $C_5H_9NO_3$, or γ-hydroxy-α-pyrrolidine-carboxylic acid. (1902, Fischer)

$$\begin{array}{l} HO\!-\!CH\!-\!\!-\!\!-\!CH_2 \\ \qquad\quad | \qquad\quad | \\ \qquad CH_2 \quad CH\!-\!COOH \\ \qquad \diagdown \qquad \diagup \\ \qquad NH \end{array}$$

19. l-Tryptophane, $C_{11}H_{12}N_2O_2$, or β-indole-α-amino-propionic acid. (1901, Hopkins and Cole)

$$\begin{array}{l} CH \\ \diagup\! \diagup \\ HC \quad C\!-\!C\!-\!CH_2\!-\!CH(NH_2)\!-\!COOH \\ | \qquad \parallel \quad \parallel \\ HC \quad C \quad CH \\ \diagdown\! \diagup\!\diagdown\!\diagup \\ CH \quad NH \end{array}$$

In the tabulation given by Vickery and Schmidt, two iodine-containing amino acids are included. *Iodogorgoic* acid (diiodo-tyrosine) was first isolated by Drechsel (1896)[7] from the products of alkaline hydrolysis of the horny skeleton of the coral *Gorgonia Cavolinii*.

[7] *Z. Biol.*, **33**, 96 (1896).

Wheeler and Mendel[8] (1909) found it in the common sponge. It was later isolated by Harington and Randall[9] from the thyroid gland, and Foster[10] obtained it among the products of the alkaline hydrolysis of partially purified thyroglobulin.

Thyroxin was discovered by Kendall[11] among the products of the alkaline hydrolysis of thyroid glands. Its chemical constitution was determined by Harington, and its synthesis was accomplished by Harington and Barger.[12]

20. Iodogorgoic acid, $C_9H_9NI_2O_3$, 3, 5-diiodo-tyrosine. (1896, Drechsel)

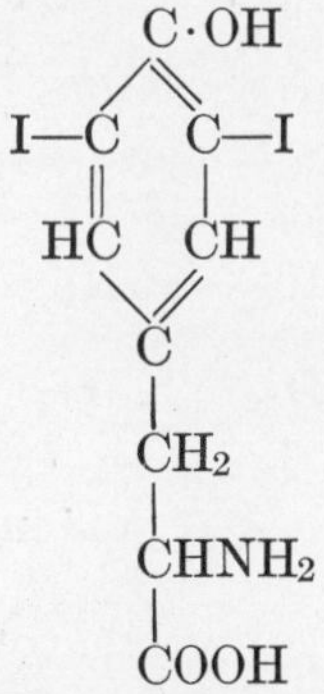

$$
\begin{array}{c}
\text{C·OH} \\
\text{I—C \quad C—I} \\
\text{HC \quad CH} \\
\text{C} \\
\text{CH}_2 \\
\text{CHNH}_2 \\
\text{COOH}
\end{array}
$$

21. Thyroxin, β-[3 : 5-diiodo-4-(3′ : 5′-diiodo-4′-hydroxyphenoxy) phenyl]-alanine. (1915, Kendall).

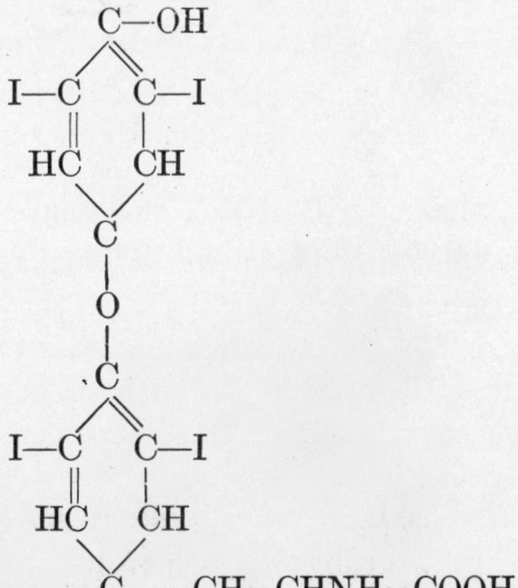

$$
\begin{array}{c}
\text{C—OH} \\
\text{I—C \quad C—I} \\
\text{HC \quad CH} \\
\text{C} \\
\text{O} \\
\text{C} \\
\text{I—C \quad C—I} \\
\text{HC \quad CH} \\
\text{C——CH}_2\text{·CHNH}_2\text{·COOH}
\end{array}
$$

[8] *J. Biol. Chem.*, **7**, 1 (1909–10).
[9] *Biochem. J.*, **23**, 373 (1929).
[10] *J. Biol. Chem.*, **83**, 345 (1929).
[11] E. C. Kendall, Collected Papers, Mayo Clinic, **7**, 393 (1915).
[12] *Biochem. J.*, **20**, 293 (1926).

The foregoing list comprises the more important cleavage products of the protein molecule. The amino acids are present in varying proportions in different proteins, and while most proteins contain all of the amino acids named (except those containing iodine) some are deficient in one or more of these. Gelatin is apparently made up of only fourteen or fifteen amino acids and contains little or no tyrosine and tryptophane. Glycine, tryptophane, and lysine are deficient or lacking in zein of corn. Then there are the protamins, which are made up of even fewer amino acids. For example, salmine yields on hydrolysis only valine, serine, proline, and arginine; sturine yields arginine, lysine, and histidine. The animal body, at least in the higher forms, is unable to synthesize certain amino acids, such as tyrosine, tryptophane, lysine, cystine, and histidine. These are required, however, in the formation of tissue and hence are essential for proper nutrition. The rôle of amino acids in nutrition will be considered in greater detail in a later chapter.

In addition to the amino acids that have been listed, others have been reported as products of protein hydrolysis. Among these are: α-amino-n-butyric acid, hydroxyamino-butyric acid, nor-valine, hydroxy-valine, nor-leucine, l-isoleucine, hydroxy-lysine, dihydroxyphenylalanine, thiol-histidine, dihydroxy-pyrrole-alanine, diamino-glutaric acid, diamino-adipic acid, dihydroxy-amino-suberic acid, dibromotyrosine, ornithine, etc. It has also been claimed that cysteine (CH_2SH—$CHNH_2$—$COOH$) may exist as such in the protein molecule.

Separation of Amino Acids. The method introduced by Fischer[13] for the separation of amino acids consists in converting the amino acids into esters and subsequently separating these by fractional distillation.

Amino acids may be separated electrolytically in a suitably constructed apparatus. The dicarboxylic acids, such as aspartic and glutamic, migrate to the anode; the basic acids, lysine, arginine, and histidine, concentrate at the cathode. Amino acids form salts with the heavy metals and may be separated as such. They also react with a large variety of other reagents to form insoluble crystalline derivatives, benzoates, picrates, picrolonates, etc.

The products of acid hydrolysis of proteins may also be separated by extraction with various solvents, such as butyl and ethyl alcohols. This is the basis of a method suggested by Dakin.[14]

In determining the proportions of mono- and diamino acids, the

[13] E. Fischer, "Untersuchungen über Aminosäuren, Polypeptide und Proteine" (1899–1906), Berlin, 1906.

[14] *Biochem. J.*, **12**, 290 (1918); *J. Biol. Chem.*, **44**, 499 (1920).

protein is hydrolyzed by boiling with hydrochloric acid.   An insoluble residue which may be removed by filtering consists largely of so-called *humin*, which contains nitrogen.   The amide and ammonia nitrogen is determined by distillation with magnesium oxide *in vacuo* at 40° C. The diamino acids are precipitated with phosphotungstic acid, and the amount of nitrogen in the precipitate as well as in the filtrate is determined by Kjeldahl's method.   The nitrogen content of the filtrate represents the monoamino acids.

The Synthesis of Polypeptides. Glycine, as the ethyl ester, in an aqueous solution forms an anhydride:

$$\begin{matrix} COOH & NH_2-CH_2 \\ | & | \\ CH_2-NH_2 & COOH \end{matrix} \quad \rightleftarrows \quad \begin{matrix} CO-NH-CH_2 \\ | \quad\quad | \\ CH_2-NH-CO \end{matrix} + 2H_2O$$

2 molecules of glycine   Diketopiperazine
(glycine anhydride)

On boiling the anhydride with concentrated hydrochloric acid, Fischer obtained the dipeptide glycyl-glycine:

$$\begin{matrix} CO-NH-CH_2 \\ | \quad\quad | \\ CH_2-NH-CO \end{matrix} + H_2O = \begin{matrix} CH_2NH_2 \\ | \\ CO \\ | \\ NH-CH_2-COOH \end{matrix}$$

Glycyl-glycine

Another method employed by Fischer for the synthesis of a dipeptide consists in treating an amino acid with an α-halogen acyl radical.   When the resulting compound is treated with ammonia a dipeptide is formed as represented by the following equations:

$$\begin{matrix} CH_2Cl \\ | \\ C=O \\ | \\ Cl \end{matrix} + \begin{matrix} COOH \\ | \\ CH-CH_2-C_6H_4-OH \\ | \\ H_2N \end{matrix} = \begin{matrix} C_6H_4-OH \\ | \\ CH_2 \\ | \\ CH-NH-C=O \\ | \quad\quad | \\ COOH \quad CH_2-Cl \end{matrix} + HCl$$

Chlor-acetyl-
chloride   Tyrosine

$$+ NH_3 = \begin{matrix} C_6H_4-OH \\ | \\ CH_2 \quad\quad CH_2-NH_2 \\ | \quad\quad\quad | \\ CH-NH-C=O \\ | \\ COOH \end{matrix} + HCl$$

Glycyl-tyrosine

The acid chloride of the halogen acyl derivative of an amino acid reacts with amino-acid esters as follows:

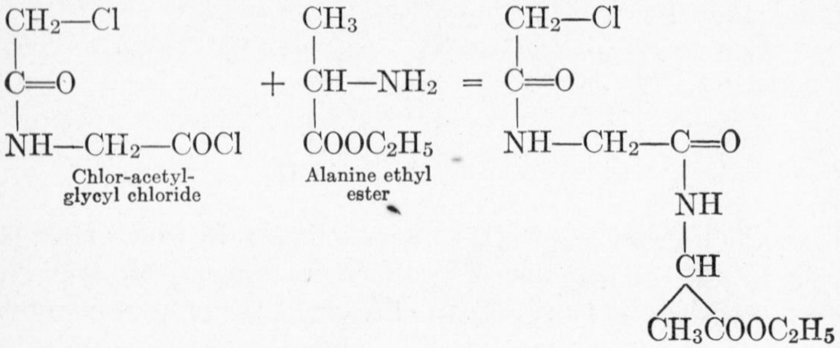

$$CH_2-Cl$$
$$|$$
$$C=O$$
$$|$$
$$NH-CH_2-COCl$$
Chlor-acetyl-
glycyl chloride

$$+ \quad CH_3$$
$$|$$
$$CH-NH_2$$
$$|$$
$$COOC_2H_5$$
Alanine ethyl
ester

$$= \quad CH_2-Cl$$
$$|$$
$$C=O$$
$$|$$
$$NH-CH_2-C=O$$
$$|$$
$$NH$$
$$|$$
$$CH$$
$$CH_3 \quad COOC_2H_5$$

The ester group of the resulting compound may be hydrolyzed, and on subsequent treatment with ammonia, a tripeptide, diglycyl-alanine is formed. By these and similar methods, Fischer and other workers have synthesized a variety of polypeptides from amino acids. Fischer prepared a chain compound of as many as eighteen amino acids, namely, *l-leucyl-triglycyl-leucyl-triglycyl-leucyl-octoglycyl-glycine.* Later, Abderhalden synthesized a polypeptide chain composed of nineteen amino acids. The more complex synthetic polypeptides have many points of resemblance to the proteins. They are non-diffusible through a parchment membrane, give certain of the color reactions characteristic of proteins, and are precipitated from solution by tannic acid, phosphotungstic acid, and other protein precipitants.

In the condensation of amino acids, compounds with cyclic structures have been formed. Glycine anhydride, or diketopiperazine, is a simple example. Substituted diketopiperazines may be obtained by the condensation of phenylalanine, aspartic acid, etc.

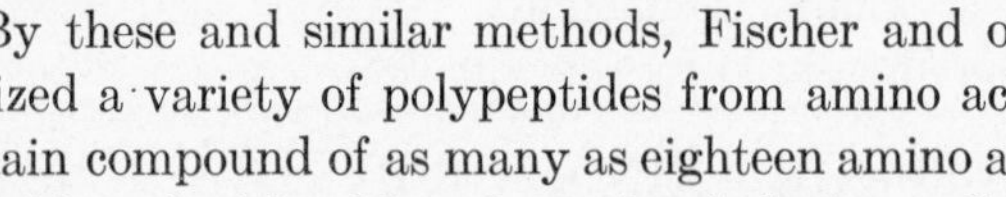

$$C_6H_5-CH_2-CH-NH-CO$$
$$| \qquad |$$
$$CO-NH-CH-CH_2-C_6H_5$$
Phenylalanine diketopiperazine

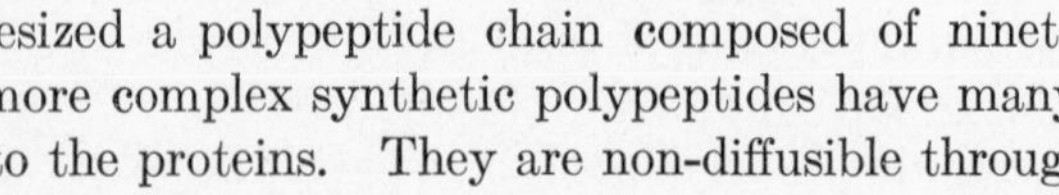

$$HOOC-CH_2-CH-CO-NH$$
$$| \qquad |$$
$$NH-CO-CH-CH_2-COOH$$
Aspartic acid diketopiperazine

The dipeptide of aspartic acid (and glutamic acid) yields yet another type of cyclic compound (Blanchetier),[15] consisting of three condensed rings, as follows:

[15] *Bull. Soc. chim. biol.*, **6**, 854 (1924).

$$
\begin{array}{llll}
\text{CH}_2\text{---} & & & \\
| & \text{CO--CH} & & \\
| & | & & \\
\text{CO------N} & \text{N--CO} & & \\
& \text{CH--CO} & | & \\
& & \text{CH}_2 &
\end{array}
$$

These, and a variety of other cyclic compounds, which have been obtained by the condensation of two or more amino acids, and which some workers claim to have isolated also among the products of protein hydrolysis, have acquired considerable interest in recent years in connection with various theories of protein structure that have been proposed.

Reactions of Amino Compounds. Nitrous acid reacts with amino compounds as represented by the equation:

$$R\text{---}NH_2 + HNO_2 = ROH + H_2O + N_2$$

This reaction is the basis of the Van Slyke method[16] for determining the free amino groups in protein. Since hydrolysis of the protein molecule results in the development of a larger number of free amino (NH_2) groups, the method may be employed in following the progress of protein digestion.

The reaction between amino acids and formaldehyde is the basis of Sørensen's formol-titration method[17] which may be employed in determining the number of free carboxyl groups. The reaction is adjusted to a definite alkalinity. Formaldehyde is then added to combine with the amino group, forming a methylene derivative in accordance with the equation:

$$
\begin{array}{cccc}
R\text{---}NH_2 & O\diagdown\diagup H & R\text{---}N{=}C{=}H_2 & \\
| & +\quad C & = \quad | & + H_2O \\
COOH & \diagup\diagdown H & COOH &
\end{array}
$$

The effect of the basic amino group having been removed, subsequent titration with standardized alkali to the original reaction of the solution gives a measure of the number of free carboxyl groups.[18]

---

[16] *J. Biol. Chem.*, **12**, 275 (1912).

[17] *Z. physiol. Chem.*, **64**, 120 (1909).

[18] According to L. J. Harris (*Proc. Roy. Soc.* [*London*], B, **95**, 500 [1923–24]) the action of formaldehyde is to increase the acid ionization constant of the amino acids and is not due to reaction with the amino group.

A reaction which appears general to α-amino acids has been described recently by Dakin and West.[19] On warming amino acids with acetic anhydride and pyridine, carbon dioxide is evolved and two acetyl groups are introduced, one attached to nitrogen and one to carbon. The compounds have the general formula $R \cdot CH \cdot (NH \cdot COCH_3) \cdot COCH_3$, and are derivatives of acetylaminoacetone. The reaction with phenylalanine may be represented as follows:

$$
\begin{array}{c}
C_6H_5 \cdot CH_2 \cdot CH \cdot COOH \qquad CH_3 \cdot CO \\
| \qquad\qquad + \qquad >O \rightarrow \\
NH_2 \qquad\qquad CH_3 \cdot CO \\[1em]
C_6H_5 \cdot CH_2 \cdot CH \cdot CO \cdot CH_3 \\
| \qquad\qquad + H_2O + CO_2 \\
NH \cdot CO \cdot CH_3
\end{array}
$$

The function of the pyridine appears to be catalytic. Proline and alkylamino acids do not react analogously, but undergo simple acetylation.

Reaction of Amino Acids with Acids and Bases; The "Zwitter Ion" Hypothesis. It has been customary to consider amino acids as amphoteric electrolytes, reacting as bases in the presence of acids and as acids in the presence of bases. In accord with the usual conception, such substances are supposed to be dissociated into ions either on the acid or basic side of a certain critical hydrogen-ion concentration, the "isoelectric point." As applied to amphoteric electrolytes, the isoelectric point has been defined as that point at which the ionization of the ampholyte is at a minimum. The following values represent the isolectric points of certain of the amino acids (after Michaelis).[20]

Amino Acid	Isoelectric Point, pH
Arginine	10.52
Lysine	9.52
Leucine	6.05
Glycine	6.09
Alanine	6.21
Histidine	7.21
Phenylalanine	5.36
Tyrosine	5.41

[19] *J. Biol. Chem.*, **78**, 91, 745 (1928); see also P. A. Levene and R. E. Steiger, *ibid.*, **79**, 95 (1928).

[20] "Die Wasserstoffionenkonzentration," Berlin, 1922, p. 60.

Selecting glycine for illustration, in its isoelectric form it may be represented as in I. It reacts with acid and with base as indicated:

In Acid

$$\text{I.} \quad H_2C \underset{NH_2}{\overset{COOH}{\Big\langle}} \xrightarrow{+HCl} H_2C \underset{NH_3{}^+Cl^-}{\overset{COOH}{\Big\langle}}$$

Isoelectric glycine

$$\xrightarrow{+NaOH} H_2C \underset{NH_2}{\overset{COO^-Na^+}{\Big\langle}}$$

In Alkali

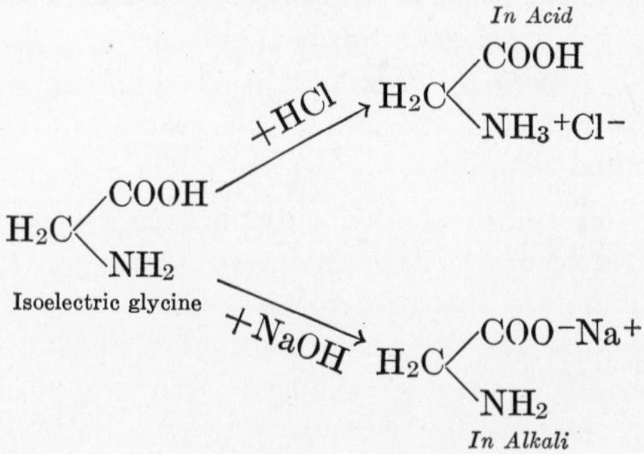

If isoelectric glycine is as represented by formula I, it should be, on theoretical grounds, a stronger acid than acetic and a stronger base than ammonia. Actually, it is much weaker than either. This and other considerations have led to the formulation of the so-called " Zwitter Ion " Hypothesis,[21] according to which isoelectric glycine is represented as in II. The molecule is neutral, but this neutrality is due to the complete and simultaneous ionization of the acid and basic groups, whereas according to the classical theory the neutrality of the molecule is assumed to be due to absence of dissociation. Although this represents a significant and fundamental difference in mechanism, the new hypothesis does not affect the products resulting on the addition of acid or base, as indicated by the following formulas:

In Acid

$$\text{II.} \quad H_2C \underset{NH_3{}^+}{\overset{COO^-}{\Big\langle}} \xrightarrow{+HCl} H_2C \underset{NH_3{}^+Cl^-}{\overset{COOH}{\Big\langle}}$$

Isoelectric glycine

$$\xrightarrow{+NaOH} H_2C \underset{NH_2}{\overset{COO^-Na^+}{\Big\langle}}$$

In Alkali

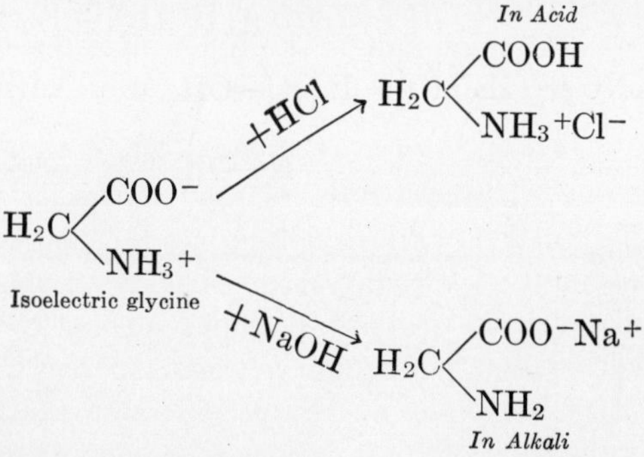

The Synthesis of Protein in Nature. Our knowledge concerning the synthesis of proteins in nature is very limited. Evidence has been

---

[21] For a fuller exposition of this hypothesis, the reader is referred to the following: N. Bjerrum, *Z. physik. Chem.*, **104**, 147 (1923); L. J. Harris, *Biochem. J.*, **24**, 1080 (1930); H. Borsook and D. A. MacFadyen, *J. Gen. Physiol.*, **13**, 509 (1930).

adduced, however, to show that the animal cell is capable of synthesizing certain amino acids, such as glycine, alanine, and serine. It seems that in the lower organisms, such as the yeasts and bacteria, the synthesis of the aromatic and heterocyclic amino acids may be accomplished, and hence protein synthesis in these organisms occurs by the utilization of carbohydrates and simple sources of nitrogen.[22] In the higher organisms, however, the amino-acid supply is largely exogenous in origin. Animal life depends on the plants for its nitrogen supply. The dependence may be a direct one as in herbivorous animals, or it may be somewhat more remote as in the carnivorous animals.

For the most part, protein synthesis takes place in the leaves of plants from nitrogen supplied to the plant in the form of simple nitrogen-containing salts, the most important of which are the nitrates. A great many factors determine the growth of plants and their capacity to form proteins and other foodstuffs. It is obvious that the supply of nitrogen to the plant is an essential factor. Much of the nitrogen is absorbed by the plant in the form of nitrate and is reduced to nitrite under the influence of sunlight. The same effect may be achieved by exposure of potassium nitrate to the rays from a quartz mercury-vapor lamp. Further reduction of the nitrite doubtless occurs. Baudisch[23] has shown that the exposure of mixtures of potassium nitrite and methyl alcohol in aqueous solution to diffused daylight and ultraviolet light results in the reduction of the nitrite to hyponitrite and the oxidation of the methyl alcohol to formaldehyde. The two products thus formed react to give the potassium salt of formhydroxamic acid:

$$KNO_2 + CH_3OH = KNO + HCHO + H_2O$$

$$KNO + HCHO = \underset{\displaystyle \underset{N-OK}{\|}}{H-C-OH}$$

Another important factor which determines the synthesis of proteins is the available supply of carbohydrate. The synthesis of proteins in the plant can take place in the dark, provided there is an adequate supply of carbohydrate and potassium. It can be seen therefore that radiant energy may have only an indirect effect on protein formation, for it will be recalled that the formation of carbohydrates is the result of photosynthetic reactions.

---

[22] See for example: E. Abderhalden and P. Rona, *Z. physiol. Chem.*, **46**, 179 (1905); S. Tamura, *ibid.*, **88**, 190 (1913); C. E. Skinner, *J. Bact.*, **19**, 149 (1930).

[23] *Ber.*, **44**, 1009 (1911); **49**, 1176 (1916); **51**, 793 (1918).

According to Treub,[24] hydrocyanic acid is the first recognizable product of nitrogen assimilation in the plant. More recently, Baly, Heilbron, and Hudson[25] have reported that formaldehyde may react with potassium nitrate or nitrite to yield potassium formhydroxamate, a compound which on hydrolysis and subsequent reduction yields a hydrate of hydrocyanic acid. These changes may be represented as follows:

$$
\begin{array}{c}
\mid \\
\mathrm{H-C-OH} \\
\mid \\
\text{Formaldehyde} \\
\text{("activated")}
\end{array}
+
\begin{array}{c}
\mathrm{O\!=\!N-OK} \\
\text{Potassium} \\
\text{nitrite}
\end{array}
\rightarrow
\begin{array}{c}
\mathrm{H-C-OH} \\
\parallel \\
\mathrm{O\!=\!N-OK}
\end{array}
\rightarrow
\begin{array}{c}
\mathrm{H-C-OH} \\
\parallel \\
\mathrm{N-OK}
\end{array}
\rightarrow
\begin{array}{c}
\mathrm{H-C-OH} \\
\parallel \\
\mathrm{N-H} \\
\text{Hydrocyanic} \\
\text{acid hydrate}
\end{array}
$$

Formhydroxamic acid is said to condense with activated formaldehyde to yield an unstable ring compound:

$$
\begin{array}{ccc}
\mathrm{OH} & & \mathrm{OH} \\
\mid & & \mid \\
\mathrm{H-C} & \!\!\!\!-\!\!\!\! & \mathrm{C-H} \\
& \diagdown\;\diagup & \\
& \mathrm{NH} &
\end{array}
$$

which by molecular rearrangement may conceivably yield glycine.

On the other hand, Björkstén[26] in a remarkable study of protein synthesis in nitrogen-starved wheat seedlings found that hydrocyanic acid was not used as a source of nitrogen. Nitrites and ammonium salts of aliphatic organic compounds were, however, well utilized.

The Structure of Proteins and the Types of Linkage in the Protein Molecule.[27] Early in the study of protein structure, Fischer arrived at the conclusion that amino acids are linked together through the amino group of one amino acid and the carboxyl group of another, forming long chains of amino acids. The union between the two constituent amino

---

[24] *Ann. Jardin Botan. Buitenzorg*, **13**, 1 (1896).

[25] *J. Chem. Soc.*, **121**, 1078 (1922).

[26] *Biochem. Z.*, **225**, 1 (1930).

[27] Two excellent reviews of the subject are especially recommended to the student. One is by E. Klarmann, *Chem. Rev.*, **4**, 51 (1927), and the other by H. B.Vickery and T. B. Osborne, *Physiol. Rev.*, **8**, 393 (1928). These reviews contain references to the work of Fischer, Kossel, Hofmeister, Abderhalden, Fodor, Bergmann, Karrer, and others who have attempted to solve the perplexing problem of the constitution of the protein molecule. See also H. B. Vickery, "Recent Contributions to the Theory of Protein Structure," *Yale J. Biol. Med.*, **4**, 595 (1932).

acids in the dipeptide, alanyl-glycine, illustrates this form of combination.

$$CH_3 \cdot CHNH_2 \cdot CO\underset{\text{Alanine}}{\underline{OH}} + \underline{H}\underset{\text{Glycine}}{NH \cdot CH_2 \cdot COOH} =$$

$$\underset{\text{Alanyl-glycine}}{CH_3 \cdot CHNH_2 \cdot CO \cdot NH \cdot CH_2 \cdot COOH} + H_2O.$$

This type of linkage (O=C—NH—) is called the peptide binding.

The view that it is the principal linkage existing between amino acids in the protein molecule is based on the following considerations, as enumerated by Vickery and Osborne:

1. Native protein itself contains very little amino nitrogen, but the end-products of protein hydrolysis contain larger amounts. The peptide bond type of union readily accounts for this.

2. The biuret reaction (p. 119) is given by many substances which contain this group, and this reaction is characteristic of proteins and their decomposition products, the proteoses. It disappears on complete hydrolysis. This strongly suggests the presence of the peptide bond in proteins and their partial hydrolysis products.

3. A number of condensation products of amino acids have been prepared which contain this group. Many of these give the biuret reaction.

4. The peptide union is also encountered in other naturally occurring substances as, for example, in hippuric acid.

5. The synthetic polypeptides obtained by Fischer from the natural isomers of optically active amino acids are hydrolyzed by the enzymes of the digestive tract.

6. Polypeptides have frequently been found among the products of incomplete hydrolysis of proteins.

7. During the hydrolysis of proteins, whether by acids or enzymes, amino groups and carboxyl groups are progressively liberated at an approximately equal rate.

8. Hydrolysis of proteins occurs without material change in the hydrogen ion concentration of the solution. This is consistent with the view that equivalent amounts of amino and carboxyl groups are thereby produced.

9. Pepsin alone liberates as a rule about 20 per cent of the total amount of amino nitrogen which can be obtained by the complete hydrolysis of a protein. Erepsin acting on a peptic digest can liberate as much as 70 per cent more. Since there is every reason to believe that the latter enzyme acts only upon peptide bonds, it is obvious that by far the

greater part of the total possible amino nitrogen of a protein has its origin in such bonds.

However, certain facts seem to point to the possibility that the protein molecule is not merely a single large polypeptide. This type of structure is believed to be inconsistent with the changes which protein undergoes in the process of denaturation by alcohol or heat. Nor is it possible to explain the insolubility in water of many proteins on the basis of a polypeptide structure. An even greater obstacle in accepting the peptide bond as being the sole link between amino acids is the behavior of pepsin toward polypeptides. Pepsin does not act on polypeptides, nor for that matter on any synthetic products formed from amino acids. In fact, it is not known which bonds in the protein molecule are attacked by this enzyme.

To explain various peculiarities in the behavior of proteins, a number of theories regarding their structure have been suggested. Of these, only two will be mentioned here. According to Abderhalden's *diketopiperazine hypothesis*,[28] the protein molecule is built up of a number of complexes containing diketopiperazine which are associated or held together by forces of secondary, or latent, valence.[29] A theory similar to Abderhalden's has been proposed by Bergmann[30] who believes that protein is composed of a variety of cyclic derivatives of piperazine held together by means of secondary valences.

Sørensen[31] holds that at least certain proteins are in a molecular condition such as may be represented by the formula $A_x B_y C_z \ldots$, in which A, B, C, and so on, represent components of a definite character and composition (e.g., polypeptides), and x, y, z, and so on, indicate the number of such components in the complexes. Within each component, strong chemical bonds unite the atoms or groups of atoms, whereas the various components are linked to each other to form the larger complex by relatively weak, residual valences. This conception has received support from Svedberg's studies of the molecular weights of proteins. Svedberg[32] is of the opinion that in *solution* a protein, as

---

[28] *Naturwissenschaften*, **12**, 716 (1924); *Z. physiol. Chem.*, **128**, 119 (1923); *ibid.*, **139**, 169, 181 (1924).

[29] According to Werner's conception there are two kinds of valence, one which he termed "primary" valence, and the residual attraction left over after the primary valence is saturated, which Werner called "secondary" valence. This idea of auxiliary or potential valence forces may be harmonized, with certain modifications, with the more modern views of atomic structure.

[30] *Naturwissenschaften*, **12**, 1155 (1924); *ibid.*, **13**, 1045 (1925).

[31] *Compt. rend. trav. lab. Carlsberg*, **18**, No. 5, 1930; see also Editorial, *J. Am. Med. Assoc.*, **99**, 998 (1932).

[32] *Nature*, **128**, 999 (1931).

for example, egg albumin, does not possess the molecular weight which characterizes the crystalline product. The implication is that, during the process of purification of a protein, it is built up from particles of a relatively small size.

There is little evidence for the presence of ester, ether, or imide linkages between amino acids in the protein molecule. However, in the individual amino acids, we have the guanidine binding (NH—CH$_2$) in arginine, and the disulfide linkage (S—S) in cystine. It is likely that the peptide group may be capable of rearrangement from the keto- to the enol-form, as follows:

$$\begin{array}{cc} -\text{C}-\text{N}- & -\text{C}=\text{N}- \\ \underset{\text{O} \quad \text{H}}{\|\ \ \ |} \rightarrow & \underset{\text{OH}}{|} \\ \text{Keto-form} & \text{Enol-form} \end{array}$$

Molecular Weights of Proteins. The physical and chemical properties of the proteins have stimulated much interest in the question of their molecular weights. Various methods have been employed in an attempt to determine the relative size of the molecules of various proteins. The minimal weight of a protein molecule may be calculated from analytical data by assuming the presence, in the molecule of protein, of but one molecule of a given amino acid. The molecular weight of hemoglobin has been calculated thus from the amino-acid content, and also from data obtained of its iron content and of the oxygen content in oxyhemoglobin. It has also been shown that 16,721 grams of hemoglobin combine with one mol of carbon monoxide. Consequently this value was formerly taken for the minimal molecular weight of hemoglobin.

Determination of the equivalent combining weights of various proteins with acids and bases may yield useful information, especially when compared with calculations of their molecular weights based on the analyses of such elementary constituents as iron (in the case of hemoglobin), copper (in hemocyanin), sulfur, and phosphorus.

The direct determination of the molecular weights of proteins by osmotic-pressure methods has yielded results approximating those obtained by analytical methods. For the determination of the relative size of protein molecules, methods of ultrafiltration and dialysis have been found very useful. Svedberg and associates[33] have determined the molecular weights of proteins by measuring their sedimentation velocities in an ultra-centrifuge. The following are illustrative data:

---

[33] T. Svedberg and associates: series of papers in *J. Am. Chem. Soc.*, **46**, to date. See also H. B. Vickery, *loc. cit.* [27] Compare with data given by C. L. A. Schmidt, *Ann. Rev. Biochem.*, **1**, 151 (1932).

	Estimated
Protein	Molecular Weight
Egg albumin	34,500
Serum albumin	67,500
Hemoglobin	68,000
Edestin	208,000
H-Hemocyanin	5,000,000

Behavior of Proteins as Electrolytes. In 1900 Hardy[34] demonstrated that particles of coagulated egg albumin were differently influenced by an electric current, depending on whether the reaction of the solution was acid or alkaline. In a slightly alkaline solution the protein moved from the cathode to the anode, whereas in the presence of acid the protein acquired a positive charge and migrated in the direction of the cathode. According to Hardy, the H^+ or OH^- ions become entangled within the colloid particle of protein, which thereby acquires a positive charge if there is an excess of H^+ ions (acid solution) or a negative charge if the OH^- ions are in excess (alkaline solution).

An explanation offered by Loeb[35] in 1904 was to the effect that proteins behaved like amphoteric electrolytes, reacting as bases in the presence of acids and as acids in the presence of bases. Owing to the presence of the amino group in the amino-acid molecule, this reacts with acids as though it were a basic substance. When placed in an alkaline solution, amino acids behave as though they were acids, because of the carboxyl group. Since the protein molecule likewise has at least one free amino group and one free carboxyl group, it will yield a protein cation in the presence of acids and will form protein chlorides, sulfates, etc. In the presence of bases it will yield a protein anion to form such compounds as sodium, potassium, or calcium proteinates. The protein molecule is obviously capable of electrolytic dissociation. The degree of dissociation of a protein and its capacity to combine with anions or cations is conditioned by the hydrogen-ion concentration, and for each protein the degree of dissociation is negligible at its *isoelectric point*.

The following are the isoelectric points of several familiar proteins (after Michaelis):[20]

Serum albumin	4.7
Serum globulin	5.4
Egg albumin	4.8
Edestin	6.9
Casein	4.7
Gelatin	4.7

[34] *Proc. Roy. Soc.*, **66**, 110 (1900).
[35] "Univ. Calif. Pub. Physiol.," **1**, 149 (1904).

Chemical Reactions of Proteins with Anions and Cations.   Assuming that proteins are amphoteric electrolytes, they should combine with anions only on the acid side of the isoelectric point, and with cations only on the alkaline side.   At its isoelectric point, the protein should combine with but negligible amounts of either acid or base.   The correctness of this assumption was proved by Jacques Loeb[36] in a very ingenious manner:

Equal amounts of commercial powdered gelatin were brought to a different pH by treatment with varying concentrations of nitric acid. Silver nitrate was then added and the excess removed by washing with cold water.   The gelatin was in turn dissolved and the solutions exposed in test-tubes to light (the previous manipulations having been carried out in a dark room).   As a result, all the gelatin solutions with a

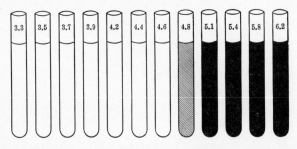

FIG. 10.—Proof that cations combine with proteins only on the alkaline side of the isoelectric point.   Powdered gelatin brought to different pH was treated in a dark room with $M/64$ AgNO$_3$ and then washed with cold water to remove the silver not in combination with gelatin.   The gelatin was liquefied, brought to a 1 per cent solution, and the pH was determined.   The solutions were then poured into test-tubes and exposed to light.   In about half an hour the gelatin of pH >4.7 was dark, while the gelatin of pH 4.7 or less remained permanently clear though exposed to light for over a year.   The pH of each gelatin solution is marked at the head of each test-tube.   (After J. Loeb, "Proteins and the Theory of Colloidal Behavior," McGraw-Hill, 1924 edition, p. 34.)

pH > 4.7 became opaque and then brown or black, while the solutions of pH < 4.7, i.e., from pH 4.6 and below, remained transparent even when exposed to light for months or years (Fig. 10).   Hence it may be concluded that the cation Ag is only in chemical combination with gelatin when the pH is > 4.7.   At pH 4.7, or below, gelatin is not able to combine with Ag ionogenically.

[36] Jacques Loeb, "Proteins and the Theory of Colloidal Behavior," McGraw-Hill Book Co., New York (1924), p. 34; see also *J. Gen. Physiol.*, **1**, 449 (1920).

Loeb has made similar tests with other cations, such as nickel and copper, and with basic dyes. Basic fuchsin and neutral red, after sufficient washing with cold water, stain only those gelatin solutions that have a pH above 4.7.

In order to bring out more fully the significance of the preceding observations, the gelatin molecule may be represented by the formula:[37]

$$\left[R\begin{array}{c} \diagup NH_2 \\ \diagdown COOH \end{array} \right]$$

in which the brackets are used to indicate the inability of isoelectric gelatin to combine with either anions or cations. On the alkaline side of the isoelectric point, only the COOH reacts, in accordance with the following equation:

$$\left[R\begin{array}{c} \diagup \overline{NH_2} \\ \diagdown COOH \end{array} + NaOH \right] = \left[R\begin{array}{c} \diagup \overline{NH_2} \\ \diagdown COONa \end{array} + H_2O \right]$$

The sodium proteinate that is formed dissociates into a protein anion and a Na^+ cation:

$$\left[R\begin{array}{c} \diagup \overline{NH_2} \\ \diagdown COONa \end{array} \right] \rightleftharpoons \left[R\begin{array}{c} \diagup \overline{NH_2} \\ \diagdown COO^- \end{array} + Na^+ \right]$$

When other electrolytes are present, as $AgNO_3$, an interchange of cations takes place with the formation in this case of silver proteinate.

When protein on the acid side of the isoelectric point is treated with a salt it combines with the anion of the salt. Loeb demonstrated this by using potassium ferrocyanide and other salts. Gelatin was treated with $M/128$ $K_4Fe(CN)_6$ and subsequently washed. From the gelatin samples 1 per cent solutions were prepared and these allowed to stand for several days. It was found that the gelatin solutions with a $pH < 4.7$ turned blue (owing to the formation of ferric ferrocyanide) whereas the gelatin samples with a $pH > 4.7$ remained perfectly clear

[37] This is based on Loeb's exposition. It may be revised in terms of the "Zwitter Ion" concept without altering the fundamental significance or interpretation of the questions involved.

(Fig. 11). This is taken as evidence that the gelatin molecule enters into chemical combination with the anion $Fe(CN)_6$ only when the pH is less than 4.7.

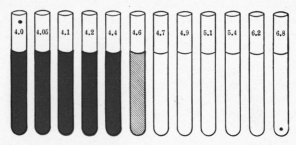

FIG. 11.—Proof that anions combine with proteins only on the acid side of the isoelectric point. Doses of powdered gelatin solutions of different pH were treated with $M/128$ $K_4Fe(CN)_6$ and then washed with cold water. All the samples of gelatin solution of pH < 4.7 turned blue (through the formation of some ferric salt), while all the gelatin solutions of pH 4.7 or above remained colorless.

On the acid side of the isoelectric point, the amino group of the protein molecule behaves like ammonia in its ability to add an acid. This may be represented by the equation:

$$\left[R\!\!<^{\text{NH}_2}_{\underline{\text{COOH}}}\right] + \text{HCl} = \left[R\!\!<^{\text{NH}_2\cdot\text{HCl}}_{\underline{\text{COOH}}}\right]$$

The hydrochloride dissociates into a protein cation and an anion (Cl^-).

$$\left[R\!\!<^{\text{NH}_3\text{Cl}}_{\underline{\text{COOH}}}\right] \rightleftarrows \left[R\!\!<^{\text{NH}_3{}^+}_{\underline{\text{COOH}}}\right] + \text{Cl}^-$$

It is to be appreciated, of course, that the protein molecule very probably contains more than one reactive carboxyl and amino group.

Reaction of Proteins with Acid. The conception that proteins undergo electrolytic dissociation was a radical departure from the views formerly held that because of the " colloidal " nature of proteins they did not react according to the " law of combining weights," that is, in *stoichiometric* proportions. The revision of this point of view was in no small measure the immediate outcome of Loeb's quantitative proof that proteins combine with acids and bases in definite and predictable proportions.

As has been stated, proteins combine with acids at a pH below that of the isoelectric point. It also happens that most weak dibasic and tribasic acids dissociate as monobasic acids in solutions more acid than that equivalent to a pH of 4.7. For example, H_3PO_4 dissociates into H^+ and $H_2PO_4^-$ ions. On the other hand, H_2SO_4, being a strong acid, splits off both hydrogen ions in dilute solutions. Oxalic acid behaves as a monobasic acid below pH 3.0 but above this value the second hydrogen atom begins to split off.

If acids combined stoichiometrically with isoelectric protein, it would require exactly three times as many cubic centimeters of 0.1 N H_3PO_4 to bring a 1.0 per cent solution of isoelectric gelatin, egg albumin, casein, or any other protein to a given hydrogen-ion concentration as it does of 0.1 N HCl, HNO$_3$ or H_2SO_4. The correctness of this assumption was demonstrated in a series of experiments in which varying amounts of acid were added to equal concentrations of isoelectric protein and the pH of the resulting solutions measured with the hydrogen electrode. The titration curves in Fig. 12 were obtained by plotting the concentration of acid against pH.

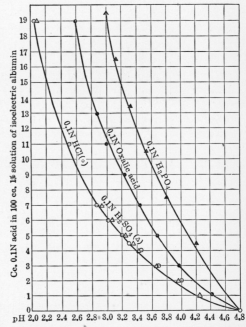

Fig. 12.—The ordinates represent the number of cubic centimeters of 0.1 N HCl, H_2SO_4, oxalic and phosphoric acids required to bring 1 gram of isoelectric crystalline egg albumin to the pH indicated on the axis of the abscissas. Enough H_2O was added to bring the albumin and acid to a volume of 100 cc. For the same pH, the ordinates for HCl, H_2SO_4, and phosphoric acid are approximately 1 : 1 : 3. The ratio of HCl to oxalic acid is a little less than 1 : 2 when pH is >3.0. (After Loeb, "Proteins and the Theory of Colloidal Behavior," 1924 edition, p. 53.)

From the curves it can be seen that it required three times as many cubic centimeters of 0.1 N H_3PO_4 as of 0.1 N HCl or H_2SO_4 to bring the albumin solution to the same pH. To bring the protein to pH 3.4 it required 4 cc. of 0.1 N HCl or H_2SO_4 and 12 cc. of 0.1 N H_3PO_4. As indicated by the titration curves, twice as much 0.1 N

oxalic acid as 0.1 N hydrochloric acid was required to bring the albumin solution to the same pH below pH 3.0.   Above pH 3.0 it required less than twice as many cubic centimeters of oxalic acid as of hydrochloric or sulfuric acid.

From the titration curves, the amount of acid actually in combination with the protein may be calculated.   The curves in Fig. 13 represent the actual amounts of each of the four acids in combination with 1 gram of originally isoelectric egg albumin in 100 cc. of solution.   The values for HCl and H_2SO_4 are practically identical.   For H_3PO_4 the values are always about three times as large as those for HCl, any slight deviations being due to the limitations in the accuracy of the method.

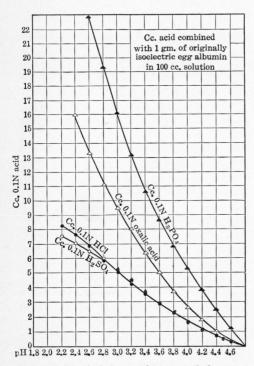

Fig. 13.—Proof of the stoichiometrical character of the combination of acids with isoelectric albumin.   The same mass of albumin combines with three times as many cubic centimeters of 0.1 N H_3PO_4 as with HCl or H_2SO_4; and with twice as many cubic centimeters of 0.1 N oxalic acid below pH 3.0.   (After Loeb, p. 56.)

Reaction of Proteins with Base. The combination of isoelectric protein with bases likewise occurs in stoichiometric proportions. Loeb has determined the number of cubic centimeters of 0.1 N KOH, NaOH, $Ca(OH)_2$, and $Ba(OH)_2$, respectively, that must be contained in 100 cc. of a 1 per cent solution of crystalline egg albumin, isoelectric albumin, casein, or gelatin to bring the solution to a given pH. He found that the number of cubic centimeters is the same in each case and that the values for the four bases lie on the same curve. This is illustrated in Fig. 14 for casein and in Fig. 15 for gelatin.

Rawlins and Schmidt[38] have titrated casein, fibrin, gelatin, and edestin with certain basic dyes, methylene blue, safranine Y, and

[38] *J. Biol. Chem.*, **82**, 709 (1929).

induline scarlet, and found that the union between protein and basic dye occurred in stoichiometric proportions.

Loeb has pointed out that the failure of the earlier investigators to recognize the stoichiometric character of the reactions of proteins with acids and bases was due to the fact that these workers were unable to measure the hydrogen-ion concentration of a protein solution and did not appreciate its significance.

Solubility of Proteins. Solutions in which the ultimate units are molecules or ions have been defined as true solutions, as distinguished from colloidal solutions in which the ultimate units are aggregates of molecules. Molecular aggregation or association is not limited, however, to colloidal particles. Many substances in the liquid state (water, acetic acid, methyl and ethyl alcohol) are not made up of discrete molecules, as can be demonstrated by comparing the molecular weights determined in the liquid state with those obtained in the vapor state. It has been generally assumed that proteins do not form true aqueous solutions but that the relatively large molecules form, by coalescence or aggregation, still larger particles, which remain in suspension.

The stability of colloidal particles suspended in water depends on the weak forces

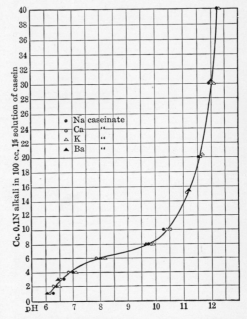

Fig. 14.—Ordinates are the cubic centimeters of 0.1 N NaOH, KOH, Ca(OH)$_2$, and Ba(OH)$_2$ in 100 cc. of 1 per cent solution of casein. Abscissas are the pH of the solution. The curves for the four alkalies are identical, proving that Ba and Ca combine with casein in equivalent proportion. (After Loeb, p. 69.)

of repulsion due to the electrical double layer, of measurable potential difference, between each colloidal particle and the water. Diminution of the potential difference of the double layer below a certain critical value results in a coalescence of the particles into larger and larger aggregates, which settle out. The neutralization of the electrical charge of the colloidal particles may be accomplished even by relatively low concentrations of neutral salts, the effect being greater in the case of polyvalent ions having a charge opposite to that of the particles in suspension.

On the other hand, the stability of individual molecules and ions in true solution in water is due to the strong forces of attraction between the molecules or ions of the solute and of the solvent. Substances in true solution are not easily precipitated, therefore, by chemically non-reacting substances. Large concentrations of salts are required to precipitate substances from true solution and emulsoids. It is not a question of the neutralization of an electric charge, for the precipitation may be accomplished by an ion having a charge similar to that of the ion or molecule that is being removed from the solution.

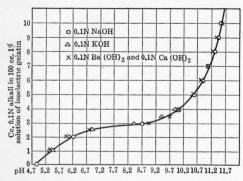

FIG. 15.—Curves for the number of cubic centimeters of 0.1 N NaOH, KOH, Ba(OH)$_2$, and Ca(OH)$_2$ required to bring the same mass of about 0.8 gram of isoelectric gelatin in a 100 cc. solution to different pH. All four curves are identical. (After Loeb, p. 70.)

We may now consider whether proteins in solution behave as crystalloids or as colloids. If, for precipitation, proteins required low concentrations of salts, this would be evidence for the suspensoid nature of their solutions. The fact that they require very large concentrations has been used in arguing for the emulsoid character of protein solutions. Some workers, however, maintain that this may also be used as an argument for the non-colloidal nature of protein solutions. In the precipitation of proteins, the active ion need not necessarily have a charge opposite to that of the protein.

Proteins are least soluble at the isoelectric point, a property which is also characteristic of other amphoteric electrolytes. It has been shown that true crystalloids, such as the amino acids, have minimum solubility at their isoelectric points. In other words, amphoteric electrolytes and ionized protein salts are more soluble than the un-ionized molecules. Quantitative evidence that proteins may form true solutions has been furnished by Cohn and Hendry.[39]

A point considered elsewhere (p. 107) may be recalled in this connection. The conceptions advanced by Sørensen and by Svedberg have

[39] *J. Gen. Physiol.* **5**, 521 (1922–23).

greatly strengthened the probability that the molecular constitution of a protein in solution may be much simpler than has been assumed on the basis of the properties of the purified product.

Denaturation and Coagulation.[40] *Denaturation* is a process peculiar to proteins. The change from the fresh or " native " (undenatured) form to the denatured protein is not clearly understood. Protein is denatured in the presence of water, by heating, exposure to ultraviolet light and to high pressures, shaking, addition of acid, alkali, alcohol, acetone, urea, and thiocyanate. In the neighborhood of the isoelectric point and within a fairly wide pH range protein will remain undenatured indefinitely. Brought outside of this range by either acid or alkali, denaturation occurs very rapidly. Whereas at ordinary temperatures (25° C.) the process of denaturation is slow, it may be greatly hastened by an increase in temperature, inasmuch as the velocity is accelerated 600 per cent for each 10° rise.

Perhaps the outstanding change is in solubility. Native protein is soluble at its isoelectric point; denatured protein on the contrary is insoluble. It is definitely known that, even though the change is invisible, denaturation of protein in solution takes place at hydrogen-ion concentrations far removed from the isoelectric point, for when the solution is brought to the isoelectric point, denatured protein is precipitated. The precipitate may be redissolved by acid or alkali; hence the process of flocculation is *reversible*, and indeed it has been so considered for a long time. On the contrary, denaturation has been generally regarded as an *irreversible* process, a view that has been effectively challenged in recent years by the work of Anson and Mirsky.[41]

Chick and Martin[42] advanced the concept that the *coagulation* of a protein occurs in two distinct steps: the first, denaturation, is a chemical change; the second, precipitation or flocculation. The latter depends on physical changes affecting the protein particles. In so far as Anson and Mirsky have succeeded in demonstrating the reversibility of denaturation, to that extent the process of coagulation may be regarded as also a reversible process. They have accomplished the complete reversal of coagulation of a protein (hemoglobin).

No clear view of the problem is possible from such isolated facts as the cleavage of sulfur from protein, or changes in the sulfhydryl groups, such as occur in denaturation of protein by alkali, or the splitting off of ammonia when protein is denatured by heating. Wu [42a] has offered the

---

[40] For a general review of the subject, the reader is referred to W. C. M. Lewis, *Chem. Rev.*, **8**, 81 (1931).

[41] *J. Phys. Chem.*, **35**, 185 (1931); *J. Gen. Physiol.*, **14**, 605, 725.

[42] *J. Physiol.*, **40**, 404 (1910); **43**, 1 (1911).

[42a] *Chinese J. Physiol.*, **5**, 321 (1931).

suggestion that in denaturation or coagulation the compact and orderly structure is disorganized. In brief, his opinion is that at least in certain cases the protein molecule is disrupted. Hendrix,[43] on the other hand, holds the view that denaturation (as well as coagulation) may involve the condensation of opposite groups of adjacent molecules. This is borne out by the apparent reduction in the number of free amino and carboxyl groups, as determined by a comparison of the combining power of native, denatured, and coagulated protein.

Regarding the significance of denaturation, physiologically, Anson and Mirsky have offered the suggestion that denaturation and its reversal are biological reactions which may be of importance in ordinary cellular processes.

The Colloidal Behavior of Proteins. It is beyond the scope of this book to enter into a detailed discussion of Loeb's work on the behavior of proteins. He has postulated that, as far as the proteins are concerned, it is incorrect to distinguish between colloids and crystalloids. With regard to their chemical reactions and solubility, the proteins behave like crystalloids. These constitute therefore the crystalloidal properties of proteins. On the other hand, the protein ion, on account of its large size, does not diffuse through membranes or gels which are permeable to smaller crystalloidal ions. This constitutes the colloidal property of the protein ion. Evidence has been adduced to show that the behavior of proteins can be explained on the basis of Donnan's theory of membrane equilibria, which applies to the equilibria established between ions on the two sides of a membrane impermeable to one of the ions. The effect of electrolytes on the swelling of proteins, osmotic pressure, membrane potentials, and the viscosity of protein solutions may be accounted for, according to the Loeb school, by application of Donnan's postulates.[44]

Hoffman and Gortner,[45] in an exhaustive study of the physico-chemical behavior of the prolamins, reach the conclusion that a chemical type of combination between proteins and acids or bases occurs only between hydrogen-ion concentrations corresponding to pH 2.5 to 10.5. Working with a large variety of proteins belonging to this group, these authors found that the amount of acid or alkali bound at any hydrogen-

[43] B. M. Hendrix and V. Wilson, *J. Biol. Chem.*, **79**, 389 (1928); M. Fay and Hendrix, *ibid.*, **93**, 667 (1931); compare with W. J. Loughlin, *Biochem. J.*, **27**, 99 (1933).

[44] See David I. Hitchcock's "Review of Proteins and the Donnan Equilibrium," *Physiol. Rev.*, **4**, 505 (1924).

[45] W. F. Hoffman and R. A. Gortner, "Colloid Symposium Monograph," Vol. 2, p. 209, etc., Chemical Catalog Co., New York, 1925.

on concentration is dependent on the chemical composition of the protein. This may be taken as evidence of a chemical type of combination within this range of pH values. However, at hydrogen-ion concentrations higher than that represented by pH 2.5 or lower than that represented by pH 10.5, all the proteins, regardless of their chemical composition, combine with the same amount of acid or alkali, as the case may be. Moreover, with increases in hydrogen-ion concentration, protein salts, such as the chloride, increase in ionization, so that at a pH of 2.5 the protein chloride is highly ionized. But when the hydrogen-ion concentration is increased above pH 2.5, there is no further increase in the ionization of the protein salt. These and similar observations, according to Hoffman and Gortner, argue for the adsorption type of combination between proteins and bases or acids outside the pH range of 2.5 to 10.5.

Color Reactions of the Proteins. Most proteins exhibit characteristic color reactions when treated with certain reagents. The colors are due to specific linkages or to amino acids, and some reactions are specific for a particular amino acid. Hence these reactions may be employed in the qualitative characterization of proteins. Among the more familiar tests are the following:

The Biuret Reaction. This is obtained by treating a protein solution first with strong alkali and then with a very dilute copper sulfate solution. A reddish violet to violet-blue color is produced. The reaction depends on the presence of the peptide linkage in the protein molecule. According to Schiff, the following groups are responsible for the reaction:

$$NH\begin{cases} CO \cdot NH_2 \\ CO \cdot NH_2 \end{cases} \quad CH_2\begin{cases} CO \cdot NH_2 \\ CO \cdot NH_2 \end{cases} \quad \begin{matrix} CO—NH_2 \\ | \\ CO—NH_2 \end{matrix} \quad NH_2—\overset{|}{C}—CO—NH—\overset{|}{C}—$$

Millon's Reaction. The addition of Millon's reagent, a solution containing mercuric nitrate and nitrite in a mixture of nitrous and concentrated nitric acids, to protein solution, with heating, results in the formation of a brick-red precipitate. This reaction is due to the presence of the tyrosine group and is exhibited, as far as the red color is concerned, by substances, other than proteins, that contain the hydroxyphenyl group.

The Xanthoproteic Reaction. Nitric acid added to proteins produces a yellow color which deepens to an orange-yellow on the addition of alkali. The yellow color is due to the formation of nitrated benzene derivatives. The reaction depends on the presence of tyrosine, phenylalanine, and tryptophane. Some authors deny that phenylalanine gives the xanthoproteic reaction.

Hopkins-Cole Reaction. The addition of a small amount of glyoxyli
acid to a protein solution stratified above concentrated sulfuric aci
results in the formation of a reddish violet ring, provided the protei
contains the amino-acid tryptophane.

Precipitation and Coagulation Reactions. The proteins are precip
itated from solution by a large variety of substances. Among these ar
the neutral salts, such as sodium sulfate, magnesium sulfate, and ammo
nium sulfate. Large amounts of these are required for the separation o
the proteins. The process is frequently spoken of as *salting out.*

The *salts of heavy metals,* such as those of copper, mercury, and lead
are good precipitants. Precipitation of proteins is also brought abou
by strong mineral acids. On the addition of nitric acid to a protei
solution, a ring of protein is formed at the junction of the acid and th
solution (*Heller's test*).

The so-called *alkaloidal reagents* precipitate proteins more or les
completely from slightly acid solution. Among these reagents are phos
photungstic acid, phosphomolybdic acid, tannic acid, picric acid, potas
sium mercuric iodide, and potassium bismuth iodide.

Ferrocyanic acid, trichloracetic acid, sulfonyl-salicylic acid, an
dinitrosalicylic acid are likewise efficient protein precipitants.

Coagulation is probably associated with dehydration of the protei
molecule and the formation of anhydrides. This may be accomplishe
by the application of heat to solutions of protein acidified with aceti
acid, or by the addition of alcohol to neutral or acid solutions.

The Proteins as Foodstuffs. The proteins of vegetable origin pla
a very important part in animal nutrition. They have been very care
fully and thoroughly studied by Osborne and his co-workers.[46] Th
proteins found in a variety of cereals enter into the human dietary
Wheat contains gliadin, glutenin, and the albumin leucosin, in addi
tion to a proteose. The mixture of gliadin and glutenin, when moist
ened, absorbs water to a greater degree than other proteins of the cereals
Rye contains a gliadin differing from that of wheat, and a glutelin
The swelling property of rye proteins is less than that of the proteins o
wheat. Rye flour therefore yields a dough which is less elastic and less
capable of becoming porous than wheat dough.[47]

The prolamin of barley is hordein. It differs markedly from the
gliadin of wheat or rye. The remaining proteins of barley resemble
those of wheat. The prolamin of corn is zein.

[46] T. B. Osborne, "The Vegetable Proteins," Longmans, Green & Co., 1924.

[47] See chapter by Carl L. Alsberg, "The Colloid Chemistry of the Cereals," in
R. H. Bogue's "The Theory and Application of Colloidal Behavior," McGraw-Hill
Book Co., New York (1924).

The biological value of proteins is largely determined by the proportions of their constituent amino acids. Deficiency in even one of the amino acids that are essential for tissue construction limits the value of a protein to the animal body. Osborne and Mendel[48] and other workers have studied this problem very exhaustively by feeding experiments performed on animals. It has been shown, for example, that maintenance and growth are difficult on a diet in which casein is the sole protein, because casein is deficient in cystine. Supplementing this diet with small amounts of cystine results in normal growth. The relation between the chemical composition of proteins and their value in nutrition will be considered in another chapter. It is desirable at this point, however, to bring out the variations in the amino-acid composition of a variety of proteins.

TABLE XII

QUANTITATIVE COMPARISON OF AMINO ACIDS OBTAINED BY HYDROLYSIS FROM PROTEINS *

	Casein	Gelatin	Gliadin	Zein	Lactal-bumin	Edestin	Salmine (Rhine salmon)	Silk-Fibroin (Italian)
Glycocoll........	0.45	25.5	0.00	0.00	0.37	3.80	....	36.0
Alanine..........	1.85	8.7	2.00	9.79	2.41	3.60	+	21.0
Valine..........	7.93	0.0	3.34	1.88	3.30	6.20	4.3	0.0
Leucine..........	9.70	7.1	6.62	19.55	14.03	14.50	+	1.5
Proline...........	7.63	9.5	13.22	9.04	3.76	4.10	11.0	0.3
Oxyproline.......	0.23	14.1	?	?	?	?	....	
Phenylalanine.....	3.88	1.4	2.35	6.55	1.25	3.09	....	1.5
Glutaminic acid...	21.77	5.8	43.66	26.17	12.89	18.74	....	0.0
Oxyglutaminic acid	10.50	0.0	2.4	?	10.00	?	....	
Aspartic acid.....	4.1	3.5	0.58	1.71	9.30	4.50	....	
Serine............	0.5	0.4	0.13	1.02	1.76	0.33	....	
Tyrosine.........	4.5	0.01	1.61	3.55	1.95	2.13	....	10.5
Cystine..........	?	?	0.45	?	1.73	1.00	....	
Histidine.........	2.5	0.9	1.49	0.82	2.61	2.19	0.0	+
Arginine..........	3.81	8.2	2.91	1.55	3.47	14.17	87.4	1.0
Lysine...........	7.62	5.9	0.63	0.00	9.87	1.65	0.0	+
Tryptophane......	1.50	0.00	1.0	0.00	2.40	1.50	....	
Ammonia.........	1.61	0.40	5.22	3.64	1.31	2.28	....	
Total........	90.17	91.31	87.61	85.27	83.41	83.78	110.5	73.4

* The data in this table are taken largely from a compilation by H. B. Vickery. The analyses are combinations of what appear to be the best determinations by various chemists. *Cf.* L. B. Mendel, "Nutrition—The Chemistry of Life," Yale Univ. Press, New Haven, 1923, p. 115. See also Plimmer, "The Chemical Constitution of the Proteins," Part I, p. 111, etc.

[48] A long series of papers in *J. Biol. Chem.*, 1910. See also Chap. XVII.

CHAPTER V

SOURCES AND COMPOSITION OF FOODSTUFFS

It seems appropriate at this stage to consider briefly the sources of the protein, carbohydrate, and fat of our diet and also the composition of some of the more important articles of food.

The extensive statistical studies of Raymond Pearl[1] have provided us with very valuable information regarding the food consumption in the United States of America for the period 1911–1918. He has shown that, despite significant fluctuations in food production and food exports and imports, the total annual consumption of food shows remarkable uniformity from year to year. The following summary is based on data contained in his book, " The Nation's Food."

Of the protein consumed in the United States, 47 per cent comes from primary food sources, i.e., food directly gathered or harvested, such as, for example, potatoes, fish, oysters; or food derived by process of manufacture from a raw plant product, such as, for example, wheat flour or cottonseed oil. The remaining 53 per cent is obtained from so-called secondary sources, i.e., edible products of animals obtained either directly (without involving the death of the producing animal), such as honey, eggs, milk, or derivatively (involving the death of the animal), such as meats.

Primary food sources provide only 18 per cent of the fats and secondary sources 82 per cent. Most of the fat of the American's diet is therefore derived from animal sources.

The condition is reversed in the case of carbohydrates, 95 per cent being furnished from primary and 5 per cent from secondary food sources.

Approximately 36 per cent of the total protein consumed comes from grain, 26 per cent from meat, and 20 per cent from dairy products. All but 18 per cent of the nation's food protein is therefore supplied by these three great commodity groups.

Meats furnish 51 per cent of the fat; dairy products, 27 per cent; vegetable oils and nuts about 12 per cent; and grains about 4 per cent.

[1] R. Pearl "The Nation's Food," Philadelphia, 1920; see also, R. Pearl, "Studies in Human Biology," Williams & Wilkins, Baltimore, 1924, Chap. XIV.

Grains provide 56 per cent of the carbohydrate; sugars, 26 per cent; vegetables about 9 per cent; dairy products, 5 per cent; and fruits, 4 per cent.

Thirty-five per cent of the energy representing the total food consumption is derived from grains; 22 per cent from meats; 15 per cent from dairy products; 13 per cent from sugars; about 5 per cent from vegetables; 5 per cent from vegetable oils and nuts; 2 per cent from poultry; and about 2 per cent from fruits.

Of the grains, wheat is by far the most important as a source of protein and carbohydrate, representing 29 per cent of the total protein and 42 per cent of the total carbohydrate consumption. Wheat provides the nation with 26 per cent of its food calories. However, it contributes only 1.8 per cent to the total fat consumption.

Corn ranks second among the grains, furnishing 5.55 per cent (6.4 per cent during the World War) of the protein, 1.9 per cent of the fat, 11 per cent of the carbohydrate and 7 per cent of the calories.

Rye, which is an important food in Russia and elsewhere in Europe, is little used in America. It supplies only 0.31 per cent of the protein, 0.03 per cent of the fat and about 0.8 per cent of the carbohydrate.

Dairy products furnish 20 per cent of the protein, 27.5 per cent of the fat, 5.5 per cent of the carbohydrate, and 15.26 per cent of the energy of the total food consumed.

Of the meats, beef is the most important from the standpoint of protein, representing 14.47 per cent of the total protein consumption. It contributes about 10 per cent to the fat consumption and provides 5.3 per cent of the total calories. Pork ranks first among all foods from the standpoint of fat; it provides 39.57 per cent of the total fat consumed in this country. It ranks fourth from the standpoint of protein, supplying 10.74 per cent of the total. The energy value represented by the pork consumption is 15.74 per cent, second only to wheat.

Of the vegetables, the potatoes are of greatest importance, representing 3.14 per cent of the total protein, 5.7 per cent of the total carbohydrate and 3.36 per cent of the total energy consumption.

As compared with other foods, fish occupy a relatively unimportant position in this country. Only 2.32 per cent of the total protein is derived from this source.

These figures represent gross consumption, being based on averages for the six years, 1911–12 to 1916–17, and do not take into account losses through wastage. Pearl has estimated the probable loss of edible food through wastage to be: for protein, about 5 per cent; fat, at least 25 per cent; carbohydrate, 20 per cent.

Composition of Some Foods.—With the relative importance of various foods in mind, we may now present the results of analyses of the protein, fat and carbohydrate contents of some of the more common foods.[2] Unless stated otherwise, the data are based on the edible portion only. The inorganic constituents and vitamins will be considered elsewhere.

TABLE XIII

COMPOSITION OF EDIBLE PORTION OF VARIOUS MEATS

	Per Cent Protein (N × 6.25)*	Per Cent Fat	Portion in Grams Equivalent to 100 Calories
Beef, chuck, thin	19.2	9	63
chuck, medium	18.6	16	45
chuck, fat	17.6	22	37
loin, thin	18.6	16	46
rib, medium	17.4	23	36
liver	20.4	4.5	78
sirloin steak	18.9	18.5	41
Porterhouse steak	21.9	20.4	37
Pork, chops	16.6	30.1	30
sausage	13.0	44.2	22
Bacon, smoked	10.5	64.8	16
Ham, fresh, lean	25.0	14.4	44
Lamb, chops, broiled	21.7	29.9	28
leg, roast	19.7	12.7	52
Mutton, leg	19.8	12.4	52
Veal, breast	20.3	11.0	56
cutlet	20.3	7.7	66

* The nitrogen content of most proteins is approximately 16 per cent, whence the factor 6.25.

[2] The sources of the data contained in these tables are: Bulletin 28 (Atwater and Bryant), of the Office of Experiment Stations, U. S. Dept. Agr., Washington; H. C. Sherman, "Chemistry of Food and Nutrition," Macmillan, New York, 1928, Appendix B; U. S. Dept. Agr. Cir., 50 and 389.

TABLE XIV

COMPOSITION OF FISH AND OYSTERS

	Per Cent Protein (N × 6.25)	Per cent Fat	Portion in Grams Equivalent to 100 Calories
Flounder	14.2	0.6	161
Haddock	17.2	0.3	140
Cod, salt	25.4	0.3	96
Halibut steaks	18.6	5.2	83
Mackerel	18.7	7.1	72
salt	21.1	22.6	35
Shad, whole	18.8	9.5	61
Salmon, whole	22.0	12.8	49
Whitefish	22.9	6.5	67
Oysters *	6.2	1.2	199

* Oysters contain about 3.7 per cent carbohydrate.

TABLE XV

COMPOSITION OF POULTRY AND EGGS

	Per Cent Protein (N × 6.25)	Per Cent Fat	Portion in Grams Equivalent to 100 Calories
Chicken, broilers	21.5	2.5	92
Fowls	19.3	16.3	45
Turkey	21.1	22.9	34
Eggs, uncooked	13.4	10.5	68

TABLE XVI
COMPOSITION OF SOME DAIRY PRODUCTS

	Per Cent Protein (N × 6.25)	Per Cent Fat	Per Cent Carbo-hydrate	Portion in Grams Equivalent to 100 Calories
Milk, whole	3.3	4.0	5.0	145
condensed, sweetened.....	8.8	8.3	54.1	31
evaporated..............	6.7	8.1	10.3	71
Cream....................	2.5	18.5	4.5	50
Butter....................	1.0	85.0	....	13
Cheese, American pale......	28.8	35.9	0.3	23
cottage..................	20.9	1.0	4.3	91
full cream..............	25.9	33.7	2.4	24
Swiss...................	27.6	34.9	1.3	23

TABLE XVII
COMPOSITION OF SOME FRUITS, BERRIES, AND NUTS

	Per Cent Protein (N × 6.25)	Per Cent Fat	Per Cent Carbo-hydrate	Portion in Grams Equivalent to 100 Calories
Apples....................	0.4	0.5	14.2	159
Bananas..................	1.3	0.6	22.0	101
Grapes...................	1.3	1.6	19.2	104
Grapefruit................	0.6	0.1	12.2	193
Cherries, fresh............	1.0	0.8	16.7	128
Figs, fresh................	1.4	0.4	19.6	115
dried..................	4.3	0.3	74.2	32
Oranges..................	0.8	0.2	11.6	195
Olives, green.............	1.1	27.6	11.6	33
ripe	1.7	25.0	4.3	40
Peaches, fresh............	0.7	0.1	9.4	242
Pears, fresh..............	0.6	0.5	14.1	158
Strawberries.............	1.0	0.6	7.4	269
Blackberries.............	1.2	1.1	7.8	160
Blueberries..............	0.6	0.6	13.9	146
Raspberries, red...........	1.0	....	12.6	184
Almonds.................	21.0	54.9	17.8	15
Brazil nuts...............	17.0	66.8	7.0	14
Peanuts..................	25.8	38.6	24.4	18
Walnuts (California or English)..................	18.4	64.4	13.0	14

TABLE XVIII

COMPOSITION OF GRAIN PRODUCTS AND CEREALS

	Per Cent Protein (N × 6.25)	Per Cent Fat	Per Cent Carbo-hydrate	Portion in Grams Equivalent to 100 Calories
Flour, wheat, patent baker's grade	13.3	1.5	72.7	28
rye	6.8	0.9	78.7	29
Corn meal	9.2	1.9	75.4	28
Bread, average white	9.2	1.3	53.1	38
whole wheat	9.7	0.9	49.7	41
Macaroni	13.4	0.9	74.1	28
Oatmeal	16.1	7.2	67.5	25
Barley	8.5	1.1	77.8	28
Rice	8.0	0.3	79.0	29

TABLE XIX

COMPOSITION OF SOME VEGETABLES AND LEGUMES*

	Per Cent Protein (N × 6.25)	Per Cent Fat	Per Cent Carbo-hydrate	Portion in Grams Equivalent to 100 Calories
Asparagus, cooked	2.1	3.3	2.2	213
Beets, cooked	2.3	0.1	7.4	252
Cabbage	1.6	0.3	5.6	317
Celery	1.1	0.1	3.3	542
Lettuce	1.2	0.3	2.9	525
Onions, fresh	1.6	0.3	9.9	206
Potatoes, white, raw	2.2	0.1	18.4	120
sweet	1.8	0.7	27.4	81
Spinach, fresh	2.1	0.3	3.2	417
Squash	1.4	0.5	9.0	217
Tomatoes, fresh	0.9	0.4	3.9	438
Beans, string, fresh	2.3	0.3	7.4	241
baked, canned	6.9	2.5	19.6	78
Peas, canned	3.6	0.2	9.8	180
dried	24.6	1.0	62.0	28
green	7.0	0.5	16.9	100

* See also C. Chatfield and G. Adams, U. S. Dept. Agr. Circ. 146 (1931).

CHAPTER VI

DIGESTION AND THE CHEMISTRY OF ENZYME ACTION

The breakdown of the three great classes of foodstuffs, after they enter the body, into substances capable of absorption from the intestinal tract and utilizable for the production of energy and living tissue is fundamentally due to the action of a group of substances known as *enzymes.*[1] So apparent is the relation between enzyme action and the processes of living organisms that at various times it has been believed that the former was dependent upon the unit structure of the latter, the cell. Thus, though Kirchhoff[2] in 1814 had discovered the catalytic action of the glutinous component of wheat meal capable of converting starch to sugar and dextrin, though Payen and Persoz[3] (1833) had separated a similar substance from malt extract, and Liebig and Wöhler[4] (1837) noted the cleavage of amygdalin by the emulsin of bitter almonds, yet Pasteur[5] many years later (1878) ascribed the processes of fermentation to the metabolism of microorganisms. It was Buchner,[6] in 1897, who established firmly the concept that the action of enzymes was independent of the cell structure. Today we broadly think of enzymes as material substances, which are formed by living cells, but the action of which is independent of their presence.

The definition given by Waldschmidt-Leitz[7] is: *Enzymes are definite material catalyzers of organic nature with specific powers of reaction, formed indeed by living cells, but independent of the presence of the latter in their operation.*

Gortner[8] supplements this definition by appending the phrase: *and when in the moist state, readily destroyed by heat.*

[1] The term, coined by Kühne, is derived from the Greek words ἐν ζύμη, meaning *in yeast.*

[2] *Schweigger's J. Chem. Physik*, **14**, 389 (1815).

[3] *Ann. chim. phys.*, **53**, 73 (1833); **56**, 337 (1837)

[4] *Ann. Chem.*, **22**, 1 (1837); *Pogg. Ann.*, **41**, 345 (1837).

[5] "Die Alkoholgärung," 2. Aufl., Stuttgart, 1878.

[6] *Ber.*, **30**, 117 (1897).

[7] E. Waldschmidt-Leitz, "Enzyme Actions and Properties," translated and extended by R. P. Walton, John Wiley & Sons, Inc., New York (1929), p. 3.

[8] R. A. Gortner, "Outlines of Biochemistry," John Wiley & Sons, Inc., New York (1929), p. 713.

Preparation and Purification of Enzymes. The general methods used in the preparation and purification of enzymes differ considerably, depending on the kind of enzyme, whether it is being separated from a secretion, such as the saliva or gastric juice, or from a tissue, depending also on its solubilities and other properties. Some of the information which we have about certain enzymes, pepsin, for example, was obtained directly by working with the gastric juice, but in most cases the enzymes, if they are to be made available for study and other uses, must be liberated from tissues. This may be accomplished by macerating the cells, as was done by Buchner in his classical experiments with yeast. Or the tissues may be allowed to undergo autolysis, a process of cellular dissolution which occurs after tissues die. In either case the juice which may be separated from the mass of disintegrated cells contains the enzyme, at least a portion.

Another procedure is to dry the tissue at low temperature, or with some non-injurious chemical agent, and subsequently grinding and extracting the preparation with a suitable solvent. Weak acids and bases, glycerol, and alcohol are commonly used for this purpose.

Enzyme preparations obtained by any of these methods contain large amounts of extraneous material, and purification methods have been developed for separating these. For the removal of inorganic impurities, dialysis is used. For the separation of enzymes from their solutions, various methods of precipitation have been employed, but these have many limitations, the most serious of which is that a large proportion of the extraneous material, such as protein, is precipitated along with the enzyme. Nevertheless considerable success has attended such methods, particularly in the case of urease, pepsin, and trypsin.

The use of suitable adsorbents, such as colloidal aluminum hydroxide and kaolin, for separating enzymes from associated substances has been adopted by many modern workers and has led to important advances in our knowledge of enzymes. Using alumina gel as an adsorbing agent, a preparation of saccharase has been obtained, 12,000 times more active than living yeast. These methods have been further developed to the point of making possible the separation of enzymes from each other. Thus, in the case of the pancreas enzymes (p. 180), Willstätter and Waldschmidt-Leitz[9] found that of the three enzymes, lipase, amylase and trypsin, the first is most readily adsorbed both by alumina and kaolin and may thus be separated from the last two. Amylase, if relatively free from concomitant foreign substances, is indifferent both to kaolin and alumina, whereas trypsin is readily adsorbed by kaolin. Repeated treatment with kaolin in an acid solution removes the trypsin,

[9] *Z. physiol. Chem.*, **125**, 132, 142 (1923).

leaving the amylase behind.   Finally, the trypsin may be freed from kaolin by elution with dilute alkali.[10]

The Chemical Nature of Enzymes.   Our first interest in enzymes as material substances is their chemical nature.   Investigation in this direction has consisted in analyzing highly active enzyme preparations with the ultimate aim of isolating and analyzing the pure principle involved. Among the earlier investigations in this field were Pekelharing's[11] (1902) and Dezani's[12] (1911) studies of pepsin.   Their preparations gave the color reactions characteristic of proteins.   Dezani obtained on hydrolysis the following amino acids: leucine, tyrosine, arginine, histidine, and lysine.   Forbes[13] and Fenger and Andrew[14] determined the isoelectric point of pepsin to be at pH 2.5.   By precipitation at this point an exceedingly active preparation of the enzyme was obtained (Fenger, Andrew and Ralston),[15] possessing a proteolytic potency as high as 1 : 65,000.[16]   Sherman[17] in the case of amylase from the saliva and from pancreatic juice and Osborne[18] in the case of malt amylase also obtained the color reactions and composition analyses of proteins. Euler and Josephson[19] found positive biuret, xanthoproteic, and ninhydrin reactions in very active preparations of invertase.   Willstätter and Kuhn,[20] however, have described a preparation of invertase entirely free from protein, carbohydrate, and phosphorus.

On the whole, investigation in this direction was very indecisive until a few years ago.   The view of Willstätter's school, the most energetic and intensive group of investigators in this field, is that enzymes are composed of a specific active group and a colloidal bearer or carrier and that the specific group binds the enzyme to the carrier.   As to the nature of the specific groups no definite information has been made available.   A somewhat similar concept is held by Fodor, according to

[10] As it is impossible to consider here the details of the methods developed by Willstätter and his school, the student is referred to Chap. VII, of Waldschmidt-Leitz's book previously cited.   The student is also referred to J. B. S. Haldane's "Enzymes," Longmans, Green & Co., Chap. IX (1930).

[11] Z. physiol. Chem., **35**, 8 (1902).

[12] Arch. ital. Biol., **54**, 15 (1911).

[13] J. Biol. Chem., **71**, 559 (1927).

[14] Ibid., **73**, 371 (1927).

[15] Ibid., **80**, 187 (1928).

[16] This means that one part of the enzyme preparation digested 65,000 times its own weight of coagulated egg albumin, the method of assay being that of the United States Pharmacopœia (10th edition, Philadelphia, 1926, p. 280).

[17] J. Am. Chem. Soc., **33**, 1195 (1911); **34**, 1104 (1912); **35**, 1790 (1913).

[18] Ibid., **17**, 587 (1895); **18**, 536 (1896).

[19] Ber. **56** B, 1097 (1923); **57** B, 299 (1924); Z. physiol. Chem., **133**, 279 (1924).

[20] Z. physiol. Chem., **125**, 28 (1923).

whom enzymes are commonly known substances existing in peculiar colloidal systems, the energies characteristic of such states being responsible for their activity.

In 1926, Sumner[21] reported the isolation of urease. Fat-free jackbean meal was extracted with 32 per cent acetone, the extract filtered and kept in a refrigerator overnight. A crystalline precipitate consisting of colorless octahedra separated out. This proved to be a globulin possessing the properties of urease to a very marked degree, the activity being 129,000 units; that is, 1 gram was capable of producing 129,000 mg. of ammonium nitrogen from a urea-phosphate solution in 5 minutes. As compared with the crude material from which the crystalline urease was prepared, there was a 700- to 800-fold increase in activity. Recrystallization did not alter the potency of the preparation. Various objections have been raised,[22] the general contention being that the crystalline protein is not the active urease, but simply a carrier of the enzyme. These objections seem to have been satisfactorily met by Sumner and his co-workers,[23] and at the present time increasing recognition is being accorded to Sumner for the first successful isolation of an enzyme. It has been shown that crystalline urease is rapidly inactivated, presumably owing to digestion, by proteolytic enzymes, pepsin, papain, and trypsin and that this occurs even in the presence of a protective colloid. The last fact has been interpreted as supporting the conception that the crystalline globulin which Sumner isolated is itself the enzyme and not a protective colloid as some have contended.

The isolation of pepsin in pure form has been described by Northrop.[24] An active preparation was first obtained by methods essentially similar to those used by earlier workers. It was then dissolved in alkali and reprecipitated with acid. Repetition of this procedure gave a product of increasing activity; however, the process could not be continued indefinitely owing to increasing instability of the enzyme. The active enzyme crystallized in regular hexahedra. It possessed the properties of protein; the isoelectric point was found to be at pH 2.75. The crystals when dissolved possessed a marked proteolytic activity. The crystalline preparation also exhibited distinct rennitic action.

[21] *J. Biol. Chem.*, **69**, 435 (1926); J. B. Sumner and J. S. Kirk, *Z. physiol. Chem.*, **205**, 219 (1931).

[22] E. Waldschmidt-Leitz and F. Steigerwaldt, *Z. physiol. Chem.*, **195**, 260 (1931); For a recent résumé of Waldschmidt-Leitz' point of view consult *Science*, **78**, 189 (1933).

[23] Sumner, Kirk, and S. F. Howell, *J. Biol. Chem.*, **98**, 543 (1932).

[24] *J. Gen. Physiol.*, **13**, 739 (1930).

Northrop and Kunitz[25] have more recently reported the isolation of trypsin in crystalline form. It too is a protein. It does not, however, possess all of the digestive properties that have been associated with trypsin.

From buffered alcohol-water solution of freshly purified pancreatic amylase, crystals have been obtained by Caldwell and Sherman.[26] The crystals are pure protein and possess amylolytic activity in a very marked degree.

Catalase[27] (liver, pumpkin) and peroxydase[28] (horse-radish) have been reported to be iron-porphyrin complexes (p. 237). Maltase, according to Tauber and Kleiner,[29] is a protein, inasmuch as it is simultaneously inactivated and digested by trypsin.

The Mode of Enzyme Action. Our second and most immediate interest in enzymes is their mode of action. Enzymes are part of a larger group of substances known as catalysts. These are defined as bodies which alter the rate of an existing reaction without themselves becoming permanently changed (Ostwald).

Although in most cases catalysis is regarded as causing an increased reaction velocity (positive catalysis), it is theoretically possible for a catalytic agent to decrease the velocity of a reaction (negative catalysis). A frequently cited example of negative catalysis is the behavior of a trace of ether vapor in depressing the oxidation of phosphorus.

J. J. Thompson attributed to catalysts the property of initiating a reaction, a view that is becoming more generally accepted. Bayliss[30] was of the opinion that this idea is not necessarily in disagreement with Ostwald's definition. It may be conceived that the catalyst overcomes an influence resisting the initiation of a reaction. From this standpoint, Bayliss defines a catalyst as a substance that changes the rate of a reaction which is actually in progress or which is capable of proceeding without any supply of energy from without, if certain resisting influences are removed. The resisting influences, according to Bayliss, may be conceived of as being somewhat analogous to the force of friction which would hold back a weight from sliding down an inclined plane.

Although the degree of acceleration of a reaction is proportional to the concentration of the catalyst present, the final amount of products

[25] *Ibid.*, **16**, 267 (1932).

[26] *Science*, **74**, 37 (1931).

[27] K. Zeile and H. Hellström, *Z. physiol. Chem.*, **192**, 171 (1930); Zeile, *ibid.*, **195**, 39 (1930–31).

[28] R. Kuhn, D. B. Hand, and M. Florkin, *ibid.*, **201**, 255 (1931).

[29] *J. Gen. Physiol.*, **16**, 767 (1933).

[30] W. M. Bayliss, "The Nature of Enzyme Action" (1925).

formed is independent of the amount of catalyst used. The time factor alone is affected by the catalyst.

Attempts to correlate our knowledge of enzyme action have resulted in the formulation of two main rival theories. Bayliss advanced a colloid chemical point of view. According to this, the substances which react are first adsorbed on the surface of the enzyme particles. The chemical reaction then takes place at the interface. Though this chemical reaction may be subject to the law of mass action—namely, that the rate of reaction at any moment is proportional to the concentration at the moment of the reacting substances—still it is the adsorbed portion of the substances which is the controlling factor.

The Michaelis school, on the other hand, has assumed that enzyme and substrate unite chemically, as ions would, to form an intermediate substance and that the rate of reaction is proportional to the concentration of this intermediate enzyme-substrate compound. These assumptions imply that the substances involved act as if they were in homogeneous solution. A good exposition of Michaelis' theory and the work upon which it is based is given by Waldschmidt-Leitz.[10]

Reversible Reactions. A characteristic feature of certain reactions is that they never reach completion. For example, acetic acid and ethyl alcohol react according to the following equation:

$$CH_3COOH + C_2H_5OH \rightleftharpoons CH_3COOC_2H_5 + HOH$$

A point of equilibrium is reached when the velocity of the reaction in one direction is equivalent to that in the opposite direction. Starting with molar concentrations of ethyl alcohol and acetic acid, equilibrium occurs when $\frac{2}{3}$ mol of ethyl alcohol and $\frac{2}{3}$ mol of acetic acid have been transformed to ethyl acetate. Increasing the concentration of either constituent on the left-hand side of the equation produces a shift to the right, until a new equilibrium is reached, whereas adding ethyl acetate to the reaction mixture results in its hydrolysis. This type of reaction is said to be *reversible*. The addition of a small amount of hydrochloric acid increases the velocity of the reaction in either direction. It is with reactions of this general type, namely those which occur relatively slowly and are reversible, that we are ordinarily concerned with in the study of catalysis, whether by inorganic catalysts or enzymes.

The Specificity of Enzyme Action. A distinction is frequently made between the enzymes and the inorganic catalysts on the basis of their relative specificity. Colloidal platinum catalyzes a variety of reactions, such as the decomposition of hydrogen peroxide, the hydrolysis of esters of the simple alcohols, and the formation of nitric acid and sulfuric acid. In other words, platinum as a catalyst is not limited to a single reaction. Similarly unspecific in their action are the inorganic acids and bases. Hydrogen and hydroxyl ions catalyze the hydrolysis of proteins, fats, and carbohydrates indiscriminately. On the other hand, a given enzyme which digests protein is never known to act on fat or carbohydrate. Catalase decomposes hydrogen peroxide, as does platinum, but it differs from platinum in having no effect on any other reaction. Invertase acts on sucrose, but not on maltose, which is hydrolyzed by maltase, or on lactose, which is specifically acted on by the enzyme lactase.

In enzymic reactions, specificity may be either with respect to the substance attacked as indicated above or the type of products formed. Thus both yeast saccharase and emulsin hydrolyze the trisaccharide, raffinose. But the first forms fructose and melibiose; the latter forms sucrose and galactose. Glucose may undergo several types of fermentations, each being caused by a specific enzyme. The substrate is the same, but the products, lactic acid, alcohol, etc., are different. On the other hand, the reaction products may be identical but the reaction path different. Both the saccharase of yeast and that of *Aspergillus oryzae* invert cane sugar to glucose and fructose. But according to Kuhn,[31] the former does so by attaching itself to the fructose component of cane sugar, whereas the enzyme of the mold fungus is supposed to attach itself to the glucose part of the molecule.

However, it should be emphasized that these distinctions in specificity are not so sharply drawn as it may appear. Inorganic catalysts also show some degree of specificity. Tungstic acid aids in the oxidation of hydriodic acid by hydrogen peroxide, but does not accelerate the oxidation of hydriodic acid by a persulfate. Iron salts catalyze the oxidation of potassium iodide by a persulfate, whereas no effect is produced by the iron in the oxidation of sulfurous acid by a persulfate. Even platinum black exhibits certain peculiarities in behavior toward esters. Hydrolysis of the esters of simple alcohols is accelerated, whereas the effect produced on the glycerol esters is hardly appreciable.

Trypsin exhibits a marked degree of specificity, its action being limited to the proteins themselves and their higher degradation products, whereas substances of the simple peptide type are attacked by erepsin, which recent work indicates is not a single enzyme, but is composed of two enzymes, a dipeptidase and a polypeptidase.

In the case of some enzymes, the specificity seems to be relative, rather than absolute. Thus, the lipases act on a variety of ester linkages, and maltase acts not only on maltose but also on other α-glucosides, whereas the enzyme emulsin hydrolyses a variety of β-glucosides. In general, the action of enzymes is limited not so much to certain

[31] *Z. physiol. Chem.*, **129**, 57 (1923).

substances as to certain atomic groups or linkages within the molecule. It is more a question of specificity for a certain group in the molecule than of substance specificity.

Owing to their specificity, the enzymes are more limited in their action than inorganic catalysts, but, on the other hand, their efficiency is much greater. Catalase prepared from red corpuscles, for example, is about 20 times more effective in decomposing hydrogen peroxide than an equivalent amount of colloidal platinum.[32]

Classification and Nomenclature. The classification and nomenclature of the enzymes are based on the type of reactions which they catalyze or on the substrate on which they act. The hydrolytic enzymes are most numerous and take part in reactions of hydrolysis. To this group belong the following:

I. The Proteases, Proteolytic or Protein-splitting Enzymes.

(a) *Pepsin.* Found in gastric juice. Pepsin acts on native proteins, usually digesting them to proteoses and peptones.

(b) *Trypsin.* Present in pancreatic juice. It digests proteins, proteoses, and peptones to polypeptides and possibly to dipeptides.

(c) *" Erepsin."* Recent work shows that the erepsin of the pancreas and intestinal mucosa is not a single enzyme, but that it is probably a mixture of two enzymes, a polypeptidase and a dipeptidase, which respectively convert polypeptides and dipeptides to amino acids.

(d) *Rennin.* Pancreatic rennin is found in the pancreatic juice and gastric rennin in the gastric juice. Rennin converts casein into paracasein.

(e) In addition to these are the plant proteases, the best known of which are *papain,* present in the melon-tree (papaw, *Carica papaya*), and *bromelin,* occurring in the pineapple.

II. The Fat and Ester-splitting Enzymes, Lipases, and Esterases. These are sometimes classed together under the general head of *esterases.* The best known is the *lipase, steapsin* of the pancreatic juice. Other lipases are especially abundant in oil-containing seeds, such as the castor bean. The liver is said to contain an esterase which acts on simple esters. Among the other known esterases are: (1) *chlorophylase,* which occurs in green leaves and hydrolyzes chlorophyll-a to chlorophylide-a and phytol; (2) *pectase,* which is widely distributed in plants and molds and hydrolyzes pectin to pectic acid and methyl alcohol; (3) *tannase,*

[32] Waldschmidt-Leitz, "Enzyme Actions and Properties," tr. by R. P. Walton, p. 213.

For an excellent discussion of specificity of enzymes, the student is referred to Haldane's "Enzymes," Chap. VI.

found in certain molds, which converts tannin into glucose and gallic acid; (4) *sulfatase*, present in *aspergillus oryzae*, which hydrolyzes sulfuric acid esters; (5) *phosphatase*, present in yeast, intestine, kidney, bone, etc., and which hydrolyzes (and may synthesize) phosphoric acid esters.

III. Carbohydrases. To this group belong the polysaccharide-digesting enzymes and those concerned with the hydrolysis of sugars, glucosides, etc.

(a) *Amylases.* These are starch-splitting enzymes. The best-known members of this group are (1) *ptyalin* of the saliva and (2) *amylopsin* of the pancreatic juice. Another is *malt amylase.* The action of amylase is the conversion of starch to maltose.

(b) *Sucrase, saccharase, or invertase,* present in the intestinal mucosa and intestinal juice, as well as in yeast. It converts sucrose into fructose and glucose. It also hydrolyzes raffinose and other trisaccharides, the former to fructose and melibiose.

(c) *Maltase,* present in the saliva, pancreatic and intestinal secretions, yeast, etc. It is actually a member of the subgroup, the *α-glucosidases.* Maltase hydrolyzes maltose to glucose and probably acts on other α-glucosides.

(d) *Emulsin,* found chiefly in bitter almonds, is a member of the subgroup of *β-glucosidases.* It hydrolyzes amygdalin to glucose and mandelonitrile and may act similarly on other β-glucosides.

(e) *Lactase,* present in intestinal mucosa and intestinal juice. It hydrolyzes lactose to glucose and galactose and may have a similar effect on other β-galactosides.

(f) Among the other carbohydrases of importance may be mentioned the *cellulases,* concerned with the hydrolysis of cellulose, and *inulinase,* which hydrolyzes the polysaccharide inulin. These enzymes do not occur in the digestive secretions of man.

Other hydrolytic enzymes are *urease,* found in the soybean and jack bean, which converts urea into carbon dioxide and ammonia. It is grouped with the *deaminases,* or *desamidases,* enzymes which hydrolyze amino acids and other nitrogen compounds into hydroxy acids and ammonia. In the latter group are included *asparaginase,* which hydrolyzes asparagine to aspartic acid and ammonia, *arginase,* which hydrolyzes arginine to urea and ornithine, and also *guanosine desamidase,* which hydrolyzes guanosine, and *adenosine desamidase,* which acts on adenosine. To this group also belongs *guanase,* which converts guanine into xanthine and ammonia, and *adenase,* which acts on adenine with the formation of hypoxanthine and ammonia.

Intestinal juice contains an enzyme, *nucleinase,* which hydrolyzes tetranucleotides into mononucleotides. The purine nucleotides are hydrolyzed into nucleosides and phosphoric acid by another group of enzymes, the *nucleotidases*, which may be classified as *phosphatases* (enzymes acting on phosphoric esters, pyrophosphates and their esters). The intestinal mucosa contains *nucleinase, nucleotidases,* and, in addition, a third group of enzymes, the *nucleosidases*, capable of hydrolyzing the purine nucleosides into sugar and purine bases.

Another important group of enzymes are the oxidizing enzymes, or *oxidases*. Of the enzymes that have been described and placed in this category there are some that are capable of converting phenols to quinones, tyrosine to black pigments, aldehydes to acids, and ethyl alcohol to acetic acid. The peroxidases reduce a variety of organic peroxides with the liberation of oxygen. The catalases behave similarly, though their action is limited to the disintegration of hydrogen peroxide. A number of enzymes concerned with the reduction of perhydrides have been described; to these the terms reductase, reducase, and hydrogenase have been applied. It is to be pointed out that the action of the oxidases and peroxidases results in the oxidation of one compound and the reduction of another. Much confusion exists in the literature with regard to the physiological significance of the oxidases, peroxidases, catalases, and reductases. Further reference to this subject will be necessary in the chapter concerned with oxidations and reductions in animal tissues.

Two enzymes have been described which are concerned in the insertion of a water molecule without producing hydrolysis. These are *fumarase* (present in *Bacillus coli*), which catalyzes the reaction, fumaric acid → malic acid, and *glyoxalase*, which converts glyoxal and substituted glyoxals into the corresponding hydroxy acids.

$$R—CO \cdot CHO + H_2O \rightarrow R—CHOH \cdot COOH$$

Still another group of enzymes are the *zymases*. These act on the simpler sugars to form a variety of products, such as lactic acid (lactic-acid fermentation), carbon dioxide, and alcohol (alcoholic fermentation).

Long usage has retained for the more familiar enzymes their former nomenclature. This is true of ptyalin, pepsin, rennin, trypsin, etc. In accordance with a suggestion made by Duclaux, most of the hydrolytic enzymes are now designated by the suffix *ase* added usually to a portion of the name of the substrate or substance on which the enzyme acts. Thus malt*ase* is the enzyme that hydrolyzes maltose; lact*ase* acts on lactose; the prote*ases* digest proteins; whereas the fat-splitting enzymes are called lip*ases*. The protein-splitting enzymes are also frequently referred to as proteo*lytic* enzymes; the enzymes that attack starch are amylo*lytic*, and those that act on fats, lipo*lytic*.

Factors Influencing Enzyme Action.   In trying to understand the nature of enzymes, not by means of their chemical composition but through a study of the actions which they exert, we are aided by a great amount of data which has been collected either empirically or in line with various theories of enzyme action.   Thus for a great many enzymes we know just how the rate at which the substrate changes, in the presence of the enzyme, varies with the following factors:

(1) Concentration of the substrate.
(2) Concentration of the enzyme.
(3) Temperature.
(4) Reaction or hydrogen-ion concentration of the medium.
(5) Light and other radiations.
(6) Electrolytes.
(7) Inhibiting agents or poisons.
(8) Products of the reaction.

Concentration of the Substrate.   In the case of most enzymic reactions it has been found that, starting with zero concentration of substrate, the velocity of the reaction increases with increasing concentration of substrate, then remains constant for a considerable variation in concentration, and finally decreases in very concentrated solutions of substrate.

In Fig. 16a are represented the results of one of Northrop's[33] experiments, showing the effect of substrate concentration on the rate of diges-

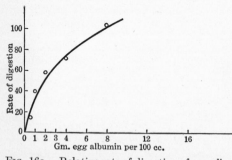

FIG. 16a.—Relative rate of digestion of egg-albumin solutions of different concentration when digested with the same concentration of pepsin solution.

tion of protein.   Protein solutions containing 8, 4, 2, 1 and 0.5 per cent egg albumin were hydrolyzed at 25° C. in the presence of 1 cc. of 2 per cent pepsin, 25 cc. of the solution being used in each case.   All solutions were brought to a pH of 1.8 with hydrochloric acid.   Since the products of protein digestion conduct the electric current better than the original protein, the specific conductivity of the digests, determined at various intervals, was used as the measure of the amount of digestion.   For purposes of comparison, the rate of digestion of the 8 per cent solution is designated in the figure as 100, and the rates of digestion of the 4, 2, 1, and 0.5 per cent egg albumin are represented on this basis.   The curve (Fig.

[33] *J. Gen. Physiol.*, **2**, 595 (1920).

16a) shows that in low concentration the increase in rate is nearly proportional to the increase in substrate concentration, but that in high concentrations the rate increases more slowly.

Concentration of the Enzyme. The final equilibrium of an enzymic reaction does not depend on the quantity of enzyme. The velocity of the reaction does depend, however, on this factor. In the case of pepsin, for example, a relationship exists between the mass of protein transformed, x; the time, t; the initial concentration of the substrate, a; and the concentration of the enzyme, E. The relationship, known as the Schütz-Borissov rule, may be expressed by the formula:

$$x = k\sqrt{aEt}$$

Northrop[34] has studied the relation between the concentration of pepsin and the rate of digestion. The latter was determined by measuring the time required to produce a given change in the conductivity of an egg-albumin solution to which pepsin had been added. The reciprocal of this time, ($1/T$ hours), being proportional to the mean rate of digestion, was taken to represent the amount of " active " pepsin. All factors, such as concentration of substrate, hydrogen-ion concentration, etc., were kept constant, the amount of pepsin alone being altered. The observations recorded by Northrop are outlined in Table XX. In the

TABLE XX

ENZYME CONCENTRATION AND RATE OF DIGESTION (after Northrop)

Pepsin solution. 10 per cent solution of Grübler's pepsin in HCl, pH 2.0.

$$K = 7.2 \qquad d = \frac{30}{v} *$$

V = volume containing 1 cc. of original pepsin solution	E = total pepsin per cc.	$Q = \dfrac{1}{T}$ = active pepsin per cc.					ET
		Observed				Cal-culated	
		1	2	3	Average		
1	26.9	9.1	9.7	10.0	9.6	9.7	269
2	13.44	6.25	6.30	6.67	6.39	6.40	206
4	6.72	4.17	3.70	3.57	3.81	4.05	175
8	3.36	2.38	2.50	2.17	2.35	2.42	145
16	1.68	1.39	1.43	1.35	1.39	1.38	120
32	0.84	0.83	0.80	0.78	0.80	0.77	106
64	0.42	0.41	0.40	0.39	0.40	0.40	100
128	[0.21]	0.22	0.20	0.20	0.20	0.20	100

* K = equilibrium constant (see equation below);
  d = concentration of peptone present at the beginning of the reaction.

[34] *J. Gen. Physiol.*, **2**, 113, 471 (1919–20).

last column, ET represents the product of the total concentration of pepsin and the time necessary to cause 10 per cent of the total change in the conductivity of the substrate. If the rate of digestion were directly proportional to the enzyme concentration, the value for ET would remain constant. From the data presented it will be seen that ET is constant only for low concentrations of pepsin. This is clearly indicated also by the curve in Fig. 16b, based on the data in Table XX.

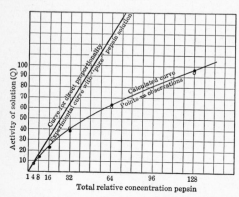

The divergence from direct proportionality is attributed to the fact that the enzyme in solution is in equilibrium with another substance, possibly peptone, and that the uncombined pepsin alone affects the hydrolysis of the protein. This equilibrium may be expressed quantitatively, according to the law of mass action, by the equation:

Fig. 16b.—Curves showing pepsin concentration and rate of digestion (cf. Table XX).

$$K = \frac{\text{concentration of pepsin} \times \text{concentration of peptone}}{\text{concentration of pepsin-peptone}}$$

Northrop has tested the Schütz-Borissov equation in the case of pepsin and finds that it holds under certain conditions only, namely, when the concentration of peptone is large with respect to pepsin, and the concentration of substrate relatively small. The causes of the divergence from the Schütz-Borissov equation are indicated in the following chart (Fig. 17). For further discussion of this work, the reader is referred to Northrop's papers.

Where the substrate is in true solution, as in the action

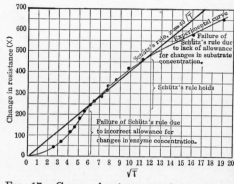

Fig. 17.—Curves showing rate of digestion of egg albumin and deviations from Schütz's rule.

of invertase on sucrose and urease on urea, the velocity of the reaction is directly proportional to the concentration of enzyme. As an illustration of this we may consider an experiment of Hudson[35] in which was determined the relation of the time required for transforming a definite amount of sucrose to the amount of invertase used. In the table given below are the data obtained with a 4.55 per cent solution of sucrose, the time being that required in each case to bring about approximately 73 per cent hydrolysis of the sucrose.

TABLE XXI

Relative concentration of the enzyme, invertase	Time in minutes required to hydrolyze approximately 73 per cent of the sucrose (initial concentration 4.55 per cent)
0.25	120
0.50	60
1.00	30
1.50	20
2.00	15

Effect of Temperature. A rise in temperature increases the velocity of a chemical reaction. Van't Hoff has formulated a rule according to which an increase in temperature of 10° C., within certain limits, about doubles or trebles the velocity of a reaction. The temperature coefficient for any given temperature range can be calculated from the formula:

$$\text{Temperature coefficient} = \frac{\text{velocity at } (T° + 10° \text{ C.})}{\text{velocity at } T°}$$

The equilibrium of an enzymic reaction is only slightly dependent on the temperature when the heat change accompanying the reaction is small. Up to a certain point, increase in temperature results in an increased velocity. Opposing this effect is the influence of heat in inactivating and destroying the enzyme. Bayliss and others relate this property to the colloidal nature of the system of which the enzyme forms a part. It has also been interpreted as being due to the protein-like nature of the enzymes.

[35] *J. Am. Chem. Soc.*, **30**, 1564 (1908).

The following temperature coefficients have been recorded for a number of enzymes:

TABLE XXII

Substrate and Enzyme	Temperature Interval	Temperature Coefficient (Q_{10}) $\dfrac{k_{t+10}}{k_t}$
Sucrose-sucrase............................	0–20°	2.0
	20–30	1.4
	30–40	1.5
	40–50	1.4
Hydrogen peroxide-catalase.................	0–10	1.5
Starch-amylase (malt).....................	20–30	1.96
	30–40	1.65
	40–50	1.43
Maltose-maltase (yeast)...................	10–20	1.90
	20–30	1.44
	30–40	1.28
Milk-rennin...............................	20–30	2.1
	30–40	3.2
Casein-trypsin............................	20.7–30.7	5.3
Glycyl-tyrosine-erepsin (pancreatic)	25–35	1.67
	35–45	1.60
Edestin-pepsin............................	0–10	2.6
	10–20	2.0
	20–30	1.8
	30–40	1.6

k = velocity constant.

The *optimum temperature* is the temperature at which the activity of an enzyme is at a maximum. Most enzymes exhibit maximum activity between 37° and 53° C. The optimum temperature may be influenced by various factors, such as the reaction of the medium, the concentration of the enzyme, and the nature and concentration of the substrate.

An experiment of Chodat on the tyrosine-tyrosinase reaction may be taken as illustrating the influence of temperature elevation on enzyme action. The time required to produce sufficient change to give a certain degree of color intensity was taken as the criterion for comparing the activity of the enzyme at various temperatures.

Temperature	0°	10°	20°	30°	45°	50° C.
Time (minutes)	180	100	60	40	20	10

Certain enzymes from vegetable sources are known to exhibit higher temperature optima than those from animal tissues. Papain and bromelin, which are proteolytic enzymes found in plants, have an optimum temperature of about 60° C. Rennin, from animal sources, has an optimum temperature of about 45° C., but the milk-coagulating enzymes obtained from plants have much higher optima, approaching 80–85° C. This is illustrated by the following data:

TABLE XXIII *

THE EFFECT OF TEMPERATURE ON THE COAGULATION OF MILK BY RENNIN (ANIMAL)

Temperature 0° C...........	25°	30°	33°	36°	39°	42°	45°
Time required for coagulation, in minutes and seconds......	1–40	1–00	0–40	0–30	0–25	0–35	0–45

Observed optimum at 39° C.

* From data obtained by Gerber and cited by Euler, "General Chemistry of the Enzymes," 1912 edition, p. 242.

TABLE XXIV *

THE EFFECT OF TEMPERATURE ON THE COAGULATION OF MILK BY RENNIN (PLANT)

Temperature, ° C.	Time, sec.	Temperature, ° C.	Time, sec.
72°	74	79°	56
73°	73	82°	53
74.5°	68	83°	52
75°	67	85°	57
78°	57	87°	78

Observed optimum at 83° C.

* From data of A. Bodansky obtained with the milk-coagulating enzyme present in *Solanum eleagnifolium, J. Biol. Chem.*, **61**, 365 (1924).

Exposure of enzymes to temperatures above 60° C. usually results in their inactivation. Here again, various factors may exert modifying influences. Invertase is more readily destroyed in the absence of sucrose (about 50° C.) than when sucrose is present (only partly inactivated at 70° C.). Trypsin is very readily destroyed by heat in an alkaline solution, but not quite as readily in an acid solution. Mellanby and Woolley,[36] as well as others, have observed that trypsin in dilute acid solution could be heated nearly to boiling with very little loss in activity. This remarkable heat stability is also shown by crystalline trypsin according to Northrop and Kunitz,[37] who reported having heated dilute solutions of their pure crystalline preparation over the whole range of acidity between pH 1 and pH 7 with little or no loss in activity as determined after cooling the solution. This result may seem inexplicable in view of the property of heat in denaturing protein and in inactivating enzymes. However, as discussed elsewhere, denaturation of protein by heat may be a reversible process (p. 117). Supported by experimental evidence, Northrop [38] has stated that at higher temperatures, accompanying denaturation of the protein, there is a corresponding loss of the enzymic activity. On cooling, denaturation is reversed, and enzymically active protein is reformed. Crystalline pepsin loses its activity when the protein is denatured, but when the denaturation is reversed on cooling, activity is regained.

Similar behavior has been observed with invertase and takadiastase; these enzymes inactivated by heating may regain a certain amount of their activity when allowed to stand in aqueous solution.

Catalase is most resistant to heat at pH 6, which according to Morgulis and Beber[39] corresponds to its isoelectric point. It is rapidly destroyed by heat in weak acids (pH 4–5) as well as in weak alkali (pH 8–9).

Effect of the Reaction or Hydrogen-ion Concentration. The activity of enzymes is markedly influenced by acids and alkalies and is usually limited to a definite range of acid or alkali concentration. Pepsin acts only in an acid medium and loses its activity in an alkaline solution, whereas trypsin digests proteins in either a neutral or an alkaline solution but not in the presence of free acid.

Sørensen[40] first pointed out that the velocity of enzymic reactions varied with the hydrogen-ion concentration, and he as well as numerous other workers have studied this relation for various enzymes.

As an illustration, one of Northrop's[41] experiments may be cited. Peptic digestion of purified egg albumin was studied at varying H-ion

[36] *J. Physiol.*, **47**, 339 (1913).
[37] *J. Gen. Physiol.*, **16**, 267 (1932).
[38] *Ibid.*, **16**, 323 (1932).
[39] *J. Biol. Chem.*, **77**, 115 (1928).
[40] *Biochem. Z.*, **21**, 131, 201 (1909); **22**, 352 (1909).
[41] *J. Gen. Physiol.*, **3**, 211 (1920).

concentrations. At the end of a four-hour interval of digestion, the amount of proteolysis was determined by analyzing the digests for the increase in amino nitrogen. The results obtained are represented in Fig. 18. The curve shows that the optimum acidity for digestion, as determined by the increase in amino nitrogen, corresponds to about pH 1.0. This is somewhat lower than the values obtained by other workers (see Table XXV) and is probably representative not only of the optimum for the digestion of

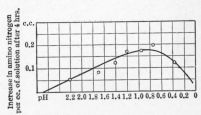

FIG. 18.—Influence of pH on the rate of digestion of egg albumin.

the protein in question, but also of some of the intermediate products of the proteolysis.

Northrop believes that the determining factor in the digestion of proteins by pepsin is the amount of ionized protein in solution. The degree of ionization is very slight in the case of most proteins at a pH of 4.5. Now it is of interest to note that pepsin becomes practically inactive at this pH, showing that it is the protein ion which is acted on by the enzyme. The optimum hydrogen-ion concentration for the activity of pepsin coincides with the hydrogen-ion concentration at which the protein solution contains the greatest number of protein ions.

The nature of the acid is not an important factor in enzymic activity. Northrop[42] has shown that at equivalent hydrogen-ion concentrations the rate of pepsin digestion of gelatin, egg albumin, casein, and edestin is the same in solutions of hydrochloric, nitric, sulfuric, oxalic, citric, and phosphoric acids. Acetic acid diminishes the rate of digestion of all proteins except gelatin. The peculiarity of acetic acid in this regard is probably due to some effect on the protein rather than on the enzyme.

Another illustration of the dependence of enzymes on hydrogen-ion concentration is the activity-pH curve in Fig. 19 for the enzyme invertase from yeast, based on the experimental data of Michaelis and Davidsohn.[43] It is to be noted that this enzyme exhibits a broad optimal zone of action, this being between pH 3.5 and 5.5.

In the following table are given a number of values which have been obtained for the optimum hydrogen-ion concentrations of various enzymes.

[42] *Ibid.*, **1**, 607 (1919).   [43] *Biochem, Z.*, **35**, 386 (1911).

TABLE XXV *

Enzyme	Optimum pH	Authority
Sucrase, yeast.................	4.4–4.6	Sørensen; Fales and Nelson
Sucrase, intestinal.............	6.8	Euler and Svanberg
Amylase, saliva................	6.0	Norris
Amylase, pancreatic............	7.0	Sherman, Thomas, and Baldwin
Pepsin (edestin, casein).........	1.4	Michaelis and Mendelssohn
Pepsin (egg albumin, $\frac{1}{2}$–1 hour)...	1.6	Sørensen
Pepsin (egg albumin, 12 hours)....	1.2	Sørensen
Pepsin (gelatin)................	3.0–3.5	Dernby
Trypsin, pancreatic.............	8.0	Lundén
Erepsin, intestinal.............	7.7	Rona and Arnheim
Catalase......................	7.0	Sørensen

* A more extensive summary is given by Haldane, [10] pp. 15–18.

These values have been obtained with the enzymes in a relatively crude state and it seems probable that totally different results might be

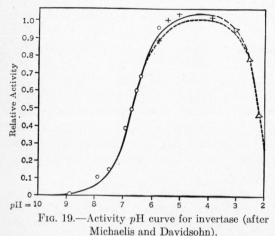

Fig. 19.—Activity pH curve for invertase (after Michaelis and Davidsohn).

obtained with highly purified preparations. In the case of at least one enzyme has this been shown to be true. Lipase extracted from the gastric mucosa was found by Willstätter and his pupils [44] to exhibit optimum activity at pH 5.5 to 6.3 and a minimum (the point at which the enzyme was completely inhibited) at pH 8.6. However, after repeated purification with kaolin, the optimum pH was found to be 7.1–7.9 (identical with pancreatic lipase) and the minimum pH, 4.7. Presumably the enzyme as secreted in the stomach is associated with a substance which inhibits its action in an alkaline medium.

The dependence of enzymes on definite concentrations of hydrogen or hydroxyl ions has been ascribed by Kuhn [45] to the influence of the latter

[44] Willstätter, Waldschmidt-Leitz, and Memmen, Z. physiol. Chem., **125**, 93 (1922–23); Willstätter, Haurowitz, and Memmen, ibid., **140**, 203 (1924).

[45] Naturwissenschaft, **11**, 713 (1923).

on the decomposition velocity of the enzyme-substrate combinations Abderhalden's view[46] of the mechanism of enzyme action is likewise suggestive of a marked hydrolytic effect on certain enzyme-substrate complexes which may be exerted by relatively low concentrations of acids and bases. Formerly this dependence was associated with the amphoteric nature of enzymes, which, as the work of several investigators has shown, behave as weak electroytes. Reference has already been made to a possible direct effect on the substrate, as in the case of peptic digestion of protein, which occurs best at the hydrogen-ion concentration at which there is maximum dissociation of the protein. These views suggest the possibility that the effect of hydrogen or hydroxyl ions may be a multiple one.

Independent of the rôle of acid and alkali in influencing enzymic reactions is their effect on the enzyme itself. It is indeed interesting that pepsin, which requires an acid medium for its action, is destroyed by acid. Employing crystalline pepsin, Northrop[47] has shown that, at pH 1.8 and 45° C., there is a decrease in protein nitrogen due to hydrolysis, the degree of hydrolysis corresponding to the decrease in activity. The products of hydrolysis thus derived from crystalline pepsin do not seem to have any proteolytic activity.

Light and Other Radiations. Most enzymes are not very sensitive to *visible* light, particularly in the absence of oxygen. In an oxygen-free medium, amylase, invertase, peroxidase, and catalase are not affected by ordinary light. In the presence of oxygen, on the contrary, these enzymes as well as pepsin, rennin, trypsin, and urease are partly inactivated. Green[48] found that red light activated salivary amylase. Blue light was less effective, whereas green and especially violet light inactivated the enzyme, the effect being less marked, however, than that produced by ultraviolet light.

Certain reducing enzymes acting on methylene blue are activated on exposure to light in the presence of oxygen. Thus Bernheim and Dixon[49] found that the reduction of methylene blue by xanthine-oxidase was accelerated by light, but only if traces of oxygen were present. Previous irradiation of the components of the system (i.e., the methylene blue and the enzyme) individually produced an increase in activity. This was even more marked when the enzyme was irradiated in the presence of the dye. However, in all cases, the effect depended on the degree of exposure. Short exposure to light increased the activ-

[46] Proc. XIII Intern. Physiol. Cong., *Am. J. Physiol.*, **90**, 258 (1929).
[47] *J. Gen. Physiol.*, **13**, 739 (1930).
[48] *Proc. Roy. Soc. London*, **61**, 25 (1897).
[49] *Biochem. J.*, **22**, 113 (1928).

ity; prolonged exposure retarded the enzyme action. In short, light and oxygen may be supposed to cause the photo-oxidation of the enzyme, the first stage of the oxidation resulting in an increased activity, the later stage in its destruction. Further investigation of the problem has revealed the formation of hydrogen peroxide during the irradiation. A very definite acceleration is produced by one-hundred-millionth molar peroxide, and the presence of one-millionth usually doubles the activity of the enzyme. In higher concentrations the peroxide destroys the enzyme, inactivation being almost complete in a thousandth molar concentration.

Inactivation of enzymes (catalase, peroxidase, etc.) by *ultraviolet* light is believed to be independent of the presence of oxygen. As a general rule, pure enzyme preparations especially if dilute are readily destroyed. The presence of substrate and of certain salts ($CaCl_2$) is said to afford protection. Activation by ultraviolet radiation has also been reported, but the conditions have not been adequately studied. Further investigation is also needed to elucidate reversible inactivation. Although ultraviolet light usually produces irreversible destruction, at least one instance of reversible inactivation has been described (amylase).[50]

X-rays have no very marked effect on enzymes; *γ-rays* produce more definite inactivation, whereas other *radium rays* and *emanations* are markedly destructive. Results even with radium have not been uniform, instances of enzyme activation having been reported. Very probably the conflicting statements in the literature are to be attributed to variations in the degree of exposure of the enzymes to these radiations.[51]

Effect of Electrolytes. Inorganic salts may either increase or diminish the velocity of enzymic reactions. Falk[52] studied the effect of various neutral salts on the action of castor-bean lipase toward ethyl butyrate. He found the change in activity to be a continuous function of the concentration of the salt added. Monovalent salts, the chlorides and nitrates of barium and calcium (except for very dilute solutions), magnesium chloride and nitrate, and dilute solutions of sodium sulfate were found to exert a depressing effect. Dilute solutions of $BaCl_2$, $CaCl_2$, $MgSO_4$, $MnCl_2$, and $MnSO_4$ produced increased activity. Lithium salts had a more depressing effect than the salts of sodium or potassium. In the case of the sodium and potassium halides, fluorides had the maximum inhibiting effect, iodides next, bromides next, and chlorides last.

[50] L. Pincussen, Fermentforschung, **8**, 181 (1926).
[51] R. G. Hussey, *J. Gen. Physiol.*, **9**, 211, 217, 309 (1925–26).
[52] *J. Am. Chem. Soc.*, **35**, 601 (1913).

Kidney phosphatase is activated by Mg ions, is unaffected by Ca and Ba and inhibited by Zn (Erdtman).[53] Cyanide activates the proteolytic enzyme, papain. Arsenate exerts a similar effect on zymase. Calcium and magnesium salts accelerate tryptic digestion.

Sodium taurocholate accelerates the activity of pancreas and liver lipase, but has no influence on serum lipase. Copper sulfate is toxic for liver and pancreas lipase and does not affect serum lipase.[54]

The interrelations of hydrogen-ion activity and concentration of salt has been the subject of a series of investigations on amylase by Sherman, Caldwell, and Adams.[55] It has long been known that the presence of electrolyte is essential to the activity of amylases. If electrolytes are completely removed from saliva (containing ptyalin) by dialysis, the ptyalin will not digest dialyzed soluble starch. The addition of a small amount of sodium chloride under these conditions will result in digestion. The complete inactivation of the enzyme in the absence of salts is questioned by Myrbäck,[56] who states that digestion will occur provided both the enzyme and starch have been buffered to about pH 6.0 before dialysis. There is, however, no doubt regarding the acceleratory effect of the electrolyte.

According to Sherman and associates, the optimal hydrogen-ion activity for pancreatic amylase is dependent both on the kind and concentration of salt present. Thus, for a concentration of 0.001 M NaCl, the optimum is pH 6.7, whereas for 0.01 M it is pH 7.1. A certain point in concentration is reached for each salt above which further increases (within specified limits) do not influence the optimum pH.

The effect of neutral salts on amylase is apparently due more to the anion than the cation, and there are indications that it is specific, either for the enzyme or the substrate. The order of efficiency of the various salts is NaCl and KCl > LiCl > NaBr > $NaNO_3$ > $NaClO_3$ > NaSCN > NaF. Moreover, the influence of these salts on the activity of pancreatic amylase seems to be the same for highly purified preparations as for commercial pancreatin, indicating that it is a property of the enzyme itself rather than of any impurities that may be present.

The term *co-enzyme* is applied to substances, including both electrolytes and non-electrolytes, that are specifically required by a particular enzyme as a condition of its activity. For example, chloride (or bromide) ions are required in the case of amylase, and magnesium ion in the action of phosphatase.

[53] *Z. physiol. Chem.*, **172**, 182 (1927); **177**, 211, 231 (1928).

[54] I. A. Parfentjev, W. C. Devrient, and B. F. Sokoloff, *J. Biol. Chem.*, **92**, 33 (1931).

[55] *J. Am. Chem. Soc.*, **50**, 2529, 2535, 2538 (1928).

[56] *Z. physiol. Chem.*, **159**, 1 (1926).

Inhibiting and Inactivating Agents, or Poisons.   Enzymes are very sensitive to a large variety of organic and inorganic substances by which they are inactivated.   In most cases the degree of inhibition depends on the concentration of the inactivating substances, but many of these are effective even in very great dilution.   The salts of mercury, silver, and gold are conspicuously toxic.   Other heavy metal salts, those of copper, lead, zinc, and cadmium, are less poisonous, though even these inactivate certain enzymes very markedly.   Still less toxic are the salts of aluminum, chromium, manganese, cobalt, and nickel. Urease is especially sensitive to mercury and its salts, as well as to other heavy metals.[57]   The inhibition of enzymes by heavy metals is believed to be due to their combination with the enzyme.   Accordingly it should be possible to reverse the process by removing the metallic ion. v. Euler and Svanberg[58] inactivated yeast invertase with $AgNO_3$.   On subsequent treatment with H_2S, the activity of the enzyme was restored.

Enzymes are inactivated by protein precipitants, such as picric and phosphotungstic acids, by alkaloids and various surface-active substances, such as urethane and the higher fatty acids.   Urease is inactivated by most basic dyestuffs.[59]

The halogens, chlorine, bromine and iodine, and other oxidizing agents, H_2O_2, $KMNO_4$, KNO_2, etc., are injurious to enzymes.   Hydrocyanic acid has a strong inhibiting effect on catalase, zymase, peroxidase and certain oxidases, excepting xanthine-oxidase.   It has no effect on rennin or pepsin and activates papain.

Fluorides exert a pronounced inhibiting action on liver and serum lipase, but exhibit a somewhat weaker effect toward pancreatic lipase. In sufficient concentration, fluorides also inhibit amylases, urease, pepsin, and other enzymes.

Certain compounds frequently employed as antiseptics are injurious to enzymes.   Chloroform destroys maltase, amylase, ptyalin, rennin, and urease.   Toluene, on the other hand, is practically inert in this respect.   Glycerol inhibits rennin; thymol is particularly destructive to the oxidases.

A certain amount of specificity is exhibited with regard to the inhibition of enzymes by poisons.   An illustration is the behavior of fluorides to various amylases, to which reference has just been made. Another example has been brought out by Rona and his co-workers,[60]

[57] Note for example the observations of J. B. Sumner and K. Myrbäck on crystalline increase, Z. *physiol. Chem.*, **189**, 218 (1930).

[58] *Fermentforschung*, **3**, 330 (1920).

[59] J. H. Quastel, *Biochem. J.*, **26**, 1685 (1932).

[60] *Biochem. Z.*, **134**, 108, 118 (1922); **141**, 222 (1923).

who have shown that pancreatic lipase is inhibited by quinine but not by atoxyl (sodium p-aminophenylarsinate), whereas liver lipase is sensitive to atoxyl. Kidney lipase, on the contrary, is not affected by quinine but is injured by atoxyl.

Enzyme inhibition was formerly believed to be due to adsorption phenomena. Although these are probably of importance, there is some reason for believing that the chief cause is the chemical combination of the inhibiting agent with the enzyme.

The behavior of heavy metals is partly explained on this basis. The inhibiting action of certain amines (aniline, paraphenylene-diamine, etc.) corresponds to their affinity for aldehydes. Then, too, enzymes are poisoned by aldehydes and substances like HNO_2 which are capable of reacting with amino groups. These properties have been considered as supporting the conception that the inactivation of enzymes may be brought about by the chemical combination of the inactivating agent with some specific group of the enzyme, to the end that the latter is thereby rendered incapable of uniting with its substrate.

Effect of Products of Digestion, Enzymic Syntheses. The accumulation of the products of an enzymic reaction is accompanied by a reduction of its velocity. This may be due, in part, to the direct effect of the combination of the enzyme with the products of digestion. It has been stated[61] that invertase enters into combination with fructose and glucose, amylase with maltose,[62] and pepsin with peptone.[63]

The reverse effect, namely, acceleration by the products of enzymic hydrolysis, is said to occur in the case of invertase (honeybee).[64] In strong solutions of sucrose, owing to the liberation of glucose and fructose, particularly the former, an increase in the velocity occurs in the early stages of the reaction. Other instances of acceleration of enzyme reactions are usually more apparent than real, being generally due to a change to a more favorable pH.

Retardation in the rate of reaction is also brought about by the approach or attainment of equilibrium, since the tendency to reversion is determined by the concentration of the products of a reaction. Removal of the products of the reaction produces a continuous shift in the equilibrium, with the result that the reaction progresses more and more toward completion.

[61] L. Michaelis and M. L. Menten, *Biochem. Z.*, **49**, 333 (1913); R. Kuhn, *Z. physiol. Chem.*, **129**, 57 (1923); J. M. Nelson and R. S. Anderson, *J. Biol. Chem.*, **69**, 443 (1926).

[62] G. McGuire and K. G. Falk, *J. Gen. Physiol.*, **2**, 224 (1919–20).

[63] J. H. Northrop, *ibid.*, **2**, 471 (1920).

[64] J. M. Nelson and D. J. Cohn, *J. Biol.*, **61**, 193 (1924); Nelson and C. T. Bottery, *ibid.*, **62**, 139 (1924).

In this connection the synthetic action of the hydrolyzing enzymes may be considered briefly. Croft-Hill,[65] in 1898, treated a very concentrated solution of glucose with yeast maltase and obtained a disaccharide, first thought to be maltose, but later shown to be isomaltose.

The equilibrium position of a reversible hydrolytic reaction is determined by the ratio $\dfrac{\text{velocity of hydrolysis}}{\text{velocity of synthesis}}$. Attainment of equilibrium in the case of a 0.5 N solution of sucrose, when subjected to the action of invertase, requires about six days; at the end of this time 99 per cent of the sucrose has been inverted. On this basis, it has been calculated, it would require ten months to attain equilibrium by the synthetic action of invertase on glucose and fructose.

Taylor[66] accomplished the synthesis of salmine by the action of trypsin prepared from the liver of a mollusc (*Schizotherus nutalli*) on the products of digestion originally obtained from salmine. In this experiment, the yield was about 0.5 per cent of the original protein.

As early as 1896, the synthesis of protein from the products of peptic proteolysis was reported by Danilewski,[67] but his proof did not seem to be complete at the time. Since then, however, his work has been confirmed by Robertson and others[68] and in a remarkable series of investigations by Wasteneys and Borsook,[69] whose work moreover has other elements of interest and importance. Wasteneys and Borsook found that peptic synthesis of protein may be accelerated if carried out in emulsions formed by certain substances, such as benzaldehyde, benzoic acid, benzene, toluene, and chloroform. Emulsions formed with oleic acid or olive oil had no accelerating effect. It appears that those emulsions which accelerate the synthesis are capable of producing some protein from suitable digests even in the absence of pepsin.

The synthetic proteins were found to vary depending on the method employed. Thus, protein synthesized by benzene alone had the highest base-combining capacity, and that synthesized by benzaldehyde alone had a somewhat lower base-combining capacity. On the other hand the proteins formed by pepsin alone, or by pepsin and benzene, combined with much less base. The proteins also differed in solubility, in the pro portion of free amino and free carboxyl groups and apparently also in

[65] *J. Chem. Soc.*, **73**, 634 (1898).

[66] *J. Biol. Chem.*, **3**, 87 (1907).

[67] Danilewski, quoted from Wasteneys and Borsook, "Colloid Symposium Monograph," **6**, 155 (1928).

[68] *J. Biol. Chem.*, **3**, 95 (1907); **5**, 493 (1908–1909); also Henriques and Gjaldbäk Z. physiol. Chem., **71**, 485 (1911); **81**, 439 (1912).

[69] *J. Biol. Chem.*, **62**, 15, 633, 675 (1924–25); **63**, 563 (1925); "Colloid Symposium Monograph," **6**, 155 (1928); *Physiol. Rev.*, **10**, 110 (1930).

their isolectric points, for they precipitated at different hydrogen-ion concentrations.

Wasteneys and Borsook attribute the effect of the emulsions essentially to adsorption or surface phenomena. They also advance the interesting speculation with regard to the proteins synthesized that the "variation in physical and chemical properties with the emulsifying agent employed suggests a possible mechanism by which the many proteins of the organism may be synthesized, as they are, *in vivo*, from a common substrate."

The following procedure has been employed in the synthesis of protein from the products of peptic hydrolysis (Borsook, MacFadyen and Wasteneys).[70] A peptic digest of egg albumin at pH 1.6 was prepared. It was boiled, the reaction adjusted to pH 4, and concentrated. Pepsin was then added. The mixture after standing for some time was found to contain protein. The greatest yield was obtained if the hydrolyzing action was stopped as soon as all the protein had disappeared. The longer the peptic hydrolysis was allowed to continue, the less was the subsequent synthesis.

The enzymic synthesis of an ester by an esterase was first reported by Kastle and Loevenhart,[71] and of fat (triolein) from glycerol and fatty acids by Hamsik.[72] Claims have also been made for the synthesis of starch- and glycogen-like substances by the action of amylase on simple sugars. Although it is true that the amount of synthesis in most of these cases has been very small, it is nevertheless a fact of great physiological importance that the enzymes capable of hydrolyzing certain substances are likewise capable of synthesizing them. In the plant and animal organism, products thus formed by the synthetic action of enzymes are for the most part insoluble and are removed from the sphere of the reaction by being laid down and stored in the tissues. Removal of the synthetic products results in a continuous shift of the equilibrium, and hence in continued synthesis.

However, in most cases, an unequivocal relationship between the enzyme content of tissues and their assumed synthetic function has not been established. The logical supposition may seem to be that tissues rich in fat would contain more lipase than tissues poor in fat, but that this is not the case has been stated by Bradley.[73] Not only is there no broad correlation between the fat and lipase content of tissues, but some fat-producing organs are relatively poorer in lipase than many organs

[70] *J. Gen. Physiol.*, **13**, 295 (1929–30).
[71] *Am. Chem. J.*, **24**, 491 (1900).
[72] *Z. physiol. Chem.*, **59**, 1 (1909); **65**, 232 (1910).
[73] *J. Biol. Chem.*, **13**, 407 (1913).

which normally never contain or produce more than a small amount of fat. Likewise, the enzymic synthesis of lactose by the mammary gland has been questioned by Bradley,[74] since he was unable to find any lactase in this tissue. On the other hand, the starch-storing tissues of plants are found to contain amylase, and there usually seems to be a correlation between the content of starch and enzyme, which has led Bradley and Kellersberger[75] to conclude that in the plant the synthesis of polysaccharides from the sugars of the sap is enzymic in character.

According to Sym,[76] in a system containing oleic acid, glycerol, water and lipase (pancreatic) the enzyme disappears from the aqueous phase and accumulates at the phase-interface, where alone it is active. Consequently the velocity of olein synthesis is to a certain extent proportional to the area of the phase-interface.

Autolysis. In 1889, Salkowski[77] described the non-bacterial, chemical liquefaction or " self-digestion " of tissues which occurs *post mortem*, and pointed out its similarity to digestion in the alimentary tract. Since then this process, termed " autolysis " by Hofmeister, has been studied by numerous investigators and certain broad generalizations have been made.[78]

Glandular tissues, such as kidney, pancreas, spleen, liver, and thyroid, autolyze more rapidly than other tissues, such as muscle. In the process, the tissue becomes acid through the formation of lactic acid and the cleavage of fatty acids from fats.

The enzymes engaged in autolysis are not limited in their action to the particular tissue undergoing dissolution. When to an autolyzing mixture are added gelatin, casein, or various protein cleavage products, these are digested. On the other hand, egg albumin is said to be unaffected and is even reported to exert an inhibiting effect.

Apparently autolysis may occur within a wide range of hydrogen-ion concentration, and it is therefore assumed that there is in the tissues at least one enzyme capable of digesting protein in an acid medium and another which is active in an alkaline medium. Amino acids and ammonia are found among the end-products of tissue autolysis. An intracellular protease, present in mammalian organs, has been described and named *kathepsin*. It is activated by H_2S, HCN, and compounds,

[74] *Ibid.*, **13**, 431 (1913); See also I. S. Kleiner and H. Tauber, *ibid.*, **99**, 241 (1932).

[75] *Ibid.*, **13**, 425 (1913).

[76] *Biochem. J.*, **24**, 1265 (1930).

[77] *Z. physiol. Chem.*, **13**, 506 (1889).

[78] For reviews of the subject, consult H. C. Bradley, *Physiol. Rev.*, **2**, 415 (1922); H. G. Wells, "Chemical Pathology," Saunders, Philadelphia, 5th edition, 1925; P. A. Levene, Harvey Lectures (1905–06), p. 73.

such as the reduced form of glutathione, containing the sulfhydryl
(SH) group.

Atrophy, which may be defined as a loss of tissue, is essentially
similar to autolysis, being likewise associated with enzymic activity.
It occurs physiologically, as in the mammary gland after lactation, or
pathologically, as in acute yellow atrophy of the liver. The process
may be very rapid, as in the disease just mentioned, or it may be
relatively slow, as in old age, starvation, in an immobilized limb, etc.

Owing to its exceptional blood supply and partly to its low protein
content, the brain is normally relatively resistant to autolysis, but any
process which produces asphyxia, such as pressure, trauma, thrombosis,
carbon-monoxide poisoning, etc., may be accompanied by autolysis,
or " softening."

DIGESTION

Of the substances taken as food, the fats, proteins, and carbohydrates
are ingested in forms not readily absorbed into the circulation and hence
are not available to the organism for purposes of nutrition until they have
become converted into small particles which can diffuse through the
intestinal epithelium. The carbohydrates are converted into monosaccharides, the fats into glycerol and fatty acids, and the proteins
into amino acids. In a measure, hydrolytic changes occur during
the process of cooking, but the major part of the disintegration of the
foodstuffs takes place in various portions of the alimentary tract. The
chemical transformations by which foods are converted into small
diffusible particles constitute the process of digestion. The enzymes
which take part in this process are secreted by various glands and pass
into the different parts of the digestive tract, the mouth, stomach, and
small intestine. In the following paragraphs the fate of the foodstuffs
in digestion will be traced.

Salivary Digestion. The saliva is a mixed secretion produced partly
by three pairs of glands, the submaxillary, sublingual, and parotid, and
partly by the mucous membrane and the buccal glands of the mouth,
throat, and esophagus. It is a viscous, frothy, slightly opalescent
fluid, containing many constituents, including the glycoprotein mucin.
The salivary glands possess two kind of cells: the serous or albuminous,
which secrete a fluid containing protein and enzyme; and the mucous
cells, which secrete a ropy fluid containing mucin. A mixed secretion
is obtained from the submaxillary gland which has both serous and
mucous cells. The sublingual glands are chiefly mucous; and the
parotid, chiefly serous.

Salivary flow is normally caused by a variety of stimuli. Psychic secretion is brought about by a reflex stimulation. The excitation, which may be caused by the sight, smell, or thought of food or by the hearing of sounds associated with the giving of food, travels along afferent paths, the stimuli being transmitted along efferent pathways to the salivary glands. During vomiting, the abdominal fibers of the vagus nerve are stimulated and cause an increased flow as a result of reflex stimulation of the salivary centers. Mechanically, salivary flow may be induced by the presence in the mouth of solid particles, such as food, sand, or paraffin. Dry food calls forth a greater amount of saliva than moist food. Many chemical agents, such as acids, salts, and flavored substances, stimulate the secretion of saliva.

The total amount of saliva secreted in twenty-four hours by a normal man has been calculated to be about 1500 cc. Among the many factors that influence the daily volume of saliva are (a) the amount of water consumed, (b) the amount of food intake and the degree of its mastication, and (c) the character of the food. Chewing and smoking usually increase the flow of saliva.

Considering the complex nervous mechanism and other factors dominating the secretory and excretory functions of the salivary glands, it is not surprising that the composition of saliva should vary appreciably in different individuals, and in the same individual from time to time, and at different times during the day. Based on the analyses of various investigators, the water content of human mixed saliva may be set at approximately 99.42 per cent; the amount of total solids is 0.58 per cent. Of the latter, about one-third is composed of inorganic constituents and the remainder of organic substances, including mucin, enzymes, and epithelial cell débris. The information regarding the inorganic composition of human saliva is relatively scanty. Such data as are available indicate that diet does not alter it markedly. The ingestion of chlorides does not affect the chloride concentration in the saliva significantly. On the other hand, the administration of sufficient inorganic phosphate to produce an increased concentration in the blood increases its excretion by the salivary glands.[79]

Starr[80] analyzed 610 specimens of human saliva, obtained from 228 healthy, normal subjects, and found the reaction to vary from pH 5.75 to 7.05. In 86 per cent of the analyses, the variations were within a

[79] The inorganic composition of dog's saliva has been studied somewhat more comprehensively. The following are references to some of the more recent papers on the subject: G. W. Clark and J. S. Shell, *Dental Cosmos*, **69**, 500 (1927); Clark and L. Levine, *Am. J. Physiol.*, **81**, 264 (1927); H. Baxter, *ibid.*, **91**, 132 (1929–30); *ibid.*, **97**, 440 (1931); M. I. Gregerson and E. N. Ingalls, *ibid.*, **98**, 441 (1931); E. J. de Beer and D. W. Wilson, *J. Biol. Chem.*, **95**, 671 (1932).

[80] *J. Biol. Chem.*, **54**, 55 (1922).

narrower range, namely, pH 6.35–6.85. That the reaction of the saliva is usually slightly acid has also been reported by Henderson and Millet,[81] who observed, moreover, that the salivary pH falls just before meals and remains low just after meals. Between meals, the reaction of the saliva approaches neutrality. The belief that an acid reaction of the saliva is harmful and that it is desirable to change it from acid to alkaline is probably without scientific basis. In fact, the saliva is a well-buffered mixture and it is practically impossible to change its reaction for periods longer than a few minutes by the addition of even moderate amounts of either acid or base.[82]

Mechanically, owing to the water and mucin, the saliva aids in the mastication of foods and serves as a solvent for some of the constituents. Chemically, the saliva takes part in the digestion of carbohydrates. The enzyme *ptyalin* in the saliva is capable of hydrolyzing starch into a variety of dextrins and ultimately into maltose which may be further digested to glucose by maltase, a second enzyme found in the saliva in small amounts.[83]

The conversion of starch into simpler products by the saliva may be demonstrated *in vitro*. This process may be followed by means of the well-known starch-iodine test. As the starch is hydrolyzed, on testing with iodine, the original blue color exhibited by starch gives way to a reddish color due to the so-called erythrodextrins. As the process continues, the digest yields paler tints, and finally it fails to yield any color whatever with iodine. Concurrently, the content of reducing sugars increases. The methods employed in studying starch digestion may be found in laboratory manuals of physiological chemistry.

In short, salivary digestion consists in the transformation, with the aid of ptyalin, of a portion of the starch of the diet into simpler polysaccharides and maltose. As the food remains in the mouth for a relatively short period, very little digestion occurs even in the case of the

[81] *Ibid.*, **75**, 559 (1927).

[82] A. L. Bloomfield and J. G. Huck, *Bull. Johns Hopkins Hosp.*, **31**, 118 (1920); R. Carlson and McKinstry, *Dental Cosmos*, **66**, 840 (1927); G. W. Clark and L. Carter, *J. Biol. Chem.*, **73**, 391 (1927); Editorial, *J. Am. Med. Assoc.*, **92** 99 (1929).

[83] Ptyalin, as well as other amylases (pancreas, malt), acting on starch does not produce a 100 per cent conversion into maltose. The yield is usually about 75 per cent, owing to the formation of an intermediate product, presumably a dextrin, which is resistant to the action of amylase. According to Pringsheim and Beiser (*Biochem.* , **148**, 336 [1924]) this dextrin is identical with tri-hexosan. Certain substances seem to promote the digestion of the residual dextrin. These are present in autolyzed yeast and peptic digests of egg albumin, serum albumin, myosin, and myogen. For further details see H. Pringsheim and G. Otto, *Biochem. Z.*, **173**, 399 (1926); Pringsheim and M. Winter, *ibid.*, **177**, 406 (1926).

carbohydrates. Carbohydrate digestion by the salivary enzymes may continue for some time in the stomach or until the food comes in contac with the hydrochloric acid of the gastric juice which inactivates the ptyalin. There is present in the parotid secretion a proteinase, resem bling trypsin. Its rôle in digestion, if any, is negligible. There are n fat-splitting enzymes in the saliva.

Gastric Digestion. Gastric digestion is concerned primarily with the partial disintegration of the protein of the diet. This is accom plished by the enzyme pepsin in the presence of hydrochloric acid A second important digestive function is the clotting of milk by rennin

Among the more significant of the earlier contributions to our knowl edge of gastric digestion are those of Réaumur (1752) and of Spallanzan (1783). These investigators studied gastric secretion in birds, fishes and mammals, and demonstrated that gastric juice is acid, that i prevents putrefaction, that the juice has digestive properties *in vitro* and that the process of digestion is essentially a chemical one.

In 1825, William Beaumont,[84] a young American surgeon, began a classical investigation of digestion, which lasted until 1833, on a patien with clinical gastrostomy. The patient's name was Alexis St. Martin and he was first observed by Beaumont in 1822. Little was known a that time concerning the mechanism of gastric secretion. Beaumon was a very careful worker and painstakingly studied the factors tha influence the flow of gastric juice. He found that the presence of foo in the stomach stimulates gastric secretion, and that irritating condi ments, alcohol, anger, fear, and fever diminish it. He failed to observe however, that gastric secretion may occur in the absence of food Beaumont recorded observations showing that gastric flow may b induced by mechanical stimulation of the gastric mucosa, a view which though later disputed by Pavlov, has been confirmed in more recen investigations.[85]

Some time before Beaumont began his experiments, Tiedemann an Gmelin and later Prout reported that the acid in the stomach wa hydrochloric acid. Beaumont, however, surmised that the gastri juice contained active chemical agents other than hydrochloric acid He thus anticipated by about six years the actual discovery of pepsi by Wassman.

Following the work of Beaumont, experimental methods were intro duced for the study of gastric secretion. The removal of juice by mean of a stomach tube is a method still employed clinically. Juice may als be collected readily from an artificial fistula. A gastric fistula is mad by cutting an opening into the stomach and sewing the cut portions to th

[84] "Experiments and Observations on the Gastric Juice," Plattsburg, 1833.
[85] Ivy, Lim, McCarthy, and Farrell, *Am. J. Physiol.*, **72**, 203, 232 (1925).

abdominal wall. The collection of pure gastric juice, uncontaminated with food, was first made possible by Heidenhain. His method consisted in cutting through the walls of the stomach, sewing the flaps into a pouch which was then sewed to the abdominal wound. By this operation, however, most of the extrinsic and intrinsic nerve connections were severed. Hence, there remained the possibility that the gastric secretion formed in the pouch was not normal. This difficulty was overcome by Pavlov, who devised an improved technique[86] for making an isolated gastric pouch.

The following diagrams illustrate the operation:

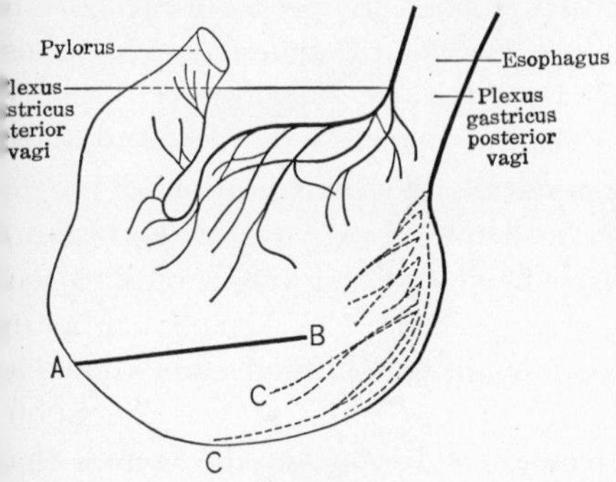

Fig. 20a.

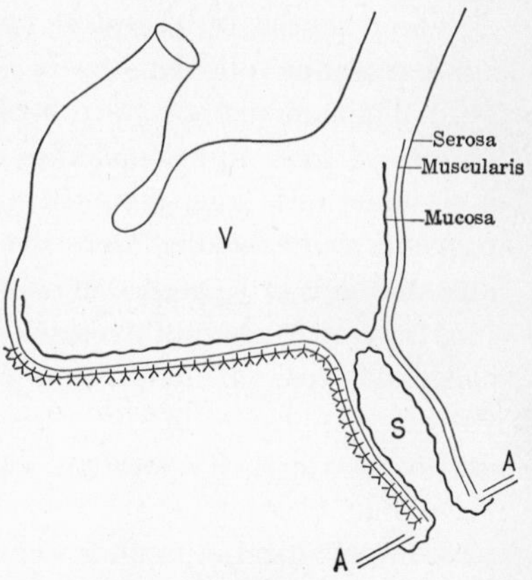

Fig. 20b.

Fig. 20a.—A-B, line of incision; C, flap for forming stomach pouch of Pavlov.

Fig. 20b.—V, cavity of the stomach; S. Pavlov's pouch. S is separated from V by a double layer of mucous membrane. A, abdominal wall. (After Pavlov.)

[86]The following is Pavlov's description of the operation (Pavlov, "The Work of the Digestive Glands," translated by Thompson, London, 1902 edition, p. 11): "The first incision, which begins in the fundus of the stomach, 2 cm. from its junction with the pyloric end, is carried in the longitudinal direction for 10 to 12 cm., and divides both the anterior and posterior walls. A triangular flap is thus formed, the apex of which lies in the long axis of the stomach. A second incision is made exactly at the base of this flap, but only through the mucous membrane, the muscular and peritoneal coats remaining intact. The margins of the mucous membrane all around these incisions are separated for a little way from the submucous tissue: on the side of the stomach for a width of 1 to 1½ cm.; on the side of the flap for 2 to 2½ cm. The raised edges of mucous membrane belonging to the large stomach are applied to each other for half their width and sewn together. Out of the piece which belongs to the flap a cupola is formed. Both the stomach and the margins of the flap are then closed by sutures along the edges of the first incision. A septum is thus made between their respective cavities, consisting of two layers of mucous membrane: one, that of the cupola, being intact, the other stitched along the middle."

Modifications of this technique have been introduced by various workers. See, for example, the improvements suggested by F. Hollander and G. R. Cowgill, *J. Biol. Chem.*, **91**, 151 (1931).

By means of the Pavlov pouch, it is possible to obtain gastric juice which is similar in character to that secreted in the main stomach and which is not contaminated with saliva or food material. In his numerous experiments, Pavlov employed dogs with gastric pouches and dogs with gastric and esophageal fistulas. If the esophagus is divided and the two ends sutured to the skin, an opening is formed. Food swallowed by dogs with esophageal fistulas does not reach the stomach but falls through the upper end of the fistula; hence, this is known as sham feeding.

The essential results of Pavlov's work on gastric digestion may be summarized as follows:

1. The amount of juice secreted is normally proportional to the amount of food and depends to a considerable extent on the character of the food to be digested.

2. In sham feeding there is no chemical or mechanical stimulation. The stimulation to gastric flow is psychic. Psychic secretion of gastric juice may be caused by the sight or smell of food or by established conditioned reflexes. If at the time of feeding, a bell is rung, a conditioned reflex is established in the course of time, so that eventually the mere ringing of the bell, without the presentation of food, causes gastric secretion.

3. Mechanical stimulation, according to Pavlov, produces no secretion. This is not in accord with Beaumont or with the recent work of Ivy.

4. Many substances, especially those having a flavor, produce secretion. [87]

The Origin of Hydrochloric Acid. The *parietal* or *border* cells found in the gastric glands are associated with the secretion of hydrochloric acid. In the concentration in which it is formed, the acid may be

---

[87] In their contribution to the subject, Lim, Ivy, and McCarthy (*Quart. J. Exp. Physiol.*, **15**, 13 [1925]) have analyzed the factors concerned in the excitation of gastric secretion as follows: (1) The cephalic phase, heretofore referred to as the "psychic secretion" demonstrated by Pavlov, which is excited chiefly by the taste, smell, and mastication of palatable food, and by sight, thought, or hypnotic suggestion of palatable food. The term "psychic secretion" is rejected because it is not necessarily psychic, having been shown to occur in the absence of the cerebral cortex. (2) The gastric phase, in which mechanical and chemical stimuli are effective. (3) The intestinal phase, in which the stimuli are certain chemical substances acting in the intestine. Ivy, Lim, and McCarthy (*Quart. J. Exp. Physiol.*, **15**, 55 [1925]) have demonstrated that the intestinal phase of gastric secretion is due to the action of the products (e.g., peptone, amino acids, and amines) of digested complex food substances and apparently, not to the food in its raw state (meat, carbohydrates, and neutral fat).

expected to be injurious to the cell protoplasm, and it is therefore doubtful that it is actually formed within the cell. Indeed, by using indicator dyes as vital stains, Harvey and Bensley[88] were able to demonstrate that the reaction in the parietal cells is alkaline. The strong acidity characteristic of the gastric juice is first observed at the mouth of the tubules of the secreting glands.[89] Concerning this there is more or less general agreement, but the question of how the hydrochloric acid is formed is still unsettled.

It has been suggested[90] that hydrochloric acid is set free from ammonium chloride by hydrolysis:

$$NH_4Cl + H_2O = NH_4OH + HCl$$

According to this view, the ammonium hydroxide is absorbed, leaving the hydrochloric acid behind. The mold *Penicillium glaucum* is capable of effecting this reaction. In further support of this view, evidence has been offered to show that the gastric mucosa contains a somewhat greater amount of ammonia than other tissues. The evidence in favor of this hypothesis is altogether too indirect and insufficient, and although a small amount of hydrochloric acid might conceivably be formed in this way, the theory, on the whole, does not appear plausible.

When a solution of phosphates is enclosed within a parchment membrane, there results a diffusion of acid with a consequent increase in the alkalinity of the fluid within the dialyzer due to the more rapid diffusion velocity of acids than of alkaline salts. A similar mechanism has been suggested for the formation of hydrochloric acid by the gastric mucosa from the alkaline phosphates of the blood. An objection to this view has been raised by Robertson,[91] who states that this theory proves too much, for, by parity of reasoning, all the secretions of the tissues should be acid in reaction, whereas, actually, the majority of the secretions are alkaline.

The formation of hydrochloric acid may possibly be accounted for

---

[88] *Biol. Bull.*, **23**, 225 (1912).

[89] It is of interest to note that Claude Bernard (1813–78) injected animals with a solution of iron ammonium citrate and at the same time with potassium ferrocyanide. Owing to the presence of free acid, the gastric contents were deeply stained with Prussian blue (ferric ferrocyanide). The staining extended to the foveola, but the lumen of the tubules and the cells lining them were quite free from the blue stain. Cited by H. C. Bradley, *Yale J. Biol. Med.*, **4**, 399 (1932).

[90] A. P. Mathews, "Physiological Chemistry," Wm. Wood and Co., Baltimore, 5th edition, p. 386.

[91] T. B. Robertson, "Principles of Biochemistry," Lea & Febiger, Philadelphia, p. 366 (1924).

by the following equations representing reactions which may occur, perhaps, between three of the blood constituents:

$$H^+HCO_3^- + Na^+Cl^- = H^+Cl^- + Na^+HCO_3^-,$$

$$Na^+H_2PO_4^- + Na^+Cl^- = H^+Cl^- + Na_2^{++}HPO_4^{--}$$

If this view is correct, the secretion of large amounts of hydrochloric acid in the stomach should be followed by an accumulation in the blood of basic radicals.   This actually occurs, frequently to such an extent that, despite the loss of alkali in the pancreatic and intestinal secretions, sufficient base remains to give the urine an alkaline reaction. The change in the reaction of the urine, following food intake, from the normal acid reaction to one that is alkaline, is referred to as the *alkaline tide*.[92]

More direct evidence of liberation of base in the gastric mucosa, simultaneously with the secretion of hydrochloric acid, has been presented by Hanke.[93]   In experiments on dogs in which gastric secretion was stimulated by the injection of histamine, the gastric venous blood contained more base bound as bicarbonate and with protein than was present in the arterial blood.   The difference was in proportion to the rate of secretion and in fact was approximately equivalent to the amount of acid formed.

A very interesting experiment and one that may have some bearing on the problem of acid formation is that of T. B. Osborne.[94]   He dis-

---

[92] Many years ago (1868) Horsford (cited by H. C. Bradley, *Yale J. Biol. Med.*, **4**, 399 [1932]) observed that when $CaHPO_4$ was subjected to dialysis, the dialyzate grew acid, whereas the contents of the dialyzing bag became alkaline and $Ca_3(PO_4)_2$ precipitated.   An even earlier experiment of this type is that of Graham, who dialyzed potassium bisulfate against water.   The dialyzate became acid owing to the diffusion of sulfuric acid.   In terms of our present knowledge the reaction may be represented as follows:

$$\begin{array}{c|c} K^+HSO_4^- & H_2SO_4 \\ - & \longrightarrow \\ HO^-H^+ & \\ \hline (KOH + KHSO_4 = K_2SO_4 + HOH) \end{array}$$

Hollander has described an experiment in which the skin of a freshly killed frog was used in separating two portions of the same solution of sodium chloride.   Presumably because of the electrochemical properties of the skin there was a shift of ions across the membrane resulting in the development of acidity on one side and alkalinity on the other.   *J. Am. Inst. Homeopathy*, **22**, 311 (1929).

[93] M. E. Hanke, R. E. Johannesen, and Maude E. Hanke, *Proc. Soc. Exp. Biol. Med.*, **28**, 698 (1931).

[94] *Am. J. Physiol.*, **5**, 180 (1901).

solved edestin in sodium chloride solution and later precipitated it with a stream of carbon dioxide. The precipitate contained edestin in combination with hydrochloric acid, whereas the solution contained $NaHCO_3$. Obviously, in the presence of the protein edestin the reaction represented by the equation $NaCl + HHCO_3 = NaHCO_3 + HCl$ was facilitated.

Behavior similar to that exhibited by edestin can be demonstrated with red blood corpuscles. If these are washed with isotonic solution of sodium chloride until the washings are neutral, then suspended in neutral sodium chloride solution and treated with a stream of carbon dioxide, it is found that the solution becomes alkaline and the corpuscles richer in chlorine. From these observations, Robertson infers that the secretion of an acid juice depends upon the existence in the secreting cells of a protein that is capable of decomposing sodium chloride in the presence of carbon dioxide, the appearance of the free hydrochloric acid in the secretion being attributable to the colloidal, indiffusible character of the protein base. The validity of this suggestion remains to be determined by further study.

If it is assumed that, in the acid-forming cells, the hydrochloric acid is combined with protein or some other cell constituent to which the cell membrane is impermeable, an explanation for the secretion of free hydrochloric acid may be based on Donnan's theory of membrane equilibria. The original state may be represented by the following diagram:

$$R^+ \parallel H^+$$
$$Cl^- \parallel OH^-$$

R represents the positively charged protein ion (or other cell constituent). The membrane being permeable to the Cl^-, H^+, and OH^- ions, an interchange of ions will occur, so that at equilibrium the situation will be as follows:

$$R^+ \parallel H^+$$
$$Cl^- \parallel Cl^-$$
$$OH^- \parallel OH^-$$

The soundness of this theory has been confirmed experimentally by Donnan,[95] who has shown that, under such conditions, hydrochloric acid may actually be " secreted " across a membrane. Donnan is of the opinion that " the proper ampholyte can easily give rise by this

[95] J. Chem. Soc., **99**, 1554 (1911); **105**, 1941 (1914); **115**, 1313 (1919); cited by Gortner, "Outlines of Biochemistry," (1929), p. 285.

mechanism alone to a concentration of hydrogen ions in the external liquid as great as that found in the gastric juice."

The formation of acid in animal organisms is not limited to the gastric mucosa. The salivary glands of the mollusc *Dolium galea* produce a secretion containing 4–5 per cent of sulfuric acid. Certain related species of molluscs produce aspartic acid in large concentration.

The Acidity of the Gastric Juice and Its Regulation. The constancy of the hydrochloric acid concentration of the gastric juice as it is *secreted* has been the subject of much discussion. Proponents of the so-called Heidenhain-Pavlov theory have adopted the view that a relatively constant acidity is characteristic of the gastric secretion. The opposing hypothesis is based on Rosemann's[96] studies and his explanation that the presence of cations in gastric juice is due to the incomplete conversion of neutral chlorides to hydrochloric acid by the parietal cells, from which follows the conclusion that even normally the acidity is subject to conspicuous variations. For example, it is implied that the concentration of acid decreases with the falling off of the secretion (i.e., in its later stages).

In recent years, the evidence in support of the Heidenhain-Pavlov view has been greatly augmented. Experimental as well as clinical studies have shown that the secretion is relatively constant with respect to the hydrochloric acid concentration, which approximates 0.55 to 0.60 per cent. This is equivalent to 0.15 to 0.16 N (pH 0.91 to 0.88).[97]

The total chloride concentration of gastric juice is approximately 0.165 N, and is practically stationary, being even more constant than the hydrochloric acid concentration. The upper value given for the latter is 0.16 N or 160 milliequivalents (m.eq.). Now it is of interest to observe that 160 to 165 m.eq. is approximately the concentration of total base in the blood, which suggests a causal relationship between the two. The obvious indication is that the gastric secretion may be in osmotic equilibrium with the blood. And indeed it is, as may be shown by changing the ionic content of the latter. Gilman and Cowgill[98] have demonstrated that in dogs as a result of water deprivation and the consequent dehydration there is a definite rise in the electrolyte content of the blood. Accompanying the variations thus produced by

---

[96] *Arch. ges. Physiol. Pharmacol.*, **118**, 467 (1907).

[97] The values obtained for the cat, dog, and man show good agreement. The problem of the constancy of gastric acidity has been especially well presented by the following authors: Hollander and Cowgill, *J. Biol. Chem.*, **91**, 151, 481 (1931); Hollander, *Am. J. Physiol.*, **98**, 551 (1931), *J. Biol. Chem.*, **104**, 33 (1934); J. L. Gamble and M. A. McIver, *J. Exp. Med.*, **48**, 837 (1928).

[98] *Am. J. Physiol.*, **99**, 172 (1931–2); **103**, 143 (1932); **104**, 476 (1933).

alternate dehydration and hydration of the animal, parallel changes in the chloride content of the secretion were observed. In one experiment the gastric chloride rose to 183.2 m.eq. The maximum acidity did not, however, greatly exceed 160 m.eq. In short, these results indicate that the osmotic pressure of the blood is the limiting factor determining the chloride concentration and the minimum pH of the gastric secretion. These results do not necessarily imply, however, that the gastric mucosa and the cells of the gastric glands are permeable to chloride ions present in the stomach. In fact, Gilman and Cowgill contend that the reverse is probably true; that the presence of chloride in the stomach is exclusively the result of the active secretory process of the parietal cells.

The hydrochloric acid concentration of the gastric contents does not remain long at the relatively high level of 0.55 to 0.6 per cent, but is rapidly diminished to a concentration which normally varies between 0.15 to 0.25 per cent. A part of the acid is neutralized by the regurgitated alkaline intestinal contents, as shown by the work of Boldyreff.[99] Evidence of the reflux of fluid from the intestine is abundant. Not infrequently intestinal and pancreatic enzymes such as trypsin and lipase, and even bile, may be demonstrated in the stomach contents. The view that the amount of regurgitation is influenced by the degree of acidity is apparently erroneous, for it has been observed that low concentration of acid may produce just as much or more regurgitation than high concentrations and that even the ingestion of alkali may be followed by more marked regurgitation than that produced by the presence of acid. Moreover, regurgitation is not uncommon in the absence of free acid.

While regurgitation of alkaline fluid from the intestine is a common occurrence, it is not the only factor concerned in the neutralization of gastric acidity. The saliva has not only a definite neutralizing, but a diluting effect as well. The foodstuffs, particularly the proteins, combine with hydrochloric acid. Perhaps the most prominent factor is the mucus, secreted by the gastric mucosa. Its effect in reducing gastric acidity has been studied by McCann,[100] who found that in the resting stomach the acid may be formed at a rate sufficiently slow that all of the acid produced combines with the mucus. Bolton and Goodhart[101] in a recent discussion of the mucus factor in the automatic regulation of the acidity of the gastric contents state that " the only means possessed by the normal stomach, whereby it is able to reduce the acidity of its contents, is by the secretion of mucus."

[99] *Ergebnisse Physiol.*, **11**, 156 (1911).   [100] *Am. J. Physiol.*, **89**, 483 (1929).
[101] *J. Physiol.*, **77**, 287 (1933).

Stimulation of Gastric Secretion; the Gastric Hormone. In the fasting stomach there occurs a continuous secretion of gastric juice; the rate is probably relatively low and subject to variation, though on this point there is admittedly not much information. Certain it is, however, that secretion is rapidly increased by a variety of stimuli, those associated with the taking of food being of particular interest.

The secretion due to psychic factors (the cephalic phase of gastric secretion described by Ivy) is usually referred to as "appetite juice." It is a discontinuous secretion and obviously significant in initiating gastric digestion. About half an hour after food-taking the rate of secretion is greatly augmented. It is not due to reflex action since it may be evoked after cutting both vagi. Nor is it due to mechanical stimulation, the presence of water or of undigested food materials. Broths, meat extract, meat juices, and the products of protein digestion, including certain amino acids, stimulate secretion. Products of starch hydrolysis do not exert an appreciable effect, and fats seem to inhibit secretion. Ivy and Javois[102] have studied the effect of protein-split products, including amino acids and certain amines, and found some of these to be potent gastric secretagogues. A certain degree of specificity was observed. For example, β-alanine was a powerful excitant, whereas α-alanine acted but feebly.

These substances contribute to the chemical stimulation of gastric secretion. But there is apparently a more important factor. Many workers have shown that the injection of extracts prepared from the pyloric mucous membrane causes increased secretion of gastric juice. The effect has been attributed to a specific secretagogue, called *gastric secretin*, or *gastrin*, described by Edkins.[103]

Gastrin is also present in the mucosa of the duodenum, though in smaller amount, as shown by Keeton and Koch.[104] These investigators could not demonstrate its presence in other tissues. More recently Murray[105] studied the effect of extracts prepared from various regions of the duodenum (cat). According to her report, only the sections which contained Brunner's glands yielded potent preparations. Attempts have been made to isolate " gastrin." Koch, Luckhardt, and Keeton[106] prepared moderately active preparations from the pyloric mucosa and,

---

[102] *Am. J. Physiol.*, 63, 182 (1924).
[103] *Proc. Roy. Soc., London*, B, 76, 376 (1905); *J. Physiol.*, 34, 133 (1906).
[104] *Am. J. Physiol.*, 37, 481 (1915).
[105] *J. Physiol.*, 69, 48 (1930).
[106] *Am. J. Physiol.*, 52, 508 (1920).

though unable to isolate the active principle, nevertheless concluded from its chemical properties that it might be an imidazole compound related to, if not identical with, histamine.

A more recent report from Ivy's laboratory[107] announces that gastrin is actually histamine. From acid extracts of the pyloric mucosa he and his co-workers have isolated this substance as the picrate. The possible formation of histamine in the process of isolation is emphatically ruled out, and evidence is presented to show that it is the sole secretory excitant. *Histaminase* (an enzyme which destroys histamine) was found to destroy the effectiveness of the crude " gastrin " solutions.

$$\begin{array}{c} \text{HC---NH} \\ \text{C---N} \\ | \\ \text{CH}_2 \\ | \\ \text{CH}_2\text{NH}_2 \end{array}$$

Histamine

The subcutaneous injection of histamine is followed by a copious gastric secretion which is very acid in character. This remarkable property was discovered by Popielski[108] in 1920 and has since been investigated in both experimental and clinical studies of gastric function. A relatively small amount of histamine is required, from 0.5 to 1 mg. (or 0.1 mg. per 10 kg. of body weight) being generally employed to produce the desired response. In man the maximum secretion of acid is usually attained between 30 and 45 minutes after the injection of histamine. In the dog, according to Gilman and Cowgill,[109] the maximum rate of secretion is reached in 30 to 45 minutes. The acid and total chloride concentrations reach their maximum values at about the same time.

Histamine apparently stimulates only the parietal, or acid-secreting, cells. Pilocarpine, on the other hand, promotes the secretion of the organic substances and enzymes. This effect is best elicited when the administration of this drug is preceded by an injection of histamine because in that way the organic substances are " washed out " from the lumen of the glands and the furrows of the mucosa. Vineberg and

---

[107] *Ibid.*, **101**, 331 (1932); see also M. S. Kim and A. C. Ivy, *ibid.*, **105**, 220 (1933).
[108] *Arch. ges. Physiol.*, **178**, 214 (1920). '
[109] *Am. J. Physiol.*, **97**, 124 (1931).

Babkin[110] state that the combination of the two excitants produces a synthetic gastric juice approaching normal.[111, 112]

The Enzymes of the Gastric Juice. Three enzymes participate in gastric digestion: *pepsin, rennin,* and *lipase.* The origin of lipase is somewhat disputed, one view being that it is secreted with the other enzymes in the stomach, while according to another view it is derived from regurgitated pancreatic and intestinal juice. The hydrogen-ion concentration in the stomach is usually unfavorable both for the emulsification of fat and for the action of lipase, so that the amount of gastric fat digestion is ordinarily slight, being limited to the partial hydrolysis of the highly emulsified fats and the more soluble glycerides of the lower fatty acids, such as are present in egg yolk, butter, and milk.

In the absence of acid in the stomach, digestion may be largely intestinal in type, being due to the pancreatic and intestinal enzymes contained in the regurgitated intestinal contents.

The *chief cells (Hauptzellen)* have been definitely associated with the secretion of pepsin and rennin. The acid furnishes a favorable hydrogen-ion concentration for the action of pepsin. Formerly it was considered that this enzyme was present in the cells in an inactive or *zymogen* form, called *pepsinogen,* which was presumably converted into the active form by hydrochloric acid.[113] The evidence for this was that neutral extracts of gastric mucosa, which had not been previously treated with acid, were more resistant to the action of alkali than activated pepsin,

---

[110] *Ibid.,* **97,** 69 (1931).

[111] Insulin, the hormone which is primarily concerned with carbohydrate metabolism, is also said to stimulate gastric secretion. J. La Barre, *Bull. acad. roy. Belgique,* **11,** 598 (1931); E. B. Boldyreff and J. F. Stewart, *J. Pharm. Exp. Therap.,* **46,** 407 (1932).

[112] A substance of protein nature, inhibiting gastric secretion, has been extracted from intestinal and colonic mucosa. Similar preparations from other sources (plain muscle, voluntary muscle, and gastric mucosa) are less effective. Extracts prepared from blood and liver have virtually no inhibitory effect. T. Kosaka, R. K. S. Lim, S. M. Ling and A. C. Lim, *Chinese J. Physiol.,* **6,** 107 (1932).

[113] Because of its alleged effect on "pepsinogen," hydrochloric acid was formerly classified as an *activator.* An activator has been conventionally defined as a substance which converts the inactive form of an enzyme into its active form. Other examples will be encountered later. In contradistinction, an agent which accelerates the action of an already active enzyme has been defined as a *co-ferment,* or *co-enzyme.* Haldane ("Enzymes," Longmans, Green & Co., London, 1930, Chap. VII), however, employs the term "activator" for non-specific substances which permit or *increase* the activity of an enzyme, thus including most of the agents formerly classified as co-enzymes. He states further that the activation may be primarily physical, as in the case of a variety of colloids which activate lipases, or chemical, as in the case of anions which activate animal amylases.

the latter being quickly decomposed in an alkaline medium.   According to Waldschmidt-Leitz the differences in the behavior of pepsin and its zymogen are attributable to the effects of hydrogen-ion concentration. Of perhaps greater significance are the observations of Northrop (p. 131) that crystalline pepsin may be completely inactivated by making the solution alkaline to pH 10.5.   If the solution is then acidified to pH 5.4 and allowed to stand at 22° C. for 24 to 48 hours, the enzyme solution recovers some of its activity.   These results indicate the reversibility of inactivation of pepsin and suggest that the difference between the active and inactive forms may reside in slight physical or chemical modifications of the protein which is pepsin.   This need not be interpreted, however, as a final settlement of the problem.

Pepsin digests protein to its primary cleavage products, the proteoses and peptones.   The food does not remain in the stomach sufficiently long for further transformation.   But even in prolonged *in vitro* digestion by pepsin the amount of the simpler polypeptides and free amino acids liberated is small.   This has led to the supposition that pepsin is restricted in its action to some specific linkage or linkages in the protein molecule.   However, peptic digestion is associated with the liberation of free carboxyl and amino groups, which are said to be liberated in approximately equivalent amounts.   This would indicate that pepsin involves the O=C—NH group, but in view of the limited amount of such cleavage it has been assumed that only certain specific bindings are thus affected.   Obviously the mode of action of pepsin has not been settled and requires further study.

Peptic digestion may be followed by observing the change in the amount of coagulable protein, or the increase in incoagulable nitrogen. The progress of digestion may also be measured by Sørensen's titration (increase in COOH groups) or the Van Slyke amino nitrogen determinations.   Another method commonly employed especially with certain substrates consists in determining the changes in viscosity of the digests. As digestion progresses, the viscosity decreases.

Rennin.   Rennin is secreted by the gastric mucosa and is said to be especially abundant in young animals.   The essential feature of the process of milk clotting, with which rennin is concerned, is the hydrolysis of the casein molecule.   Calcium is essential for rennitic action, and if it is removed by treating the milk with oxalate, clotting does not occur on the addition of rennin.   When to milk so treated calcium is added, clotting occurs.   If milk, to which rennin has been added after the removal of the calcium, is allowed to stand for some time and then boiled to destroy the enzyme, and calcium is finally added, clotting occurs.   This shows that the rennin must have acted

on the casein in some way in the absence of calcium. Many theories
have been advanced for the clotting process of milk, but tentatively,
the changes may be represented by the following equations:

$$\text{Casein} + \text{rennin} = \text{paracasein (soluble)}$$

$$\text{Paracasein} + \text{Ca} = \text{Ca-paracasein (insoluble)}$$

The action of rennin may also be represented by the equation:

$$\text{Ca-casein} + \text{rennin} = \text{Ca-paracasein}$$

The curdling of milk may be brought about likewise by the addition
of acid. In the precipitation of calcium caseinate by hydrochloric
acid, isoelectric casein, which is insoluble, is formed:

$$\text{Ca-casein} + \text{HCl} = \text{casein} + \text{CaCl}_2$$

The Question of the Identity of Pepsin and Rennin. Hammarsten
considered rennin to be a special proteolytic enzyme distinct from
pepsin. This view was supported by the fact that pepsin preparations
without rennitic action and rennin preparations without peptic activity
have been obtained. A contrary view was proposed by Pavlov. It
postulated that both activities were due to the same enzyme. This
conception was based partly on the wide distribution and co-existence
of pepsin and rennin in plants and animals. Indeed, the property of
clotting milk has been attributed not only to pepsin, but also to trypsin
and the autolytic proteases of tissues.

Obviously the non-identity of pepsin and rennin can be established
only by the complete separation of the two enzymes. The crystalline
pepsin of Northrop possesses rennitic action (p. 131.) However,
Tauber and Kleiner[114] have recently obtained an active preparation of
rennin from the fourth stomach of the calf. Their product is relatively
pure, is practically devoid of peptic activity, and is much more powerful
in coagulating milk than any rennin previously described. It differs
from pepsin in being not a protein, but a thioproteose, in containing
neither calcium nor phosphorus, in being soluble in 0.04 per cent hydrochloric acid, non-coagulable by heat, and diffusible through a dialyzing
membrane. Unlike pepsin it yields negative Millon and Hopkins-Cole
reactions and weaker xanthoproteic and biuret tests. The isoelectric
point of rennin is given as pH 5.4, whereas that of pepsin is pH 2.75.
Rennin is more resistant than pepsin to destruction by acid.

Summarizing the available information, it may be stated that pepsin,

[114] *J. Biol. Chem.*, **96**, 745 (1932).

as represented by Northrop's crystalline preparation, has both proteolytic and rennitic action, but that a separate and distinct enzyme is
elaborated by the gastric mucosa which possesses only rennitic activity.

Gastric Motility, Hunger Contractions. Carlson[115] has shown
that hunger is a sensation accompanying movements of the stomach, and
that in conditions where hunger is abnormally keen, the contractions of
the stomach are increased both in height and frequency. It has been
suggested that the increased gastric tonus and contractions are associated with the reduction of the tissue glycogen. A relationship has
even been assumed to exist between the blood-sugar level and gastric
motility, but this has been denied recently by Quigley and Halloran,[116]
who were unable to modify spontaneous gastric motility in dogs by the
intravenous injection of glucose.

Gastric hunger contractions may be augmented by fasting, moderate
exercise, hemorrhage, and exposure to cold. Insulin stimulates motility
of the stomach, as well as of other parts of the gastro-intestinal tract.
Marked reduction of gastric motility, and in fact long-continued gastric
atony, accompanied by loss of appetite (anorexia), occur in dogs (and
probably in man) deprived of the antineuritic factor (vitamin B).
This has been the subject of a long series of investigations by Cowgill
and associates and will be considered in another connection.

Discharge of Food from the Stomach. Factors which increase the intensity and frequency of the contractions of the stomach, such as hunger,
fasting, or the administration of thyroid substance or insulin, also hasten
the rate at which the food is discharged into the intestine. Constriction
waves propel the semi-liquefied food, or chyme, toward the pyloric
sphincter, which is apparently able to resist the passage of large or solid
food fragments, but which opens from time to time to permit the
passage of small amounts of chyme. On the basis of Cannon's work the
stimulus for opening of the pyloric sphincter was until recently attributed
to the accumulation of acid on the stomach side, whereas the stimulus
for closure was thought to be the presence of acid on the duodenal side.
During the period of relaxation, there probably is not only the ejection
of material from the stomach, but the reverse passage of intestinal
contents into the stomach. The view that the acid is the essential
factor for the alternate opening and closing of the sphincter is no longer
generally accepted, for it appears that contraction of the sphincter may
be produced not only by acid, but also by mechanical irritation, and
even by alkali. The stomach, moreover, can also empty itself of

[115] A. J. Carlson, "The Control of Hunger in Health and Disease," *Univ. of
Chicago Press*, 1916.
[116] *Am. J. Physiol.*, **100**, 102 (1932).

alkaline contents.   Carlson and Litt[117] believe that ordinary sensory stimuli may induce contraction of the pylorus.

This view finds some support in the work of McCann.[118]   In animals in which the pyloric sphincter is resected, there is only partial reduction in the efficiency of food retention in the stomach.   This observation, adequately controlled by fluoroscopic examinations and fractional analyses of the gastric contents, has led McCann to conclude that the emptying of the stomach is not controlled by the sphincter alone, but that the whole pyloric antrum is actively engaged in the process.   The vigorous tonic and peristaltic contractions of the pylorus observed early in digestion, McCann believes to be due to its irritability. As digestion progresses and the food is reduced to a semi-fluid consistency, this stimulus gradually diminishes, giving way to a progressive relaxation of the pars pylorica, including the sphincter, and results in the more rapid emptying of the stomach.   Neither the free hydrochloric acid or the products of digestion seem to be the specific influence for the relaxation.

The type and amount of food determine the rate of evacuation of the stomach.   When fed separately, carbohydrate food remains in the stomach for a shorter period than protein food.   Fat remains in the stomach for a longer period that proteins.   The digestion of protein food is markedly delayed on a high-fat diet.   In part, the differences in the rate of emptying of the stomach are due to the variations in the time required for mechanical disintegration and enzyme action.

Gastric Analysis.   Departures from the normal composition of the gastric contents have long been considered of significance in clinical diagnosis.   Accordingly, various methods and functional tests have been devised for the purpose of obtaining information on one or more of the following points: presence or absence of free hydrochloric acid and its amount; total acidity; peptic and rennitic activity; abnormal retention of food in the stomach, and the character, including the microscopic appearance, of the residuum; evidence of regurgitation, presence of blood, and organic acids, such as lactic and butyric, particularly the former.

Gastric flow may be stimulated by the ingestion of a so-called test meal.   The one proposed by Ewald consists of a dry piece of toast or a roll and a cup of weak tea (about 250 cc.).   The test is performed in the morning on an empty stomach; one hour after the meal, the complete stomach contents are removed (by means of a suitable stomach

---

[117] *Arch. Int. Med.*, **33**, 281 (1924).

[118] *Am. J. Physiol.*, **89**, 497 (1929);   compare with B. A. McSwiney and L. N. Pyrah, *J. Physiol.*, **76**, 127 (1932).

tube, such as the Rehfuss tube) and analyzed. The procedure may be modified to advantage by removing the stomach contents before giving the meal.

Dilute oatmeal gruel as the test meal (Boas) is also widely used. The Riegal test meal consists of beef broth, beefsteak, and mashed potatoes. A wide variety of other test meals have been proposed.

The information derived from a single analysis is often inadequate. To meet this objection, Rehfuss introduced a method of fractional analysis. The stomach is emptied and the contents kept for analysis; the meal is given, after which specimens are withdrawn at 15-minute intervals for one hour. Should it seem desirable to continue the test for a longer period (2 to 3 hours), the last specimens may be collected at intervals of 30 minutes.

Gastric secretion may also be stimulated by the administration of dilute alcohol, a procedure that has been applied clinically. Special advantages have been pointed out in the use of histamine (p. 175).

The subject of gastric analysis will be treated only briefly in this connection, as it belongs more properly in manuals devoted to clinical laboratory methods. A general inspection of the specimens withdrawn may yield useful information. For example, the stomach contents removed before the test meal may be abnormal in volume. Whereas ordinarily the amount of juice in the resting stomach varies between 15 and 40 cc., it may be many times this as a result of obstruction. This would be further indicated by the presence of food particles. The test meal is normally evacuated in 1.5 to 2 hours. Should there be no evidence of the test meal in about an hour, it signifies increased motility. If, on the contrary, a residue is present after 2 to 3 hours, it shows diminished motility, or obstruction usually at the pyloric sphincter.

Although appropriate tests are available for the detection of blood and bile, these may be readily recognized grossly. A bright red color indicates recent bleeding, such as may occur from an ulcer or an esophageal varix. Bleeding due to these causes is profuse. Very frequently a small amount of blood may be detected. This results from the slight trauma that is often produced in passing the stomach tube. If bleeding occurs slowly, but continually, there may be present a considerable amount of blood possessing a color that has been likened to that of coffee-grounds. Considerable significance may also be attached to the odor. It may be characteristic of fermentation (lactic or butyric acid), or may be even more disagreeable, as in cancer, severe catarrhal gastritis, etc.

For analysis the stomach contents are usually strained through cheesecloth. The free hydrochloric acid is determined by titration with standard alkali, using dimethyl-aminoazobenzene (Töpfer's reagent) as the indicator. This shows a change from red (acid) to salmon-pink and yellow at pH 3 to 4. The results are conventionally expressed in terms of the number of cubic centimeters of 0.1 N acid present in 100 cc. of gastric contents.

Not all the hydrochloric acid is free. Some occurs in combination with protein. By using phenolphthalein as the indicator, the value for total acidity may be obtained. Titration with alizarin as the indicator is supposed to represent the free hydrochloric acid plus the organic acids and acid salts. The difference between this titration and the one with Töpfer's reagent is a measure of the organic acidity. From the difference in the titration values with phenolphthalein and alizarin may be calculated the combined hydrochloric acid. For most purposes, the titrations for free and total acidity are sufficient.

Physiological and Pathological Variations. In considering physiological standards it is necessary to recall that the acidity of the gastric juice as it is secreted is close to and approaches as a maximum the value of 160 units or m.eq. (160 cc. 0.1 N acid per 100 cc.). This is reduced in various ways so that the total acidity ordinarily encountered after a test meal amounts to 60 to 90 units as a maximum, and depending on various factors previously discussed, the free acidity may be decreased to an average value of about 40 to 50 units.

Vanzant and associates[119] have analyzed the data of nearly four thousand test meals performed on individuals of all ages who were presumably free from gastro-intestinal disease. The free acidity, which is low in childhood, increases rapidly up to the age of 20 years, when the adult values are reached. Achlorhydria (absence of free hydrochloric acid) was encountered in all age groups, but showed a steady increase in incidence up to the age 60 to 65 years. At the age of 60 years, 23 per cent of the men and 28 per cent of the women were achlorhydric. For other ages, too, achlorhydria was somewhat more frequent in women than in men. As an upper limit the free acidity rarely exceeded 90. This illustrates the broad range of values encountered in apparently normal individuals and emphasizes the necessity for caution and discrimination in the interpretation of the data of gastric analysis.

Excluding the cases of achlorhydria from the calculations Vanzant determined the mean value for free acidity for men between the ages of 20 and 40 years to be about 45 to 50 units. From this the level falls off to about 30 to 35 for aged men. The total acidity is ordinarily 15 to 20 units higher than the free acidity. In women throughout adult

[119] *Arch. Int. Med.*, 49, 345 (1932).

life the mode is approximately 35 units of free acidity, with an average of about 18 units for combined acid.

Fractional Analysis. About 40 per cent of normal individuals show the following response to a test meal: increase in free HCl, sometimes from an initial value which is as low as zero, to a maximum of 45 to 55 at the end of 60 to 90 minutes. This is followed by a rapid decrease in the next 30 to 60 minutes to a level of about 15 to 20 units. In about one-third of normal persons, a relative hypersecretion and hyperchlorhydria occur, with maximum values for free HCl of 90 to 100. On the other hand, a certain proportion (25 to 30 per cent) show a tendency to hypochlorhydria.

As an extreme of hypoacidity, there is the condition of achlorhydria in which free hydrochloric acid is entirely absent. In true achlorhydria, even histamine fails to provoke any secretion and the total acidity rises very little, if at all. Occasionally a case is encountered showing an almost normal rise in total acidity, but the absence of free HCl. Neutralization by regurgitated duodenal fluid, or by mucus, secreted in abnormal amounts is the usual explanation. Pernicious anemia, gastric carcinoma, and chronic gastritis are among the conditions in which achlorhydria is a prominent feature.

In hyperacidity, or hyperchlorhydria, the concentration of free acid may rise from an initial value of 20 to 40 to over 100 units, within 60 to 90 minutes, and remain at a relatively high level for several hours. Such a response is commonly obtained in gastric and duodenal ulcer.

The Histamine Test. The use of test meals in determining gastric function has certain limitations. Psychic elements, such as lack of appetite, distaste for the food, the speed of eating, and the buffer value of the meal are disturbing factors. Other factors are the amount of saliva swallowed, regurgitation from the duodenum, and the speed with which the stomach empties itself. Because of so many variables, repeated tests often yield divergent results. Another factor which prevents uniformity is that the test meal does not ordinarily provide a maximum stimulus. In discussing this problem Bloomfield and Polland,[120] as well as others, have emphasized the point that one criterion of a satisfactory functional test is that the stimulus which makes up the test must impose a load on the function to be tested. Only when there is a maximal stimulus, i.e., under strain, is it possible to demonstrate early or partial impairment in function.

The histamine test is of especial value in establishing true achlorhydria. Its most serious limitation is that it gives no information con-

[120] *J. Am. Med. Assoc.*, **92**, 1508 (1929); see also Klumpp and Bowie, *J. Clin. Investigation*, **12**, 1 (1933).

cerning the motor activity of the stomach. Moreover, should it be firmly established that histamine is the gastric secretagogue, it will be possible to dismiss the objection raised that histamine is not a physiological stimulus.

Tests for Enzymes, etc. The absence of pepsin, as well as hydrochloric acid, is termed *achylia*. For the determination of peptic activity, a commonly used procedure is the Nierenstein and Schiff modification of Mett's method. Small glass tubes, filled with coagulated egg albumin, are introduced into small flasks containing a definite amount of gastric juice, adjusted to approximately $0.05 N$ HCl. Digestion occurs at both ends of the tube; the portion of the column digested at each end is measured and used as the basis for calculating the peptic activity.[121]

Rennin is rarely determined for purposes of clinical diagnosis. Qualitatively it may be readily detected by neutralizing the gastric juice and adding 5 drops of it to 5 cc. of fresh milk in a test-tube. If placed in an incubator or water bath at 40° C., clotting should occur within a few minutes.

Evidence of regurgitation may be obtained by testing the gastric contents for bile, or the pancreatic enzymes, notably trypsin. The presence of blood is detected by appropriate tests described in laboratory manuals. Lactic acid occurs commonly in the later stages of gastric carcinoma, but may occur in non-malignant pyloric obstruction associated with achlorhydria. In the absence of hydrochloric acid, bacterial fermentation is unchecked.

Germicidal Properties of Gastric Juice. The hydrochloric acid of the stomach is said to have germicidal properties. Although this is true to some extent, as evidenced by the fact that gastric juice, when allowed to stand, does not putrefy readily, nevertheless, the antiseptic properties have been overestimated. The presence of yeasts and bacteria in normal gastric juice has frequently been demonstrated.

Anti-enzymes. In view of the proteolytic action of pepsin, the question may be raised as to the failure of the stomach mucosa to digest itself. One explanation offered is that the gastric mucosa contains an anti-enzyme which inhibits the action of pepsin. Another explanation is that the blood and lymph bathing the cells of the stomach have an alkaline reaction which is unfavorable to peptic digestion. It is obvious, however, that the latter explanation cannot hold in the case of the

---

[121] A more elaborate method has been described by Polland and Bloomfield (*J. Clin. Investigation,* **7,** 45 [1932]). An edestin solution is used as the substrate, the undigested portion being precipitated in tubes designed for this purpose and measured after centrifuging.

intestinal mucosa, which is not attacked by either the intestinal or the pancreatic enzymes despite the favorable reaction.[122]   Many regard the mucins to be of much importance in preventing autodigestion of the gastric mucosa.   Powdered mucin, prepared from hog's stomach, has been employed in the treatment of peptic ulcer.[123]

Digestion in the Intestine.   There is practically no absorption of foodstuffs from the stomach.   Accordingly, the partly digested food material enters the small intestine where it is subjected to the action of three separate secretions, the pancreatic juice, the intestinal juice or *succus entericus*, and the bile.   The pancreas is a long, irregularly shaped gland lying close to the duodenum.   In the adult, the organ usually weighs about 70–90 grams.   Two secretions are formed by the pancreas, an internal secretion which is concerned with regulating carbohydrate metabolism, and an external secretion which has digestive properties and which is conveyed to the duodenum by one or more ducts.

Mechanism of Pancreatic Secretion.   Pancreatic secretion, although, in part, under the control of the nervous system, does not seem to be influenced by psychic stimuli, as is the case with salivary and gastric secretion.   It has been shown (Pavlov) that the presence of acid chyme in the intestine normally causes active secretion by the pancreas. This excitation Pavlov thought to be due to a reflex stimulation, since the pancreas is under the control of both the vagi and the splanchnic nerves.   However, in 1902, Bayliss and Starling[124] were able to show that, even after nervous communication with the pancreas had been destroyed, secretion could be induced by the introduction of acid into the intestine.   Working on the assumption that the secretory mechanism was under chemical control, Bayliss and Starling prepared an acid extract from the intestinal mucosa, and after neutralizing it, injected it into the circulation of dogs.   This resulted in copious secretion of pancreatic juice.

This chemical mechanism is believed to consist in the transformation of a substance known as *prosecretin,*[125] present in the intestinal mucosa,

---

[122] According to Banting and Gairns, *Am. J. Physiol.*, **94**, 241 (1930), normal serum contains an antitrypsin.   The skin of white rabbits contains a substance which is specifically antagonistic to the oxidase found in the skin of black rabbits.   Kirk and Sumner, *J. Biol. Chem.*, **94**, 21 (1931–2) immunized rabbits to crystalline urease and produced an antibody which definitely inhibited the hydrolysis of urea by urease *in vitro* as well as *in vivo*.   See also S. F. Howell, "Antiurease Formation in the Hen," *Proc. Soc. Exp. Biol. Med.*, **29**, 759 (1931–2).

[123] S. J. Fogelson, *J. Am. Med. Assoc.*, **96**, 673 (1931).

[124] *J. Physiol.*, **28**, 325 (1902).

[125] The evidence for the pre-stage of secretin is inconclusive, although the observations of Still and Keith support this idea (cited by E. U. Still, *Physiol. Rev.*,

into secretin. Secretin is a hormone, or "chemical messenger," which enters the circulation and is carried to the pancreas which it rouses to activity.

Of the many experiments which have confirmed the work of Bayliss and Starling, several reported by Ivy and Farrell[126] are especially convincing. These workers transplanted the tail of the pancreas of dogs, subcutaneously, beneath the mammary gland, and in the same animals made a Thiry fistula of the jejunum. When dilute acid was applied to the Thiry fistula, the pancreatic transplant was stimulated to secrete. As this occurred after ligation of the bile duct and injection of atropine (the latter inhibits gastric secretion), the secretion of the transplant could not have been due to bile or to gastric juice flowing into the duodenum. In another experiment, loops of the jejunum were transplanted subcutaneously in animals with a pancreatic transplant. The original blood and nerve supply to both transplants was then severed. Application of dilute acid to the intestinal transplant provoked copious secretion by the pancreatic transplant, whereas the application of water had no effect.

Bayliss and Starling prepared secretin by scraping the intestinal mucosa (duodenum and jejunum), grinding with sand, then boiling with 0.4 per cent HCl. The mixture was neutralized, acidified with acetic acid, cooled, and filtered. The filtrate contained the pancreatic secretagogue, but also many unknown substances.

Crude secretin preparations have a marked vasodilating effect as well as other physiological properties unrelated to pancreatic stimulation. The problem has therefore been to separate secretin, not only from inert material, but also from other physiologically active substances. Luckhardt, Barlow, and Weaver[127] obtained an active preparation by the following simple method. An excised duodeno-jejunal loop was washed by passing through it a rapid stream of water. One end was then clamped and the loop filled with 0.4 per cent HCl and the other end clamped. After 30 minutes the acid was removed, neutralized, and filtered. The filtrate was an effective secretagogue and practically free from vasodilating substances. This extract has formed the starting-

---

11, 328 [1931]). Intestinal mucosa was frozen (the freezing destroys the cellular continuity of the tissue) and dropped into (a) hot 0.4 per cent HCl and (b) hot 0.9 per cent NaCl. The HCl extract contained twenty times as much activity as the saline extract. When the latter was acidified, its activity increased several times.

[126] *Am. J. Physiol.*, **77**, 474 (1926); **78**, 325 (1926); *J. Am. Med. Assoc.*, **89**, 1030 (1927); A. C. Ivy, J. I. Farrell, and H. C. Lueth, *Am. J. Physiol.*, **82**, 27 (1927).

[127] *Am. J. Physiol.*, **76**, 182 (1926).

point for other investigators who have attempted to prepare more active products, with the ultimate aim of obtaining pure secretin.

Weaver, Luckhardt, and Koch[128] saturated the acid extract with sodium chloride. The flocculent precipitate which formed was dried and preserved. It was soluble in water, and was relatively free from vasodilatins. This salt concentrate has been subjected to further purification and study by Still[129] and Ivy.[130] Working independently and employing somewhat different methods these investigators obtained products of about equal potency. Their preparations are also pure, at least physiologically. Still has shown his product to be free from vasodilator substances, cholecystokinin (see p. 192), oxytocic and hypoglycemic substances. In addition to its effect on the pancreas, secretin seems to have a specific cholagogue action, i.e., it stimulates the hepatic cells to produce bile.

Mellanby[131] has likewise prepared an active secretin. His product has the percentage composition of a protein. Employing in part the same procedures as other investigators, Cunningham[132] has carried the process of purification still further and has recently reported the isolation in crystalline form of a secondary proteose which he believes to be the hormone secretin.

Composition of the Pancreatic Juice. The pancreatic juice is a clear liquid having an alkalinity corresponding to a pH of about 7.5 to 8.0.[133] The specific gravity is approximately 1.007 and subject to slight variation. Water constitutes about 98.7 per cent, the remainder consisting of coagulable protein, organic substances, enzymes, and inorganic compounds.

Recent studies of the inorganic constituents are of particular interest. The concentration of base is fairly constant and is practically equivalent to the concentration in the blood plasma (about 160 millimols per liter). Gamble and McIver[134] have reported the following data for the distribution of the various ions:

[128] *J. Am. Med. Assoc.*, **87**, 640 (1926).

[129] E. U. Still, *Am. J. Physiol.*, **91**, 405 (1930); *Physiol. Rev.*, **11**, 328 (1931); Still and J. La Barre, *Am. J. Physiol.*, **91**, 649 (1930).

[130] Ivy *et al.*, *Am. J. Physiol.*, **95**, 35 (1930).

[131] *J. Physiol.*, **66**, 1 (1928); *Proc. Roy. Soc.* (*London*), **111**, 429 (1932).

[132] *Biochem. J.*, **26**, 1081 (1932).

[153] C. G. Johnston and E. G. Ball (*J. Biol. Chem.*, **86**, 643 [1930]) in a study of pancreatic juice obtained from permanent pancreatic fistulas in dogs observed a range of values between pH 7.16 and 8.04.

[134] *J. Exp. Med.*, **48**, 849 (1928).

TABLE XXVI

Acid-Base Composition of Pancreatic Juice from Dog

Base Cc. 0.1 N per 100 cc.		Acid Cc. 0.1 N per 100 cc.	
Na·	148	Cl'	81
K·	7	HPO$_4$''	1
Ca··	6	HCO$_3$'	79
	161		161

In these analyses the HCO$_3$' was taken to be the difference between the values for total base and for Cl' + HPO$_4$''. Mg, which was not determined, is present in relatively small concentration. Values between 0.3 and 0.7 mM. (millimols) per liter were obtained by Johnston and Ball.

Somewhat higher values for HCO$_3$' were obtained by Gamble and McIver in direct determinations after equilibration of the pancreatic juice with alveolar air.

Similar results were obtained in analyses of human pancreatic juice. The total base amounted to 164 mM. and the Cl content averaged 87 mM. per liter.

Pancreatic Digestion. The rôle of pancreatic juice in protein digestion has been mainly associated with the enzyme *trypsin*, secreted in the inactive form, described as *trypsinogen*. In 1899 Schepovalnikov, a pupil of Pavlov, discovered a substance in the intestinal mucosa, having the properties of an enzyme, which specifically activated trypsinogen. The activator was called *enterokinase*.

A second proteolytic enzyme, known to occur in the pancreatic secretion, is *erepsin*. Though apparently capable of hydrolyzing poly-peptides, its digestive function was not clearly defined until recently.

It has developed from the work of Waldschmit-Leitz[135] and others that the pancreatic juice may contain several proteolytic enzymes. These are said to be separable from one another by means of suitable methods based on selective adsorption. One of the group is a proteinase. It is totally inactive when formed and requires enterokinase for its activation. This enzyme digests native proteins, such as albumin, glob-ulin, and casein. The properties of this proteinase are essentially anal-ogous to those of the classical trypsinogen.

Differing from the trypsin proteinase is the enzyme *protaminase*, the activity of which does not depend on enterokinase. This enzyme,

[135] For a summary of Waldschmidt-Leitz' work and theories the reader is referred to his review in *Physiol. Rev.*, **11**, 358 (1931).

like trypsin, digests protamines, such as clupein, salmin, and scombrin, but is incapable of digesting such proteins as globulin, albumin, and casein.

Four additional proteolytic enzymes are described by Waldschmidt-Leitz under the general term of *peptidases*. They are said to differ in their mode of attacking the peptide molecule and otherwise exhibit considerable specificity of action. These enzymes are: carboxy-polypeptidase, amino-polypeptidase, imino-peptidase, and dipeptidase. Of these, carboxy-polypeptidase occurs partially in an inactive form and requires enterokinase for the development of its full activity.

Waldschmidt-Leitz holds the view that the activation of proteinase and carboxy-polypeptidase by enterokinase depends upon the formation of a dissociable addition product. After the " trypsin " is thus activated (i.e., by the formation of trypsin-kinase), it is possible to separate the components by means of adsorption methods and to obtain again the inactive enzyme.

Crystalline Trypsin. Northrop and Kunitz[136] have isolated from beef pancreas a crystalline protein with constant physical and chemical properties (a criterion of purity), including constant proteolytic activity. This product is obviously a protease; and inasmuch as the protease of pancreas has always been called trypsin, Northrop and Kunitz have designated their crystalline product as such. It is admitted, however, that the crystalline enzyme does not carry the hydrolysis of protein nearly so far as does the trypsin-kinase (proteinase-enterokinase) of Waldschmidt-Leitz. Moreover, the activity of the crystalline trypsin is not increased by the addition of enterokinase. The explanation is offered by Northrop and Kunitz that the raw material for their preparation of the enzyme had been obtained from pancreas which had stood for some time and probably the activation had already occurred.

Crystalline trypsin digests casein, gelatin, edestin, denatured hemoglobin, but not native hemoglobin. It digests peptone prepared by the action of pepsin on casein, edestin, or gelatin. The molecular weight of the enzyme is about 34,000. Its isoelectric point is probably between pH 7.0 and 8.0. The optimum pH for the digestion of casein is from pH 8.0 to 9.0. The enzyme is more stable in an acid than in alkaline solution; the optimum solubility is at pH 1.8.

The work of recent years on the subject of proteolytic enzymes of the pancreas has shown the problem to be somewhat more complex than was formerly supposed. Until further progress has been made it will not be possible to formulate precisely the chemical, including the diges-

[136] *J. Gen. Physiol.*, **16**, 267, 295, 313, 323, 339 (1932), compare I. S. Kleiner, and H. Tauber, *J. Biol. Chem.*, **104**, 367, 271 (1934).

tive, properties of the individual enzymes. Considered as a group, the proteolytic enzymes of the pancreatic juice digest the protein and protein cleavage products which reach the intestine, through successive stages to relatively simple polypeptides, dipeptides, and amino acids. Such peptide linkages as remain unaffected are in turn hydrolyzed by " erepsin " of the intestinal juice.

Pancreatic Lipase, Steapsin. The fat-splitting enzyme of the pancreas, *steapsin*, is relatively inactive in the form in which it is secreted. However, in the presence of certain substances, such as bile, bile salts, egg albumin, calcium salts, and calcium soaps, the enzyme seems to be activated. This type of activation is obviously non-specific. Willstätter[137] and his pupils have shown that these activating agents exert their effect on pancreatic lipase by providing a specially favorable adsorption condition for the contact of the water-soluble enzyme with its insoluble substrate, the fats. This conception is a departure from the view, which until recently has been generally accepted, that the bile salts transform the inactive zymogen, steapsinogen, into steapsin, and that, in addition, the bile salts accelerate fat hydrolysis because of their co-ferment action toward the active steapsin. Glick and King[138] obtained a definite correlation between activating effect and the property of reducing surface tension in a study of the activation of lipase by various organic compounds. They found, moreover, that substances which activated lipase inhibited esterase and *vice versa.*[139]

Amylopsin and Other Enzymes. *Amylopsin* is the starch-splitting enzyme or amylase of the pancreatic juice. It is active in a neutral or slightly alkaline solution. The starchy food reaching the small intestine is digested by pancreatic amylase through the maltose stage. The maltose is hydrolyzed to glucose by the pancreatic and intestinal *maltases.* *Lactase* is not found uniformly in pancreatic tissue of adults, but occurs more consistently in children and other young mammals. This enzyme converts lactose into glucose and galactose. For the most part, the disaccharides are acted on by the intestinal enzymes. However, *invertase* is occasionally found in pancreatic juice. A rennin is likewise present. The pancreatic juice is without influence upon nucleic acids.

---

[137] *Z. physiol. Chem.*, **125**, 93 (1922–23).

[138] *J. Biol. Chem.*, **97**, 675 (1932).

[139] The blood contains an esterase, capable of splitting ethyl butyrate, but no true lipase is present. Following injury to the pancreas, or ligation of the pancreatic duct, the blood acquires fat-splitting properties. This may be interpreted as being due to the appearance either of a lipase or of a lipase-activating substance. A similar, though less pronounced, effect follows liver injury. I. A. Cherry and L. A. Crandall, *Am. J. Physiol.*, **100**, 266 (1932); *Proc. Soc. Exp. Biol. Med.*, **28**, 570 (1931).

The quantity of pancreatic juice is said to vary with the type of food, probably because of an interrelationship with gastric secretion. The secretion of the pancreatic juice begins when the acid chyme enters the duodenum, the quantity secreted being more or less conditioned by the amount of acid admitted. Cessation of pancreatic secretion in pathological conditions, as in obstruction of the pancreatic duct by a tumor, or in experimental occlusion of the pancreatic ducts by ligation, is usually followed by a reduction in the digestion of protein and fat. It has been stated (Yesko)[140] that under such conditions there is a delayed emptying time of the stomach which permits gastric digestion to proceed further than normally. Nevertheless, large amounts of material remain undigested and are found in the feces. This occurs, likewise, in animals after pancreatectomy. Even in these animals, with special care in the selection of the diet, fair nutrition may be maintained by virtue of the digestive powers of the gastric and intestinal secretions.

The Enzymes of the Intestinal Juice. Closely associated with the pancreatic juice in the digestive processes that occur in the intestines is the intestinal juice, or *succus entericus*. This secretion is produced most abundantly in the duodenum and is formed in progressively smaller quantities in the lower portions, the jejunum and the ileum. The juice, which is alkaline in reaction, is produced by two types of glands present in the mucous membrane of the entire small intestine, the so-called Brunner's and Lieberkühn's glands. There are apparently two distinct types of secretions, only one of which is associated with digestion. The other, which is periodic, occurring about every two hours even during starvation, is rich in the glycoprotein, mucin, and poor in enzymes, and contains a number of constituents which are very probably products of excretion. This periodic secretion and the bile form the major portion of the feces eliminated in starvation.

The discharge of food into the intestine results in the rapid secretion of a juice possessing marked digestive properties. Amylase, maltase, invertase, " erepsin," lipase, rennin, the nucleinases and nucleotidases, and possibly lactase are found in the intestinal juice and intestinal mucosa. The nucleosidases, which act on purine nucleosides, are found only in the intestinal mucosa. A peptic enzyme, active in acid solution, has been found to be produced by Brunner's glands. The function of this enzyme in intestinal digestion is probably insignificant. There are, in addition, a number of less well-defined enzymes, including emulsin, which is capable of hydrolyzing β-glucoside linkages. Enterokinase, the enzyme which activates trypsin, is an important constituent of the intestinal mucosa.

[140] *Am. J. Physiol.*, **86**, 483 (1928).

The digestive properties of intestinal " erepsin," discovered by Cohnheim[141] in 1901, are of especial importance. It will be recalled that the pancreatic enzymes fail to act on certain peptide linkages. In tryptic digestion, the unhydrolyzed portion may be equivalent to as much as 10–20 per cent of the total protein nitrogen. This fraction constitutes the so-called resistant group of polypeptides. Erepsin is capable of completing protein digestion by cleaving these resistant polypeptides. Erepsin is said to hydrolyze, in addition, peptones, casein, fibrin, the protamins, and the histones, but is not capable of acting on native proteins such as the albumins, globulins, and muscle proteins.

Waldschmidt-Leitz, Balls, and Graser[142] have reported that the so-called erepsin of the animal intestinal tract and of other tissues is not a single enzyme, but a mixture of at least two independently acting enzymes, a polypeptidase and a dipeptidase. The former splits tri-, tetra-, penta-, and hexapeptides composed of leucine and glycine residues, and, according to these authors, would, in all probability, split the still higher members of these series.

Somewhat earlier Grassmann[143] showed that erepsin of yeast could be separated into two fractions, a dipeptidase and polypeptidase.

Cajori[144] has recently studied the digestive properties of intestinal juice from Thiry loops of the jejunum and ileum. He found the enzyme activity from jejunal loops much greater than from the ileal loops. Starch disappeared from the intestinal loops at a rate commensurate with the concentration of the amylase content of the juice, but the amount of peptone that was apparently hydrolyzed was much greater than could be accounted for on the basis of the " ereptic " activity of the juice. Sucrose and lactose were also absorbed more rapidly than was to be expected from the activities of invertase and lactase. When intestinal secretion was augmented as a result of histamine injections, there was no corresponding increase in enzymes. Lactase was encountered only once, the remaining samples being devoid of this enzyme. Although there have been occasional reports of the presence of lactase in intestinal juice, its occurrence in this fluid is not generally conceded.

The Bile. The bile is continually formed by the liver cells and, between periods of digestion, is stored in the gall-bladder. As it reaches the intestine, it is composed not only of the secretions of the liver cells, but likewise of the mucosa of the gall-bladder and the biliary passages. The quantity of bile secreted is subject to great variation, and

[141] Z. physiol. Chem., 33, 451 (1901).

[142] Ber., 62, 956 (1929); Am. J. Physiol., 90, 549 (1929). See also reviews by Waldschmidt-Leitz, "Annual Review of Biochemistry," Stanford University Press, 1932, p. 69; Physiol. Rev., 11, 358 (1931).

[143] Z. physiol. Chem., 167, 202 (1927).

[144] Am. J. Physiol., 104, 659 (1933).

accurate determinations are not available. In man, the secretion for twenty-four hours has been estimated at between 500 and 1200 cc.

Bile obtained from the hepatic duct differs in composition from that found in the gall-bladder, chiefly with regard to the solid constituents, liver bile containing a much lower percentage of total solids. While in the gall-bladder, the bile becomes concentrated by the reabsorption of a certain amount of water. Mucin and possibly other substances are added to the bile, being secreted from the wall of the gall-bladder. Whereas gall-bladder bile is nearly neutral, or even slightly acid, hepatic duct bile is decidedly alkaline.

Bile is usually golden yellow, but may be brownish yellow or olive green in color. It is very bitter to the taste.

The following are analyses of human gall-bladder bile obtained from normal individuals who had been either executed or accidentally killed. The data are in parts per hundred.

TABLE XXVII

	I*	II	III	IV
Water...............................	86.00	85.92	82.27	89.81
Solids...............................	14.00	14.08	17.73	10.19
Bile salts............................	7.22	9.14	10.79	5.65
Mucin and pigments.................	2.66	2.98	2.21	1.45
Cholesterol..........................	0.16	0.26	} 4.73	3.09
Fat.................................	0.32	0.92		
Inorganic substances.................	0.65	0.75	1.08	0.62

* Analysis I and II are those of Frerichs; Analyses III and IV are from the work of v. Gorup-Besanez. These data are taken from Hammarsten-Mandel's " Physiological Chemistry," 1915 edition, p. 437.

The composition of human liver bile (according to Hammarsten) is given below:

TABLE XXVIII

Water...............................	97.48	96.47	97.46
Solids...............................	2.52	3.53	2.54
Mucin and pigments.................	0.53	0.43	0.52
Bile salts............................	0.93	1.82	0.90
Taurocholate........................	0.30	0.21	0.22
Glycocholate........................	0.63	0.16	0.15
Fatty acids from soaps...............	0.12	0.14	0.10
Cholesterol..........................	0.06	0.16	0.15
Lecithin.............................	} 0.02	{ 0.06	0.07
Fat.................................		{ 0.10	0.06
Soluble salts........................	0.81	0.68	0.73
Insoluble salts......................	0.03	0.05	0.02

It has been shown that the content of total base (Na + K + Ca) in hepatic bile is approximately equivalent to,[145] or is somewhat higher[146] than, that of the plasma, i.e., about 170 mM. per liter. The principal anions are chloride, bicarbonate, and bile-acid radicals. These show considerable individual variability in content, but in the aggregate approximate the total concentration of base.

In the gall-bladder, there is reabsorption of water and of the bicarbonate and chloride ions. Indeed, the last may be reduced to an almost negligible quantity. However, the bile salts are not reabsorbed and hence increase in amount. There is likewise an increase in the amount of base, which not infrequently attains a level of over 300 m.eq. Inasmuch as the base is largely in combination as bile salts, which are weakly dissociated, the osmotic pressure of gall-bladder bile is not much different from that of hepatic bile.[147]

There is also a marked increase in calcium and cholesterol. The absorption of chloride and bicarbonate and the non-absorption of calcium, bile pigment and cholesterol from the normal gall-bladder have been demonstrated by Ravdin and associates.[148] In the diseased gall-bladder, on the other hand, the normal relations are not found; substances which are ordinarily reabsorbed remain in the gall-bladder.[149]

The Bile Pigments. The color of bile is due to the presence of a variety of pigments, chief among which is bilirubin, $C_{33}H_{36}N_4O_6$, a substance closely related to porphyrin (p. 239). On oxidation, this yields a green pigment, biliverdin, $C_{33}H_{36}N_4O_8$. The latter, on oxidation, forms a number of compounds, among which is the blue pigment, bilicyanin. Bilicyanin does not occur in normal bile, but is found in gallstones, together with bilirubin and biliverdin, as well as with certain other pigments, choleprasin, bilifuscin, biliprasin and bilihumin. In diarrhea, the feces may have a greenish color due to biliverdin. The brown color of normal feces is due to stercobilin, which is hydrobilirubin.

---

[145] J. L. Gamble and M. A. McIver, *J. Exp. Med.*, **48**, 837 (1928).

[146] I. S., Ravdin, C. G. Johnston, *et al.*, *Am. J. Physiol.*, **100**, 317 (1932).

[147] Gilman and Cowgill (*Am. J. Physiol.*, **104**, 476 [1933]) have determined the osmotic pressure of blood, hepatic bile, pancreatic juice, and lymph collected simultaneously. All of these fluids were found to be practically isotonic. When the osmotic pressure of the blood was temporarily raised or lowered, as by the injection of hypertonic saline, or water, corresponding changes occurred in the bile, pancreatic juice, and lymph. Evidently the secretions of the alimentary tract, though characteristic in composition, are nevertheless in osmotic equilibrium with the circulating fluid.

[148] Ravdin, Johnston, J. H. Austin and C. Riegel, *Am. J. Physiol.*, **99**, 638, 648, 656 (1932); *J. Exp. Med.*, **56**, 1 (1932).

[149] Johnston, Ravdin, Riegel and C. L. Allison, *J. Clin. Investigation*, **12**, 67 (1933).

Another reduction product of bilirubin is urobilin, a pigment found in the urine.

It was formerly believed that the bile pigments were formed exclusively in the liver. It now seems probable, however, that they may be formed in other tissues as well (spleen, bone marrow, lymph glands, etc.), and that the reticulo-endothelial system is principally involved in the process.

Bilirubin is derived mainly from the hemoglobin liberated in the process of red cell destruction. That this is not the only source has been suggested by Whipple and Robscheit-Robbins,[150] who consider muscle hemoglobin (myohemoglobin) as a precursor of bilirubin. Myohemoglobin and red cell hemoglobin are probably identical. It has also been suggested that foods, notably proteins and green vegetables, may provide precursors for bilirubin (Whipple and Hooper).[151] The exogenous origin of bilirubin is not generally accepted.

After reaching the intestine, some of the bilirubin is probably reabsorbed. A portion is reduced to stercobilin and excreted as such in the feces. Another reduction product, urobilinogen, is partly reabsorbed, oxidized to urobilin (and urochrome), and excreted in the urine.

The blood serum of adults contains between 0.1 to 0.5 mg. of bilirubin in 100 cc. of serum. When the concentration is abnormally high the pigment diffuses through the blood capillaries and gives to the skin and mucous surfaces a characteristic yellow color, designated by the term " jaundice." The accumulation of pigment in the blood may result from an obstruction to the bile passages, as for example by a gallstone filling the lumen of the common bile duct or by a tumor obliterating either the common or the hepatic duct. This is the obstructive type of jaundice. Retention of bilirubin may also result from disease or injury of the polygonal cells of the liver and their consequent failure to excrete the pigment. Or the excretion may not keep pace with the excessive production of bile pigment resulting from unusual destruction of the red blood cells. These conditions constitute the so-called nonobstructive and hemolytic types of jaundice.

Bilirubin gives a characteristic color reaction (red-violet) when treated with a mixture of sulfanilic acid, hydrochloric acid, and sodium nitrite. This is the well-known diazo reaction of Ehrlich. It has been adapted by van den Bergh and his associates to the detection of abnormal amounts of bile pigment in the serum, as well as to their quantitative estimation. The addition of a small amount of the diazo reagent to serum may result in the immediate development of a red-violet color,

---

[150] *Am. J. Physiol.*, **78**, 675 (1926).　　[151] *Ibid.*, **40**, 349 (1916).

reaching its maximum intensity in 30 seconds.   This has been described as the *direct reaction* and is indicative, clinically, of the obstructive type of jaundice.

No color may develop, or it may develop very slowly and incompletely, in a serum which after treatment with alcohol responds readily and completely.   This is the *indirect reaction*.   It has been associated clinically with non-obstructive, or hemolytic, jaundice.

Intermediate between the direct and indirect reactions is the *biphasic* reaction.   In this type, the color develops as in the direct reaction immediately or within 30 seconds, but the maximum intensity is reached after a variable period.

What is the underlying cause for the difference in the direct and indirect reactions?   This question has interested many investigators and has stimulated considerable discussion, but no definite explanation has yet been reached.   The more generally accepted theory is that the bilirubin which normally circulates in the blood differs from the bilirubin that has passed through the liver cells in that the former is bound up in some manner with protein or lipids so that the bilirubin is prevented from reacting with the diazo reagent.   After the complex is dissociated by alcohol, it is assumed, the reaction can take place.

Sodium bilirubinate gives a direct van den Bergh reaction.   In an interesting series of experiments, Barron[152] added to serum increasing amounts of this pigment in a solution buffered to pH 8.43.   The serum gave an indirect reaction until the concentration exceeded 12 mg. per 100 cc.   As it increased to 16 mg., the reaction became biphasic.   When the concentration exceeded this amount a direct reaction was obtained. Accordingly Barron suggests that " some constituent of the serum has a tendency to adsorb bilirubin, and this adsorption prevents coupling with the diazonium salt."[153]

The Bile Salts.   Among the constituents of bile are the salts of the bile acids.   Human bile contains glycocholic acid ($C_{26}H_{43}NO_6$) and taurocholic acid ($C_{26}H_{45}NSO_7$).   In addition, glycocholeic acid ($C_{26}H_{43}NO_5$ or $C_{27}H_{45}NO_5$) has been detected in human bile, and, more recently, many new bile acids have been described.   Glycocholeic is present in considerable amount in ox bile.   Taurocholeic acid ($C_{26}H_{45}NSO_6$ or $C_{27}H_{47}NSO_6$) is present in dog bile and ox bile but has not been found in human bile.   Hyo-glycocholic acid ($C_{27}H_{43}NO_5$)

[152] *Medicine,* **10**, 77 (1931).

[153] On the other hand, Griffiths has reported the isolation from gall-bladder bile of a pigment giving the direct van den Bergh reaction, which is distinct from bilirubin.   The formula $C_{32}H_{50}O_{11}N_2$ is tentatively suggested, and the name *cholebilirubin* is proposed.   *Biochem. J.,* **26**, 1155 (1932).

occurs in the bile of pigs and cheno-taurocholic acid ($C_{29}H_{49}NSO_6$) in the bile of geese.

On hydrolysis, glycocholic acid yields cholic acid and glycine, whereas taurocholic acid is converted into cholic acid and taurine (amino-ethyl-sulfonic acid).

$$C_{23}H_{39}O_3 \cdot CO \cdot HN \cdot CH_2 \cdot COOH + H_2O = C_{23}H_{39}O_3 \cdot COOH + CH_2NH_2 \cdot COOH$$

Glycocholic acid   Cholic acid   Glycine

$$C_{23}H_{39}O_3 \cdot CO \cdot HN \cdot CH_2CH_2SO_2 \cdot OH + H_2O$$

Taurocholic acid

$$= C_{23}H_{39}O_3COOH + H_2N \cdot CH_2 \cdot CH_2 \cdot SO_2OH$$

Cholic acid   Taurine

The structural relationship of cholic acid to cholesterol (p. 85) is shown by the following formula (Windaus):[154]

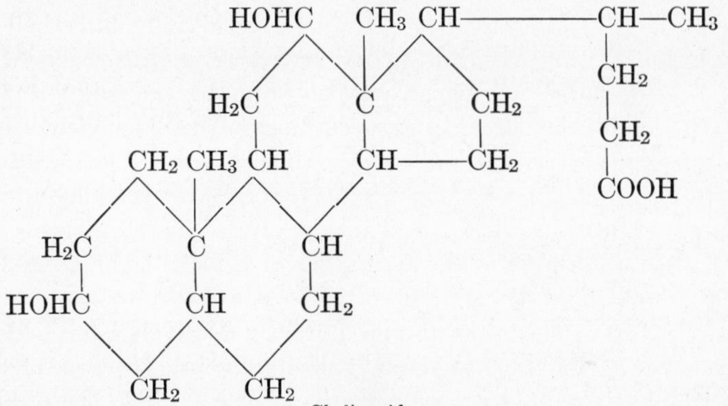

Cholic acid

The bile salts possess the remarkable property of stimulating the secretion of bile; for this reason they have been classified among cholagogues.

It may be recalled at this point that secretin, in addition to its effect in stimulating the pancreas, is believed to exert a specific effect in stimulating bile secretion.

The bile salts diminish the surface tension of the limiting membrane of red corpuscles and most other cells. In sufficient quantity they may exert a solvent effect on the cell lipids, causing the complete disintegration of the cells. To these properties of the bile salts Horrall and Carlson[155] have attributed the toxicity of bile when it leaves its normal channels, the biliary tract and alimentary canal, as in bile peritonitis and obstructive jaundice.

[154] Z. physiol. Chem., **213**, 147 (1932–33).

[155] Am. J. Physiol., **85**, 591 (1928).

Injected intravenously into experimental animals, bile salts cause marked circulatory depression and eventually failure, muscular twitching, spasms, and other symptoms. The neuromuscular junction and the reflex centers of the cord are the structures most susceptible, according to the observations of Ries and Still.[156]

Functions of the Bile. Normal bile flow appears to be necessary for life; yet bile-fistula animals may tolerate the exclusion of bile over considerable periods. Especially is this true when the diet is carefully selected. Whereas fistula dogs kept on a diet of kitchen scraps usually die within two months, they may live in good condition for four to ten months when fed a diet of milk, cooked potatoes, rice, and bread. These animals usually develop bony abnormalities, however, the essential features of the condition being a loss of inorganic salts from the bones, which thus become thin and fragile. This is due largely to failure in the reabsorption of the calcium excreted in the intestinal juice.

Exclusion of the bile leads to serious digestive disturbances. The bile is a good emulsifying agent; it also promotes the solution of fats, fatty acids, and other lipids, and, according to the older view, exerts a direct effect in activating and accelerating lipases. Because of these properties the bile plays a very important rôle in the digestion and absorption of fats. Fat digestion is intimately associated with the digestion of other foodstuffs. The formation of a fatty layer around food particles diminishes the amount of surface exposed to the action of enzymes. As a result, in the absence of bile, a relatively large amount of undigested or partially digested food finds its way into the large intestine, where it is likely to undergo putrefactive changes. The bile ordinarily diminishes putrefaction by aiding in the digestion and absorption of fats as well as by its natural laxative properties. The bile stimulates peristalsis.

In his review of the extra-hepatic functions of the bile, Schmidt[157] has emphasized the importance of the bile as a reservoir for alkali. Together with the pancreatic and intestinal juices, bile neutralizes the hydrochloric acid which enters the intestines from the stomach. Owing to its recirculation, the bile affords a method of bringing alkali to the intestinal tract.

The bile is a channel for the elimination of a variety of excretory products—cholesterol, lecithin, drugs, toxins, bile pigments, copper, iron, and other inorganic substances.

Another function which has been mentioned is the cholagogue effect of the bile acids. Bile taken internally stimulates biliary secretion.

---

[156] *Ibid.*, **91**, 609 (1930).   [157] *Physiol. Rev.*, **7**, 129 (1927).

Functions of the Gall-bladder.   The sphincter of Oddi, a muscular band surrounding the common bile duct near its duodenal end, closes when digestion ceases.   The continuous secretion of bile raises the pressure in the ducts, and, it is believed, after a certain pressure is reached, namely one of about 70 mm. of water, bile begins to flow into the gall-bladder.   Discharge of bile into the duodenum occurs when the pressure in the ducts rises above 100 to 120 mm., which is presumably the pressure maintained during digestion.   Considerable variations in pressure in the bile passages have been observed under different conditions.

Not all animals have a gall-bladder.   The horse, certain deer, and the rat are among the species of animals in which it is absent.

As to the functions of the gall-bladder, there are differences of opinion, as may be judged from various reviews of the subject.[158] The oldest and probably still the most widely accepted view is that the gall-bladder serves as a reservoir during the intervals between digestion, when the bile is not needed.   However, the gall-bladder is not a reservoir in the same sense as the urinary bladder, for the bile which it can hold is only a portion of the total which enters the intestinal tract.   In man the capacity of the gall-bladder is approximately 3 per cent of the total daily bile flow.   Actually, however, the importance of the gall-bladder as a reservoir may be much greater than this figure would indicate, if due account is taken of the fact that the bladder bile is much more concentrated than hepatic bile.

The observation that the gall-bladder is an organ of absorption of bile constituents has led many investigators to consider absorption as its main function, by virtue of which certain valuable materials, secreted in the bile, are restored to the organism.

On the other hand, various substances, such as mucus and toxic agents, are added to the bile during its stay in the gall-bladder.   Accordingly, it has been suggested that the gall-bladder is secretory, and perhaps also excretory, in function.

The view has been advanced that the gall-bladder is concerned in regulating the flow of bile, making possible an intermittent rather than a continuous flow into the intestine.   Finally, there is the plausible theory that, because it is an expansible chamber, the gall-bladder regulates the pressure in the biliary passages.

Both nervous and hormone mechanisms are said to control the flow of bile.   The afferent nerve endings of the mucous membrane of the intestine are thought to be excited by the acid chyme when it enters the duodenum, resulting in a reflex contraction of the gall-bladder and the flow

---

[158] See for example F. C. Mann, *Physiol. Rev.*, **4**, 251 (1924); B. Halpert, *Arch. Surgery*, **19**, 1037 (1929).

of bile into the duodenum.   Many workers have questioned the importance of this factor.

The hormone secretin, which, we have seen, stimulates the pancreas
and intestinal glands, has been thought to act also on the liver cells,
causing increased bile formation.   However, Ivy and Oldberg[159] prepared an extract of the upper intestinal mucosa which when injected
intravenously caused the contraction and evacuation of the gall-bladder.
The view has been advanced by these workers that when acid is injected
into the duodenum something gets into the blood which causes the gall-
bladder (in cats, dogs, and guinea-pigs, but not in rabbits) to contract.
The active principle, presumably a hormone, has been named " cholecystokinin."

The introduction of fat into the duodenum is said to stimulate a
copious flow of bile.

Gallstones.   Biliary concretions, or gallstones, are occasionally
formed in the gall-bladder, usually around some foreign body, injured
epithelial cells, or bacteria.   Although gallstones may contain a preponderance of one constituent, as in the case of cholesterol stones, or of
two constituents, as in the calcium carbonate-bile pigment stones, they
all contain small, although at times only minute, amounts of other substances.   Fats, soaps, fatty acids, lecithin, mucin, copper, zinc, iron, and
manganese are among the organic and inorganic substances which may
be present.   Strictly, therefore, there are no *pure* gallstones, but for
purposes of classification, it is convenient to designate as such certain concretions which consist mainly of one substance.   The cholesterol stones,
for example, may contain as much as 98 per cent of pure cholesterol.
A convenient classification of gallstones has been proposed by Halpert.[160]

One species of whale (*Physeta macrocephalus*) develops biliary concretions containing a substance, ambrine, which closely resembles cholesterol.   These concretions are often found in the excreta of these animals
and are known as ambergris.

Summary of Digestion.   Reactions of living tissues are catalyzed by
certain substances known as enzymes, which behave, in some respects,
like inorganic catalysts.

Most of the reactions of physiological importance are those of
hydrolysis.   To the group of hydrolytic enzymes belong the proteolytic,
lipolytic, and amylolytic enzymes.

The activity of enzymes is influenced by a variety of factors, such as
the concentration of the substrate, the concentration of the enzyme,

---

[159] *Am. J. Physiol.*, **86**, 599 (1928); see also A. C. Ivy, "Factors Concerned in the
Evacuation of the Gall-bladder," *Physiol. Rev.*, **11**, 345 (1932).

[160] *Arch. Pathol.*, **6**, 623 (1928).

the temperature, the reaction of the medium, and the presence of inhibiting or accelerating agents.

It has been shown that the very same enzymes that are capable of bringing about the hydrolysis of a given substance may be capable of accelerating the reaction of synthesis of the substance from the hydrolytic products. Thus protein or protein-like substances have been synthesized with the aid of pepsin and trypsin, and ester formation has been accomplished with the aid of lipases.

The chemical transformations by which the foods are converted into small diffusible particles constitute the process of digestion. These changes are accomplished with the aid of enzymes distributed in the upper portion of the alimentary tract. By this means, the food becomes available for absorption and subsequently for metabolism.

The enzymes concerned in the digestion of starch are the ptyalin of the saliva and the amylopsin of the pancreatic juice. The maltase and lactase of the pancreatic juice, and the maltase, lactase, and invertase of the intestinal juice and intestinal mucosa, are concerned with hydrolysis of the disaccharides. Thus, the carbohydrates of the diet are reduced to monosaccharides.

Protein digestion occurs in the stomach and small intestine. The pepsin of the gastric juice, the trypsin of the pancreatic juice, and the polypeptidases and dipeptidases of the intestinal secretions are primarily concerned with the hydrolysis of proteins. Rennins are found in all three of these secretions. Rennin takes part in the clotting of milk, a process associated with the conversion of casein into paracasein.

The nucleoproteins are partly digested by the proteolytic enzymes of the stomach and pancreas. The nucleic acids that are split off are hydrolyzed by an enzyme, nucleinase, of the intestinal juice. The change consists in the hydrolysis of the tetranucleotide molecule into four mononucleotide molecules. The mononucleotides are further acted upon by an enzyme or a group of enzymes, the nucleotidases. It is not certain whether the pyrimidine nucleotides are acted upon by the intestinal juice. At any rate, the purine nucleotides are broken down to phosphoric acid and nucleosides. The purine nucleosides are hydrolyzed by the nucleosidases which are present in the intestinal mucosa, yielding a sugar and a purine base. These changes will be considered in more detail in a later chapter.

Lipases are found in the secretions of the stomach, pancreas, and intestine. Fat digestion is accomplished almost entirely, however, by the enzymes secreted into the intestine. The bile aids both in the digestion and in the absorption of fat.

TABLE XXIX

THE RÔLE OF ENZYMES IN DIGESTION

Site	Secretion	Reaction	Enzyme	Substrate	Amount of Digestion	Products of Digestion
Mouth	Saliva	Neutral, acid or slightly alkaline ($pH = 5.75$–7.05)	Ptyalin	Starch	Slight	Dextrins, maltose
			Maltase	Maltose	Very slight	Glucose
Stomach	Gastric Juice	Acid	Pepsin	Protein	Incomplete	Proteose, peptones, some polypeptides
			Rennin	Casein	Usually complete	Paracasein
			Lipase	Highly emulsified fat	Very slight	Fatty acids, glycerol
Intestine	Pancreatic Juice	Alkaline	Trypsin	Protein, proteoses, peptones and polypeptides	Nearly complete	Polypeptides, amino acids
			Steapsin	Fat	Nearly complete	Fatty acids, glycerol
			Amylopsin	Starch	Nearly complete	Dextrins, maltose
			Maltase	Maltose	Fairly marked	Glucose
			Lactase	Lactose	Appreciable	Glucose and galactose
			Invertase (?)	Sucrose	(?)	Glucose and fructose
			Rennin 'Erepsin' (polypeptidase and dipeptidase)	Casein		
			'Erepsin' (polypeptidase and dipeptidase)	Certain proteins, casein, protamins, etc., polypeptides, dipeptides	Complete	Amino acids
			Amylase	Starch	Nearly complete	Maltose
Intestine	Intestinal Juice and Intestinal Mucosa	Alkaline	Rennin Enterokinase Lipase	Fat	Nearly complete	Fatty acids, glycerol
			Maltase	Maltose	Complete	Glucose
			Lactase	Lactose	Complete	Glucose galactose
			Invertase	Sucrose	Complete (usually)	Glucose, fructose
			Nucleinases	Nucleic acids	....	Mono-nucleotides
			Nucleotidases	Mono-nucleotides	....	Nucleosides, phosphoric acid
			Nucleosidases in mucosa)	Nucleosides	....	Purine bases, sugar

CHAPTER VII

ABSORPTION AND INTESTINAL RESIDUES

The end-products of digestion diffuse through the wall of the small intestine, pass into the small blood and lymph vessels of the intestinal wall, and are then transported by the blood and lymph to the tissues. The undigested, unabsorbed residue is propelled to the large intestine and finally excreted as feces.

So much of the general plan is known. As to the precise mechanism involved in intestinal absorption, we are very much in the dark. Essentially, the problem is but one phase of the more general problem of cell permeability. Some of the more puzzling questions, pertaining to this subject, which we are as yet unable to answer satisfactorily, are set forth in the excellent review of Jacobs,[1] here quoted:

Beginning with the alimentary system, the problem of cell permeability arises in many forms. Why, for example, does practically no absorption, even of water, occur in the stomach, while taking place with the greatest ease in the small intestine? Why, in the latter, are some substances absorbed much more rapidly than others; for example, $NaCl$ more rapidly than Na_2SO_4, dextrose more rapidly than sucrose, etc.? Why does $NaCl$ readily enter the blood stream from a solution introduced into the gut but pass with difficulty in the reverse direction? Does the wall of the intestine show evidence of a one-sided permeability to water? What are the means by which water is taken up, not merely from hypotonic, but from isotonic and hypertonic solutions as well? What is the mechanism of normal absorption of the different kinds of digested food materials? . . .

Factors in Absorption. Among the more important factors influencing the amount of absorption from various parts of the alimentary canal may be mentioned the following:

1. Character of the lining epithelium.

2. Area of the absorbing surface.

3. Time during which food remains in contact with the absorbing surface in a particular region.

4. Amount of digested material present.

[1] In Cowdry's "General Cytology," 1924 edition, p. 99.

195

Absorption from the Upper Alimentary Tract. The epithelium of the mouth, pharynx, and esophagus is relatively thick. There is but a very slight amount of the carbohydrate digestion and no protein and fat hydrolysis has occurred. Moreover, the food remains in this region a very short time, with the result that no food is absorbed from these areas. Certain drugs, however, are absorbed, owing to their ready penetration and the vascularity of the tongue and the lining of the oral cavity.

There is, likewise, very little absorption from the stomach. While the gastric mucosa secretes large amounts of water, it normally absorbs but little or none. The gastric mucosa is somewhat permeable to alcohol and alcoholic solutions, as well as to very small amounts of sugar, amino acids, and other organic compounds. It is stated that condiments, such as mustard, increase the permeability of the gastric mucosa.

Absorption from the Small Intestine; Function of the Villi. The small intestine is best adapted for absorption, especially the lower part of the duodenum and the jejunum. Superficially, the surface of the small intestine measures about $\frac{1}{2}$ sq. meter, but the mucous coat is so irregular, because of its folds (*plicae circulares*) and its numerous smaller projections or *villi*, that the actual absorbing surface is about 10 sq. meters. Moreover, the food remains in the small intestine for several hours. It usually requires four to six hours, from the time the stomach begins to discharge its contents or acid chyme, before intestinal digestion and absorption are complete. The distribution of the chyme over so large an area as is offered by the small intestine greatly facilitates the absorption of diffusible substances.

The villi are of primary importance in absorption. They are small finger-like projections consisting largely of a framework of reticular tissue containing many leucocytes in its meshes. The lining is simple columnar epithelium, containing many goblet cells. In size, the villi may vary between 0.5 and 0.7 mm. In man, the villi number between four and five millions.

Two channels take part in the removal of material. In the center of each villus is the central lacteal which opens into a plexus of lymphatics lying in the muscularis mucosae. Fluid is forced from the lacteal toward the larger lymphatics by the contraction of muscle fibers which run lengthwise in the villus. The flow of fluid in the reverse direction is prevented by valves present in the deeper plexuses. After reaching the larger lymph vessels, the absorbed material, consisting largely of fat in emulsion, flows to the thoracic duct and enters the blood near the junction of the left subclavian with the jugular vein.

The capillary blood vessels of the villus constitute the second channel of absorption. The material diffusing into the capillaries is carried

to the radicles of the portal vein and subsequently by the portal vein
to the liver.   The circulation of blood in capillaries is very rapid as compared with the sluggish flow of lymph.   This is, no doubt, an important
factor determining the distribution of material between the lymph
stream and the blood.

Carbohydrate Absorption.   Only the monosaccharides are readily
absorbed.   The disaccharides are not found in appreciable amount in
the blood except when excessively large amounts are fed or when they
are injected directly into the circulation.   Under these conditions,
sucrose and lactose behave as foreign substances and are excreted as
such by the kidneys.   Maltose behaves somewhat similarly, although
a certain amount is said to be transformed into glucose by a maltase
present in the blood.   Disaccharides present in intestinal contents
washed free from enzymes are readily absorbed, but as monosaccharides.
Evidently the intestinal mucosa takes part in intracellular hydrolysis of
disaccharides.   No absorption of starch or dextrin occurs under similar
conditions.   The transformation of levulose and galactose to d-glucose
has also been affirmed but is probably not complete when large amounts
of these sugars are taken.   The absorbed sugar is carried by the blood
of the portal vein to the liver where much of it is removed and stored
as glycogen.   Other tissues, particularly muscle, likewise convert glucose into glycogen.

The sugar also enters the lymph circulation, as has been shown by
Hendrix and Sweet,[2] who observed that during the absorption of glucose,
its concentration in the lymph and blood rises to about the same level.
A marked increase in the concentration of sugar in the blood occurs soon
after large amounts have been fed, but in the normal individual the
blood sugar soon returns to normal levels even while absorption still
continues.   This shows that the liver and other tissues are capable of
removing the sugar at a faster rate than it is absorbed.   This capacity is
markedly diminished in diabetes and in conditions in which the liver
is involved.

In a quantitative study of carbohydrate absorption, Cori[3] found
that sugars are removed from the intestine at a rate which is constant
for each sugar and which is independent of the initial concentration of
the sugar in the intestine.   The following is the order of the rates of
absorption of the sugars studied by Cori: galactose > glucose > fructose > mannose > xylose > arabinose (see p. 309).

Fat Absorption.   The possibility of the passage of unsplit fat across
the intestinal wall cannot be overlooked entirely, but, as Bloor[4] has

[2] *J. Biol. Chem.*, **32**, 299 (1917).   [3] *Ibid.*, **66**, 691 (1925).
[4] *Physiol. Rev.*, **2**, 103 (1922).

pointed out, there is every reason to believe that fat is completely hydrolyzed before it passes from the intestine.   This view is opposed to the
doctrine advanced by Munk nearly forty years ago that neutral fat in
fine emulsion is absorbed by the villous epithelium.

Pflüger[5] proposed the theory that fatty acids were not absorbed
as such but as soaps.   This conception was practically unchallenged by
students of the subjects who differed with Munk, inasmuch as it was
generally assumed that the intestinal contents were alkaline.   Actually
the reaction is almost always slightly acid.   Even in the ileum the pH
rarely rises above neutrality (McClendon,[6] Verzar[7]).   Moreover, it has
been shown that soaps dissociate at pH 8, and hence it is impossible
for them to exist in the physiological range of pH 6–8.[8]   The
evidence therefore points strongly to the absorption of fatty acids
as such.

Absorption of fatty acids is greatly facilitated by the presence of
bile.   Whereas the higher fatty acids are quite insoluble in water, they
readily dissolve in an aqueous solution of bile acids.   The property of
the bile acids in bringing the otherwise insoluble fatty acids into solution in water has been described by Neuberg[9] as an example of *hydro-
tropism*.   The effect seems to be due largely to the formation of bile
acid-fatty acid complexes which are characterized by their diffusibility
through membranes and by their stability in slightly acid solution.   The
bile acids, moreover, lower surface tension, thereby increasing the
permeability of the epithelial cells and in this way probably promote
the absorption of other substances as well.

Within the cell the bile acid-fatty acid complex is dissociated and
the fatty acid released.   Resynthesis of neutral fat occurs immediately
and may be demonstrated histologically.   How the fat is transferred
from the lining epithelium into the lacteals is not clearly understood.
According to the view of Heidenhain the fat globules are expelled from
the epithelial cells by the contraction of the cell protoplasm.   Shäfer
considered the leukocytes to play the dominant rôle in the transfer of
the fat to the lacteals.   A third explanation is the hydrolysis-resynthesis
theory of Loevenhart which is based on the reversible action of lipase.
According to this theory, the transfer of fat is made possible because
of its hydrolysis at cell boundaries and its resynthesis within the cell.
A critical examination of these rival theories leaves much to be desired.

[5] *Arch. ges. Physiol. Pharm.*, **80**, 111 (1900); **82**, 303 (1900).
[6] *Am. J. Physiol.*, **38**, 191 (1915).
[7] *Nutr. Abst. and Rev.*, **2**, 441 (1933).
[8] A. Jarisch, *Biochem. Z.*, **134**, 163 (1923).
[9] *Ibid.*, **76**, 107 (1916).

The problem of the transference of fat to the lacteals remains to be solved.

After entering the lacteals, the fat appears as a milk-white emulsion to which the term *chyle* has been applied. The chyle enters the larger lymphatics of the mesentery, passes to the receptaculum chyli, then by way of the left thoracic duct enters the blood at the junction of the left subclavian and jugular veins.

However, only about 60 per cent of the absorbed fat can be accounted for in the chyle. What happens to the remainder has always been somewhat of a mystery. A considerable portion is doubtless absorbed directly by the blood as shown by the higher concentration of fat in portal blood than in the general circulation. Eckstein[10] has studied the question of fat absorption through channels other than the left thoracic duct. While his results are admittedly not altogether consistent, they show, nevertheless, that when all of the thoracic lymph is diverted from the blood stream, an appreciable, though small, augmentation of the fatty-acid content of the blood follows the absorption of neutral fat from the duodenum. It has been suggested, likewise, that a portion of the fat that is unaccounted for may be stored somewhere along the path of transport to the blood, or that it may be catabolized in the tissues before reaching the blood.   In the blood, the fat is transported as neutral fat, fatty acid, and lecithin, and in the form of cholesterol esters. This question will be considered again in relation to the intermediary metabolism of fat.

Absorption of Proteins. The digestion of protein to amino acids serves many purposes. Except for minute amounts, the intestinal epithelium is normally impermeable to protein as well as to its intermediate digestion products—proteoses, peptones, and higher polypeptides.[11] For the most part, only amino acids are absorbed, although the simpler peptides are no doubt also diffusible through the intestinal epithelium. Were it not for this exclusion of nearly everything except the amino acids, much of the protein ingested would be of little use to the animal organism. To synthesize proteins characteristic of itself, the organism must begin with the simplest building-stones possible. The building specifications, so to speak, must be observed most rigidly, a difference in even a single peptide bond being sufficient to alter the architecture and properties of the protein molecule.

[10] *J. Biol. Chem.*, **62**, 737 (1925).

[11] According to Sussman, Davidson, and Walzer (*Arch. Internal Med.*, **42**, 409 [1928]), absorption of detectable amounts of unaltered egg protein from the digestive tract was noted in 85.3 per cent of 34 subjects tested and may, according to these authors, therefore, be considered a normal phenomenon. The absorption of fish protein was likewise noted.

The amino acids are absorbed into the blood capillaries of the villi, the rate of absorption in all probability being somewhat different for individual amino acids (Wilson and Lewis).[12] Several hours after a meal, the amino-acid content of the blood, and especially of the corpuscles, is increased considerably. This does not mean, as is commonly supposed, that the blood is the only channel of amino-acid absorption. Evidence of absorption into the lacteals has been adduced by Hendrix and Sweet,[2] who found the amino nitrogen of the chyle to increase considerably during absorption, becoming much greater in concentration than in the blood of the systemic circulation.

Not only would the absorption of proteins, proteoses, and peptones as such prove useless to the animal organism, but their entrance into the blood is usually attended by a severe form of intoxication, termed "shock." Proteins differ in their toxicity and in the manner in which they act. This effect is especially pronounced in the case of the proteoses and peptones and has been attributed to a variety of constituents which may be supposed to arise during the hydrolysis of protein. It has been suggested that either histamine or substances related to it may be the fundamental cause of peptone shock.

Proteins, therefore, are foods when absorbed in the usual way as amino acids, and poisons when introduced directly into the blood. One of the most violent poisons known is ricin, the protein of the castor bean. The injection of a protein that is foreign to the tissues of an animal results in the excretion of most of it in the urine. If the injection is repeated a few days later, no ill effects ensue. Continued injection of small amounts of a given protein at short intervals establishes an immunity for that protein, due, it is believed, to the formation of a precipitin, in the presence of which the foreign protein is precipitated. If, however, the second injection is administered several weeks after the first, severe shock is induced. This phenomenon is termed *anaphylaxis* and has among its symptoms a marked fall in blood pressure and a reduction in the coagulability of the blood. According to some investigators anaphylactic shock and peptone shock are essentially the same, the former being due to the development in the sensitized animal of an enzyme capable of converting the foreign protein in question into proteoses and peptones. "Serum-sickness" frequently occurs in individuals sensitized against horse-serum proteins, and develops after the injection of antitoxins, such as diphtheria antitoxin. Under these conditions typical anaphylactic shock may occur and may terminate fatally.

[12] *J. Biol. Chem.*, **84**, 511 (1929).

Idiosyncrasies toward food proteins are likewise known. Certain individuals are unable to tolerate egg or milk proteins. Others, after eating strawberries or sea food, develop skin eruptions, asthma, and other anaphylactic reactions. These idiosyncrasies are attributed to the absorption of native or unchanged proteins found in these foods. Exceedingly small amounts (less than one milligram) are frequently sufficient to produce typical intoxications.

Occasionally, therefore, unchanged protein may be absorbed from the intestine. When this happens, the protein behaves as a foreign substance, or, where the individual has been previously sensitized to that protein, it behaves as a poison. Ordinarily, however, protein is absorbed almost entirely in the form of amino acids.

Mechanism of Intestinal Absorption. In the present state of our knowledge, we cannot speak with assurance concerning the forces involved in the absorptive process. No doubt, diffusion or osmotic forces play an important part, but other factors are likewise involved.

Only when the intestinal epithelium is injured, as in poisoning with sodium fluoride, is it possible to demonstrate a definite relationship between osmotic forces and absorption. Dead intestinal epithelium behaves in many respects like an artificial gelatin membrane. Neither exhibit the characteristics of selective absorption shown by the living intestinal wall.

Cohnheim[13] studied the interchange of substances between the intestine and the circulating fluid in dead animals by pumping through the blood vessels a solution of sodium chloride (0.94 per cent). A sugar solution was placed in an isolated loop of the intestine, with the result that interchange of material occurred in both directions, sugar passing into the circulating fluid and sodium chloride into the intestine. There was no diminution in the volume of the intestinal contents. These observations have led many to the conclusion that absorption is due to some specific activity of the living epithelium.

The absorption of amino acids, glucose, sodium chloride, and similar substances from hypertonic solutions is easy to understand, but their absorption from isotonic or hypotonic solutions has always been somewhat of a puzzle. Why does absorption continue under these circumstances? It has been surmised that water is absorbed from isotonic or hypotonic solutions until the concentration in the intestinal contents again attains hypertonicity, when absorption is again possible, this process presumably continuing until all of the solute is absorbed.

Starling[14] advanced the idea that the absorption of fluid from the

[13] Z. Biol., **37**, 443 (1899).
[14] E. H. Starling, "Fluids of the Body," London, 1909, p. 49; cited by Magee.[16]

intestines may be explained on the basis of the colloid osmotic pressure of the blood or lymph of the villi. This conception anticipated by many years the later deductions based on the theory of membrane equilibria developed by Donnan. Starling's conception has received considerable support from the recent work of Wells,[15] which indicates that the absorbing force of the intestine is proportional to and corresponds with the osmotic pressure exerted by the colloids of the lacteal lymph. The colloid osmotic effect is due to protein derived from the plasma. The presence of protein in the lymph, according to Wells, causes an inward transfer of water, a process which apparently may continue indefinitely because of the rapid transfer of the water to other tissues and the organs of excretion (kidney, lung, skin).

In a recent review of the subject, Magee[16] has considered the various factors (permeability, temperature, concentration of solute, diffusibility of the solute) which he believes should influence the rate and direction of the transfer of the solute through the intestinal wall, on the assumption that the rôle of the epithelial membrane in absorption is purely passive. In summarizing the evidence he states that the majority of the experimental results cannot be explained by known physical laws and that "the conclusion may therefore be drawn that the phenomena of absorption are due partly to some special property of the epithelial cells."

Formation of Feces. The intestinal contents, upon reaching the ileocaecal valve, are not like feces in appearance and composition. They are semi-fluid in consistency, and frequently acid in reaction, whereas the feces are usually alkaline. At this stage the intestinal contents consist largely of undigested food remnants, the remains of the digestive and intestinal secretions, and cellular elements, including cell débris from the alimentary tract. The transformation of this material into feces occurs in the large intestine where the food residues remain for one or more days. Here, certain substances, especially water, are partly reabsorbed.

The character of the feces depends only partly on the food eaten. Thus, on a diet consisting exclusively of rice, the feces may have nearly the same composition as on an exclusively meat diet. The two foods, which differ in composition, are presumably almost completely digested and the feces are derived largely from the secretions of the alimentary tract. In a starving animal, the feces are diminished in amount, but the

---

[15] *Am. J. Physiol.*, **99**, 209 (1931–32); **101**, 421, 434 (1932).

[16] *Physiol. Rev.*, **10**, 473 (1930). An earlier review of the literature is that of S. Goldschmidt, *ibid.*, **1**, 421 (1921).

composition may be the same as in a normally fed animal. The feces are bulky when the food contains much indigestible material, like cellulose. Normally, the color is dark brown, but when much fat is present the stool acquires a characteristic lighter color. The composition of feces is about 60–70 per cent water, 5–10 per cent nitrogen, 10–20 per cent fatty material, and 10–20 per cent ash. Human feces are approximately neutral in reaction. According to Robinson[17] the normal fecal reaction of healthy men lies between pH 7.0–7.5.

Feces may contain the following food residues: cellulose, fruit seeds and skins (also made up largely of cellulose), muscle fibers, shreds of connective tissue, starch, fat, fatty acids, and soap. Among the remains of bile and intestinal secretions are to be found bile acids, bile pigments, cholesterol, coprosterol, mucin, and a variety of inorganic constituents, especially iron. Cellular elements derived from the alimentary tract are likewise present. One-fourth or more of the feces consists of bacteria, the number excreted per day having been estimated to vary between 50 and 500 billions.[18]

The fecal excretion of fat has been the subject of careful study. Hill and Bloor[19] and Sperry and Bloor[20] have shown that the amount and composition of fecal fat are to a large extent independent of the fat in the diet. In an experiment in which the effect of diet was studied, the amount of fecal fat on a fat-free diet was 1.76 grams, having an iodine number of 32.7. When this diet was supplemented with 50 grams of coconut oil, which has an iodine number of 8.8, the fat excretion was 2.50 grams, and its iodine number was 24.8. When 50 grams of olive oil (iodine number, 88.2) was added to the diet, the feces contained 2.24 grams of fat, having an iodine number of 44.6.

Fecal fat differs in composition from food fat, but resembles closely the lipids of the blood. Approximately one-third of the fecal lipids is unsaponifiable.[21] The endogenous fecal lipids do not originate, as might be suspected, from bacterial synthesis, desquamated epithelium, or other cellular débris of the intestines, but are for the most part secreted into the small intestine. A portion of this secretion is reab-

[17] J. Biol. Chem., **52**, 445 (1922).

[18] For an excellent account of the nature and composition of the feces, the student is referred to Chap. II of Lusk's "Science of Nutrition," 4th edition, Saunders, Philadelphia (1928).

[19] J. Biol. Chem., **53**, 171 (1922).

[20] Ibid., **60**, 261 (1924).

[21] Ibid., **68**, 357 (1926); **71**, 351 (1926–27); **81**, 299 (1929); **96**, 759 (1932); Sperry and R. W. Angevine, ibid., **96**, 769 (1932).

sorbed, apparently from the large intestine, but this is not certain. The unabsorbed residue, together with the relatively small amount secreted in the colon, make up the endogenous lipids found in the feces.

Products of Intestinal Putrefaction.[22]   The contents of the large intestine undergo bacterial or putrefactive changes. Concerning bacterial action on fat, little can be said except that it results in the formation of fatty acids and glycerol. From lecithin may be formed choline, neurine, muscarine, and related compounds.

$$
\begin{array}{ccc}
CH_3 \quad CH_2{-}CH_2OH & CH_3 \quad CH{=}CH_2 & CH_3 \quad CH_2CHO \\
CH_3{-}N & CH_3{-}N & CH_3{-}N \\
CH_3 \quad OH & CH_3 \quad OH & CH_3 \quad OH \\
\text{Choline} & \text{Neurine} & \text{Muscarine}
\end{array}
$$

The carbohydrates yield a variety of substances, including oxalic acid, the lower fatty acids[23] and their derivatives—formic, acetic, propionic, lactic, butyric, oxybutyric, and succinic—acetone, and the gases carbon dioxide, methane, and hydrogen. If present in sufficient amount, some of the products of carbohydrate fermentation may act as irritants to the intestinal tract and cause diarrhea.

Bacterial enzymes acting on protein yield proteoses, peptones, amino acids, ammonia, and hydrogen sulfide. From the aromatic amino acids are formed indole, skatole, phenol, cresol, and tyramine. Cadaverine, putrescine, and ethylidene-diamine are among the toxic amines, or ptomaines, formed from amino acids in putrefaction. Ethyl mercaptan (C_2H_5SH), methyl mercaptan (CH_3SH), and hydrogen sulfide owe their origin to the putrefaction of cystine.

With regard to the formation of these substances, much remains to be learned, but sufficient is known to enable us to consider briefly the chemistry of some of the reactions involved. Among the more important of these is one involving the removal of a carboxyl group (decarboxylation), presumably due to an enzyme, carboxylase, present in the bacteria. Another reaction consists in the splitting off of an amino group by deaminization. Reduction, due to a reductase, and reactions of hydrolysis as well as of oxidation are also believed to occur.

---

[22] For a comprehensive survey of the subject, the student is referred to Marjory Stephenson's monograph "Bacterial Metabolism," Longmans, Green & Co., London, 1930.

[23] Grove, Olmsted and Koenig, *J. Biol. Chem.*, **85**, 127 (1929–30).

The following substances result from bacterial action on tyrosine:

$$
\begin{array}{ccc}
\text{OH} & \text{OH} & \text{OH} \\
| & | & | \\
\text{CH}_2 & \text{CH}_2 & \text{CH}_3 \\
| & | & \text{Cresol} \\
\text{CH}_2 & \text{COOH} & \\
| & \text{Para-oxyphenyl} & \\
\text{COOH} & \text{acetic acid} & \\
\text{Para-oxyphenyl} & & \\
\text{propionic acid} & &
\end{array}
$$

OH / CH₂ | CHNH₂ | COOH — Tyrosine

Para-oxyphenyl propionic acid → Para-oxyphenyl acetic acid → Cresol → Phenol

$$
\begin{array}{ccc}
\text{OH} & \text{OH} & \text{OH} \\
| & | & | \\
\text{CH}_2 & \text{CH}_3 & \text{Phenol} \\
| & + & \\
\text{CH}_2\text{NH}_2 & \text{CH}_3\text{NH}_2 & \\
\text{Tyramine} & &
\end{array}
$$

Tyramine is formed in the putrefaction of cheese and is known to be a constituent of certain cheeses—Camembert, Roquefort, Emmenthal, etc.[24] It is also a constituent of ergot. It has likewise been isolated from intestinal contents. Tyramine is a pressor base (raises blood pressure) but is weaker in its action than epinephrin (p. 487), to which it is closely related chemically. Tyramine is detoxified in the liver, being at least partly converted into hydroxyphenylacetic acid.

Hanke and Koessler[25] in an examination of 26 stools found 17 to contain a microorganism capable of decarboxylating tyrosine.

Cresol, phenol, and probably phenylacetic acid, after absorption, are partly conjugated with sulfuric acid and glycuronic acid (with the latter especially in herbivorous animals). Folin and Denis,[26] as well as Dubin,[27] have shown that 30–90 per cent of the phenols (this term is here applied to phenol and its derivatives) are excreted in the urine in the free form, the total amount eliminated usually varying between 200–400 mm. per day. Quantitatively, paracresol is most important. The process of conjugation with sulfuric acid, which takes place in the liver primarily but in other tissues as well, is a mechanism which

[24] F. P. Underhill, "The Physiology of the Amino Acids," 1915, Yale Univ. Press, New Haven, p. 42.

[25] J. Biol. Chem., **59**, 835 (1924).

[26] J. Biol. Chem., **22**, 309 (1915).

[27] Ibid., **26**, 69 (1916); **31**, 255 (1917).

the organism employs in detoxifying relatively toxic substances.[28]   The fate of foreign organic compounds in the animal organism has been discussed by Sherwin[29] and will be referred to again.

Indole and Skatole.   The disagreeable and characteristic odor of feces is said to be due partly to two compounds, indole and skatole.   These are formed from tryptophane, as indicated by the following formulas:

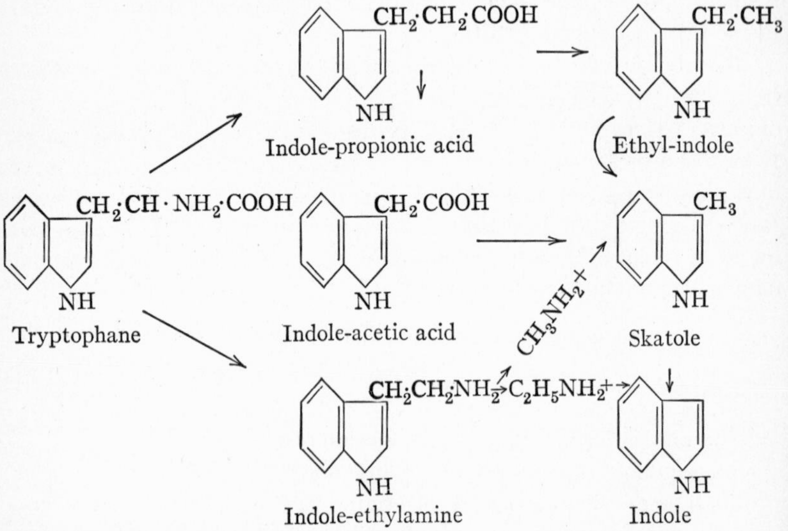

$CH_2 \cdot CH_2 COOH$

Indole-propionic acid

$CH_2 \cdot CH_3$

Ethyl-indole

$CH_2 \cdot CH \cdot NH_2 \cdot COOH$

Tryptophane

$CH_2 \cdot COOH$

Indole-acetic acid

CH_3

Skatole

$CH_2 CH_2 NH_2^+ \rightarrow C_2H_5NH_2^+ \rightarrow$

Indole-ethylamine

Indole

A portion of the indole is oxidized either before or after absorption and is subsequently conjugated to form the potassium salt of indoxyl-sulfuric acid (indican), in which form it is excreted in the urine.   The daily elimination of indican varies considerably, but is usually between 12 and 20 mg.   The indole content of the feces averages about 50–60 mg. on an ordinary diet.   In carcinoma of the liver, large amounts of indican appear in the urine.

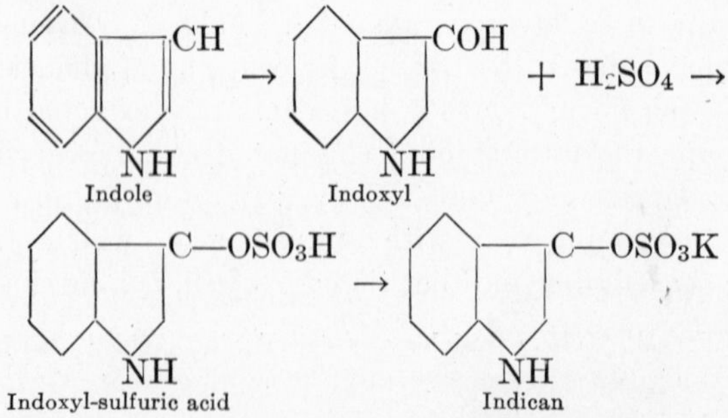

CH

Indole

COH

Indoxyl

$+ \ H_2SO_4 \ \rightarrow$

$C-OSO_3H$

Indoxyl-sulfuric acid

$C-OSO_3K$

Indican

[28] K. F. Pelkan and G. H. Whipple, *ibid.*, **50**, 513 (1922).

[29] *Physiol. Rev.*, **2**, 238 (1922); see also A. M. Ambrose and C. P. Sherwin, *Ann., Rev. Biochem.*, **2**, 377 (1933).

As much as 1 gram of indole may be administered to a dog without producing unusual symptoms. Larger amounts (2 grams) produce diarrhea and hematuria. The quantities normally absorbed from the intestine are probably insufficient to produce any effect in man. Very large amounts, however, are said to produce torpor, feeble heart action, and lower temperature. Skatole behaves very much like indole but is somewhat less toxic. The amount of this substance normally excreted in the urine is less than 10 mg.

Histamine. Histamine (β-iminazolyl-ethylamine) was first isolated from ergot by Barger and Dale.[30] Its formation through the action of putrefactive bacteria on histidine was first described by Ackermann.[31] It has been further shown by other investigators that a bacillus is present in the intestinal contents which is capable of decarboxylating histidine. Indeed, Hanke and Koessler[32] in an examination of 26 human stools found 16 to contain such a microorganism. The formation of histamine may be represented as follows:

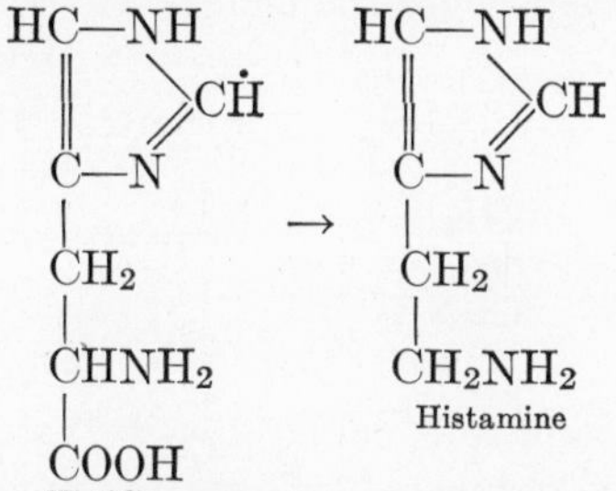

Histamine has been isolated from intestinal contents, as well as from loops of the large and small intestine. Human feces contain appreciable amounts. Hanke and Koessler found 500 to 600 grams of feces from normal individuals to yield 6 to 20 mg. of histamine.

In variable amounts the presence of histamine has been reported in different organs (lung, muscle, heart, spleen, and intestinal and gastric mucosa). Its identity with the gastric hormone has been considered elsewhere (p. 167).

When injected intravenously, it is toxic, even in small amounts, producing, particularly in anesthetized animals, a condition of shock, simulating traumatic or surgical shock. However, when given by mouth, it is relatively inert, large amounts being tolerated. The histamine disappears. Its detoxication by the animal organism has aroused considerable interest. Unlike tyramine it is not destroyed by

[30] *J. Physiol.*, **40** (Proc.) xxxviii (1910); **41**, 499 (1911).
[31] *Z. physiol. Chem.*, **65**, 504 (1910).
[32] *J. Biol. Chem.*, **59**, 879, 889 (1924).

perfusion through the liver. It is, however, rendered physiologically inert by incubation with minced beef, lung, or kidney. The effect is due to an enzyme, histaminase, described by Best.[33] This is present in abundance, not only in lung and kidney, but also in intestinal mucosa, spleen, muscle, adrenals, and blood. Little, if any, is present in the liver and gastric mucosa. Best and McHenry have suggested that the histaminase of intestinal mucosa may serve as a protection against the small amounts which normally might be formed. It is therefore doubtful that histamine formed in intestinal putrefaction can be a factor in systemic intoxications.

Cadaverine and Putrescine. Ptomaines is the term that has been applied to the basic substances derived from putrefying flesh. As we have seen in the case of tyramine and histamine they are derived from amino acids by the removal of a carboxyl group.

Of the more familiar ptomaines, one is cadaverine, a diamine (penta-methylene-diamine), formed from lysine and first discovered in putrefying human cadavers, whence the name. Its formation may be represented as follows:

$$
\begin{array}{ccc}
\mathrm{CH_2NH_2} & & \mathrm{CH_2NH_2} \\
| & & | \\
\mathrm{(CH_2)_3} & \longrightarrow & \mathrm{(CH_2)_3} \\
| & & | \\
\mathrm{CHNH_2} & & \mathrm{CH_2NH_2} \\
| & & + \\
\mathrm{COOH} & & \mathrm{CO_2}
\end{array}
$$

Lysine   Cadaverine

A closely related substance is putrescine (tetramethylene-diamine) derived from arginine.

$$
\begin{array}{cccc}
 & \mathrm{NH_2} \diagup OH \diagdown & \mathrm{C=O} & \\
\mathrm{HN=C} & & \mathrm{NH_2} & \\
 & \diagdown \mathrm{NH} & \mathrm{Urea} & \\
 & | & \mathrm{NH_2} & \mathrm{CH_2NH_2} \\
 & \mathrm{(CH_2)_3} & | & | \\
 & | \longrightarrow & \mathrm{CH_2} & \mathrm{CH_2} \\
 & \mathrm{CHNH_2} & | & | \\
 & | & \mathrm{(CH_2)_2} \longrightarrow & \mathrm{CH_2} \\
 & \mathrm{COOH} & | & | \\
 & \mathrm{Arginine} & \mathrm{CHNH_2} & \mathrm{CH_2NH_2} \\
 & & | & \mathrm{Putrescine} \\
 & & \mathrm{COOH} & \\
 & & \mathrm{Ornithine} & \\
\end{array}
$$

[33] *J. Physiol.*, **67**, 256 (1929); Best and E. W. McHenry, *ibid.*, **70**, 349 (1930); *Physiol. Rev.*, **11**, 371 (1931).

Another product formed in the putrefaction of arginine is agmatine,

$$NH_2—C—NH—CH_2CH_2CH_2CH_2NH_2.$$
$$\underset{NH}{||}$$

Cadaverine and putrescine have been found in the urine in cholera. *Mercaptans.* Cystine undergoes the following changes when acted upon by bacteria:

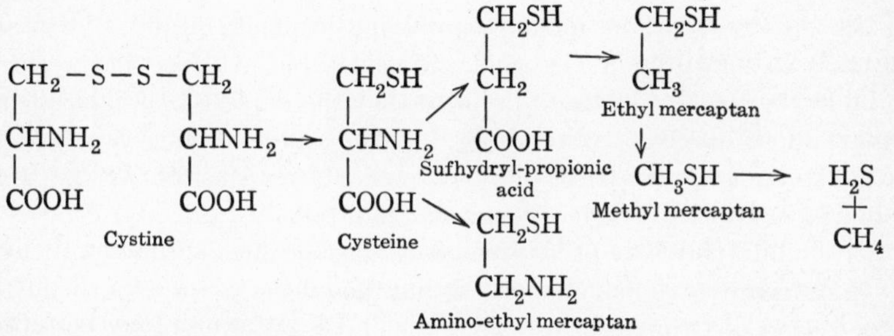

It is a popular belief that the absorption of products of intestinal putrefaction is responsible for many ills, as well as for the symptoms associated with constipation—headache, malaise, irritability, nausea, insomnia, drowsiness, etc. Actually, there is very little experimental evidence to support this view, as has been pointed out by Alvarez in reviewing the literature on the subject of intestinal auto-intoxication. Very little absorption takes place from the colon, especially when the feces are hard. If auto-intoxication were due to the absorption of toxic substances from the colon it would be more frequent in diarrhea than otherwise. Alvarez[34] ascribes the symptoms of constipation to the mere plugging of the lower end of the alimentary canal. A plug of cotton introduced into the rectum produces the same effect. He has also observed that individuals with jejunal fistulas become sleepy when the intestine is made to contract on a small balloon inserted through the fistula. Muscular activity and nervous stimuli arising in the digestive tract are probably important factors in producing the symptoms ordinarily associated with constipation.

Intestinal Obstruction. Occlusion of the intestine results in severe toxic symptoms, anorexia, weakness, profound depression, oliguria, continuous vomiting, sometimes muscular twitching and tetany, etc. The rapid onset, severity, and usually fatal outcome have led to two views as to the cause of the toxemia, one being that it is due to a toxic agent formed above the point of obstruction and the other that the

[34] *Physiol. Rev.*, **4**, 352 (1924); see also W. C. Alvarez, "The Mechanics of the Digestive Tract," 2d edition, Hoeber, New York, 1928.

noxious substance has its origin in the mucosa of the intestine or stomach. However, a closer study of the problem has revealed totally different factors to which the symptoms may be attributed.   In the first place, it seems that the intestinal contents in obstruction are not more toxic than normal intestinal contents.   Then it has been observed that in pyloric obstruction, or in obstruction of the duodenum or upper ileum, there are definite chemical changes in the blood.   These include a striking fall in the concentration of chloride, a marked increase in the alkali reserve (carbon dioxide-combining capacity), and a terminal increase in non-protein nitrogen.   Considerable evidence has accumulated in the last few years to indicate that the depletion of chloride and water, due to the copious vomiting, and the accompanying derangement of the water and acid-base balance are chiefly responsible for the symptoms in acute intestinal obstruction and possibly are also factors in other conditions where excessive loss of gastric juice occurs.

A crucial experiment demonstrating the effects of total loss of gastric juice is that of Dragstedt and Ellis.[35]   These workers isolated the stomach of dogs by section at the cardia and pylorus.   The duodenum was anastomosed to the lower end of the esophagus.   The cardiac end of the isolated stomach was closed and the pyloric end brought to the surface as a fistula.   Precautions were taken not to interfere with the vagus nerves or blood vessels supplying the isolated stomach.   The total loss of the gastric secretion which was drained away through the fistula resulted in symptoms of weakness, anorexia, loss of weight (chiefly because of anhydremia), oliguria, and profound depression.   Death occurred in five to eight days.   Accompanying these symptoms and proportionate to their intensity, the following changes were noted in the blood: decrease in concentration of chloride, the values ranging between 340–108 mg. per 100 cc., an increase of the CO_2-combining capacity, reaching a value as high as 140 cc., an increase in pH (7.3–7.75), and a terminal increase in non-protein nitrogen.   The changes in the blood chemistry thus resulting from the loss of gastric juice were therefore similar to those occurring in pyloric or intestinal obstruction.   It was observed, moreover, that the gastric glands continued to secrete a juice of high acidity even when the blood chloride was reduced to less than one-third of its normal concentration.   Dragstedt was able to relieve the symptoms, restore the blood constituents toward the normal, and prolong the lives of the animals (in one case to over 76 days) simply by intravenous injection of Ringer's solution.   It was therefore concluded that although food deprivation was one of the main effects of this experimental procedure,

[35] *Am. J. Physiol.*, **90**, 331 (1929); **93**, 407 (1930).

the symptoms and fatal outcome could be attributed to hypochloremia, alkalosis, and dehydration.

Scott, Holinger, and Ivy[36] have described an experiment on a dog having a pouch of the stomach and a jejunal fistula. Through the fistula the dog was given an adequate diet and sufficient salt (6 to 10 gm. daily) to maintain the normal level of blood chloride. Despite the complete loss of gastric juice (400 to 600 cc. daily), the animal continued in good health and maintained its normal weight for the period of the experiment (18 weeks).[37]

Loss of Pancreatic Juice. The loss of pancreatic juice leads to as conspicuous effects as does the loss of gastric juice. Dogs with pancreatic fistulas invariably die within a short time (15 to 42 days in Pavlov's experiments;[38] 7 to 8 days in Elman and McCaughan's experiments).[39] Gamble and McIver[40] have definitely associated the symptoms and fatal outcome with the loss of water and electrolytes. Inasmuch as there is a relatively greater loss of basic (chiefly $Na^{\cdot}$) than of acid radicles (chiefly Cl' and HCO'_3), acidosis develops. Thus Dragstedt and associates[41] have observed a reduction in total plasma base from 155 to 130 mM., a decrease in chloride from 101 to 84 mM., a decrease in HCO_3 from 23.0 to 8.3 mM., and a shift in the pH from 7.35 to 6.95. In short, the loss of either gastric or pancreatic juice results in dehydration. In the former case, depletion of the chloride ion predominates; hence alkalosis develops. In the latter case, there is a predominant loss of base; hence there is a shift of the acid-base balance in the blood to the acid side (see p. 265).

The loss of bile by continuous drainage may be expected to produce changes similar to those obtained when pancreatic juice is drained away.

---

[36] *Proc. Soc. Exp. Biol. Med.*, **28**, 569 (1930–31).

[37] The theory that the absorption of a toxin is a factor in the toxemia observed in intestinal obstruction is not supported by the experiments of White and Fender (*Arch. Surgery*, **20**, 897 [1930]). These investigators produced high intestinal absorption in animals and kept them alive by the simple expedient of reinjecting the vomitus below the point of obstruction through a jejunal fistula. See, also H. P. Jenkins, *Proc. Soc. Exp. Biol. Med.*, **28**, 111 (1930–31).

[38] "The Work of the Digestive Glands," translation by Thompson, London, 1902.

[39] *J. Exp. Med.*, **45**, 561 (1927).

[40] *Ibid.*, **48**, 859 (1928).

[41] *Proc. Soc. Exp. Biol. Med.*, **28**, 110 (1930–31).

CHAPTER VIII

THE BLOOD AND LYMPH

The interchange and transport of material in the animal organism are accomplished through the blood, lymph, and tissue fluid. The blood circulates in what is practically a closed system of vessels (the vascular system), and although there is an exchange of material through the endothelium lining the capillaries, the blood itself does not come in direct contact with the cells of the tissues, except in the liver and spleen, where in part the endothelium is non-continuous in some of the blood spaces. It is now believed by many physiologists and anatomists that the lymphatics also constitute a closed system of vessels and that they do not open directly into the tissue spaces as was formerly supposed. In the tissue spaces and bathing the cells is a fluid, the composition of which is supposed to resemble that of the lymph circulating in the lymphatics and which, according to Starling's theory, is derived from the blood by a process of passive filtration. The tissue fluid plays an important rôle in the exchange of material between the blood and tissues. Nutritive substances, including oxygen, brought by the blood pass through it on their way to the tissues, and, in turn, the metabolic products of the cells are carried into the blood and lymph streams through the reabsorption of the tissue fluid.

Functions of the Blood. Among the more important functions of the blood are the following:

1. The blood transports food material and other substances absorbed from the intestine to the tissues.

2. It is concerned with the transportation of oxygen from the lungs to the tissues.

3. The waste products formed in metabolism are carried by the blood to the organs of excretion—kidneys, lungs, intestine, and skin.

4. The blood is the channel for the exchange of products formed in one tissue or organ and used by another. The hormones are transported in the blood.

5. The white corpuscles of the blood constitute a defense mechanism against invading bacteria. Other defenses of the body against toxic

212

agents include antitoxins, agglutinins, precipitins, etc., contained in the blood.

6. The blood takes part in maintaining the temperature of the body at a fairly constant level.

7. It aids in the regulation of the normal reaction, or acid-base balance, of the tissues.

8. Owing to the plasma proteins, it is concerned in the regulation of the water balance of the tissues.

Volume. Various methods have been employed in attempts to determine the total volume of blood in the body. The direct procedure of measuring all the blood that could be removed by bleeding and subsequent extraction of the tissues has been used in experiments on animals and in executed criminals. Another method has been based on the property of carbon-monoxide of reacting with oxyhemoglobin, replacing the oxygen and forming carbon-monoxide hemoglobin. The amount of carbon-monoxide thus combined may be determined quantitatively, and the amount of the gas inhaled being known, the amount of blood may be estimated by appropriate calculations. Dyestuffs, such as vital red, have also been introduced for this purpose. A definite amount of the dye is injected intravenously and after a short interval a specimen of blood is collected and centrifuged, the proportion of cells measured, and the concentration of dye in the plasma determined. On the assumption that no dye is taken up by the cells or escapes from the blood, the blood volume is calculated. Similar in principle to the dye method is the procedure of Lee and Whipple[1] in which a solution of hemoglobin is injected.

Results reported by different workers have been very divergent. The discussion of Fleischer-Hansen[2] calls attention to the technical errors of the exsanguination method. In the other methods the fundamental error is made of assuming that the ratio of cells to plasma is the same in all parts of the body. In consequence, the carbon-monoxide method, though giving a reasonably accurate measure of the body hemoglobin (and volume of red cells) affords no accurate information concerning plasma volume. Likewise, the dye- or hemoglobin-injection methods give at best an accurate measure of the circulating blood plasma only, as shown by Whipple and associates.[3] More dependable information should therefore be obtained, according to these investigators, by a combination of the two methods, a small allowance being made for the volume occupied by the white blood cells.

[1] *Am. J. Physiol.*, **56**, 328 (1921).
[2] *Skand. Arch. Physiol.*, **59**, 243 (1930).
[3] *Am. J. Physiol.*, **56**, 313, 336 (1921).

The quantity of blood in the body is thus estimated to be about 8.8–9.2 per cent, or between one-eleventh and one-twelfth, of the body weight. It is apparently not subject to much fluctuation, physiologically, or otherwise. Dehydration occurs particularly in infancy and childhood, due to water deprivation, diarrhea, or vomiting, and is accompanied by a concentration of the blood and a reduction in its volume. The blood volume is also diminished during severe and rapid hemorrhage and in surgical shock. It is increased in polycythemia vera, in fever, and during pregnancy. The cellular elements of the blood become more concentrated in influenza, following the inhalation of war gases,[4] following severe burns, and in intestinal obstruction. The term anhydremia has been applied to the condition in which the concentration of the blood is greater than normal. For a review of the literature on the subject, the student is referred to the article by W. McKim Marriott.[5]

Formed Elements. The formed elements are the red corpuscles or erythrocytes, the white corpuscles or leukocytes, and the blood platelets. Together these constitute about 40–45 per cent by volume of the whole blood, the remainder being occupied by the plasma. In men, there are normally 5,000,000 red cells per cubic millimeter of blood; the count is somewhat lower in women. Variations occur frequently, especially after exercise or a heavy meal, or at high altitudes. The shape of the mammalian corpuscle is commonly that of a circular, non-nucleated, biconcave disk. The average diameter usually given is 7.7 μ, a value obtained by examining dried preparations of blood and considered by Ponder[6] to be too low. Ponder's own observations, made on red cells in the fresh state, show the human corpuscle to have an average diameter of about 8.8 μ. When circulating in the blood vessels, the red cell does not maintain a fixed shape but changes its form continually, especially in the small capillaries. The red blood corpuscles are continually undergoing destruction, new corpuscles being formed to replace them.[7] The average life of red corpuscles has been estimated to be between three and four months (A. S. Wiener). Preceding destruction, changes in the composition of the cells are believed to occur which render them less resistant. To a large extent, the

[4] F. P. Underhill, "The Lethal War Gases, Physiology and Experimental Treatment," Yale Univ. Press, New Haven, 1920.

[5] *Physiol. Rev.*, **3**, 275 (1923).

[6] "The Erythrocyte and the Action of the Simple Hemolysins," Oliver and Boyd, Edinburgh, 1924, p. 21.

[7] A recent review on the subject of red cell regeneration is that of F. S. Robscheit-Robbins, *Physiol. Rev.*, **9**, 666 (1929).

corpuscles are taken up by the phagocytic cells of the reticulo-endothelial system, such as the Kupffer cells of the liver. In the process of destruction, the lipids of the membrane are dissolved, and the hemoglobin which is liberated is the most important, though probably not the only, source of bilirubin. Formerly the liver was believed to be the only site of red-cell disintegration. This view is no longer generally held, for it seems that the destruction of corpuscles may occur in the blood stream, as well as in other tissues.

During rapid red-cell disintegration and in certain diseases of the blood-forming system various types of nucleated erythrocytes (normoblasts, microblasts, macroblasts, megaloblasts) may appear in the circulation. The presence of reticulocytes (immature red cells showing a reticulum under vital staining) is likewise an indication of marked erythropoesis. Normally less than 0.5 per cent of the red blood cells are reticulocytes.

Hemolysis. Erythrocytes undergo *hemolysis*, or laking, when blood is diluted with water or treated with ether, chloroform, soap, fatty acids, ultraviolet rays, bile acids, snake venom, specific hemolysins, and other substances. Sometimes partial hemolysis is due to the disruption of erythrocytes by purely mechanical influences. When placed in a hypotonic solution, the red corpuscle swells, thus stretching the membrane. If the stretching is sufficient, the membrane bursts. There is some reason to believe that the distended membrane is more permeable than the normal membrane. Under these conditions, the hemoglobin may pass out of the corpuscle into the plasma. However, it does not seem that the red cell undergoes complete destruction at once, for there remain behind the so-called " ghosts." From their appearance, it seems possible that the " ghosts," are made up of the stroma, or network, of the original corpuscles. The disintegration of the stroma, or *stromatolysis*, probably follows hemolysis when red corpuscles are subjected to the action of hemolytic agents.

Clinical application has been made of the resistance of erythrocytes to hypotonic solutions (fragility test). In concentrations higher than 0.42–0.44 per cent sodium chloride, human erythrocytes resist hemolysis at ordinary temperatures for as long as two hours. Beginning hemolysis is shown at about 0.40 per cent, but in more hypotonic solutions (0.32–0.36) hemolysis is carried to completion. Diminished resistance (increased fragility) is observed in hemolytic jaundice. Increased resistance seems to be a characteristic of the red blood cells in various forms of anemia.

The *leukocytes*, of which there are several forms (granulocytes— neutrophile, eosinophile, basophile; lymphocytes and monocytes) usually number between 5000 and 10,000. Wide fluctuations occur physiologically, but when the subject is at complete rest, the white blood cell count tends to be at a minimum and relatively steady. Food intake is thought to produce an increase (digestive leukocytosis), but it has been shown that if food is taken in the resting state, leukocytosis does not occur. Inflammation, and bacterial infection, in general, are usually accompanied by a sharp rise in the white count. The type of response varies. In most septic infections, the increase may be almost exclusively due to neutrophiles, whereas in tuberculosis and whooping-cough there is a relative increase in lymphocytes. There may also be a reduction in white cells (leukopenia), as in typhoid fever, and it is even possible for one type of cell to diminish or practically disappear from the circulation (granulopenia).

In a large measure the function of the leukocytes in the destruction of bacteria and in the liquefaction and removal of dead tissue is due to the various enzymes which they contain, particularly proteases and lipases.

Normally the platelets number 250,000 to 400,000. Increases up to a million and more have been reported in Hodgkins' disease and in myeloid leukemia. The most pronounced reduction, and even disappearance, of platelets occurs in *purpura hemorrhagica*, a condition in which spontaneous bleeding occurs from the mucous membranes and subcutaneously. The platelets are of biochemical interest because they contain the phospholipid, kephalin (p. 82), which as we shall see is a requisite in the process of blood clotting.

Serum, Plasma. If blood, after being removed from the blood vessels, is allowed to stand, it soon forms a clot in which the cellular elements are enmeshed. Clot formation is due essentially to the conversion of the soluble protein, fibrinogen, into the insoluble protein, fibrin. Calcium is needed for this process. If the effect of the calcium is removed by its combination with an oxalate or citrate radical, the blood remains fluid. Blood treated in this way is referred to as *oxalated* or *citrated*.

Blood may also be kept from clotting by adding *hirudin*, the function of which will be considered presently (p. 226).

The formed elements may be separated from the plasma by centrifuging the whole blood.

When allowed to stand, a blood clot eventually retracts and shrinks; in the process of shrinking, a pale yellow liquid, the serum, is expressed. A similar phenomenon is exhibited by other colloidal gels and is termed *syneresis*. Serum is blood from which the corpuscles and fibrinogen have been removed. Plasma is blood from which the corpuscles have been removed; it differs from serum in that it contains fibrinogen.

The fibrin may be removed in the form of stringy masses, without enmeshing the cellular elements, by rapidly stirring freshly drawn blood with a rod or some other contrivance. As a result *defibrinated* or " *whipped* " blood is obtained.

Composition. A discussion of the chemical constituents of the blood without reference to their physiological significance would have little meaning. The composition of the blood is so intimately related to its diverse functions that it is only logical to consider the various compounds individually and each from several angles.

Certain of the blood constituents have specific, though not necessarily limited, functions. Whereas fibrinogen is almost exclusively concerned in the clotting process, another blood protein, hemoglobin, not only has the specific function of transporting oxygen, but is also an important participant in the buffer mechanism of the blood and indirectly in the transportation of carbon dioxide. Similarly, the plasma proteins, inorganic salts, cell lipids, etc., are each connected with several properties of the blood.

Then there are those constituents which are primarily of nutrient value to the organism and may be regarded as being *en route* from the intestine, liver, or other organ to some tissue for utilization. Amino acids, glucose, fats, oxygen, and inorganic salts belong to this category.

A third group of constituents may be considered as waste products of metabolism, in transit from the tissues to the organs of excretion. Blood contains approximately 45 to 65 volumes per cent of carbon dioxide. The total non-protein nitrogen of the blood, which, as the term implies, represents all the nitrogenous constituents of the blood, except the proteins, varies normally between 30 and 35 mg. per 100 cc. The amino acids, which are not waste products, account for a certain proportion, but about 14 to 20 mg., or roughly 50 to 60 per cent, represents urea nitrogen. The amount of urea in the blood is therefore approximately 30 to 40 mg. per 100 cc. Blood of normal individuals contains 2 to 3 mg. of uric acid, 1 to 2 mg. of creatinine, 3 to 6 mg. of creatine (which is not to be regarded as a waste product necessarily), an exceedingly small amount of ammonia (about 0.1 mg. per 100 cc.) and small amounts of other nitrogenous constituents, constituting the " undetermined nitrogen " fraction.

The chemistry of the blood is of much importance in relation to intermediary metabolism and the functional activity of the organs of excretion, notably the kidneys. In diabetes, owing to a derangement in carbohydrate metabolism, the sugar in the blood may increase considerably above normal. When fat oxidation is not carried to completion, such substances as acetone, acetoacetic acid, and β-hydroxybutyric acid, normally present in insignificant amounts, appear in the blood (and urine) in relatively large quantity. More than normal amounts of uric acid are formed and excreted when there is excessive metabolism of glandular material Retention of the non-protein nitrogenous constituents of the blood may occur in disease of the kidney. The detailed study of certain of the blood constituents, such as urea, creatine, creatinine, uric acid, etc., will be deferred at this time for the reason that their significance will be more fully appreciated after their origin has been considered in the chapters on intermediary metabolism.

Specific Gravity. The specific gravity of whole blood is normally between 1.054 and 1.060. The plasma has a specific gravity of 1.026±.002.[8] For erythrocytes the value is approximately 1.090.

Water. Quantitively water is the most important constituent. The plasma (or serum) of mammalian blood, including that of man, contains 90–92 per cent of water; the red corpuscles, 64–65 per cent. The similarity in composition of human, dog, and horse blood is shown by the data in Table XXX.

TABLE XXX

SPECIFIC GRAVITY AND WATER CONTENT, IN PERCENTAGE BY WEIGHT, OF WHOLE BLOOD, SERUM, AND RED BLOOD CELLS IN DOG, MAN, AND HORSE*

	Whole Blood		Serum		Cells	
	Sp. Gr.	H_2O	Sp. Gr.	H_2O	Sp. Gr.	H_2O
Dog............	1.054	79.2	1.021	92.2	1.100	64.6
Horse..........	1.0548	80.93	1.028	91.39	.....	63.8
Man............	1.055	79.1	1.027	90.7	1.090	64.8

* The data for dog blood are based on the analyses of Austin, Cullen, Gram, and Robinson (*J. Biol. Chem.*, **61**, 829 [1924]), with the exception of the value for the specific gravity of the cells. The data for horse blood are based on the analyses of Van Slyke, Wu, and McLean (*J. Biol. Chem.*, **56**, 765 [1923]). The data for human blood and dog blood cells are the author's and are in good agreement with data to be found in the literature. See, for example, L. J. Henderson, "Blood, A Study in General Physiology," Chap. VI, Yale Univ. Press, New Haven, 1928.

[8] The specific gravity of the plasma corresponds to the protein content. When the latter exceeds 7.5 grams per cent, the specific gravity is correspondingly high, 1.028; and with values of over 8 grams, it may be about 1.030. On the contrary a protein content of 6 grams per cent is associated with a specific gravity of about 1.024; 5 grams with 1.022; 4 grams with 1.019. See J. P. Peters and D. D. Van Slyke, "Quantitative Clinical Chemistry," Vol. I, p. 683, Williams & Wilkins, Baltimore. 1931.

Solids. The solid constituents of the human red blood corpuscle comprise approximately 35 per cent of the weight and may be roughly distributed as follows:

Hemoglobin......................................	31–33	per cent
Phospholipids, cholesterol, and other lipids.............	1	"
Protein*...	0.5–1	"
Inorganic constituents, ionized or combined, chiefly potassium and chloride...............................	0.5–0.6	"
Organic constituents, glucose, glutathione, urea, etc......	0.2	"

* Globulin, globin, and nucleoprotein have been described as constituents of the stroma or red cell membrane, but according to E. Jorpes, *Biochem. J.*, **26**, 1488 (1932), the protein of the stroma differs from these, as well as from hemoglobin and fibrin.

Blood plasma contains 8–9 per cent of solids, of which all but about 1.5 grams consists of protein. A rough approximation of the distribution follows:

Plasma protein....................................	7 ± 0.5	per cent
Phospholipids, cholesterol, and other lipids..............	0.7	"
Inorganic constituents...............................	0.75	"
Organic constituents, such as glucose, urea, amino, acids, etc..	0.15	"

PLASMA PROTEINS

An accurate method for determining total protein in plasma or serum consists in separating the protein from the lipids by precipitation in acetone, and subsequent coagulation with acetic acid (and removal of contaminants), drying and weighing.[9]

Probably the most widely used procedure is the well-known Kjeldahl method for nitrogen, both in its original macro-form and in the micro-form, of which there are several variants. From the value for total nitrogen, the protein nitrogen is obtained by subtracting the non-protein nitrogen. There is also a colorimetric method based on the reaction of Folin and Denis' so-called phenol reagent with the tyrosine of the protein molecule. Several modifications of this indirect procedure have been described. Physical methods of measurement, employing the interferometer, viscosimeter, and refractometer, have been introduced, but these have not proved to be entirely reliable. Finally, the

[9] C. O. Guillaumin, R. Wohl, and M. L. Laurencin, *Bull. soc. chim. biol.*, **11**, 387 (1929). See also Peters and Van Slyke, "Quantitative Clinical Chemistry," Vol. II, p. 688, Williams & Wilkins, Baltimore, 1932, for various methods for the determination of plasma protein.

apparent relationship of the specific gravity of plasma to its protein content shows possibilities of wider application.[10] The relationship is expressed by the following formula:

$$\text{Total protein} = (\text{specific gravity} - 1.007)\ 343$$

The normal variation of the total protein of plasma is indicated by the following data:

TABLE XXXI

PLASMA PROTEIN CONTENT IN NORMAL INDIVIDUALS, IN GRAMS PER 100 CC.

Authority	Number of Subjects	Minimum	Maximum	Average
Salvesen[11]	32 (16 men and 16 women, 42 analyses)	6.34	7.96	7.00
Moore and Van Slyke[12]	9	6.5	7.7	7.1

The plasma proteins may be separated into three major fractions:

1. Fibrinogen.
2. Globulin.
3. Albumin.

Fibrinogen and the Clotting of Blood. Fibrinogen resembles the globulins; indeed it may be classed with them. Like the globulins it is precipitated by half saturation with ammonium sulfate; it differs in being precipitated in a 0.75 molar solution of sodium sulfate and by half saturation with sodium chloride. This property may be utilized in its quantitative estimation, but a more accurate procedure consists in diluting the plasma with sodium chloride solution, and adding a certain amount of calcium chloride. The fibrinogen is thus converted into fibrin, which may be separated, dried, and weighed. Or the nitrogen may be determined by the Kjeldahl method and from the result the amount of fibrinogen calculated.[13]

[10] N. S. Moore and D. D. Van Slyke, *J. Clin. Investigation*, **8**, 337 (1929–30); A. A. Weech, C. E. Snelling, and E. Goettsch, *ibid.*, **12**, 193 (1933).

[11] *Acta Med. Scand.*, **65**, 147 (1926); cited by Moore and Van Slyke.

[12] *Loc. cit.*; see also Linder, Lundsgaard, and Van Slyke, *J. Exp. Med.*, **39**, 887 (1924); Bruckman, d'Esopo, and Peters, *J. Clin. Investigation*, **8**, 577 (1929–30).

[13] G. E. Cullen and D. D. Van Slyke, *J. Biol. Chem.*, **41**, 587 (1920); see also T. B. Jones and H. P. Smith, *Am. J. Physiol.*, **94**, 144 (1930), and Peters and Van Slyke, Vol. II, p. 696.

In human plasma the amount of fibrinogen varies between 0.2 and 0.4 per cent, though somewhat higher values are not uncommon. The following data are illustrative:

TABLE XXXII

FIBRINOGEN PERCENTAGE IN PLASMA OF NORMAL INDIVIDUALS[14]

Authority	Number of Subjects	Minimum	Maximum	Average
Gram[15]	25 (men)	0.20	0.36	0.27
	25 (women)	0.21	0.38	0.29
McLester[16]	15	0.272	0.385	0.333

The maintenance of the normal quantity of fibrinogen in the blood depends upon the integrity of the liver. Destruction of liver tissue, whether by disease or through the action of such poisons as chloroform, phosphorus, or hydrazine, leads to an impairment in the mechanism for the production of fibrinogen and results in a sharp fall of its content in the blood. On the contrary, in sufficiently small doses, these liver poisons may exert an irritant or stimulating effect on the liver parenchyma and cause a definite rise in the amount of blood fibrinogen (Foster and Whipple). [14]

Direct evidence of the rôle of the liver in the production of fibrinogen has been obtained in experiments on animals (rabbits, dogs) in which the liver had been completely extirpated. Such animals may be kept alive for many hours after the operation, provided the sugar content of the blood is maintained at its normal level, or somewhat higher, which may be done by the administration of glucose. In hepatectomized animals a progressive decrease of blood fibrinogen occurs invariably. A disappearance of 20 to 50 per cent has been observed in dogs (Jones and Smith)[17] within 12 to 20 hours. In rabbits, the rate of disappearance has been found to be even more rapid (Drury and McMaster),[18] though it is interesting to note that, in animals in which the liver had been only

[14] Foster and Whipple (*Am. J. Physiol.*, **58**, 407 [1921-22]) obtained the following data for fibrinogen in 13 dogs, maintained on a liberal mixed diet: minimum 0.306 per cent; maximum 0.506 per cent; average 0.390 per cent. Lower values—average 0.358 per cent—were observed in fasting animals.

[15] *J. Biol. Chem.*, **49**, 279 (1921).

[16] *J. Am. Med. Assoc.*, **79**, 17 (1922).

[17] *Am. J. Physiol.*, **94**, 144 (1930).

[18] *J. Exp. Med.*, **50**, 569 (1929).

partly removed (70 per cent), the blood fibrinogen remained unchanged. The depletion of fibrinogen in liverless animals is clearly an index of the rapidity of its normal utilization by the organism.

Equally remarkable is the capacity of the organism to regenerate fibrinogen. In studying this problem several investigators have employed the procedure of replacing the blood of an animal with its defibrinated blood, or with the defibrinated blood of compatible donors. Drury and McMaster found that after a 90 per cent reduction of fibrinogen by this procedure (in rabbits), a complete return to the previous amount occurred within 5 to 6 hours. Indeed an enormous overproduction of fibrinogen ensued in the animals thus stimulated to regeneration of this protein. No such regeneration occurred, however, in hepatectomized animals subjected to the same defibrination procedure (Drury and McMaster, Jones and Smith). Not only was there no new formation of fibrinogen, such as occurred in the normal animals, but a swift fall in the amount of the substance signified a rapid utilization of the fibrinogen remaining in the organism. As emphasized by Drury and McMaster, had there been any other important source of fibrinogen, regeneration should have been observed in the liverless animals. Moreover, the body is apparently without any great reserve of fibrinogen, for otherwise the speedy decrease of this substance in the blood would have been prevented. In short, there is no evidence of fibrinogen regeneration in the absence of the liver. Consequently it is to be assumed that this organ either controls its production, or is actually the seat of its formation.

Physiological and Pathological Variations. Foster and Whipple have reported that diets rich in animal protein (meat, liver, beef, heart) favor a high blood fibrin level, as contrasted with fasting, or carbohydrate or fat feeding. According to Vars,[19] this effect may be produced by any kind of protein, including casein, but the dietary stimulus to increased fibrinogen formation is transient and the high fibrin level cannot be maintained indefinitely.

The problem of fibrinogen utilization has not been studied adequately, but such knowledge as has been gained in recent years points to its participation, not only in disease, but normally, in the reparative processes of tissues and organs and particularly in the repair of injuries to the vascular system. Tissue injury and inflammation stimulate an increase in fibrinogen production; indeed, Foster and Whipple regard tissue injury as the most powerful single stimulus to overproduction of fibrinogen, a stimulus which far exceeds that of a low fibrin level such as results from severe hemorrhage. Moreover, these investigators have

[19]*Am. J. Physiol.*, **93**, 554 (1930).

shown that bacteria are not directly concerned in the reaction, which is identical whether an inflammation is sterile or septic. Under these conditions there is an exaggerated utilization of fibrinogen in the formation of fibrinous exudate and in the deposition of fibrin in and about the disturbed or injured tissues.

That almost any kind of infection or inflammation in the body leads to an increase in blood fibrinogen is supported by clinical observations. The following are data reported by McLester:[20]

	Fibrinogen, Milligrams per 100 cc.		
	Minimum	Maximum	Average
Septic inflammation: various forms, (20 patients).................................	624	1120	829
convalescent, for instance after drainage of abscess (4 patients)....................	....	....	540
Pneumonia (8 patients).....................	726	1447	1069

Menstruation and pregnancy are likewise associated with a rise in plasma fibrinogen. In acute hepatitis the blood fibrinogen is elevated, but in the more severe forms of liver disease (acute yellow atrophy, phosphorus poisoning, etc.), low values are the rule.

The injection of proteose or peptone intravenously causes a severe and usually fatal intoxication, which is not accompanied by an inflammatory reaction, but by a marked destruction of tissue protein and a reduction in fibrinogen. The disappearance of this constituent is attributed to two factors (Foster and Whipple): a passive escape with other blood constituents from the blood vessels; an active escape due to precipitation of fibrin in certain areas injured by the proteose.

The Clotting or Coagulation of Blood.[21] The immediate cause of clotting is the change from *fibrinogen* to *fibrin*. Clotting does not occur in the absence of *ionizable calcium*, as may be shown by converting the calcium into the oxalate or citrate. The significance of calcium is as important here as in the curdling of milk by rennin. However, fibrinogen and calcium in themselves do not form a clot; another substance is essential. This other substance is believed to be a protein or

[20] *J. Am. Med. Assoc.*, **79**, 17 (1922); *Arch. Internal Med.*, **35**, 177 (1925).
[21] For a comprehensive discussion and review of the literature the student is referred to E. Wöhlisch, "Die Physiologie und Pathologie der Blutgerinnung," *Ergebnisse Physiol.*, **28**, 443–624 (1929).

a proteose and is called *thrombin*. It may be extracted from water-washed fibrin with an 8 per cent solution of sodium chloride.

Examination with the aid of the ultra-microscope has revealed that when a fibrin clot is being formed the fibrin first separates in the form of needle-like crystals, later assuming the appearance of threads. The chemical aspects of the phenomenon are of unusual interest.

From a consideration of these facts, one is naturally led to inquire why the blood does not clot in the blood vessels. To explain this, it has been assumed that thrombin does not exist as such in the circulating blood but is present in an inactive form which has been named *thrombogen* or *prothrombin*.[22] The cause for the change from prothrombin to thrombin has long been sought without success; it is known, however, that blood in contact with dead or injured tissue or with disintegrated blood corpuscles, and especially with broken-down blood platelets, clots more readily than otherwise. Howell has suggested that when blood platelets or tissue cells disintegrate, a substance is liberated which hastens the coagulation process and for which he suggested the name *thromboplastin*. This constituent is soluble in fat-solvents and appears to be the familiar substance, kephalin (cephalin). The function of the kephalin in the clotting process is not known definitely, but it is believed by Howell[23] that it neutralizes the effect of *heparin*, a constituent of the blood which in some way prevents the transformation of *prothrombin* into *thrombin*. Heparin has been prepared from the liver (and other organs) and is believed to be responsible for maintaining the normal fluidity of the blood.[24] Formerly this alleged effect of heparin on prothrombin was

---

[22] Prothrombin may be prepared from oxalated plasma by the addition of an equal volume of acetone. The precipitate which is formed is filtered off and washed with ether. It is a protein or protein-like substance. The difference between it and thrombin may be readily demonstrated. Thrombin added to fibrinogen results in the prompt formation of a clot. Prothrombin added to fibrinogen produces no effect unless calcium ions are also added.

In a recent study of the properties of thrombin, J. Mellanby has advanced the hypothesis that it is a proteolytic enzyme which splits fibrinogen into fibrin and serum globulin. Thrombin, or "*thrombase*," is a protein, soluble in water and destroyed by heat at temperatures above 50° C. 1 mg. of thrombase coagulates 100 c.c. of oxalated plasma in 30 seconds. The intravenous injection of 2 mg. into a rabbit causes intravascular clotting and death. *Proc. Roy. Soc.* (*London*), B, **113**, 93 (1933). Compare with A. Fischer, Biochem. Z., **264**, 169, 178, 184 (1933).

[23] *Bull. Johns Hopkins Hosp.*, **42**, 199 (1928).

[24] The isolation of heparin has been reported by A. Schmitz and A. Fischer, Z. *physiol. Chem.*, **216**, 264 (1933). They consider it to be a monobasic acid of the formula $C_{18}H_{32}O_{17} \cdot 6H_2O$. A very active preparation of heparin has also been obtained by A. F. Charles and D. A. Scott, *J. Biol. Chem.*, **102**, 425, 431, 437 (1933). The analysis of their product does not coincide with that of Schmitz and Fischer.

attributed to an hypothetical substance termed *antiprothrombin.*[25]
Another possibility is that heparin combines with some other substance
to form *antithrombin* and that this too is neutralized by kephalin. It
is to be admitted that our conception of the process of clotting is not
necessarily clarified by the introduction of so many terms to represent
alleged substances, or rather effects.

In short, according to Howell's theory there are found in the blood
fibrinogen, prothrombin, calcium salts, kephalin, heparin, and antithrombin. When blood is shed, owing to the disintegration of the blood
platelets, or in some other fashion, kephalin is liberated. This combines
with heparin and possibly antithrombin, with the result that prothrombin is formed and in the presence of the calcium salts is converted into
thrombin. The thrombin then transforms the fibrinogen into fibrin.

The following is a schematic representation of the essential postulates of Howell's theory:

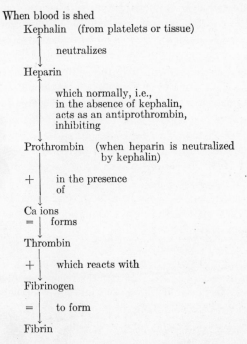

When blood is shed
    Kephalin   (from platelets or tissue)

            neutralizes

    Heparin

            which normally, i.e.,
            in the absence of kephalin,
            acts as an antiprothrombin,
            inhibiting

    Prothrombin   (when heparin is neutralized
                        by kephalin)

    +   in the presence
            of

    Ca ions
    =   forms

    Thrombin

    +   which reacts with

    Fibrinogen

    =   to form

    Fibrin

Other theories have been suggested. According to Bordet, the
plasma contains fibrinogen and proserozyme, the latter being converted
to serozyme by the action of calcium salts. The tissues, and particularly

[25] Antithrombin is said to be present in circulating blood in traces. Its function
is presumably to neutralize any small traces of thrombin that may be formed.

the platelets, contain a lipoprotein which Bordet[26] named cytozyme and which he believed to be lecithin, but which really belongs to the group of kephalins. Cytozyme unites with the serozyme to yield thrombin, which transforms fibrinogen to fibrin.

That there are two distinct mechanisms concerned with the coagulation of blood seems likely from the observations of Mills[27] and others. In addition to the thrombin mechanism, clotting may be produced by the action of tissue fibrinogen on plasma fibrinogen, even in the absence of thrombin or prothrombin.

Anticoagulants. The coagulability of the blood may be experimentally inhibited by the injection of sodium or potassium oxalate or citrate, peptone, hirudin, heparin, and other substances. With the exception of peptone, which acts only *in vivo*, the substances named are effective both *in vivo* and *in vitro*.

Oxalate is commonly used as an anticoagulant in obtaining blood for analysis. The effect is due to the precipitation of calcium, which is essential in the clotting process, as insoluble calcium oxalate.

Sodium citrate is chiefly used as an anticoagulant in blood transfusions. Its effect is due to the conversion of ionizable calcium salts into the much less ionized calcium citrate. Apparently, only the calcium ions are effective in the transformation of prothrombin into thrombin.

Heparin (antiprothrombin) is effective in very small amounts, 1 mg. added to 25–50 cc. of blood being sufficient to delay coagulation for as long as 24 hours.

Hirudin is the active principle derived from the salivary gland of the medicinal leech. It is said to be a proteose, preventing coagulation by neutralizing thrombin.

The injection of toxic doses of proteose or peptone renders the blood incoagulable, presumably through a reduction in fibrinogen. Whether this is the only factor is not clearly established. Peptone is said to increase the amount of antithrombin.

At low temperatures blood tends to remain fluid for a long time. This has been associated with the greater resistance of platelets in the cold and the consequent delay in the liberation of kephalin. On the contrary, heat favors the clotting of blood.

Clotting may also be delayed by collecting blood in a paraffin-coated vessel (non-wettable surface). This condition is also believed to diminish the fragility of the platelets.

Coagulation Time, Hemophilia, Thrombocytopenia, etc. In man the clotting time of blood is normally 2–10 minutes, varying somewhat according to the method used for its determination.

[26] *Ann. inst. Pasteur*, **34**, 561 (1920).   [27] *Am. J. Physiol.*, **57**, 395 (1921).

The most striking departure from the normal occurs in *hemophilia*. This disease is manifested clinically by a tendency to excessive bleeding. Hemorrhage may be spontaneous, or may follow an injury, even of the most trivial kind. The condition is hereditary, the transmission being sex-linked, manifested only in males, but transmitted through females.

The blood of an hemophiliac frequently requires 40–50 minutes, and occasionally even more than two hours, for clotting. And yet, it apparently contains all the necessary elements for the coagulation process. The number of platelets is normal, but they are abnormally resistant to disintegration. In consequence the kephalin does not become readily available for the process of clotting. The addition of normal platelets, or hemophiliac platelets mechanically disintegrated by macerating in a mortar, or kephalin, to hemophilic blood hastens its clotting.

The use of various kinds of ovarian preparations in the treatment of hemophilia has been recently proposed, [28, 29] the basis being that though females potentially have this disease, it is held in abeyance by an internal secretion from the ovary. More direct evidence of the control of the ovaries on the resistance of blood platelets is still lacking.

In conditions of severe liver damage, such as occur in chloroform and phosphorus poisoning and in acute yellow atrophy, there is deficient formation of fibrinogen, as a result of which its content in the blood may fall to very low values. To this reduction of fibrinogen is attributed the delayed clotting time and hemorrhagic tendency in these conditions.

As has been mentioned, the removal of calcium from the blood as the oxalate or citrate prevents its clotting. However, physiologically, diminished clotting of the blood is not frequently attributable to a diminished calcium content of the blood. It is perhaps a factor in obstructive jaundice, for the " coagulability " of the blood of patients with this disease may be increased by the administration of calcium salts.

Of the various hemorrhagic diseases classified under the head of *"purpura,"* the relation to blood clotting is understood only in the so-called *purpura hemorrhagica*, or *thrombocytopenic purpura*. In this condition the blood may have a normal clotting time, although the clot is usually soft and fails to retract, but the bleeding time is greatly prolonged. Normally after a slight puncture there is rapid diminution in the intensity of the hemorrhage, successive drops of the blood being smaller and smaller, and soon the bleeding stops altogether. Cessation of the bleeding is brought about by the formation of small thrombi in the injured capillaries, the thrombi being made up essentially of aggregations of

[28] C. L. Birch, *J. Am. Med. Assoc.*, **99**, 1566 (1932); *Proc. Soc. Exp. Biol. Med.*, **28**, 752 (1931).

[29] H. T. Kimm and C. M. van Allen, *J. Am. Med. Assoc.*, **99**, 991 (1932).

blood platelets. In the hemorrhagic diseases referred to, there is no prompt checking of the hemorrhage, which may continue for hours, the drops showing little or no tendency to diminish in size. This prolongation in the bleeding time is attributed to a deficiency of platelets, which in severe hemorrhagic diseases have often been found to be as low as 10,000 per cubic millimeter, or even less.

Intravascular Clotting. Certain circumstances favor the clotting of blood in the blood vessels, clots thus formed being called *thrombi* and the process, *thrombosis.* Intravascular clotting may result from the slowing down of the blood flow, such as may occur in heart disease, or where there is an abnormal dilation of the blood vessels, as in varicose veins, or where there is some obstruction in the vessel. A thrombus also tends to form around an area of injury, such as an atheromatous patch in an artery, a sclerosed coronary vessel, or on a damaged heart valve. Infections, such as typhoid fever, predispose to thrombus formation, and there are other causes which are described in textbooks of pathology.

The formation of intravascular clots differs from clotting outside the blood vessels. At first, there is a clumping together of blood platelets, forming a framework, which becomes infiltrated by white blood cells. At this stage, the thrombus is whitish in color and is called a white thrombus. When its size is sufficient, it causes obstruction of the blood vessel, the flow of blood is stopped, and a red blood clot, the red thrombus, is formed. This consists of fibrin and all the blood elements. It fills the obstructed blood vessel to the point of its nearest anastomosis with some other vessel.

Globulin and Albumin. The separation of serum protein into two fractions may be accomplished by half-saturation with ammonium sulfate. The globulin is salted out while the albumin remains in solution. Separation of these two fractions may also be performed in 1.5 molar sodium sulfate (approximately 22 per cent). In turn the globulin may be divided into two fractions, *euglobulin* and *pseudoglobulin,* the former being precipitated in 1.0 molar sodium sulfate. Although this classification is quite generally employed, the chemical individuality of the fractions is still under discussion. The further subdivision of the albumin and globulin into fractions has been questioned even more from the standpoint of the chemical identity of the various fractions.[30]

However, most workers who have attempted to determine the molecular weight of serum albumin have regarded it as an entity. Thus

[30] Compare P. E. Howe, *Physiol. Rev.,* **5,** 439 (1925); S. P. L. Sørensen, "Proteins," Fleischman Co., New York, cited by Adair and Robinson; T. Svedberg and B. Sjögren, *J. Am. Chem. Soc.,* **50,** 3318 (1928); H. K. and L. Reiner, *J. Biol. Chem.,* **95,** 345 (1932).

Svedberg and Sjögren have stated that once-crystallized serum albumin is a homogeneous substance of molecular weight 68,000. In their hands repeated crystallization apparently resulted in the decomposition of the protein. This was not observed by Adair and Robinson,[31] who found serum albumin to remain stable through several crystallizations. Moreover, they could detect no change in the osmotic pressure of serum albumin preparations, crystallized once, twice, and four times. The mean molecular weight obtained in a series of 27 determinations with horse-serum albumin was 72,000 ± 3000. Serum albumin of the ox and sheep yielded approximately the same result (molecular weight about 70,000). These observations are in agreement with other recent measurements. Burk[32] found the mean molecular weight of horse-serum albumin to be 74,600.

For unfractionated serum globulin Adair and Robinson obtained a mean molecular weight of 175,000, the range of values in 17 experiments being from 154,000 to 192,000. Euglobulin resembled total globulin. These investigators could find no explanation for the discrepancy between their result and Svedberg's value for total globulin of only 103,000.

Normal Distribution of Albumin and Globulin. Moore and Van Slyke[33] observed the following range of values in nine normal subjects:

	Total Plasma Protein per cent	Albumin per cent	Globulin per cent	Albumin / Globulin
Minimum............	6.5	4.0		
Maximum............	7.7	4.5		
Average.............	7.1	4.3	2.8	1.53

The amount of albumin normally exceeds the globulin; the proportion though variable is usually from 1.5 to 2.0.

Functions of the Plasma Proteins. One of the important functions of the plasma proteins is to maintain the normal osmotic relations between the blood and tissues. Starling[34] was the first to recognize the significance of the protein of the blood as a controlling factor in the distribution of fluids between the plasma and tissues. The hydrostatic pressure

[31] *Biochem. J.*, **24**, 1864 (1930).

[32] *J. Biol. Chem.*, **98**, 353 (1932).

[33] *J. Clin. Investigation*, **8**, 337 (1929–30); see also A. E. Kumpf, *Arch. Pathol.*, **11**, 335 (1931).

[34] *J. Physiol.*, **19**, 312 (1895–6).

in the capillaries tends to force water into the tissues; the osmotic pressure of the plasma proteins tends to draw fluid from the tissue spaces into the blood. A delicate balance normally exists between these opposing forces.

There are few accurate measurements of arterial capillary pressure. It is known to vary in different parts of the body and is uniformly somewhat higher in the arterial than in the venous limb. A sufficient pressure gradient exists to favor the outward filtration of water from the arterioles and the passage of water from the tissues into the venules. Landis[35] determined the pressure of the capillaries of the frog's mesentery to be 14.5 cm. (H_2O) in the arterial end and 10 cm. in the venous. Filtration outward occurred when the pressure was about 11.5 cm., which is to be expected from the relatively low plasma protein osmotic pressure of the frog (10 to 12 cm., according to White).[36]

The capillary pressure in human skin is 32 mm. (Hg) in the arterial limb and 12 mm. in the venous limb (Landis). The former is somewhat above the osmotic pressure of the plasma proteins; the latter is considerably below. A sufficient rise in capillary pressure is accompanied by an increased filtration. In a series of experiments, Landis[37] raised the venous pressure in one arm by means of an armlet to 20, 40, 60, or 80 mm. Hg and compared the composition of the blood in that arm with that of blood collected from the control arm, where the pressure had remained at its normal value of 9 mm. Loss of fluid could be detected at venous pressures as low as 20 mm. The loss was conspicuously increased at higher venous pressures, as much as 19.5 per cent passing out into the tissues when the venous pressure was raised to 80 mm. The amount of protein lost was negligible below 60 mm. At that point the capillary filtrate contained only 0.3 per cent protein; at 80 mm., however, the filtrate contained an average of 1.5 per cent of protein.

It is thus seen that increased hydrostatic pressure in the capillaries may be accompanied by a loss of fluid to the tissues, and up to a certain point by an increased concentration of protein in the plasma because of a proportionately smaller loss of this constituent. The greater concentration of protein tends to balance the effect of the heightened hydrostatic pressure, so that within certain limits a new balance is soon attained.

Significant as is the factor of hydrostatic capillary pressure, disturbance in the equilibrium is usually the result of changes in the plasma protein. The osmotic pressure of plasma is about 6.5 atmospheres

[35] *Am. J. Physiol.*, **75**, 548 (1926).

[36] *Ibid.*, **68**, 523 (1924).

[37] E. M. Landis, L. Jonas, M. Angevine and W. Erb., *J. Clin. Investigation*, **11**, 17 (1932).

(494 cm. Hg). This tremendous force is due to dissolved electrolytes and organic crystalloids, but does not produce the calculated effect, inasmuch as the tissues and tissue fluids likewise contain about the same concentration of these constituents. Such osmotic effect as is produced by the blood is, however, of incalculable importance, although it amounts to a very small fraction of the total, being due to the difference in the concentration of protein in the plasma and tissue fluids, a difference which is maintained because of the relative impermeability of the capillary endothelium to protein.

Krogh[38] states that in his laboratory determinations of the osmotic pressure of the serum protein in 12 normal subjects gave an average result of 380 mm. of water (equivalent to 27.94 mm. Hg). Together with other data in the literature based on measurements with various types of osmometers, the normal variations are given as 265 to 420 mm. of water pressure. In a series of determinations on 11 normal subjects (medical students), Fellows[39] obtained values ranging from 321 to 380 mm. The total serum proteins in these subjects varied from 6.32 to 6.81 g.[40]

Of the serum proteins, albumin is osmotically more active than the globulin on account of its relatively smaller molecular size. According to the molecular weights recently determined by Adair and Robinson, albumin should be approximately 2.5 times as active as globulin. This does not agree, however, with the observation of Govaerts,[41] who found that a 1 g. per cent solution of albumin in serum gave an osmotic pressure of 75.4 mm. of water (5.54 mm. Hg), whereas 1 g. per cent of globulin exerted a pressure of only 19.5 mm. of water (1.43 mm. Hg). According to these figures, the osmotic activity of serum albumin is nearly four times that of globulin. Using these constants as a basis for calculation, Govaerts was able to predict the osmometric reading from the chemical analysis of the serum for albumin and globulin. In a similar comparison recently made by Fellows,[39] Govaerts' constants yielded somewhat higher results than those obtained by osmometry.[42]

[38] "The Anatomy and Physiology of Capillaries," Yale Univ. Press, New Haven, 1929, pp. 286–290.

[39] *Proc. Soc. Exp. Biol. Med.*, **29**, 1175 (1931–32).

[40] Turner has recently discussed the validity of determinations by the osmometer method as well as the reliability of different types of membranes. *J. Biol. Chem.*, **96**, 487 (1932).

[41] *Compt. rend. soc. biol.*, **93**, 441 (1925); **95**, 724 (1926).

[42] H. S. Wells, J. B. Youmans and D. G. Miller, *J. Clin. Investigation*, **12**, 1103 (1933), consider the formula of Govaerts unreliable. They propose the following formula: $P = C(21.4 + 5.9A)$, where P is the osmotic pressure in millimeters of water, C is the total protein concentration, and A is the albumin concentration, in grams per 100 cc.

Despite such discrepancies, Govaerts' data have proved very useful, particularly in explaining what otherwise would have seemed to be an inconsistency in the relationship between the concentration of total protein and the development of edema. It remains, of course, to reconcile the four-fold difference in the osmotic activity of albumin and globulin with the smaller difference of their molecular weights.

According to the observations of Iversen and Nakazawa[43] in a series of cases of various types of renal disease, edema develops when the effective osmotic pressure of the serum (serum due to proteins) falls below 250 mm. H_2O.

Protein Depletion and Regeneration. Serum protein may be reduced to a very low level by repeated bleeding and simultaneous injection of the washed blood cells suspended in a protein-free medium, such as Locke's solution. This procedure, termed *plasmapharesis*, was employed by Kerr, Hurwitz, and Whipple[44] in a study of serum protein regeneration. It will be recalled that the regeneration of fibrinogen is very rapid. Not so with the other proteins. Following a 50 per cent depletion, it required, after an initial rise of about 1 per cent during the first 24 hours, 7 to 14 days to restore the lost protein. Regeneration was more rapid on a meat diet than on a protein-free diet. It was somewhat delayed in the presence of liver injury. Globulin was regenerated more rapidly than albumin.

Whipple and associates found that the body cannot tolerate too great a reduction of its plasma protein. Depletion to a concentration of 1 per cent was almost always accompanied by fatal shock; this often supervened long before the minimum figure of 1 per cent was reached.

Edema. We are not concerned at this stage with the types of edema associated with heart disease, venous or lymphatic obstruction, acute glomerular nephritis, or other causes, but with the forms of fluid accumulation in the tissues in which low plasma protein is the dominant factor.

Plasmapharesis as a method of producing experimental edema was first developed by Leiter,[45] who found that in dogs palpable edema usually begins when the plasma protein has fallen to 3 per cent, or less, and recedes with a rise above this critical level. The edema fluid was characterized by its low protein content. The mechanism of the development of this form of edema may be adequately explained on the basis of the lowered osmotic pressure of the plasma proteins; however, the degree of fluid accumulation in the tissues and the rate are modified

---

[43] *Biochem. Z.*, **191**, 307 (1927).

[44] *Am. J. Physiol.*, **47**, 356, 370, 379 (1918–19); see also H. P. Smith, A. E. Belt, and G. H. Whipple, *ibid.*, **52**, 54 (1920).

[45] *Proc. Soc. Exp. Biol. Med.*, **26**, 173 (1928); *Arch. Internal Med.*, **48**, 1 (1931).

by the intake of water and salt, the chief constituents of the edema fluid.

Edema Due to Malnutrition. Chronic malnutrition, from whatever cause, and particularly dietary deficiency of protein, is invariably associated with a decrease in plasma protein. The albumin fraction is especially affected because it is formed with greater difficulty than globulin. If the reduction in plasma protein, and especially of albumin, is sufficient, edema develops.

This correlation has been established quite recently. During and after the World War, nutritional edema, commonly called " war edema," was prevalent in famine areas and in prison camps.[46] Authorities at first attributed it to various causes, but there is now little doubt that the underlying factor was protein deficiency. Moreover, nutritional edema has been produced experimentally in rats and dogs maintained on low-protein diets.[47]

Edema Associated with Nephrosis. Nephrosis is a chronic disease in which two of the chief manifestations are the excretion of large quantities of protein in the urine and edema. Beginning with the work of Epstein,[48] who first explained nephrotic edema on the basis of Starling's hypothesis (p. 229), there has accumulated a large body of evidence proving that it is due to the lowered osmotic pressure of the plasma. The protein fraction excreted by the kidney in greater proportion is albumin, which possesses the greater osmotic effect. It is also the protein that is less easily regenerated. In consequence, the albumin-globulin ratio tends to become very low, values of 0.3 being observed not infrequently. The osmotic pressure is correspondingly lowered. Krogh has recorded a colloid osmotic pressure in one case of only 100 mm. of water, as compared with a capillary blood pressure of 150 mm. There was therefore in this case a head pressure of 50 mm. in favor of filtration from the blood into the tissue spaces.[49]

Accumulation of fluid in the tissues in man usually begins when the level of serum protein falls below 5 gm. per 100 cc. This so-called " edema level " is subject, however, to variation, depending on the relative proportions of albumin and globulin.

[46] The historical aspects of nutritional edema have been reviewed by M. B. Maver, *J. Am. Med. Assoc.*, **74**, 934 (1932).

[47] E. A. Kohman, *Am. J. Physiol.*, **51**, 378 (1920); R. A. Frisch, L. B. Mendel, and J. P. Peters, *J. Biol. Chem.*, **84**, 167 (1929); Shelbourne and Egloff, *Arch. Internal Med.*, **48**, 51 (1931); Weech, Snelling, and Goettsch, *J. Clin. Investigation*, **12**, 193 (1933).

[48] *Am. J. Med. Sci.*, **154**, 638 (1917).

[49] For a review of the literature on nephrosis, the reader is referred to L. Leiter, *Medicine*, **10**, 135 (1931).

The edema fluid in nephrosis is characteristically low in its protein content, just as in the edemas resulting from malnutrition or plasma-pharesis.   All respond favorably to a high meat intake.

Other Physiological and Pathological Variations.   A reduction in plasma protein occurs during pregnancy, this being partly attributed to blood dilution and partly to protein depletion, the latter because of the fetal requirements.   The albumin-globulin ratio is diminished and the fibrinogen increased.   These changes are particularly marked in eclampsia.

The plasma protein concentration is low in infancy, but attains adult values within the first two years of life.

Dehydration resulting from water deprivation, muscular activity, diarrhea, vomiting, and other causes is associated with a diminished plasma volume and an increased protein concentration.

In acute hemorrhagic nephritis (acute glomerular nephritis), there seems to be a generalized increase in capillary permeability, presumably due to some toxic factor.   There is an escape of protein not only through the glomeruli, but also through the capillaries into the tissues generally, so that the edema fluid in this condition tends to be relatively high (1 per cent, or more).   The development of edema is therefore not related primarily to protein deficit, though it is obvious that, with the loss of protein from the blood, its content is thereby diminished.

Plasma protein remains unchanged in so-called arteriosclerotic Bright's disease.[50]

HEMOGLOBIN

Hemoglobin, the pigment of the red blood corpuscles, belongs to the group of conjugated proteins.   One of its most characteristic properties is that of combining with oxygen to form oxyhemoglobin, a compound which is readily dissociated when exposed to an environment of low oxygen tension.   The iron content of hemoglobin is practically the same for many species of animals and amounts to about 0.0335 per cent. On the assumption that the hemoglobin molecule contains at least one atom of Fe, the minimum molecular weight has been calculated to be about 17,000.   However, it is very probable that the hemoglobin molecule contains not one but four atoms of iron.   The osmotic pressure determinations of Adair[51] have led to the value of 68,000, or four times the minimal molecular weight.   Confirmation of this value has been

[50] The chemical changes occurring in different types of Bright's disease are discussed in an article by Van Slyke and associates, *Medicine*, **9**, 257 (1930).

[51] *Proc. Roy. Soc. (London)*, A, **109**, 292 (1925).

obtained by several investigators, employing different experimental methods.[52]

Crystallization of Hemoglobin. Although a protein, hemoglobin may be crystallized with relative ease from the blood of certain animals, such as the horse, dog, and guinea-pig. The hemoglobins of the ox and rat crystallize with difficulty, whereas other hemoglobins, such as that of

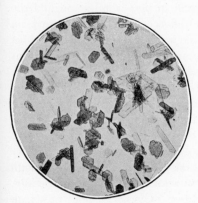

FIG. 21.—Oxyhemoglobin of the White Rat.

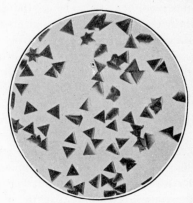

FIG. 22.—Oxyhemoglobin of the Guinea-pig.

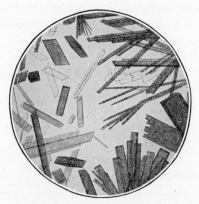

FIG. 23.—Oxyhemoglobin of Man. (After Otto Funke, "Atlas of Physiological Chemistry." Printed for the Cavendish Society, London [1853], Plate X.)

the frog, have not been obtained in crystalline form. The most important study of the crystalline structure of the hemoglobins is that of

[52] Svedberg and Fahraeus, *J. Am. Chem. Soc.*, **48**, 430 (1926); Svedberg and Nichols, *ibid.*, **49**, 2920 (1927); Vickery and Leavenworth, *J. Biol. Chem.*, **79**, 377 (1928); Northrop and Anson, *J. Gen. Physiol.*, **12**, 543 (1929).

Reichert and Brown,[53] who showed that oxyhemoglobin crystals differ not only with the species but also with the genus of the animal from which they are obtained, no two hemoglobins forming identical crystals. There is, however, similarity in the crystal structure of the hemoglobins of genetically related animals, as for example the horse and donkey. Indeed the hemoglobin of these animals cannot be differentiated immunologically.[54] Since heme, the non-protein part of all hemoglobins, is the same, the specificity and possible differences in the constitution of different hemoglobins presumably reside in the globin. When Reichert and Brown were engaged in their monumental work, the importance of the reaction and salt concentration was not fully appreciated. As has been pointed out by Hastings,[55] it would be of considerable importance if a crystallographic study comparable to that of Reichert and Brown were made today on crystals from isoelectric, salt-free solutions of hemoglobin.

Absorption Spectra. When white light is transmitted through solutions of hemoglobin, or of compounds related to it, certain wavelengths are absorbed, with the result that these solutions, when examined spectroscopically, exhibit absorption spectra. Oxyhemoglobin or diluted arterial blood shows two absorption bands between the Fraunhofer lines D and E, one narrower than the other. The center of the narrower or α band corresponds to the wavelength $\lambda = 579$ mμ, and that of the second or β band to $\lambda = 542$ mμ. The β band disappears first on dilution. A third band, having its center at $\lambda = 415$ mμ, i.e., in the extreme violet region, may be seen in spectrophotographs of oxyhemoglobin.[56]

Hemoglobin (reduced hemoglobin) shows a spectrum with one broad band between D and E and nearer to D. The center and darkest part of the band corresponds to the wavelength $\lambda = 559$ mμ.

Methemoglobin is formed when blood is treated with ozone, potassium permanganate, potassium ferricyanide, chlorates, nitrites, nitrobenzene, pyrogallol, acetanilide, and many other substances. These compounds when introduced into the organism cause the appearance

[53] "The Crystallography of Hemoglobins," Carnegie Institution of Washington (1909).

[54] Boor and Hektoen in a recent study of the antigenic properties of carbonmonoxide hemoglobin (carefully purified by repeated crystallization) have confirmed the species specificity of hemoglobin and its derivatives. They obtained cross reactions in closely related species, as duck, chicken, and turkey; beef and sheep. *J. Infectious Diseases*, **46**, 1 (1930).

[55] "Colloid Symposium Monograph," **6**, 140 (1928).

[56] The amount of light transmitted may be accurately measured by modern spectrophotometric methods. See for example D. L. Drabkin and J. H. Austin, *J. Biol. Chem.*, **98**, 719 (1932).

of methemoglobin both in the blood and urine. One hydrogen equivalent of oxidizing agent is presumably required in the conversion of reduced hemoglobin into methemoglobin. The Fe in methemoglobin is in the ferric state, Fe^{+++}, whereas in hemoglobin and oxyhemoglobin it is in the ferrous condition, Fe^{++}. In acid solution, methemoglobin shows one band, the center of which corresponds to a wavelength of about $\lambda = 634$ mμ.

The carbon monoxide-hemoglobin spectrum shows two bands; the middle of the first corresponds to wavelength $\lambda = 570$ mμ, and that of the second to $\lambda = 542$ mμ. Carbon-monoxide hemoglobin absorption spectra can be distinguished from oxyhemoglobin spectra by the fact that reducing substances, such as ammoniacal ferrous tartrate (Stokes' reagent), have a less marked effect on the absorption bands of carbon-monoxide hemoglobin than on those of oxyhemoglobin.[57] Hydrogen sulfide hemoglobin and cyanhemoglobin (hydrocyanic acid hemoglobin) likewise give characteristic absorption spectra. They are formed in the blood of individuals poisoned with hydrogen sulfide and cyanide, respectively.

Chemistry of Hemoglobin; Relation to Heme and the Porphyrins. When hemoglobin is treated, under appropriate conditions, with glacial acetic acid and sodium chloride, and the mixture warmed gently, a substance is obtained which crystallizes readily as brown crystals (Fig. 24). This substance is hemin, $C_{34}H_{32}N_4O_4FeCl$.

The other product of the cleavage is globin. Hemin has been re-

---

[57] Carbon monoxide has a greater affinity for hemoglobin than oxygen. The relationship between the proportions of hemoglobin that would unite with oxygen and carbon monoxide at varying gas pressures has been formulated by Douglas, Haldane, and Haldane (*J. Physiol.*, **44**, 275 [1912]), and is expressed mathematically by the equation:

$$\frac{[\text{HbCO}]}{[\text{HbO}_2]} = K\frac{p\text{CO}}{p\text{O}_2}$$

The brackets indicate the concentrations of hemoglobin combined as carbon-monoxide-hemoglobin and as oxyhemoglobin; $p\text{CO}$ and $p\text{O}_2$ the gas tensions, and K the relative affinity constant for hemoglobin for the two gases.

A recently estimated value of K shows that the tendency of hemoglobin (of hemolyzed human blood) to form carbon monoxide-hemoglobin is approximately 210 times greater than the tendency to form oxyhemoglobin (J. Sendroy, S. H. Liu, and D. D. Van Slyke, *Am. J. Physiol.*, **90**, 511 [1929]). When carbon monoxide is breathed, a large proportion of the hemoglobin combines with it. If thereby the amount left to combine with oxygen is sufficiently diminished, the tissues do not obtain sufficient oxygen to maintain life, and death from asphyxiation results. In non-fatal cases of severe carbon monoxide poisoning, permanent injury to the central nervous system may occur, often consisting of a softening of the lenticular nuclei, with a resulting syndrome of paralysis agitans.

cently synthesized by Fischer and Zeile.[58] It contains four methyl-pyrrol radicals and an atom of iron and may be represented by the following structural formula:

Hemin

If the crystals of hemin are treated with sodium hydroxide, the corresponding base is liberated. The reaction may be represented by the equation:

$$C_{34}H_{32}N_4O_4FeCl + NaOH = C_{34}H_{32}N_4O_4FeOH + NaCl$$
Hemin   Heme

Although the free base has not been isolated, its properties and derivatives are well known. It was formerly called *hematin* and the term is still adhered to by some. *Heme* is the name that has been given to it by Anson and Mirsky.[59]

Hematin (or heme) may be reduced to a substance which some call *reduced hematin* or *reduced alkali hematin*, but which Anson and Mirsky

[58] *Ann.*, **468**, 98 (1929). It is not definitely known to which pair of nitrogen atoms the iron atom is attached.

[59] *J. Physiol.*, **60**, 50, 161, 221 (1925); Anson, Barcroft, Mirsky, and Onuma, *Proc. Roy. Soc. (London)*, B, **97**, 61 (1925); *J. Gen. Physiol.*, **12**, 273 (1928–29); *ibid.*, **12**, 581 (1929).

have called *reduced heme*. This may also be produced directly from hemin by treatment of the latter with sodium hydroxide, in the presence of a reducing agent, such as sodium hydrosulfite, $Na_2S_2O_4$. The formation of reduced heme is indicated as follows:

$$C_{34}H_{32}N_4O_4FeOH \rightarrow C_{34}H_{32}N_4O_4Fe$$

Heme   Reduced Heme

The relation of these compounds to hemoglobin will be considered shortly.

The Porphyrins. An iron-free pigment is obtained when blood, hemoglobin, hemochromogen, hematin, or hemin is treated with strong acids. This pigment, which has been called *hematoporphyrin*, is also formed by the action of bacteria on hemoglobin, and it may be extracted from putrefying blood with ether and acetic acid. Hematoporphyrin has the formula $C_{34}H_{38}O_6N_4$. Its derivation from hemin may be indicated as follows, representing for convenience only the parts of the structural formula (p. 238) involved in the transformation.

FIG. 24. — Hemin crystals. (After Nencki and Zaleski, *Z. physiol. Chem.* **30**, 423 (1900).)

1.

2. Each of the two vinyl groups of hemin takes up a molecule of H_2O:

When hematoporphyrin is heated with soda lime, it yields a porphyrin having the formula $C_{32}H_{38}N_4$. This is identical with *ætioporphyrin* derived from chlorophyll. Thus we see the close chemical relationship of chlorophyll to hemoglobin.

The porphyrin related to hemin is *protoporphyrin*, $C_{34}H_{34}N_4O_4$. With the introduction of an iron atom into the molecule, neutral heme is formed, which may be isolated as hemin, indistinguishable from the product derived from hemoglobin.

Other porphyrins occur naturally. Egg-shells contain *ooporphyrin*, an isomer of protoporphyrin. *Coproporphyrin*, $C_{36}H_{36}O_8N_4$, is said to be a product of intestinal putrefaction and a constituent of feces. It has also been isolated from certain yeasts and is said to be present in the serum of various animals,[60] including man, and in the urine of individuals with congenital porphyrinuria.[61]

Aetioporphyrin

Uroporphyrin, $C_{40}H_{38}O_{16}N_4$, is likewise excreted in the urine in congenital porphyrinuria. The copper salt of this compound is the pigment turacin,[62] present in the feathers of the turaco, a South African bird. These are but a few of the many examples which may be cited to illustrate the widespread distribution and chemical relationship of the porphyrin derivatives in nature.

[60] H. Fink, *Biochem. Z.*, **211**, 65 (1929).

[61] A. A. H. van den Bergh, *Proc. Acad. Sci. Amsterdam*; cited in *Chem. Ann.*, **26**, 245 (1929).

A review entitled "The Porphyrins in Human Disease" has been recently prepared by V. R. Mason, C. Courville, and E. Ziskind, *Medicine*, **12**, 355 (1933).

In the presence of light and oxygen, hematoporphyrin is said to possess proteolytic activity, being capable of hydrolyzing fibrinogen, as well as serum albumin. W. H. Howell, *Arch. Internat. physiol.*, **18**, 269 (1931); M. J. Boyd, *J. Biol. Chem.*, **103**, 249 (1933).

[62] This pigment and the related metaloporphyrins have been studied by P. P. Laidlaw, *J. Physiol.*, **31**, 464 (1904); J. A. Milroy, *ibid.*, **38**, 384 (1909); D. Keilin, *Proc. Roy. Soc. (London)*, *B*, **100**, 129 (1926). It was first described by A. H. Church, *Proc. Roy. Soc. (London)*, **51**, 399 (1892); *Phil. Trans.*, *B*, **183**, 511 (1892). The relationship to uroporphyrin is discussed by Fischer and Hilger, *Z. physiol Chem.*, **138**, 49 (1924).

Isomeric Modifications. On examining the structural formula of ætioporphyrin it will be seen that, by altering the sequence of the methyl and ethyl side-chain groups, a series of isomers would be obtained. In the case of this pigment, four isomeric forms are theoretically possible, and all four have been synthesized by Hans Fischer and his pupils. Protoporphyrin and hematoporphyrin each have fifteen possible isomers, but only two of each have been synthesized so far. Mesoporphyrin, $C_{34}H_{38}O_4N_4$ (containing the following side chains: $4CH_3$, $2C_2H_5$, $2CH=CH_2$), has fifteen possible isomers, of which twelve have been synthesized. All four theoretical isomers of coproporphyrin have been prepared and two of the fifteen isomers of ooporphyrin.

Corresponding to the fifteen protoporphyrins, an equal number of hemins is theoretically possible. Two have been synthesized, one being the natural derivative of hemoglobin. Similarly from the many other porphyrins, natural and synthetic, it is theoretically possible to prepare a series of hemes (and hemins) through their union with iron. This has been done in many cases; from mesoporphyrin and ætioporphyrin, mesohemin and ætiohemin have been prepared. Of the extremely large number of possible hemes, we are, however, primarily concerned with only one, the heme of hemoglobin.

Bilirubin. It is permissible to digress at this point in order to consider the relation of the bile pigments to heme. It has been pointed out elsewhere that bilirubin is formed in the breakdown of hemoglobin in the cells of the reticulo-endothelial system, especially in the liver. Bilirubin gives no absorption spectrum, from which it has been inferred that the porphyrin ring system is probably absent. On the basis of the present knowledge of its chemical properties, the following formula has been tentatively suggested ($X = CH_3 \cdot CH_2 \cdot COOH$).

Structurally this is related to an unnatural isomer of ætiporphyrin. Accordingly the assumption has been made that the formation of bilirubin may involve the intermediary degradation of heme to pyrrole units.[63]

Heme and Its Derivatives. Heme combines with a large variety of organic nitrogenous substances to form a series of compounds that

[63] A brief summary of the subject of pyrrole pigments with a complete bibliography of recent work is to be found in the Annual Reports of the Chemical Society of London, **29**, 209–219 (1932).

are now described as *hemochromogens*. These substances exhibit the same absorption spectrum pattern, but for individual members of the group, the absorption bands occupy somewhat different positions. The most familiar hemochromogen is derived from hemoglobin by the action of alkali and a reducing agent.[64] Hoppe-Seyler (1870)[65] thought that the product of this reaction was a substance represented by the formula $C_{34}H_{35}N_4O_4Fe$, and that it was this which gave the characteristic absorption spectrum. Accordingly the name " hemochromogen " was at first associated with this compound only. This conception was, however, erroneous.

Largely to the work of Anson and Mirsky[66] we owe a more correct understanding of the relationship between hemoglobin and hemochromogen. Several years before our knowledge of the heme compounds, as summarized in the preceding pages, had advanced to the present stage, they showed that when hemin is reduced in an alkaline solution, the resulting compound does not give the spectrum of hemochromogen. However, when globin is added the spectrum of hemochromogen appears. The work of these investigators, the details of which cannot be considered here, established the fact that the substance which gave what until then had been called the hemochromogen spectrum was a conjugated protein, consisting of globin and the base $C_{34}H_{32}N_4O_4Fe$.

In hemoglobin, heme is attached to *native*, i.e., undenatured, globin; in globin-hemochromogen the combination is with *denatured* globin. There is no clear evidence that the two differ in other respects, as for example in their molecular weights, or in the manner in which the globin and heme are combined.

The synthetic hemochromogens include combinations of heme with albumin, pyridine, nicotine, piperidine, hydrazine, cyanide, ammonia, glycine, and other organic nitrogenous compounds. The relation of heme to these hemochromogens may be represented as follows:

$$\text{Heme} + \text{nitrogenous substance} \rightleftarrows \text{hemochromogen}$$

The various synthetic hemochromogens do not give identical absorption spectra, but they are sufficiently close to explain why the older workers, using less accurate spectroscopes, did not recognize the true

---

[64] This reaction and the resulting absorption spectrum were first studied by the physicist G. Stokes: *Proc. Roy. Soc. (London)*, **13**, 355 (1863–4).

[65] *Ber.*, **3**, 229 (1870).

[66] *J. Physiol.*, **60**, 50, 161, 221 (1925); Anson, Barcroft, Mirsky, and Onuma, *Proc. Roy. Soc. (London)*, *B*, **97**, 61 (1925); *J. Gen. Physiol.*, **12**, 273 (1928–29); *ibid.*, **12**, 581 (1929).

nature of hemochromogen.   In liberating the base from hemin, ammonia was often used.   On subsequent reduction, instead of obtaining the reduced base, as was thought, a complex of this substance with ammonia, or as it would now be called, ammonia-hemochromogen, was formed. This substance gives an absorption spectrum which sufficiently resembles that given by the hemochromogen obtained directly from hemoglobin to have been mistaken for it.

Undenatured globin combines with heme to form crystallizable hemoglobin.[67]

Helicorubin, Actiniohematin, Chlorocruorin, and Hemocyanin. *Helicorubin* is a respiratory pigment found in the liver and gut of the snail (*Helix pomatia*) and other pulmonate molluscs, as well as in the liver of the crayfish.   It is a hemochromogen composed of globin and heme.   Artificial hemochromogens prepared from this pigment are identical with those derived from hemoglobin.   Helicorubin combines with oxygen, forming a compound capable of dissociation, thus resembling hemoglobin.   However, it differs from hemoglobin in that its affinity for oxygen is greatest in a slightly acid medium.

Actiniohematin is a respiratory pigment, resembling helicorubin, which occurs in certain actinia.   *Chlorocruorin* occurs in marine worms of the polychæte family.   In concentrated solution it is reddish, whereas in dilute solution it has a green color.   It may be oxidized and reduced like hemoglobin, which it resembles in other ways.   Chlorocruorin yields derivatives corresponding to methemoglobin, hemochromogen, hematin, and hematoporphyrin.   The artificial hemochromogens prepared from chlorocruorin, however, yield an absorption spectrum differing from the hemochromogen derived from hemoglobin, and it is therefore concluded that the porphyrin of chlorocruorin is different from protoporphyrin.[68]

Hemocyanin is a copper-containing respiratory pigment found in certain crustaceans and molluscs.   In the oxidized state it is blue; in the reduced state it is colorless.   The hemocyanins derived from *Limulus polyphemus* (king-crab), and *Helix pomatia* (snail) are among the more familiar examples.   Formerly hemocyanin was considered to be an analogue of hemoglobin, but this is unlikely inasmuch as there is no

[67] For further details the student is referred to a review by Anson and Mirsky, "Hemoglobin, the Heme Pigments and Cellular Respiration," *Physiol. Rev.*, **10**, 506 (1930); see also Anson and Mirsky, *J. Gen. Physiol.*, **14**, 605 (1931); R. Hill and H. Holden, *Biochem. J.*, **20**, 1326 (1926); *ibid.*, **21**, 625 (1927).

[68] Warburg and Christian have pointed out a relationship of the heme of chlorocruorin to the iron addition compound of pheohemin *b*, a chlorophyll derivative. *Biochem. Z.*, **235**, 240 (1931).

evidence for the existence of a copper-porphyrin nucleus in the molecule, as was supposed. Some of the more recent observations have added both to the confusion and interest of the subject. The hemocyanin of *Octopus* has pH 4.8 as its isoelectric point; the hemocyanin of *Limulus* has its isoelectric point between 6.2 and 6.4. The hemocyanin of *Helix pomatia* may be readily crystallized; yet determinations of its molecular weight have yielded a value of 4,930,000 (Svedberg). Whether this represents the actual molecule or an aggregate of many molecules is an open question. The copper may be removed from the hemocyanin molecule in an acid solution (pH 2.5).[69]

The Biological Significance of Heme Compounds; Cytochrome. If the occurrence of heme were limited only to hemoglobin, it would still be one of the most widely distributed and most important substances in nature. However, hemoglobin is not the only heme compound; there are others which are much more widely distributed. There exists an intracellular pigment in aerobic bacteria, yeast, higher plants, and animals. It was first observed in muscle and other tissues by MacMunn[70] in 1886 and named histohematin, but it is to the more recent work of Keilin[71] that we owe most of our knowledge of the subject. This pigment, renamed cytochrome, is capable of existing in an oxidized and in a reduced form. In the latter condition, it exhibits an absorption spectrum of four bands. Whatever the source of the cytochrome, these bands occupy approximately the same positions, namely, $a = 6046$; $b = 5665$; $c = 5502$; $d = 5210$, expressed in Ångstrom units.

The work of Keilin has shown that cytochrome is not one substance, but a mixture of three independent hemochromogen-like compounds, a', b', c', capable of being oxidized and reduced independently from one another. In addition to these hemochromogens, or even in their absence, all cells of aerobic organisms contain a free unbound heme, which is apparently identical with the heme of hemoglobin.

The pigments designated collectively as cytochrome are found in highest concentration in cells capable of active metabolism. Heart muscle of mammals and birds, the pectoral muscle of flying birds, the thoracic muscles of flying insects, baker's yeast, and certain bacteria are

[69] Recent studies of the chemistry of hemocyanins include the following: J. B. Conant and W. G. Humphrey, *Proc. Nat. Acad. Sci.*, **16**, 543 (1930); A. Schmitz, *Naturwissenchaften*, **18**, 798 (1930); J. Roche, *Arch. phys. biol.*, **7**, 207 (1930); F. Herneler and E. Philippi, *Z. physiol. Chem.*, **191**, 23 (1930); T. Svedberg, *J. Biol. Chem.*, **103**, 311 (1933). The last includes a study of the molecular weights and isoelectric points of other respiratory pigments, as well.

[70] *Phil. Trans. Roy. Soc.*, **177**, 267 (1886)

[71] *Proc. Roy. Soc.* (*London*), B, **98**, 312 (1925); **100**, 206 (1928–29); *Nature*, **119**, 670 (1927).

among the active tissues that are especially rich in cytochrome. This striking relation of the concentration of pigment to tissue activity, as well as other experimental data, has led to the conclusion that cytochrome plays an important rôle in physiological oxidations, a view strengthened by recent reports that certain enzymes associated with cellular respiration (catalase, peroxidase, Warburg's so-called respiratory ferment) are derivatives of heme. In the succeeding chapter this phase of the subject will receive further attention.

THE CHEMISTRY OF RESPIRATION

Mechanism for the Transportation of Oxygen. Hemoglobin is not a catalyst of oxidations, but a passive carrier of oxygen. The transportation of oxygen by the blood from the lungs to the tissues depends on a reversible chemical reaction between hemoglobin and oxygen, as represented by the equation:

$$Hb + O_2 \rightleftharpoons HbO_2$$

where Hb stands for hemoglobin.[72] Reduced hemoglobin is readily oxidized to oxyhemoglobin when exposed to oxygen of such concentration as exists in the lungs; oxyhemoglobin is, in turn, dissociated at low oxygen tensions, such as obtain in the tissues. These reactions occur with extreme rapidity, requiring but a fraction of a second, as has been shown by Hartridge and Roughton.[73] It should also be mentioned at the outset that not all of the hemoglobin is oxidized in the lungs, nor is all of the oxygen given up in the tissues.

[72] Since it has been shown that the molecular weight of hemoglobin is four times what it was formerly thought to be, oxyhemoglobin is more accurately represented by the formula Hb_4O_8, where Hb_4 denotes a molecule of reduced hemoglobin having a molecular weight of 66,800. The question has been raised whether this is the only form of combination of hemoglobin with oxygen. Indeed, Adair (*J. Biol. Chem.*, **63**, 529 [1925]) has attempted to explain the equilibrium between oxygen and hemoglobin on the assumption that the latter combines with oxygen in steps to form Hb_4O_2, Hb_4O_4, Hb_4O_6, and Hb_4O_8. The equilibrium relations between oxygen and hemoglobin have also been studied recently by Ferry and Green (*J. Biol. Chem.*, **81**, 175 [1929]) and by Conant and McGrew (*ibid.*, **85**, 421 [1929–30]). The latter workers found that if solutions of oxyhemoglobin are deoxygenated, the Hb_4O_8 persists and does not disappear as would happen if it were converted into the intermediate products (Hb_4O_6, Hb_4O_4, Hb_4O_2), which have much higher solubilities than the fully oxidized hemoglobin. Conant and McGrew have suggested that, if intermediate oxidation products of hemoglobin are formed, they are present in very small quantities.

[73] *Proc. Roy. Soc.* (*London*), A, **104**, 395 (1923).

In a mixture of gases, each gas exerts its own partial pressure. The oxygen content of the air at sea level is about 21 per cent. From this it follows that the partial pressure of the oxygen in the air is about 160 mm. of mercury, when the atmospheric pressure is 760 mm. In the alveoli of the lungs the oxygen content is only about 14 per cent; this is equivalent to approximately 106 mm. of mercury. Ordinarily, this is the maximum oxygen tension to which the hemoglobin of the blood is exposed in the course of its circulation.

One liter of plasma saturated with alveolar air takes up about 3 cc. of oxygen. The oxygen capacity of the blood is about 1 liter, this amount of oxygen being ordinarily sufficient for tissue needs. If we were dependent, therefore, upon the solubility of oxygen in the blood alone, our circulatory system would have to contain about 300 liters of fluid or about four times our body weight. Due to the presence of hemoglobin the enormous quantity of oxygen which we need is handled by about 6 liters of blood. As stated by Barcroft, "the warm-blooded creation owes its existence, or at all events its activity, to hemoglobin."[74]

In passing through the capillaries of the lungs, the blood is exposed to an oxygen tension of about 100–110 mm. of mercury. As it leaves the lungs, the blood (i.e., arterial blood) has an oxygen content of about 19 volumes per cent; the tension is about 80 mm. of mercury; the percentage saturation of the hemoglobin is 93–98 per cent.[75] In the tissues

[74] In man, and perhaps in other animals, the quantity of hemoglobin appears to be regulated by the demand for oxygen and its supply. Thus, at high altitudes, where the amount of oxygen is reduced, the quantity of hemoglobin in the blood is increased. A striking illustration of this is to be found in the observations of Barcroft and his associates, who studied the blood of the natives in the Cerro de Pasco region of the Peruvian Andes, 14,000–15,000 feet above sea level. Of twelve cases studied, one had 150 per cent of the normal amount of hemoglobin; three had from 140–149 per cent; four gave hemoglobin values from 130 to 139 per cent; and the remaining four had from 120 to 129 per cent of the normal amount observed in man at sea level. *Phil. Trans. Royal Soc.*, B, **211**, 351 (1922–23). A fascinating account of the expedition to Cerro de Pasco is given in J. Barcroft's "The Respiratory Function of the Blood," Part I, Lessons from High Altitudes, 2d Edition, Cambridge, 1925.

A. Grollman, *Am. J. Physiol.*, **93**, 19 (1930), in a series of determinations found a steady increase in hemoglobin to 140 per cent during the first two weeks of a prolonged stay on Pike's Peak (altitude, 14,109 feet).

A. Hurtado, *Am. J. Physiol.*, **100**, 487 (1932) has made a large number of observations on the Indian natives of the Peruvian Andes. His results are in conflict with those obtained by Barcroft.

[75] These are approximately the values obtained in the resting subject. Compare L. J. Henderson, "Blood, A Study in General Physiology," pp. 195, 201. For the changes occurring during work, see Chap. IX.

the oxygen tension is much lower, perhaps of the magnitude of 0–10 mm. of mercury.[76] Consequently when the blood reaches the tissues, a part of the oxyhemoglobin is dissociated, and, as the oxygen is liberated, there is a progressive fall in the oxygen tension of the blood. The blood returning from the tissues to the lungs, i.e., venous blood, has an oxygen content about 15 volumes per cent and a tension of about 40 mm. of mercury; the percentage saturation of the hemoglobin is usually 60–70 per cent. The liberated oxygen passes from the blood to the lymph and from the lymph to the tissues, and there takes part in the processes of oxidation, which we shall consider in succeeding chapters.

Factors Influencing the Combination of Hemoglobin and Oxygen.— *Effect of Temperature.* As is true of many other chemical combinations, the union of oxygen and hemoglobin is less the higher the temperature. Thus, when blood is allowed to come to equilibrium with oxygen at a tension of 100 mm. of mercury, 93 per cent will become saturated at 38° C., and 98 per cent at 25° C. Under a pressure of 10 mm., at a temperature of 38° C., 56 per cent of the hemoglobin will still be in combination with oxygen, whereas at 25° C. the amount in combination will be 88 per cent. This means that, with a drop in oxygen tension commensurate with the difference between the pressure in the lungs and in the tissues, the amount of oxygen that becomes available for purposes of metabolism is greater at the higher than at the lower temperature. From this point of view, the advantage of being a warm-blooded animal is fairly obvious. These relationships are more completely illustrated in the accompanying diagram (Fig. 25) in which are presented a number of oxyhemoglobin-dissociation curves obtained at different temperatures.

Effect of Electrolytes. At low oxygen tensions, oxyhemoglobin is more readily dissociated in the presence of salts than in pure solution. If the temperature is maintained constant at 38° C., the saturation of hemoglobin in the presence of electrolytes may be reduced to less than one-half of what it is in pure solution, at an oxygen tension of 10 mm. of mercury. That this effect is not operative at higher pressures is shown by the curves in Fig. 26, where an increase in the combining capacity of the hemoglobin is actually indicated at 100 mm.

Effect of Carbon Dioxide. A third factor influencing the efficiency of hemoglobin as a carrier of oxygen is carbon dioxide. In view of the

[76] Much higher values have been cited, namely 50–20 mm. (or less) for extra-cellular tissue fluid and 40–20 mm. for the oxygen tension within the cell. J. A. Campbell, "Gas Tension in the Tissues," *Physiol. Rev.*, **11**, 1 (1931).

acidity of carbonic acid, the effect of carbon dioxide may be referred to the hydrogen-ion concentration changes. This relationship has been studied by Barcroft and Poulton[77] and others. More recently, Bock, Field, and Adair[78] obtained oxygen-dissociation curves for normal blood at carbon-dioxide tensions of 3, 20, 40, and 80 mm. of mercury. From

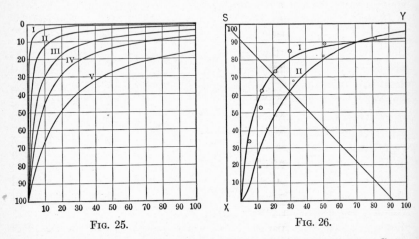

FIG. 25.   FIG. 26.

FIG. 25.—Dissociation curves of oxyhemoglobin at different temperatures. Curves I, II, III, IV, and V correspond to 16°, 25°, 32°, 38°, and 49° C., respectively. Ordinates = percentage of reduced hemoglobin; abscissas = tension of oxygen in millimeters of mercury. (After Barcroft and Hill, *J. Physiol.*, **39**, 422 [1909–10].)
FIG. 26.—Effect of electrolytes on the dissociation curve of oxyhemoglobin. Ordinates = percentage saturation of hemoglobin with oxygen; abscissas = tension of oxygen in millimeters of mercury. ° Points determined from dialyzed solution. ° Points determined from undialyzed solution. Curve I (electrolytes absent) = rectangular hyperbola; $xy = 800$. Curve II (electrolytes present in low concentration) = Bohr's dissociation curve for hemoglobin (see *Zentr. Physiol.*, **17**, 682, 688 (1903–04)). (After Barcroft and Roberts, *J. Physiol.*, **39**, 146 (1909–10).)

their results, some of which are reproduced below (Fig. 27), it may be seen that carbon dioxide, while not hindering, to any appreciable extent, the formation of oxyhemoglobin in the lungs, greatly facilitates its dissociation in the tissues. In the removal of carbon dioxide from the tissues, which is intimately associated with its rôle in the transportation of oxygen, hemoglobin plays an important part. This function will be discussed presently.

The isoelectric point of oxyhemoglobin as given by Adair is 6.6, and of reduced hemoglobin, 6.81. On the acid side of the isoelectric

77 *J. Physiol.*, **46**, iv (1913).
78 *J. Biol. Chem.*, **59**, 353 (1924).

point of hemoglobin its affinity for oxygen is less than on the alkaline side. The oxyhemoglobin dissociation curves obtained at various hydrogen-ion concentrations have been described by Adair.[79]

Mechanism for the Transportation of Carbon Dioxide. The carbon dioxide content of atmospheric air is about 0.02 to 0.03 per cent, corresponding to a tension which is negligible (0.15 to 0.23 mm. of mercury). At rest the alveolar air contains about 5.5 per cent carbon dioxide, equivalent to a tension of 40–42 mm. This is essentially the same in arterial blood, which, however, has a total carbon dioxide content of 45 to 50 volumes per cent. Venous blood contains 50 to 55 volumes per cent of carbon dioxide and the pressure is about 45–47 mm. of mercury.[80] Presumably the carbon dioxide tension is somewhat above this value in the intracellular and extracellular fluid of the tissues. In short, if diffusion plays an important part in gaseous exchange, as it evidently does, the direction for carbon dioxide would be from the tissues to the blood and in turn to the lungs and the outside air.

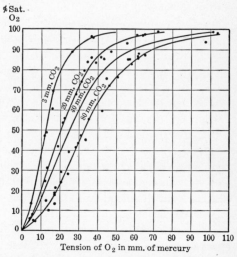

FIG. 27.—Effect of carbon dioxide on the dissociation of oxyhemoglobin. (After Bock, Field and Adair.)

Does Hemoglobin Combine with Carbon Dioxide? The relatively large amounts of carbon dioxide carried in the blood at the corresponding low tensions indicates that the greater proportion is not in solution,

---

[79] *Ibid.*, **63**, 529 (1925).

[80] Data are given by Henderson (p. 259) comparing the pCO_2 (CO_2 tension in millimeters of mercury) of the blood at work and at rest (subject A. V.).

	Arterial	Venous
Work................	38	54.8
Rest................	40	45.4

but in some form of combination. Considering also that the transportation of oxygen depends almost exclusively on its reversible chemical union with hemoglobin, it is logical to inquire whether a similar combination does not occur with carbon dioxide. Indeed such a reaction was assumed by Bohr,[81] who based his conclusions partly on the observation that hemoglobin solutions, even if they are first rendered slightly acid, will combine with considerable amounts of carbon dioxide.

The present supporters of this idea have been particularly impressed with the effect of hemoglobin in increasing enormously the rate of liberation of CO_2 from solutions containing carbonic acid and bicarbonate. The reactions $H_2CO_3 \rightleftharpoons H_2O + CO_2$, or $HCO_3^- \rightleftharpoons CO_2 + OH^-$, are ordinarily slow ones. Two divergent explanations have been advanced for the rapid evolution of carbon dioxide in the lungs and in artificial systems containing hemoglobin. Henriques[82] has been prominently associated with the conception of the existence of an $Hb \cdot CO_2$ compound capable of rapid dissociation. Others[83] have considered this view untenable and have attributed the rapid dissociation of carbon dioxide from the blood to the catalytic action of hemoglobin.

On the other hand, Margaria and Green[84] have reported that the presence or absence of hemoglobin influences the first dissociation constant of carbonic acid. This is suggestive of the existence of a carbon dioxide-hemoglobin complex. The point of attachment is apparently not the same as for oxygen. Other considerations of a physicochemical nature have been brought into the discussion in support of the conception that carbon dioxide combines chemically with hemoglobin.

Weighing the evidence, the possibility of the existence of an $Hb \cdot CO_2$ complex cannot be excluded. Nevertheless the amount thus formed

[81] C. Bohr, in Nagel's "Handbuch der Physiologie," 2, 106 (1905); Bohr's theory is also discussed in J. S. Haldane's "Respiration," p. 87, Yale Univ. Press, New Haven, 1922.

[82] *Ergebnisse Physiol.*, 28, 624 (1929); *J. Biol. Chem.*, 92, 1 (1931). See also M. N. J. Dirken and H. W. Mook, *J. Physiol.*, 70, 373 (1930).

[83] D. D. Van Slyke and J. A. Hawkins, *J. Biol. Chem.*, 87. 265 (1930); W. C. Stadie and H. O'Brien, *ibid.*, 92 (Proc.), xxvii (1931). More recently Stadie and O'Brien in a reconsideration of the catalytic mechanism for the uptake (hydration) or release (dehydration) of carbon dioxide in the tissues and lungs respectively have reported the isolation from the red blood cell of an active principle presumably an enzyme which accelerates greatly the velocity of this reaction (*J. Biol. Chem.*, 100 (Proc.), lxxxviii (1933); 103, 521 (1933). N. U. Meldrum and F. J. W. Roughton, however, were the first to report the isolation of an enzyme ("carbonic anhydrase") which catalyzes the dehydration of H_2CO_3 and the hydration of CO_2. Proc. Roy. Soc. (*London*), 111, 296 (1932); *J. Physiol.*, 75, Proc., 3 P (1932).

[84] *J. Biol. Chem.*, 102, 611 (1933); see also R. Brinkman and R. Margaria, *J. Physiol.*, 72, Proc. 6 P (1931); Margaria, 73, 311 (1931).

is apparently relatively small, and it is hence probably safe to assume that the transportation of carbon dioxide in the organism does not depend upon it. From this it should not be inferred that hemoglobin does not participate in the transportation of carbon dioxide, for indeed it does and in a very significant manner, but as we shall see shortly the mechanism involved is of a different type from that concerned in the carrying of oxygen.

State of Carbon Dioxide in the Blood. If the amount of carbon dioxide ordinarily carried in the blood were dissolved in an equivalent volume of water, the hydrogen-ion concentration of the resulting solution would approximate 3.0×10^{-5}. Were the blood to become as acid as this, life would cease immediately. Actually, the hydrogen-ion concentration of the blood is only about one-thousandth of this value. How, then, is the blood able to carry so much carbon dioxide and yet remain an alkaline solution? In attempting to answer this question, we become involved in another very important problem which has to do with the mechanism whereby the blood maintains its hydrogen-ion concentration within fixed limits.

There are four forms in which carbon dioxide can exist in solution: (1) as free anhydrous carbon dioxide; (2) as carbonic acid (H_2CO_3); (3) as bicarbonate; and (4) as carbonate. It may be assumed that, in water, a constant amount, if not all, of the free CO_2 would change into H_2CO_3, particularly as the water concentration remains constant. It is also apparent that, in the presence of carbonic acid, carbonates are changed to bicarbonates as follows:

$$B_2CO_3 + H_2CO_3 = 2BHCO_3$$

where B is used to represent a monovalent base such as sodium or potassium. The conditions in the blood are such that only H_2CO_3 and $BHCO_3$ can possibly exist.[85] It is very important that both of these be present

[85] Peters and Van Slyke ("Quantitative Clinical Chemistry," Vol. 1, p. 885) give the following proportions of total CO_2 in the forms of free carbonic acid, bicarbonate, and carbonate at physiological reactions:

	Percentage of Total CO_2 as		
pH	H_2CO_3	$BHCO_3$	B_2CO_3
7.0	11.0	88.8	0.16
7.4	4.8	94.8	0.4
7.8	2.0	97.0	1.0

in certain more or less definite proportions. As Van Slyke[86] points out, if the CO_2 were all present as H_2CO_3, the blood would be a thousand times more acid than it is. If the CO_2 were all present as bicarbonate, the blood would be hundreds of times too alkaline. There is normally a definite balance or ratio between the amount of CO_2 present as H_2CO_3 and the amount present as $BHCO_3$. Because there is a mechanism which makes this balance possible, the blood is able to carry large amounts of carbon dioxide from the tissues to the lungs, to be excreted, without the production of any very marked change in its hydrogen-ion concentration. We shall now examine the nature of this mechanism.

The Nature of Buffers. Buffer action may be defined as the resistance to change in hydrogen-ion concentration. Solutions may be prepared of mixtures of acids or bases with an excess of alkali salts in the case of the acids, and, in the case of the bases, an excess of their salts with strong acids. Such solutions are termed " buffer solutions " and are distinguished by the fact that upon dilution, or the addition of moderate amounts of acid or base, but little effect upon their hydrogen-ion concentration is produced.

Buffer action may be illustrated by the following example. If, to a liter of pure water of pH 7.0, we should add 1 cc. of 0.01 N hydrochloric acid, the hydrogen-ion concentration of the resulting solution would become equivalent to a pH of about 5.0. If, however, instead of using pure water, we should add the same amount of acid to water containing potassium acid phosphate (KH_2PO_4) and potassium hydroxide in such proportion as to give the solution a pH value of 7.0, the resulting change in hydrogen-ion concentration would be hardly measurable.

The behavior of sodium acetate as a buffer is similar. When added to acetic acid, sodium acetate reduces the ionization of the acid and consequently the C_H of the solution. If, to a solution of acetic acid and sodium acetate, hydrochloric acid is added, little effect is produced on the hydrogen-ion concentration, as the hydrogen ions combine with acetate ions to form the weakly ionized acetic acid. On the other hand, the same amount of hydrochloric acid added to water or to a solution of sodium chloride would cause a marked increase in hydrogen ions. The sodium acetate-acetic acid solution would also be effective against hydroxyl ions. The addition of a base like sodium hydroxide would result in its reaction with the acetic acid to give sodium acetate.

Fernbach and Hubert,[87] who first studied the power of certain solutions to resist changes in reaction, compared their action to that of a tampon. Sørensen translated this by the German word " Puffer."

[86] *Physiol. Rev.*, **1**, 141 (1921).　　　　[87] *Compt. rend.*, **131**, 293 (1900).

In translating this into English, the word " buffer " has been adopted. Various analogies have been employed to explain buffer action. A buffer has been compared to a sponge having the capacity of " soaking up " hydrogen and hydroxyl ions. It has also been likened to a shock absorber. Just as a shock absorber blocks the transmission of the full force of an impact, so a chemical buffer resists the change in H^+ ion concentration which tends to occur when acid or alkali is added.

The Buffers of the Blood.   The buffers of the blood are salts of weak acids. These are the bicarbonates, phosphates, and alkali salts of the proteins, including both hemoglobin and oxyhemoglobin. In each case, however, part of the buffer is present as the free acid, the remainder as the salt of the weak acid with a strong base. We thus have a number of what we might term buffer pairs. These are:

$$\frac{H_2CO_3}{BHCO_3}, \quad \frac{BH_2PO_4}{B_2HPO_4}, \quad \frac{HHbO_2}{BHbO_2}, \quad \frac{HHb}{BHb}, \quad \frac{H\text{ protein}}{B\text{ protein}}$$

B is used here to indicate any monovalent base such as sodium or potassium, $HHbO_2$ the free oxyhemoglobin, $BHbO_2$ the alkali salt of oxyhemoglobin, HHb the free or acid hemoglobin, BHb the basic salt of hemoglobin, H protein the free protein, and B protein the alkali proteinate, respectively.

The maintenance of the acid-base balance of the blood is not dependent upon any one buffer pair, but rather upon the total effect of several such pairs. The advantage of such an arrangement in providing security against acidosis or alkalosis may be likened to the advantage of having five sentinels on duty instead of one. It is obviously unsafe to leave a single individual to safeguard a treasure or to hold and defend a mountain pass against an enemy. No matter how well armed he may be, he is always in great danger of being overcome. Five guards strategically placed would constitute a much more solid defense. If one or two of the guards were overcome there would still be a few left to hold the enemy back for a time, perhaps even until help arrived. This analogy, crude as it may be, is quite apropos if we suppose the enemy to be H^+ or OH^- ions, and the mountain pass the outer limits of the normal pH range of the blood. Of course, all five guards in our analogy might be overcome. Translated into terms of acid-base balance, this is what happens when severe acidosis or alkalosis develops.

General Laws.   There are two general laws which may be applied to buffer solutions:[88]

---

[88] L. J. Henderson, *Ergebnisse Physiol.*, **8**, 254 (1909), see also Van Slyke.[86]

1. The hydrogen-ion concentration of a buffer solution is proportional to the ratio $\dfrac{\text{free buffer acid}}{\text{buffer salt}} = \dfrac{\text{HA}}{\text{BA}}$, where A represents the acid radical and B a monovalent base.

2. A given buffer mixture is most efficient in maintaining constancy of pH when the ratio $\dfrac{\text{HA}}{\text{BA}}$ is equal to 1, and when H^+ approximates K, the dissociation constant of the free acid forming one of the buffer pairs.

Relationship between pH and the Ratio $\dfrac{\text{HA}}{\text{BA}}$. The proof of the first law will be considered at this point. The dissociation of an acid HA may be represented by the equation $HA = H^+ + A^-$. From the law of mass action, it follows that, when equilibrium is reached,

$$K \times \text{HA} = H^+ \times A^- \tag{1}$$

where K is the dissociation constant of the acid. Therefore,

$$H^+ = K \frac{\text{HA}}{A^-} \tag{2}$$

However, in buffer mixtures of the type with which we are concerned, there is to be considered not only the weak acid, but the salt of the acid as well. No matter which of the buffer pairs we may select, the dissociation of the free acid is negligible as compared with the dissociation of the salt BA (salt of a weak acid and a strong base). It is to be noted here that the salts are present in the blood in low concentration, which means that they are, relatively speaking highly dissociated (60–90 per cent). The degree of dissociation, which may be represented by λ, will not vary appreciably for any given base over the range of its concentration in the blood. The concentration of the anions A^- is therefore equal to λBA. Substituting in Equation (2),

$$H^+ = K \frac{\text{HA}}{\lambda \text{BA}} \tag{3}$$

As λ remains practically constant, the above equation may be simplified by substituting K_1 for K/λ. Thus,

$$H^+ = K_1 \frac{\text{HA}}{\text{BA}} \tag{4}$$

Expressed in terms of pH, Equation (4) becomes

$$p\text{H} = - \log K_1 - \log \frac{\text{HA}}{\text{BA}} \tag{5}$$

The symbol pK_1 may be used to signify the logarithm of the reciprocal of K_1. Hence Equation (5) may be written

$$pH = pK_1 + \log \frac{BA}{HA}. \tag{6}$$

For any given buffer pair, pK_1 remains practically constant. It is 6.1 for $BHCO_3 : H_2CO_3$ (Hasselbach corrected by Van Slyke). For the phosphates it is 6.8. By substituting these values for pK_1 in Equation (6), it becomes possible to calculate the ratio of a buffer mixture for any given pH, or, if the ratio is known, the pH may be calculated.

Efficiency of Buffers. According to the second generalization, the maximum efficiency of a buffer is obtained when $\dfrac{BA}{HA} = 1$, and $[H]^+ = K_1$. The bicarbonate : carbonic acid ratio is 1 at a pH of 6.1, while at a pH of 7.4 it is equal to $\frac{20}{1}$. Offhand it may be supposed that the bicarbonate, as a buffer, does not act with its maximum efficiency in the blood, where the pH is about 7.35. However, owing to the fact that the solubility of carbonic acid in water is limited to 2.75 volumes per cent, the generalization applying to the efficiency of buffers does not hold in this particular case. And indeed the maximum efficiency of this buffer mechanism is at the pH of the blood (7.35). At the same pH the ratio $Na_2HPO_4 : NaH_2PO_4$ is 3.55, whereas at 6.8 the ratio is 1. This means that the closer the reaction of the blood approaches the danger zone, the more efficient is the buffer action of the phosphates.

Two factors contribute to the buffer mechanism of the blood. The first is the buffer action of the bicarbonate and proteins of the plasma, and of the bicarbonate, phosphates, and proteins of the cells. The second factor depends upon the property of hemoglobin to change from a weak acid to a relatively strong one when it changes from the reduced to the oxidized form. The dissociation constant of reduced hemoglobin (of the horse) is approximately 1/29 of that of oxyhemoglobin.

The Transportation of Carbon Dioxide and the Neutralization of Acid. Intimately connected with the buffer action of these substances is their rôle in the transportation of carbon dioxide. According to the definition given by Van Slyke, a carbon-dioxide carrier is a constituent of the blood that increases the amount of carbon dioxide which may be taken up by arterial blood with a change in reaction equal only to the normal pH difference between arterial and venous blood. The maintenance of the reaction of the blood at a constant level and the transportation of carbon dioxide are both due to the giving up, by the buffer salts, of part of their reserves of alkali for the purpose of neutralizing any acid, including carbonic acid.

All buffers act in essentially the same manner in neutralizing acid. Let us assume that a large amount of lactic acid is being formed which requires neutralization. The sodium bicarbonate will react with it as follows:

$$NaHCO_3 + \text{lactic acid} = Na\cdot\text{lactate} + H_2CO_3$$

The basic phosphates would react similarly:

$$B_2HPO_4 + \text{lactic acid} = B\cdot\text{lactate} + BH_2PO_4$$

The plasma proteins would neutralize a portion according to the equation:

$$B\cdot\text{protein} + \text{lactic acid} = B\cdot\text{lactate} + H\cdot\text{protein}$$

The remaining buffers would act in the same way.

The Action of Buffers as Carriers of Carbon Dioxide. All buffers act in essentially the same manner as carriers of carbon dioxide. For the purpose of illustration, we shall consider the behavior of the phosphates and calculate the changes that occur when the H_2CO_3 is increased sufficiently to lower the pH from 7.35 to 7.25. *Of course, it is to be clearly understood that changes of this magnitude do not actually occur in the blood.* This marked shift, which is several times the normal pH difference between arterial and venous blood, is selected mainly in order to make the calculations somewhat more striking and the illustration somewhat clearer.

In these calculations it will be assumed that the concentration of total phosphate ($Na_2HPO_4 + NaH_2PO_4$) is 0.05 M; and of $NaHCO_3$, 0.03 M.

Recalling the relation between the ratio of a buffer pair and pH, and substituting 6.80 for pK_1 in the equation representing this relation, we have

$$\log \frac{Na_2HPO_4}{NaH_2PO_4} = 7.35 - 6.80 = 0.55$$

or

$$\frac{Na_2HPO_4}{NaH_2PO_4} = 3.55$$

As the total concentration of PO_4 is 0.05 M, the concentration of NaH_2PO_4 is obviously $0.05 - Na_2HPO_4$. Calculating, we find that at pH 7.35,

$$\frac{Na_2HPO_4}{NaH_2PO_4} = \frac{0.0390}{0.0110} = 3.55$$

The ratio changes with pH, being but 2.82 at pH 7.25. Calculating as before, we find that at pH 7.25,

$$\frac{Na_2HPO_4}{NaH_2PO_4} = \frac{0.0369}{0.0131} = 2.82$$

That the change in pH is accompanied by the release of a certain amount of base can be seen from the fact that, in the equation above, NaH_2PO_4 has one less sodium than Na_2HPO_4. The amount of alkali which is thus set free to combine with H_2CO_3 to form bicarbonate is calculated as follows:

$$0.0390 \ M \ Na_2HPO_4$$
$$- \ 0.0369 \ M \ Na_2HPO_4$$

Difference $= 0.0021 \ M$ Na set free to form $NaHCO_3$.

We began with an initial bicarbonate concentration of 0.03 M. At the higher pH,

$$\log \frac{NaHCO_3}{H_2CO_3} = 7.35 - 6.10 = 1.25$$

hence

$$\frac{NaHCO_3}{H_2CO_3} = 17.8$$

It therefore follows that

$$H_2CO_3 = \frac{0.03}{17.8} = 0.00169 \ M$$

At pH 7.25 the ratio $NaHCO_3 : H_2CO_3$ is equal to 14.1. Had the $NaHCO_3$ concentration remained constant, the H_2CO_3 would have been

$$H_2CO_3 = \frac{0.03}{14.1} = 0.00212$$

This is not the case, however, for it has just been shown that, with the change in pH from 7.35 to 7.25, the $NaHCO_3$ concentration increased to 0.0321 M. Therefore, at pH 7.25,

$$H_2CO_3 = \frac{0.0321}{14.1} = 0.00228 \ M$$

The difference between 0.00212 and 0.00169 $= 0.00043 \ M$ represents the amount of free H_2CO_3 that is added to 0.03 N $NaHCO_3$ solution with a change in pH from 7.35 to 7.25.   The difference between 0.00228 and 0.00212 = 0.00016 M represents the amount of free H_2CO_3 added because of the buffer effect of the phosphates and the consequent increase of the $NaHCO_3$ concentration.   Thus, the additional amount of carbon dioxide that can be carried on account of the presence of phosphates is

$$0.00210 \ M \ CO_2 \ as \ NaHCO_3,$$
$$+ \ 0.00016 \ M \ CO_2 \ as \ H_2CO_3$$
$$\overline{0.00226 \ M \ CO_2 \ = \ CO_2 \ capacity \ of \ the \ phosphates}$$

between pH 7.35 and 7.25.

To avoid misconceptions it is again emphasized that the foregoing calculations are intended merely to illustrate the manner in which the buffers of the blood contribute their quotas of base, in order that the removal of carbon dioxide may proceed at a more or less constant rate. In reality, the phosphates play a very minor rôle as carriers of carbon dioxide, the amount of base liberated from this source in the tissues in a normal respiratory cycle representing less than 0.5 per cent of the total.

The Hemoglobin-oxyhemoglobin Change. Oxyhemoglobin is a stronger acid than reduced hemoglobin, as evidenced by the following values for their dissociation constants:[89]

$$K \ for \ oxyhemoglobin \quad = 2.4 \times 10^{-7}$$
$$K \ for \ reduced \ hemoglobin = 6.6 \times 10^{-9}$$

Both the reduced and the oxidized forms exist partly as free acids and partly as the salts of strong bases.   The tendency of oxyhemoglobin to combine with base is greater, however, than that of reduced hemoglobin, and hence, at a given pH, the proportion of salt to acid will be greater in the former case than in the latter.

$$\frac{BHbO_2}{HHbO_2} > \frac{BHb}{HHb}$$

This is very significant, for, in changing to the reduced form in the tissues, oxyhemoglobin liberates sufficient base to neutralize a considerable part of the carbon dioxide that is present.   Subsequently, when the reduced hemoglobin reaches the lungs and is oxidized, it

[89] These values are based on data given by Hastings, Sendroy, Murray, and Heidelberger, *J. Biol. Chem.*, **61**, 317 (1924).   See also *ibid.*, **60**, 89 (1924).

reacts with bicarbonate, with the consequent liberation of carbon dioxide. The cycle may be represented as follows:

Lungs   Tissues

(From Air) $O_2 \longrightarrow O_2 + HHb$ HHb
                           +

$HHbO_2$ $BHCO_3$
   +   ↑

$BHCO_3$ $H_2CO_3 \longleftarrow CO_2$ (From Tissues)
   ‖   +

$BHbO_2$ $BHb + O_2 \longrightarrow O_2$ (To Tissues)
   +   ↑

H_2CO_3 → $BHbO_2$

(To Air) $CO_2 \longleftarrow CO_2 + H_2O$

Estimates have been made of the approximate distribution of the carbon dioxide carrying power among the buffers of the blood. The calculations of Van Slyke, based on the most reliable data available in 1921, show that the base furnished by hemoglobin accounts for 84–94 per cent of the total carbon dioxide absorbed. For details, the student is referred to the reviews of Van Slyke[86] and Wilson[90] as well as to L. J. Henderson's monograph.[91] Suffice it to say here that in the transportation of carbon dioxide, hemoglobin plays a dual rôle. Owing to its action as a buffer, it contributes materially to the carbon-dioxide capacity of the blood; but even more important than this is the fact that half or more of the carbon dioxide is carried in combination with the base liberated as a result of the change in the oxygenation of the hemoglobin in the tissues and lungs. This is the so-called *isohydric* change of oxyhemoglobin to hemoglobin.

Doisy, Briggs, Eaton, and Chambers[92] have obtained fairly close approximations of the carbon dioxide carried by various buffer systems in the blood. Their results, which are somewhat lower than those obtained by others, are presented in Table XXXIII and show that about 53 per cent of the total carbon dioxide carried is due to the change

$$BHbO_2 \rightleftarrows HHb$$

and that about 20–30 per cent more is carried by the base liberated

[90] *Physiol. Rev.*, **3**, 295 (1923).

[91] L. J. Henderson, "Blood, A Study in General Physiology," Yale Univ. Press, New Haven, 1928.

[92] *J. Biol. Chem.*, **54**, 305 (1922).

from hemoglobin as a result of the change in pH.[93] That the most important buffer of the blood is isolated within the corpuscles is a matter worthy of note.

TABLE XXXIII

CARBON DIOXIDE CARRIED BY BUFFER SYSTEMS OF THE BLOOD

	E. A. D.		W. H. C.		J. M.	
	Volumes, Per Cent	Per Cent of Total	Volumes, Per Cent	Per Cent of Total	Volumes, Per Cent	Per Cent of Total
Total CO_2 carried for R. Q. of 0.75...	2.32	......	4.23	......	5.08	
$BHCO_3$ carried isohydrically.........	1.233	53.1	2.262	53.5	2.72	53.5
$\quad BHbO_2 \rightleftharpoons HHb$						
$BHCO_3$ carried by change of pH:						
$\quad$ By hemoglobin: $BHbO_2 \rightleftharpoons HHbO_2$						
$\qquad\qquad\qquad\quad BHb \rightleftharpoons HHb$...	0.439	18.9	1.070	25.3	1.384	27.2
$\quad$ By B_2HPO_4 in cells..............	0.010	0.43	0.012	0.3	0.013	0.25
$\quad$ By separated serum..............	0.089	3.84	0.198	4.7	0.142	2.8
CO_2 physically dissolved............	0.249	10.7	0.511	12.1	0.657	12.9
Sum, per cent of total..............	2.020	87.0	4.053	96.0	4.196	97.0
Per cent of total CO_2 carried by hemoglobin..........................	72.0		78.8		80.7	
	pH		pH		pH	
Arterial blood (pH values recalculated)	7.296		7.310		7.281	
Venous blood (pH values recalculated)	7.283		7.280		7.244	
Difference........................	0.013		0.030		0.037	

Buffer Effect of Plasma and Corpuscles. Although the major part of the buffer effect of the blood resides in the corpuscles, both the plasma and the corpuscles take part in the transportation of carbon dioxide. The plasma, according to the observations of Bock, Field, and

---

[93] L. J. Henderson by introducing certain simplifying assumptions has analyzed the conditions accompanying the respiratory exchange of carbonic acid in the blood. With a change between arterial and venous blood of 2.08 mM. of $BHCO_3$ per liter, 1.71 mM. of base or 82 per cent is provided through the change in oxygenation of the hemoglobin in the tissues. Added to this is the true buffer action of hemoglobin, amounting to 13 per cent, in the case cited, so that fully 95 per cent of the transportation of carbon dioxide is due to hemoglobin. In Henderson's calculations, the serum proteins (because of the base liberated with the change in pH from arterial to venous blood) are responsible for nearly all of the remaining 5 per cent.

Adair,[94] carries about 60 per cent, and the corpuscles about 40 per cent, of the carbon dioxide which arterial blood takes on when it becomes venous blood.

When plasma or serum is in contact with red cells (" true " plasma or serum), its capacity for taking up carbon dioxide is much greater than in the absence of cells (" separated " plasma or serum). This is because the cells pass on their buffer effect to the plasma in accordance with the mechanisms that have been discussed. Some features of these mechanisms still remain to be considered, however.

Zuntz[95] and Schmidt[96] found that they could increase the titratable alkalinity of serum by subjecting the blood to high tensions of carbon dioxide. Zuntz concluded that the carbonic acid passed into the corpuscles, where it split off alkali from the cell proteins, and that the alkali then diffused into the serum. That the corpuscles are freely permeable to carbonic acid has been well established. The transfer of cations between the corpuscles and the plasma or serum seems very improbable.

Chloride Shift. In seeking an explanation for the increased titratable alkalinity of the serum when carbon dioxide is passed through blood, Gürber[97] studied the ash of the serum and determined that no sodium or potassium diffused from the corpuscles. These observations have been confirmed by many workers. Gürber found, however, that sufficient chloride passed into the corpuscles to account for the increase in serum bicarbonate. That this is not entirely correct has been shown by Van Slyke and Cullen,[98] who were able to account for only 72 per cent of the alkali increase of the plasma on the basis of the chloride shift. Other anions, SO_4 and PO_4, are also capable of migration through the red-cell membrane. When the reaction of the blood is changed artificially from 7.45 to 7.25 by the absorption of carbon dioxide, the base furnished to form the additional plasma bicarbonate comes from the following sources, according to the calculations of Doisy, Eaton, and Chouke:[99]

1. Due to non-migrating serum buffers (plasma proteins, amino acids, and organic acids)..16 per cent
2. Due to migration of Cl into corpuscles.........................80 per cent
3. Due to the migration of other acid radicals such as SO_4 (de Boer[100]), and PO_4 (Doisy and Eaton[101])..................... 4 per cent

[94] *J. Biol. Chem.*, **59**, 353 (1924).
[95] *Centr. med. Wiss.* (1867), 529; Dissertation, Bonn (1868).
[96] *Ber. sächs. Ges. Wiss., Math.-phys.*, **19**, 30 (1867).
[97] Maly's Jahresb., **25**, 165 (1895).
[98] Cited by Van Slyke, *Physiol. Rev.*, **1**, 161 (1921).
[99] *J. Biol. Chem.*, **53**, 61 (1922).
[100] *J. Physiol.*, **51**, 211 (1917).
[101] *J. Biol. Chem.*, **47**, 377 (1921).

That the transfer of chloride between plasma and corpuscles under the influence of changing tensions of carbon dioxide occurs *in vivo* has been demonstrated by numerous workers who compared arterial with venous blood and found more chloride in the plasma of the former than in that of the latter.

The reactions which may be supposed to occur in the plasma and corpuscles, when CO_2 and O_2 are either absorbed or given off, have been summarized in a diagram which is reproduced below.[102] In interpreting this diagram it is to be appreciated that HCl and H_2CO_3 do not diffuse through the membrane as such, but as H^+, Cl^-, and $HCO_3{}^-$ ions.

Plasma	Red-cell Wall	Cell
(1) H_2CO_3 + Na Protein $\leftrightarrows$ H Protein + $NaHCO_3$		
(2) H_2CO_3 + NaCl $\leftrightarrows$ $NaHCO_3$ + HCl $\longleftarrow$ $\longrightarrow$ HCl $\leftarrow\rightarrow$		(3) HCl + K_2HPO_4 $\leftrightarrows$ KH_2PO_4 + KCl (4) 2HCl + $2KHbO_2$ $\leftrightarrows$ 2KCl + $\begin{cases} HHbO_2 \\ HHb + O_2\leftarrow \end{cases}$
H_2CO_3 $\longleftarrow$ $\longrightarrow$ H_2CO_3 $\leftarrow\rightarrow$		(5) H_2CO_3 + K_2HPO_4 $\leftrightarrows$ $KHCO_3$ + KH_2PO_4 (6) $2H_2CO_3$ + $2KHbO_2$ $\leftrightarrows$ $2KHCO_3$ + $\begin{cases} HHbO_2 \\ HHb + O_2\leftarrow \end{cases}$
$O_2\leftarrow$ $\longrightarrow$ $O_2 \leftarrow$		

Electrolyte and Gas Equilibria. The distribution of electrolytes in the blood, including the transfer of chloride, hydrogen ions, carbon dioxide, and water between the plasma and corpuscles, can be explained partly on the basis of Donnan's theory of membrane equilibrium, by assuming that the membrane of the red cell is the semi-permeable membrane which separates the plasma from the fluid in the corpuscles. This membrane, as we have seen, is impermeable to proteins and cations, with the exception of H^+ ions. It is permeable to $HCO_3{}^-$ and other anions (Cl^-, $SO_4{}^-$, and $PO_4{}^-$). Electrolytes that are present on either side of the membrane will tend to distribute themselves equally on the two sides. This tendency will be opposed, however, by the attractive forces of the non-diffusible ions, with the result that when equilibrium is reached there will be an uneven distribution of ions on the two sides of the membrane.

[102] Austin, Cullen, Hastings, McLean, Peters, and Van Slyke, *ibid.*, **54**, 121 (1922).

As is evident from what has been stated earlier in this chapter, the equilibria established between the cells and serum (or plasma) are due in a large measure to the base-binding power of hemoglobin and its variation with changing pH and oxygenation. These properties explain the following facts, as summarized by Van Slyke:[103] (1) The cells contain more base in proportion to water than serum, but much less Cl^- and HCO_3^-; (2) the cell contents are more acid than serum; (3) the cells carry most of the buffer alkali (as BHb) of the blood which is available to combine with carbonic or other acids entering the blood; (4) the cells absorb water from the serum when CO_2 or other acids enter the blood; (5) at the same time Cl^- passes from serum to cells; (6) oxygenation of reduced blood, by increasing the acidity of hemoglobin, has the same effect as acidification in driving CO_2 out of the blood, but has the effect of alkalization on the distribution of diffusible ions and water.

In short, considering that the concentration of base bound by hemoglobin is about five times the base combined with the plasma proteins and also that the two phases (plasma and corpuscles) are in osmotic equilibrium, it follows that there must be other inequalities in concentration on the two sides of the red-cell membrane. The study of the blood as a physicochemical system by several groups of investigators in this country and abroad has materially advanced our knowledge of its properties. The relations involved in the distribution of gases and electrolytes between the cells and serum are very complex and do not lend themselves to a brief formulation. For this reason they cannot be further considered here, but if the student is to gain an appreciation of the scope of the subject he is urged to consult the recently published monograph of L. J. Henderson.[91] The composition of the cells and serum with respect to any given constituent, at any stage in the respiratory cycle, is quantitatively dependent on practically all the other constituents. In other words, each is variable and the relations of all the variables may be mathematically formulated and graphically represented. An idea may be gained of the complexity of the situation if some of the variables are listed. These are:

1. Concentration of Cl in serum (Cl_s).
2. Concentration of Cl in cells (Cl_c).
3. The percentage of total blood chloride or bicarbonate present in the cells (A).
4. Volume of cells (V).
5. Percentage of H_2O in cells.
6. The base combined with cell protein (BP_c).
7. The combined carbonic acid of the cells ($[BHCO_3]_c$).

[103] D. D. Van Slyke, "Factors Affecting the Distribution of Electrolytes, Water and Gases in the Animal Body," Lippincott, Philadelphia and London, 1926, p. 28.

8. The combined carbonic acid of the serum ($[BHCO_3]_s$).
9. Total CO_2 of the blood.
10. Free CO_2 of the blood.
11. Base bound by protein of serum (BP_s).
12. pH in the serum.
13. pH in the cells.
14. Oxygen pressure.
15. Combined oxygen (HbO_2).

Hydrogen-ion Concentration of the Blood. The blood is slightly alkaline in reaction, the serum being more alkaline than the corpuscles, arterial blood more than venous. This is shown by the following illustrative data obtained in two normal subjects at rest:

TABLE XXXIV

COMPARISON OF pH IN NORMAL RESTING INDIVIDUALS*

	I		II	
	Serum	Cells	Serum	Cells
Arterial...................	7.455	7.118	7.442	7.108
Venous...................	7.429	7.110	7.416	7.098
Difference.................	0.026	0.008	0.026	0.010

* After L. J. Henderson, "The Blood," Yale Univ. Press, 1928, pp. 195, 201.

The pH of normal serum is usually between 7.4 and 7.5 (Earle and Cullen).[104] It varies during the day, increasing from early morning, before rising, to late evening. The total increase varies from 0.01 to 0.07 pH and is not constant, being interrupted by fluctuations due to digestion, exercise, and other factors.

As indicated by the data in the preceding table the difference in pH between arterial and venous blood is small, the cells being affected even less than the plasma. The data of Peters, Barr, and Rule[105] show differences between arterial and venous blood of 0.01 to 0.04 and those of Doisy and associates[106] differences ranging from 0.013 to 0.037.

A greater shift in pH between arterial and venous blood as well as increased acidity above that in the resting state occur as a result of work. This is illustrated by the following data:

[104] *J. Biol. Chem.*, **83**, 539, 545 (1929).   [105] *Ibid.*, **45**, 489 (1920–1).
[106] *Ibid.*, **54**, 305 (1922).

TABLE XXXV

COMPARISON OF THE pH OF THE BLOOD OF A NORMAL MALE INDIVIDUAL, AT REST AND AT WORK*

	Rest		Work	
	Serum	Cells	Serum	Cells
Arterial..................	7.425	7.124	7.351	7.062
Venous....................	7.399	7.106	7.278	7.027
Difference...............	0.026	0.008	0.078	0.035

* Based on data given by L. J. Henderson, Chap. IX.

Even more conspicuous changes in the hydrogen-ion concentration of the blood may occur as a result of very strenuous exercise.[107] An increase in alkalinity of the blood may be produced physiologically by forced breathing. In this way, Davies, Haldane, and Kennaway[108] obtained values as high as pH 7.85. Ordinarily, any marked divergence from the normal is indicative of serious disturbance in the acid-base equilibrium of the body. A value higher than pH 7.5 indicates a condition of *alkalosis*. It may be due, as will be shown presently, either to an uncompensated excess of alkali or to an uncompensated deficit of carbon dioxide. On the other hand, a pH below 7.3 indicates a condition of *acidosis*, due either to an uncompensated deficit of alkali or to an uncompensated excess of carbon dioxide. Values lower than pH 7.0 are rarely encountered in individuals who later recover. Such values are indicative of extreme acidosis and have been observed almost exclusively in cases of diabetic or uremic coma which terminated fatally.

Acid-base Balance. *Alkali Reserve.* The alkali reserve refers to the amount of base combined as bicarbonate and not to all of the base stored in the blood, as is sometimes supposed.[109] Bicarbonates afford

[107] Barr, Himwich, and Green have reported a value as low as 7.05 (*J. Biol. Chem.*, **55**, 495 [1923]). Compare these observations with those of H. A. Rice, and A. H. Steinhaus, *Am. J. Physiol.*, **96**, 529 (1931).

[108] *J. Physiol.*, **54**, 32 (1920).

[109] This is evident from the methods used in its determination, one of the simplest being the method introduced by Van Slyke and Cullen in 1917. This procedure is based upon the assumption that the CO_2-combining power of the blood depends upon the amount of alkali which is available. The essential features of the method consist in saturating the blood, after it is drawn, with carbon dioxide, and liberating the CO_2 in a definite amount of blood by treating it with acid *in vacuo* in an apparatus devised for this purpose. *J. Biol. Chem.*, **30**, 289 (1917). This method has been modified so that the CO_2 liberated is measured manometrically (*ibid.*, **61**, 523, 575 [1924]).

a readily available source of base for the neutralization of acids stronger than carbonic acid. Base present in excess of acids other than carbonic takes the form of bicarbonate. The designation of this source of base as "alkali reserve" receives added justification in the fact that it reflects more or less closely the reserve of available alkali present in the body as a whole.

According to Peters and Van Slyke,[110] "*acidosis* may be broadly defined as an abnormal condition caused by the accumulation in the body of an excess of acid or the loss from the body of alkali." Acids tend to accumulate when they are formed or absorbed more rapidly than they are destroyed or eliminated. When this process has caused either the bicarbonate of the blood to fall (decreased alkali reserve), or the hydrogen-ion concentration to rise above the normal limits, a state of acidosis is said to exist.

Similarly, *alkalosis* may be defined as an abnormal condition caused by the accumulation in the body of an excess of alkali (increased alkali reserve), or by the loss of acid. Either the accumulation of alkali or the loss of acid exerts the same effect, namely to increase the bicarbonate and usually to diminish the hydrogen-ion concentration of the blood.

We shall consider in particular the relation between carbonic acid and base in the blood, inasmuch as this constitutes the principal factor in the acid-base equilibrium. As ordinarily employed the term blood pH actually refers to the plasma or serum pH. As has been stated elsewhere, the normal pH is approximately 7.4, corresponding to an hydrogen-ion concentration of 4×10^{-8}. For the extreme normal range, the values pH 7.3 to 7.5 are usually cited. In a series of determinations on the serum of blood drawn without stasis, Earle and Cullen obtained results varying from pH 7.33 to 7.51, with pH 7.4 to 7.5 predominating. The carbon dioxide content varied between 55 and 74 volumes per cent and the carbon dioxide tension from 37 to 58 mm. Hg.

Deviation from the normal acid-base balance is of two general types:

(1) Metabolic, due primarily to (*a*) alkali excess, (*b*) alkali deficit.
(2) Respiratory, due primarily to (*a*) CO_2 excess, (*b*) CO_2 deficit.

Primary alkali excess may be due either to the retention of alkali or the loss of acid. The administration of alkaline substances, such as sodium bicarbonate, in sufficient amount, results in an alkali excess. The condition is characterized by an increased CO_2 content due primarily to the rise in bicarbonate. Corresponding to this is a rise in pH, which if sufficient may be accompanied by the development of tetany. Values as high as pH 7.8 have been encountered, not infrequently.

[110] Quantitative Clinical Chemistry," p. 870.

Copious vomiting of HCl, as in pyloric obstruction, may cause a *relative* excess of alkali and a corresponding rise in pH.

In an earlier classification, Van Slyke described primary alkali excess that was not balanced by a change in CO_2 tension as *uncompensated* alkali excess. As the primary alkali change is followed by a corresponding increase in CO_2, or by the excretion of alkali, the ratio $\dfrac{HHCO_3}{BHCO_3}$ tends to return to normal, as does also the pH of the blood. When the normal ratio is thus restored, even though the content of base remain high, the condition is one of *compensated* alkali excess.

Primary alkali deficit represents a condition in which the most conspicuous and constant change is the reduction of the bicarbonate (and CO_2) concentration. When the reduction in bicarbonate is not balanced by a corresponding change in carbonic acid, the pH diminishes. The condition may result from (a) acid retention, (b) alkali loss. In most instances acid formation occurs first, followed by neutralization and the excretion of the salts thus formed. In consequence there is a loss of base from the body. The two factors, namely, acid formation and alkali depletion, are frequently co-existent.

In diabetes, as the result of faulty fat metabolism, large amounts of aceto-acetic acid and β-hydroxybutyric acid are formed. These are eliminated in combination with base, thus depleting the alkali reserve of the body. The same factors are involved in starvation and carbohydrate deprivation (p. 364).

The immediate effect of the administration of acids, or acid-forming salts, such as NH_4Cl, is the retention of acid. NH_4Cl is converted into urea and HCl. Neutralization of the latter involves a loss of available base.

Retention of NaH_2PO_4 through the failure of the kidneys to excrete it, as in terminal nephritis, causes a relative increase of the ratio $\dfrac{NaH_2PO_4}{Na_2HPO_4}$, as well as a similar change with respect to other buffer pairs. There is an accompanying reduction in the pH. The end result is a relative alkali deficit.

During pregnancy the total serum base is somewhat diminished, but this is compensated by a comparable reduction in H_2CO_3, so that the pH tends to remain within normal limits.

Primary CO_2 excess is a condition characterized by a low pH and a high or normal CO_2. It occurs when the excretion of CO_2 is retarded, usually as a result of some obstruction to the passage of air to and from the lungs. Though relatively uncommon, this condition has also been observed in cases of cardiac decompensation accompanied by dyspnea,[111] and in morphine narcosis. In essential emphysema a condition of CO_2 excess may develop, but it is usually compensated. Scott[112] has recorded one such instance with a CO_2 content of 82.7 volumes per cent and with a normal pH of 7.4.

Primary CO₂ deficit is a condition of abnormally high pH (7.6 to 7.8) with a normal or low CO_2 content. The latter may fall to as low a level as 20 to 30 volumes per cent. The condition may result from voluntary or involuntary over-ventilation of the lungs.[113] If the degree of alkalosis is sufficient, symptoms of tetany may develop. Primary CO_2 deficit is also observed at high altitudes (or in atmospheres with low oxygen tension) and may likewise be associated with an increase in body temperature, due to hot baths, fever, etc. The disturbance in acid-base balance occurring under all of these circumstances is gradually modified by a diminution in alkali reserve (through the excretion of base), corresponding more or less to the reduction in H_2CO_3, and a consequent restoration to the normal pH range (" compensated CO_2 deficit ").

COMPOSITION OF THE BLOOD

Hemoglobin. Normally the amount of hemoglobin varies with age and sex. The highest values are encountered during the first 2 to 3 days of life (22 to 23 g. per 100 cc. of blood, corresponding to an oxygen capacity of 27 to 29 volumes per cent). Available data indicate a gradual diminution to about 13 g. (oxygen capacity of 16 volumes per cent), followed after the fourth or fifth year by a gradual rise to the adult values, attained at about the age of 16 years. For males, the adult level is 16.5 to 17 g. per 100 cc. (oxygen content of 20.4 to 21 volumes per cent); for females about 15 to 16 g. (oxygen content of 18.5 to 19.8 volumes per cent).

Physiologically the hemoglobin content increases at high altitudes, and as a result of vigorous exercise, largely because of a corresponding change in the concentration of the blood (diminished plasma volume), particularly in the latter case. Diurnal variations and changes associated with digestion, water administration, dehydration, pregnancy, and emotional, seasonal, climatic, and other factors have been described.

Pathologically the amount of hemoglobin is reduced in various forms of anemia.

[111] J. P. Peters and D. P. Barr, *J. Biol. Chem.*, **45**, 537 (1921).

[112] *Arch. Internal Med.*, **26**, 544 (1920).

[113] H. W. Davies, J. B. S. Haldane, and E. Kennaway, *J. Physiol.*, **54**, 32 (1920–21).

Inorganic Constituents. Sodium, potassium, calcium, and magnesium are the quantitatively important basic constituents of the tissues and body fluids and exist in combination with the following inorganic and organic anions: HCO_3', Cl', PO_4''', SO_4'', protein, lactic acid, and other organic acid radicals. Of these the monovalent ions, $K^·$, $Na^·$, Cl', HCO_3', and monovalent organic acid anions (lactic acid, etc.), compose about 95 per cent of the total electrolytes of the blood plasma and other extracellular fluids. Accordingly, if the amount of total base (B) is determined, a fairly accurate measure is also obtained of the total osmotically active ions (2B), since:

$$B = Na + K + Ca + Mg = HCO_3 + Cl + PO_4 + SO_4 + \text{protein} + \text{organic acid anions}$$

The relative distribution of inorganic cations and anions in human blood is represented by the following data:

TABLE XXXVI

	Serum Mg. per 100 cc.	Cells Mg. per 100 cc.
$Na^·$	335 ± 15	0
$K^·$	19 ± 3	$420 \pm$
$Ca^{··}$	10 ± 1	0 $(.53)$
$Mg^{··}$	$2.74 \pm .3$	$6.61 \pm .53$
HCO_3'	$164 \pm$	$112 \pm$
Cl'	370 ± 20	190 ± 20
PO_4'''	$10 \pm$	$18 \pm$
SO_4''	19	

In terms of milli-equivalent concentrations, average plasma has approximately the following electrolyte content:[114]

$$B = Na^· + K^· + Ca^{··} + Mg^{··} = Cl' + HCO_3' + PO_4''' + \text{protein} + SO_4'' + \text{organic acids}$$
$$155 = 142 + 5 + 5 + 3 = 103 + 28 + 2 + 16 + 6$$

[114] The numbers under the symbols indicate the milli-equivalents per liter of plasma (after Peters and Van Slyke, p. 762).

In the form in which the quantitative relation of these constituents is expressed in the Table XXXVI, it is not apparent that a balance exists between the acid and basic radicals. Indeed the conventional method of expressing the results of quantative analysis in terms of proportion by weight is unsatisfactory, especially in

Sodium and Potassium. In human blood, the sodium is confined almost exclusively to the plasma. It is also the predominant base in lymph, edema fluid, cerebrospinal and other extracellular fluids. Muscle contains about 80 mg. per 100 g., which corresponds to approximately 50 m.eq. per liter of muscle water. In contrast, the potassium content of muscle is approximately 320 mg. per 100 g., corresponding to 112.5 m.eq. per liter of muscle water. It is assumed that muscle contains in the neighborhood of 72.5 per cent of water. As regards the distribution of sodium and potassium between the plasma and corpuscles, horse's blood resembles human. However, in the cat and dog, sodium instead of potassium is present in greater abundance in the corpuscles. This is indicated by the following data for dog's blood.[115]

	Na	K
Serum....................	141	5.19
Corpuscles...............	109	7.77

A diminished alkali reserve, from whatever cause, is accompanied by a definite reduction of the sodium and potassium concentrations of the blood. Profuse sweating, or diarrhea, may produce a similar effect

certain cases where it is desirable to bring out the relations of the various constituents to one another.

A better method is to express the amounts in terms of their equivalence. The significance of the term *molar* (*molal*) and *normal*, as applied to solutions is probably familiar to the student. A *normal* solution of acid contains 1.008 g. of replaceable hydrogen per liter. This is approximately equivalent to 35.5 g. of reactive chloride, 23 g. of sodium, or 20.03 g. of calcium. Ordinarily, the various constituents of the body fluids are present in small concentration and it is therefore more convenient to express the results in *millimols* (one-thousandth of a mol per liter) or still better in milli-equivalents (*m. eq.*). A few simple examples will illustrate the point:

Serum contains 335 mg. of sodium per 100 cc. This is equivalent to 3350 mg. per liter. Inasmuch as 1 *m. eq.* of sodium weighs 23 mg., the concentration is $3350/23 = 146$ *m. eq.* per liter.

The concentration of chloride is 360 mg. per 100 cc. of serum. This corresponds to $3600/35.5 = 101$ *m. eq.* per liter.

The value for serum calcium is 10.6 mg. per 100 cc. The atomic weight of Ca is 40.7; 1 *m. eq.* therefore weighs 20.35 mg. Hence $10.6 \times 10/20.35 = 5.2$ *m. eq.* per liter.

For certain purposes it is desirable to express the concentrations in terms of milli-equivalents per 1000 cc. of water. Thus, if the chloride concentration of serum is 101 *m. eq.* and the content of water 92 per cent, $101/92 \times 100 = 109.8$ *m. eq.* is the chloride content of 1000 cc. of serum H_2O.

[115] After S. E. Kerr, *J. Biol. Chem.*, **67**, 689 (1926); see also A. R. McIntyre, *ibid.*, **98**, 115 (1932).

despite the marked dehydration which may co-exist. In adrenal insufficiency, the concentration of sodium in the serum is conspicuously diminished. The potassium and calcium tend to rise above normal. *Calcium.* The blood serum normally contains from 9 to 11.5 mg. of calcium per 100 cc. Apparently the red-cell membrane is impermeable to calcium ions. The analyses of Leiboff[116] indicate that human red blood corpuscles contain no calcium. Rymer and Lewis[117] found on an average only 0.53 mg. per 100 cc. of corpuscles.

Of the total serum calcium, 42 to 68 per cent is diffusible through a collodion membrane (Greenberg and Gunther).[118] Nicholas,[119] employing a somewhat different procedure for ultrafiltration, found the diffusible calcium to vary from 60 to 67 per cent. Presumably the diffusible fraction exists as readily ionizable salts, while the remainder is firmly combined with protein. Indeed various formulas have been proposed for calculating the calcium content from the amount of protein in the serum.

Edema fluid contains 5 to 7 mg. of calcium and cerebrospinal fluid about 5 mg., nearly all of which is diffusible.

The constancy of serum calcium is very striking. Even though considerable amounts of calcium (and phosphorus) are lost from the body as a result of undernutrition or starvation, the content in the blood remains unchanged. However, when the period of starvation is prolonged, accompanying the reduction in protein, there is a decrease in calcium. Only a slight increase of the diffusible fraction occurs after feeding calcium salts. Gunther and Greenberg[120] observed an increase of about 1 mg. per cent after taking 1 liter of acidified milk, but not after taking a similar amount of sweet milk.

Serum calcium tends to be low in the last months of pregnancy, this being presumably related to the calcium utilization by the developing fetus, and partly to the reduction in serum protein. The lowered serum calcium observed in jaundice, malignancy, nephritis, and nephrosis is ordinarily confined to the non-diffusible fraction and is obviously related to serum-protein deficiency.

Low calcium values are often accompanied by a high inorganic phosphate. This reciprocal relation is noted especially after extirpation of the parathyroid glands. When the serum calcium falls to 7 mg., or less, tetany develops. Actually the onset of the convulsions depends not so much upon the total calcium as upon the diffusible fraction. A reduction of the latter to 3.5 mg. per 100 cc., or less, is associated with

[116] *J. Biol. Chem.*, **85**, 759 (1929–30).
[117] *Ibid.*, **95**, 441 (1932).
[118] *Ibid.*, **85**, 491 (1930).
[119] *Ibid.*, **97**, 457 (1932).
[120] *Arch. Internal Med.*, **50**, 855 (1932).

clinical symptoms of active tetany. The effect of the hypocalcemia may be overcome, at least temporarily, by the administration of calcium salts. Milk has also been reported to exert a beneficial effect. It is thus seen that the serum calcium is influenced more readily when it is low than when normal.

Tetany associated with rickets and osteomalacia is due to hypocalcemia resulting from nutritional deficiency with respect to calcium (see p. 590).

The most striking increases in serum calcium (20 mg. per 100 cc., and higher) have been observed in clinical hyperparathyroidism and following the administration of parathyroid extract to experimental animals.

Magnesium. In recent analyses, Greenberg and associates [121] found the average magnesium content of human serum to be 2.74 mg. per 100 cc. In 70 per cent of their 58 subjects, the values fell between 2.45 and 3.05 mg., that is, the standard deviation was ±0.3 mg. The extreme range observed was 2 to 3.6 mg. The magnesium content of the red blood corpuscles averaged 6.61 mg., with a standard deviation of ±0.53 mg. This high value is at variance with nearly all other data previously reported. Greenberg has asserted, moreover, that there is no loss of magnesium from corpuscles when they are washed with isotonic magnesium-free salt solutions and that there is no relation between the level of magnesium in the plasma and corpuscles. This would indicate that the cell membrane is relatively impermeable to this ion. It is considered highly probable that the magnesium may play some special physiological rôle in the corpuscle where it is the sole representative of the alkaline earth elements, the calcium content being negligible.

The magnesium level is practically unaffected by the concentrations of serum protein or phosphate. Very little is known of its variations physiologically and in disease.

Chloride and Bicarbonate. The anions Cl^- and HCO_3^- may be considered jointly because of their interdependence. Factors which alter the concentration of one tend to produce a reciprocal change in the other. This is indicated by the data in table XXXVII.

The concentration of chloride in normal human serum may vary from about 350 to 380 mg. per 100 cc. (99 to 108 m.eq. per liter) corresponding to 0.56 to 0.63 per cent of sodium chloride. Ordinarily, however, the range of values is somewhat narrower, 362 to 376 mg. Cl^-, or 596 to 620 mg. NaCl, per 100 cc. (102 to 106 m.eq. per liter).

[121] *J. Biol. Chem.*, **100**, 139 (1933).

TABLE XXXVII

RELATION OF Cl⁻ AND HCO₃⁻ IN ARTERIAL AND VENOUS BLOOD, AT REST AND
AT WORK [122]

	Subject I at Rest		Subject II at Rest		Subject I at Work	
	Arterial	Venous	Arterial	Venous	Arterial	Venous
Cl⁻, mM. per liter serum...	99.32	98.49	102.56	102.03	102.7	100.3
Total CO_2 (HCO_3^-) mM. per liter serum.........	26.57	28.50	27.16	28.79	20.86	25.84
Cl⁻, mM. per liter cells...	45.27	47.00	47.03	48.27	49.42	53.22
Total CO_2 (HCO_3^-) mM. per liter cells..........	13.98	15.40	15.59	17.07	13.08	17.03

On a salt-free diet, the Cl⁻ concentration is lowered to about
98 mM., at which " threshold " level it remains fairly constant, inasmuch as little or no chloride is excreted in the urine under the circumstances. In contrast, if large amounts of salt are administered (40 g.
daily, or more), the serum Cl⁻ concentration may be raised to 110 mM.,
but above this point it is difficult to cause a further increase in the normal
individual, because of the rapid excretion of the excess by the kidneys.
The intravenous administration of hypertonic salt solution causes a
temporary increase in concentration, followed rapidly by the withdrawal
of water from the tissues and an increase in blood volume.

During the early stages of digestion, associated with gastric activity
and the secretion of HCl, the serum chloride diminishes. This is accompanied by a compensatory increase in bicarbonate. The reverse occurs
during anesthesia, namely an increase in Cl⁻ and a decrease in HCO₃⁻
ions. As a result of the administration of bicarbonate, a reduction in
plasma chloride occurs.

Subnormal chloride values are observed during starvation, but the
most striking change is caused by the vomiting in obstruction to the
gastro-intestinal tract. A 50 per cent reduction of the serum chloride
concentration is not an uncommon finding. Though a compensatory
increase in bicarbonate occurs, it is usually less than the fall in chloride.
The chloride concentration is also reduced in diabetic acidosis, acute
glomerular nephritis, emphysema, and pneumonia.

[122] See also p. 263. The data are after L. J. Henderson, "Blood," Yale Univ.
Press, New Haven, 1928. For a discussion of the distribution of these ions between
cells and plasma from the standpoint of the Donnan theory of membrane equilibria,
see Peters and Van Slyke, loc. cit., Chap. XIX.

Phosphate.   The blood serum of adults normally contains 2 to 5 mg. of inorganic phosphorus; in children the values are somewhat higher, 4 to 7 mg.   The concentration in the corpuscles has been a matter of dispute.   According to Kramer and Tisdall,[123] it is approximately twice that in the serum.   Youngburg and Youngburg[124] in a series of 12 normal subjects found the serum inorganic phosphate to vary between 2.56 and 4.43 mg. per 100 cc. (average 3.73), whereas the content in the corpuscles varied between 1.08 and 4.69 mg. (average 3.32).

An increase occurs in terminal nephritis.   In rickets and osteomalacia, the phosphorus is low,[125] if the condition is primarily due to phosphorus deficiency.   Physiologically a slight fall accompanies the active utilization of glucose.   In the diabetic, depending on the capacity to metabolize carbohydrate, this fall is not so marked, and the return to normal is more delayed than in the normal individual.

The inorganic (orthophosphate) phosphorus constitutes but a small fraction of the total.   Various organic phosphorus fractions are present, chiefly in the corpuscles.   The phosphorus compounds of the blood have been subdivided into two main fractions:

(*a*) Acid soluble, including inorganic phosphate, nucleotides, phosphate esters, and other undetermined compounds.

(*b*) Alcohol-ether soluble, or lipid phosphorus.

Nucleic acid is not a constituent of the normal erythrocyte.   Reticulated cells may, however, contain it, according to Kay.[126]

Further subdivision into fractions, such as enzyme-hydrolyzable, enzyme-non-hydrolyzable, etc., has been attempted, but on the whole our present knowledge of the constituents composing these fractions is fragmentary.

Such data as are to be found in the literature indicate the normal total phosphorus of the serum to be 8 to 18 mg., and of the corpuscles, 47 to 114 mg.

Sulfate.   Blood contains 0.5 to 1.0 mg. per 100 cc. of inorganic sulfate sulfur.   The amount of ethereal sulfate is approximately the same. About 2 to 4 mg. of sulfur is in the unoxidized, or so-called neutral, form and is present somewhat more abundantly in the cells than in the plasma.   Increased concentrations have been reported in pyloric and

---

[123] *J. Biol. Chem.*, **53**, 241 (1922).

[124] *J. Lab. Clin. Med.*, **16**, 253 (1930).

[125] Bakwin, O. Bodansky, and Turner obtained an average of 5.41 mg. of inorganic (orthophosphate) P per 100 cc. of serum in non-rachitic children (36 subjects).   The concentration in the cells averaged 2.48 mg.   In contrast, values of 2.95 mg. for serum and 1.05 for cells were obtained in a group of 19 infants with rickets.   *Proc. Soc. Exp. Biol. Med.*, **29**, 1238 (1931–32).

[126] *Brit. J. Exp. Pathol.*, **11**, 148 (1930).

intestinal obstruction, diabetes, and leukemia, but the most striking retention has been observed in cases of terminal nephritis.[127]

Organic Constituents. The proteins of the plasma having been considered elsewhere, we shall restrict our attention to the (a) non-protein nitrogenous constituents, (b) glucose, (c) lipids. Removal of the protein by suitable precipitants, under appropriate conditions, leaves in solution, besides inorganic salts, glucose and a group of nitrogen-containing substances. The latter are determined by analyzing the protein-free filtrate for total nitrogen; hence the term non-protein nitrogen (or total non-protein nitrogen, or N.P.N.). It represents the nitrogen of urea, uric acid, ammonia, the amino acids, creatine and creatinine, and certain undetermined substances (peptides, nucleotides, etc.). It is customary to record the concentration of at least some of these constituents, for example, urea, in terms of milligrams of nitrogen per 100 cc. of serum, plasma, or blood, as the case may be. Creatine, creatinine, and uric acid are usually expressed as such.[128]

Non-protein Nitrogen. For whole blood the normal variation is from 25 to 35 mg., with an average of about 30 mg. Plasma contains 18 to 30 mg. (average about 25 mg.). Folin and Svedberg[128] analyzed the blood of 19 normal individuals and obtained the following data for non-protein nitrogen:[129]

TABLE XXXVIII

Time	Plasma			Laked Blood			Unlaked Blood		
	Maximum	Minimum	Average	Maximum	Minimum	Average	Maximum	Minimum	Average
Before breakfast..........	25.0	19.1	22.6	35.3	25.6	30.7	20.8	13.8	18.5
$2\frac{1}{2}$ hours after breakfast....	28.3	20.2	24.2	42.0	26.4	30.8	20.2	14.6	18.0

One factor influencing the level of non-protein nitrogen is the rate of protein metabolism. On a restricted protein intake, provided the diet is adequate otherwise, the blood N.P.N. may be reduced to approxi-

[127] W. Denis, *J. Biol. Chem.*, **49**, 311 (1921).

[128] Most of the data on the distribution of the various blood constituents have been obtained by the method of Folin and Wu, which involves preliminary laking of the blood. More recently Folin has pointed out that certain errors are inherent in the method. In the process of laking, unknown products are presumably formed or liberated from the disintegrated cells and constitute the major part of the undetermined nitrogen fraction. *J. Biol. Chem.*, **38**, 81 (1919); Folin, *ibid.*, **86**, 173 (1930); Folin and A. Svedberg, *ibid.*, **88**, 715 (1930).

[129] Compare these results with those of Wu, *J. Biol. Chem.*, **51**, 21 (1922).

mately half the normal value. In contrast, when protein metabolism is increased, as in starvation, fever, and untreated severe diabetes, the N.P.N. tends to rise above normal.

The rate of excretion of nitrogen by the kidney is even more important in determining the level of N.P.N. Diuresis tends to lower it. Diminished urinary flow, accompanying dehydration, as in severe diarrhea, persistent vomiting, fever, etc., tends to raise it. The increased N.P.N. observed in intestinal obstruction and in fever may also be due to impaired renal function. Obstruction to the urinary passages (prostatic hypertrophy, stricture of the urethra, etc.) may be accompanied by a marked rise in N.P.N., values of 100 mg. or more being encountered not infrequently. As the obstruction is relieved, the blood N.P.N. tends to return to normal. The most conspicuous changes are observed, however, in disease of the kidney. In non-hemorrhagic Bright's disease (nephrosis), renal function remains fairly normal and the N.P.N. is unchanged and often somewhat diminished, unless the urine output is markedly decreased. Even in acute glomerular nephritis, the ability to excrete the nitrogenous constituents may remain unimpaired, and hence no change occurs in the blood. Frequently, however, this is not the case; nitrogen retention develops, and, as in chronic nephritis, there is a rise in N.P.N. that is more or less commensurate with the degree of renal insufficiency. When the capacity of the kidney to concentrate the nitrogen, or to form urine, is reduced to an extremely low point, as in terminal nephritis, or in bichloride of mercury poisoning, the non-protein nitrogen rapidly attains very high values, 300 mg. or even more.

Amino-acid Nitrogen. The amino acids of the blood are to be regarded as nutrient material *en route* to the tissues. During digestion of a protein-rich meal, there is an increase in the amino-acid nitrogen of the blood, as has been shown by György and Zunz,[130] Van Slyke and Meyer,[131] and others. In the work of György and Zunz, the distribution of amino acids between the plasma and the corpuscles was studied before and four hours after the ingestion of raw beef. Dogs were used as the experimental animals. The results of one of these experiments are given below; they show the marked increase in the amino-acid nitrogen both in the plasma and in the corpuscles.

Van Slyke and Meyer[131] found the blood of fasting dogs to contain 3–5 mg. of amino-acid nitrogen in 100 cc. In one of their experiments, 12 grams of alanine were injected, the injection lasting thirteen minutes. Five minutes after the injection was over, the blood was analyzed. Only 1.5 grams of the alanine could be accounted for at this time. At the end of thirty-five minutes only 0.4 gram remained. During this

[130] *J. Biol. Chem.*, **21**, 511 (1915).   [131] *Ibid.*, **12**, 399 (1912).

interval 1.5 grams of the amino acid were excreted. These observations show that the tissues are capable of removing amino acids with great rapidity.

TABLE XXXIX

AMINO-ACID N PER 100 CC. OF CAROTID BLOOD

	Whole Blood	Plasma	Corpuscles
Three to four hours after bleeding....	6.1	2.1	4.0
Four hours after bleeding followed immediately by ingestion of raw beef.	11.6	3.8	8.0

In a series of 20 analyses of the blood of normal individuals, Greene, Sandiford, and Ross[132] found the amino-acid nitrogen to vary between 5.2 and 7.2 mg. per 100 cc. Approximately the same results were obtained in a series of more than 400 observations on individuals suffering from various pathological conditions, the concentrations varying between 4.8 and 7.8 mg. per 100 cc. of whole blood. The concentration of amino acids is greater in the corpuscles than in the plasma, according to Wu,[129] who obtained an average of 5.52 mg. per 100 cc. of plasma and 9.47 mg. per 100 cc. of corpuscles. However, data indicating that diffusible amino acids are more abundant in the plasma than in the corpuscles have been published by Folin and Svedberg.[133] Danielson,[134] working in Folin's laboratory, has concluded that the values based on analysis of laked blood are too high. Analyzing unlaked blood, he obtained the following data for the amino nitrogen in normal *fasting* individuals:

TABLE XL

	Whole Blood		Plasma		Corpuscles	
	Average	Range	Average	Range	Average	Range
Young men (29 analyses) ..	3.0	2.3 –3.73	4.84	4.0 –5.65	1.04	0.34–2.19
Young women (8 analyses)....	2.89	2.32–3.3	4.78	3.86–5.46	0.37	0.05–0.834

[132] *J. Biol. Chem.*, **58**, 845 (1923–24); see also Blau, *ibid.*, **56**, 861 (1923).
[133] *J. Biol. Chem.*, **88**, 715 (1930).
[134] *Ibid.*, **101**, 523 (1933). Compare D. D. Van Slyke and E. Kirk, *ibid.*, **102**, 651 (1933).

A marked increase in amino-acid nitrogen and a corresponding reduction in urea nitrogen occur in acute yellow atrophy. It is only in the most severe forms of liver disease that destruction of the tissue is sufficient to interefere with the function of the liver in the metabolism of amino acids and in the production of urea (p. 413).

Urea. The concentration of urea in the blood varies within rather wide limits, as indicated by the data in Table XLI, but as a rule it represents about 50 to 60 per cent of the total non-protein nitrogen.

TABLE XLI

UREA NITROGEN IN MILLIGRAMS PER 100 CC.

Authority	Whole Blood			Plasma		
	Max.	Min.	Aver.	Max.	Min.	Aver.
Wu[129] (20 subjects)......	22	12	17.1	23	13	19.3
Folin and Svedberg[133] (19 subjects)..........	14.5	9.8	13	16	10.5	13.8
MacKay and MacKay[135]						
114 male subjects......	21.6	12.05	15.4			
47 female subjects....	18.2	5.14	11.4			

The data of MacKay and MacKay show that the average for the male group is about 35 per cent above that for the female group.

Urea is about equally distributed between the water of the corpuscles and of the plasma.

The concentration of blood urea is influenced by (1) the amount of protein metabolism and (2) the rate of excretion. It tends to be high when protein metabolism is increased by diet, fever, etc., and is somewhat diminished when protein metabolism is at a low level. With impairment in renal function and retention of nitrogen, the urea accumulates in greater proportion than the rest of the nitrogenous constituents, so that the ratio of $\dfrac{\text{Urea N}}{\text{N P N}} \times 100$ increases above 50 to 60.

Normally the concentration of blood urea is related to the excretion. This relation has been utilized clinically in estimating the functional activity of the kidneys (p. 463).

As has been stated elsewhere, blood urea is markedly diminished in acute yellow atrophy.

[135] *J. Clin. Investigation,* **4**, 127 (1927).

Uric Acid. The normal variations are represented by the following data:

TABLE XLII

BLOOD URIC ACID IN MILLIGRAMS PER 100 CC.

	Whole Blood			Plasma			Corpuscles		
	Max.	Min.	Aver.	Max.	Min.	Aver.	Max.	Min.	Aver.
Wu[129] (20 subjects)..	.....	.....	......	5.7	2.3	3.92	3.8	1.2	1.93
Folin and Svedberg[133].......	3.2	2.2	2.6	3.9	3.3				
Benedict and Behre[135a].....	5.2	3.0	3.8	5.5	3.4	4.4	.....	.....	3.17

In the new-born infant, during starvation, after exercise, during pregnancy, and especially at the end of labor the uric acid content of the blood is increased above normal. High uric acid values, due either to increased nuclear metabolism or retention, have been observed in various diseases, notably leukemia, polycythemia, arteriosclerosis, gout, toxemias of pregnancy, especially eclampsia of the nephritic type, and nephritis. In the terminal stages of nephritis it is not unusual to find the uric acid in the vicinity of 20 mg. per 100 cc., or even higher.

Creatine and Creatinine. Blood of normal individuals contains 1.0 to 1.5 mg. of creatinine per 100 cc., the distribution between the plasma and corpuscles being about equal.[136]

The concentration of creatinine is relatively constant and unlike other nitrogenous blood constituents is not subject to physiological variation. Even in nephritis, the creatinine level may remain unchanged so long as renal function is only moderately impaired. But when marked retention occurs, the creatinine tends to rise. Values above 2 mg. are definitely abnormal; 3 mg. indicates severe impairment in function, and 5 mg. is considered by clinicians of grave signifi-

[135a] *J. Biol. Chem.*, **92**, 161 (1931).

[136] Compare Folin and Svedberg,[133] Wu[129] and Hammett, *J. Biol. Chem.*, **41**, 599 (1920).

The determination of creatinine depends on a reaction with alkaline picrate (Jaffé's reaction). As this is a non-specific reaction, various authorities have questioned the existence of creatinine, as such, in the blood (Behre and Benedict, *J. Biol. Chem.*, **52**, 11 (1922); O. H. Gaebler, *ibid.*, **89**, 451 (1930). Although Gaebler and Keltch have isolated creatinine as the picrate from blood (*J. Biol. Chem.*, **76**, 337 [1928]), Gaebler nevertheless believes it to be derived, not from creatinine, or creatine, but from an unknown creatinine-yielding substance.

cance. In a case of bichloride of mercury poisoning in which there was almost complete anuria for 10 days, a creatinine value of 19.2 mg. per 100 cc. has been recorded (Looney).[137]

Creatine, unlike creatinine, is not an end-product of metabolism, nor is it a urinary constituent in the normal male adult. The concentration in the blood is usually about 4 mg. per 100 cc., more being present in the corpuscles than in the plasma. In severe nephritis, the content is somewhat increased though evidently this is not due to retention by the kidneys.

Glucose. The methods for determining blood sugar are based on the reducing action of glucose, under controlled conditions, on such reagents as an alkaline solution of copper tartrate. Several methods in common use give somewhat different results. Actually, the results obtained by such methods are a measure, not only of the amount of glucose, but of other reducing substances as well. In order to differentiate between the so-called " true sugar " of the blood and other reducing constituents, especially non-sugars, advantage is taken of the fact that glucose is readily fermentable by yeast. Suitably prepared blood filtrates are analyzed before and after being subjected to the action of yeast, and in this way values are obtained for the total reducing substances (or apparent sugar) of the blood and for the non-sugar reducing substances. The difference between the two represents the concentration of glucose. According to Somogyi,[138] the amount of reducing non-sugars of the blood is very uniform, averaging 27 mg. per 100 cc. (expressed in terms of glucose). The concentration of " true sugar " in the blood, according to the data given by Somogyi, is frequently less than 90 mg. per 100 cc. In a group of 11 normal subjects, West[139] obtained " blood sugar " values varying from 87 to 119 mg., of which 16 to 25 mg. represented non-sugar reducing substances. The " true sugar " varied between 68 and 94 mg. per 100 cc.

Employing Benedict's procedure,[140] which apparently excludes the non-sugar reducing substances, the normal blood-sugar level in the fasting state may be fixed at 70 to 90 mg. per 100 cc.

The concentration of glucose in the corpuscle is less than in the plasma, but calculated on the basis of the water content of each, there is equal distribution between the cells and the plasma.[141]

[137] *J. Biol. Chem.*, **70**, 513 (1931).

[138] *J. Biol. Chem.*, **75**, 33 (1927); **78**, 117 (1928).

[139] E. S. West, F. H. Scharles, and V. L. Peterson, *ibid.*, **82**, 137 (1929).

[140] S. R. Benedict, *J. Biol. Chem.*, **92**, 141 (1931). See also Folin and H. Malmros, *ibid.*, **83**, 121 (1929).

[141] Compare M. Somogyi, *J. Biol. Chem.*, **90**, 731 (1931); M. H. Power and C. H. Greene, *ibid.*, **94**, 281 (1931–32).

A man weighing 70 kg. has about 6 grams of sugar in circulation
When moderate amounts of carbohydrate are ingested, the sugar con
tent of the blood in the portal vein increases appreciably, but in the
systemic circulation little change is noted, owing to the rapid removal
of excessive amounts of sugar by the liver and other tissues. However,
when more than moderate amounts of sugar are taken—50 to 100
grams—the sugar in the blood may increase to as much as 0.15 per cent
or even higher (see p. 316). The increase occurs during the first hour
and is soon followed by a return of the blood sugar to normal levels.

Mention should also be made of the probable occurrence of hydrolyzable sugars in the blood. The analyses of Everett and Sheppard[142]
indicate the presence of about 3 mg. of such carbohydrates per 100 cc.
of plasma and about 10 mg. per 100 cc. of corpuscles.

The significance of data for blood sugar should therefore be clearly
understood. Glucose is not the only reducing substance present in the
blood, although it undoubtedly predominates. In the present discussion
the point may be emphasized that the glucose of the blood is on its
way to the liver, muscles, and other tissues, either to be stored or
oxidized. The blood going to the tissues (arterial blood) normally contains more sugar than the blood returning from the tissues (venous
blood), as shown by the work of Foster[143] and others.

Blood Lipids. Blood plasma usually contains 0.5 to 0.8 per cent of
fat. The fatty acid content is from 0.2 to 0.45 per cent, being almost
entirely in combination as phosphatide, neutral fat, and cholesterol
esters. The total cholesterol normally varies between 150 and 200 mg.
per 100 cc., but wider variations are not uncommon. It is about equally
distributed between the cells and plasma; in the corpuscles the cholesterol is present in the free form, whereas in the plasma the greater
part (50 to 80 per cent) is combined with fatty acids, as esters.

The following average data have been obtained by Boyd[144] in eight
normal young women:

Total lipid, mg. per cent... 589
Neutral fat, mg. per cent... 154
Total fatty acid, mg. per cent.. 353
   Phospholipid fatty acid, mg. per cent............................. 130
   Cholesterol ester, fatty acid, mg. per cent....................... 77
   Neutral fat fatty acid, mg. per cent.............................. 146
Total cholesterol, mg. per cent....................................... 162

[142] *J. Biol. Chem.*, **80**, 255 (1928).

[143] *Ibid.*, **55**, 303 (1923); see also Friedenson, Rosenbaum, Thalheimer, and Peters
ibid., **80**, 269 (1928).

[144] *J. Biol. Chem.*, **101**, 323 (1933).

Combined cholesterol, mg. per cent...................................... 115
Free cholesterol, mg. per cent.. 47
Phospholipid, mg. per cent... 196
Iodine number of total fatty acids...................................... 88.5
Iodine number of phospholipid fatty acids.............................. 124

The following physiological and pathological conditions are associated with an increased concentration of blood lipids (lipemia, or hyperlipemia) and usually by an increase in cholesterol (hypercholesterolemia): food ingestion, high fat diet, high meat diet, exercise, ether anesthesia, pregnancy, prolonged fasting, cachexia, diabetes, anemia, nephritis, nephrosis, hypothyroidism. Very high values for cholesterol, 500 mg. per 100 cc. of plasma, and above, are encountered not infrequently in hypothyroidism and nephrosis. In hyperthyroidism, the cholesterol concentration tends to be low.

Lactic acid occurs normally in amounts of 10 to 20 mg. per 100 cc. of blood. In the resting individual the variation is from about 6 to 14 mg., with an average of 10 mg.[145] The concentration is increased with exercise and depends on its intensity. Very strenuous exercise may raise the concentration above 100 mg. The ingestion of carbohydrate, the administration of insulin, ether anesthesia, and pregnancy are associated with an increased content. High values have also been observed in heart failure, pneumonia, and tuberculosis.

Normal blood contains about 1 mg. per 100 cc. of the so-called *ketone bodies* (acetone, aceto-acetic acid, and β-hydroxybutyric acid. The concentration is markedly increased in fasting individuals, particularly in children, in toxemias of pregnancy, persistent vomiting, and diabetes. In severe diabetes values of 300 mg. per 100 cc. have been recorded.

THE WATER BALANCE OF THE BODY

This subject has been reviewed by Rowntree,[146] Marriott,[147] and more recently by Adolph.[148] Water balance may be defined as the daily relation between the total amount of water entering the organism, through the ingestion of liquids and food, and the total output of water lost from the body by way of the kidneys, bowels, lungs, and skin. The water that results from the oxidation of the foodstuffs must also be included in the intake. Water is essential to life, and the supply,

---

[145] A. V. Bock, D. B. Dill, and H. T. Edwards, *J. Clin. Investigation*, **11**, 775 (1932).

[146] L. G. Rowntree, *Physiol. Rev.*, **2**, 116 (1922).

[147] W. McKim Marriott, *ibid.*, **3**, 275 (1923).

[148] E. F. Adolph, *ibid.*, **13**, 336 (1933).

in most animals, must keep up with the demand. Voluntary abstinence from food for periods as long as two months has been endured by man, but deprivation of water for much shorter periods brings on serious effects. Rowntree cites the case of Viterbi, an Italian political prisoner who refrained from food and drink for eighteen days and died as a result. He is said to have suffered but little from hunger after the first day, but to have experienced terrible thirst until he died. Death from thirst, in the case of individuals who are lost in the desert, is believed to result after 36 to 72 hours of water deprivation.[149]

It is estimated that from 7500 to 10,000 cc. of water per day are excreted into various parts of the alimentary tract as saliva, gastric juice, pancreatic juice, and intestinal juice. Nearly all of this water, which is about two to three times the usual water intake, is reabsorbed. Water is lost to the body chiefly by way of the skin, respiratory tract, and kidneys. The kidneys are the most important, except under unusual conditions of heat and exercise, when the amount of water lost as sweat may exceed the amount in the urine.

Numerous attempts have been made to alter the composition of the blood by forced water administration. For example, in the experiment of Haldane and Priestley[150] 5500 cc. of water was taken in a period of four hours. Marked diuresis followed, so that at one time the rate of urine secretion was 2500 cc. per hour. And yet they observed no evidence of blood dilution. Similar results were obtained by Adolph.[151] These experiments show the remarkable control exercised by the kidneys in maintaining the normal water balance.

However, Greene and Rowntree,[152] and more recently, Calvin, Smith, and Mendel,[153] succeeded in producing blood dilution in the dog by forced administration of water. Finally, the experiments of Margaria[154] on human subjects prove that the blood may be definitely diluted as a result of drinking large quantities of water (p. 15).

The water lost through vaporization constitutes 80 per cent, or more, of the so-called " insensible loss of weight." This is represented by the combined output of water vapor and carbon dioxide *minus* the weight of oxygen simultaneously absorbed. Under ordinary conditions,

---

[149] The student is referred to W. B. Cannon, "The Physiological Basis of Thirst," *Proc. Roy. Soc.*, (London) *B*, **90**, 283 (1918).

[150] *J. Physiol.*, **50**, 296 (1915–16).

[151] *Ibid.*, **55**, 114 (1921).

[152] *Am. J. Physiol.*, **80**, 209 (1927).

[153] *Ibid.*, **105**, 135 (1933); see also Chanutin, Smith, and Mendel, *ibid.*, **68**, 444 (1924).

[154] *J. Physiol.*, **70**, 417 (1930).

the insensible loss of weight of an adult during 24 hours may amount to about 1 kg.[155]

There are many phases to the problem of water exchange, of which only a few can be referred to even briefly. The relation between water equilibrium and acid-base balance has been emphasized by a number of investigators.[156] Acidosis and dehydration are often associated phenomena, and alkalosis may be accompanied by sufficient water retention to show an increase in body weight. In another connection mention has been made of the effects resulting from the loss of water and hydrochloric acid in intestinal obstruction (p. 210).

Water retention due to lowered barometric pressure has been observed in rats and dogs by C. S. Smith.[157] Associated with this disturbance in water balance is marked restlessness, which has led to the interesting speculation as to the possibility of a similar relationship existing in those animals which are capable of anticipating a change in weather.

Larson, Weir, and Rowntree[158] have described a form of water intoxication which may be produced in dogs, cats, rabbits, and guinea-pigs by the administration of excessive amounts of water. The symptoms are nausea, vomiting, salivation, convulsions, stupor, and coma; death ensues if water administration is continued after the onset of the convulsions. On the other hand, the convulsions may be prevented by the injection of hypertonic saline when the first symptoms of the intoxication become apparent. The convulsions are believed to be cerebral in origin.[159]

The factors of water retention and tissue hydration have also been associated with the convulsive seizures in epilepsy.

[155] According to Benedict and Root, *Arch. Internal Med.*, **38**, 1 (1926), the insensible perspiration bears a quantitative relationship to the basal metabolic rate (p. 508) and may therefore be applied as an indirect method of determining the basal metabolism. This aspect of the subject, as well as the question of water balance, have received attention in various connections: M. W. Johnston and L. H. Newburgh, *J. Clin. Investigation*, **8**, 147, 161 (1929–30); F. H. Wiley and Newburgh, *ibid.*, **10**, 723 (1931); S. Z. Levine, J. R. Wilson, and M. Kelly, "The Insensible Perspiration in Infancy and Childhood," *Am. J. Diseases Children*, **33**, 204 (1927); **37**, 791 (1929); **39**, 917 (1930); I. McQuarrie, *et al.*, "Water Balance in Epilepsy," *ibid.*, **43**, 1519 (1932); *J. Nutrition*, **4**, 39 (1931).

[156] E. J. Stieglitz, *Arch. Internal Med.*, **41**, 10 (1928); W. McKim Marriott and A. F. Hartmann, *J. Am. Med. Assoc.*, **91**, 1675 (1928); L. Schoenthal, *Am. J. Diseases Children*, **37**, 244 (1929); Editorials in *J. Am. Med. Assoc.*, **90**, 1294, 1378; **91**, 2066 (1928); **92**, 148, 724, 898 (1929).

[157] *Am. J. Physiol.*, **87**, 200 (1928).

[158] Cited by Rowntree.[146]

[159] F. S. Smyth, W. C. Deames, and N. K. Phatak, *J. Clin. Investigation*, **12**, 55 (1933), are inclined to relate the convulsive symptoms in water intoxication to the loss of chloride by way of the gastric secretion and to the resulting alkalosis.

It was shown by Weed and McKibben[160] that the intravenous injection of strong hypertonic solutions of salt or glucose produces a marked lowering of the cerebrospinal fluid pressure, together with a diminution in the volume of the brain. These effects, which are brought about by the withdrawal of water from the brain, as well as from other tissues, may also be obtained by the intra-intestinal administration of hypertonic solutions.[161] Clinical application of these physiological observations has been made, particularly in brain surgery, where occasionally a modification of the pressure of the cerebrospinal fluid or a diminution of the brain bulk is desired.

A marked disturbance in water balance results from burns. The capillaries become abnormally permeable and a large proportion of fluid, rich in protein, is withdrawn from the circulation and localized in the tissues beneath the burned area. This is accompanied by a decrease in plasma protein, blood volume, and blood pressure. If the last is severe enough a condition of " shock " develops.[162]

---

[160]*Am. J. Physiol.*, **48**, 512, 531 (1919).

[161] Foley and Putnam, *ibid.*, **53**, 464 (1920).

[162] An experimental study of the mechanism of water exchange in the animal organism, accompanying burns, has been reported by Underhill, Kapsinow, and Fisk, *Am. J. Physiol.*, **95**, 302 *et seq.* (1930); see also Blalock *et al.*, *Arch. Surgery*, **22**, 598 *et seq.* (1931).

The following description by Haldane illustrates the effects of derangement of the salt and water balance:

"Perhaps the hottest place in England is about a mile under Salford, where the coal-miners work in boots and bathing-drawers, and empty the sweat from their boots at lunch—or snapping-time. One man sweated eighteen pounds in the course of a shift, and it is probable that even this figure has been exceeded. This sweat contained about an ounce of salt—twice what the average man consumes in all forms per day. The salt loss was instinctively made up above ground by means of bacon, kippers, salted beer, and the like. And as long as they did not drink more than a quart of water underground, no harm came to the miners. But a man who has sweated nearly two gallons is thirsty, and coal-dust dries the throat, so this amount was often exceeded, and the excess occasionally led to appalling attacks of cramp, often in the stomach, but sometimes in the limb or back. The victims had taken more water than was needed to adjust the salt concentration in their blood, and the diversion of blood from their kidneys to their muscles and skin was so great that they were unable to excrete the excess. The miners in question were offered a solution of salt in water which was about the composition of sweat, and would be somewhat unappetizing to the average man. They drank it by quarts and asked for more. And now that it has become their regular beverage underground there is no more cramp, and far less fatigue. It is almost certain that the cramp of stokers, and of iron and glass workers, which is known to be due to excessive water-drinking, could be prevented in the same way." J. B. S. Haldane, "Possible Worlds," Harper, New York and London, 1928, p. 82. A fairly full account of "Some Effects of High Air Temperatures and Muscular Exertion upon Colliers" is given by K. N. Moss, *Proc. Roy. Soc.*, *B*, **95**, 181 (1924). See also, E. F. Adolph, *J. Physiol.*, **55**, 114 (1921).

Water and Heat Regulation. Rowntree states that water regulates heat distribution and dissipation because of its mobility and thermal properties. The high specific heat of water favors the storage of heat. The high caloric demands for the evaporation of water permit rapid elimination of heat when necessary. The high heat conductivity provides rapid equalization of heat within the tissues of the body, according to Barbour.[163] Rowntree points out that the latent heat of vaporization of water is of universal significance in relation to the dissipation of body heat, because of the fact that evaporation occurs at all temperatures.

Severe diuresis, owing to the depletion of water, produces a febrile condition in man and animals. In this way, Balcar, Sansum, and Woodyatt[164] produced a fever as high as 125.6° F. in dogs through the intravenous administration of concentrated solutions of glucose. An elevation in temperature also develops in infants deprived of food and water, but in new-born puppies Pucher[165] obtained an opposite effect, namely a rapid fall in temperature. In dogs, Greene and Rowntree[166] have observed a fall in temperature to result from the forced administration of water, even though the water given was at a temperature equal to or slightly above that of the body.

THE LYMPH AND OTHER FLUIDS

The lymph is fundamentally a transudate, formed from the plasma by filtration through the capillary wall.[167] It therefore resembles the plasma in composition, except as this is modified by the impermeability of the capillary endothelium for protein. In accordance with Donnan's theory of membrane equilibria, differences in ionic concentrations (Na^+, H^+, Cl^-, HCO_3^-, etc.) are to be expected, but the non-electrolytes, such as sugar and urea, should be equally distributed between the two fluids, an equal distribution conforming with the idea that the lymph is a filtrate and not a secretion, as was supposed by many of the earlier physiologists.

[163] *Physiol. Reviews*, **1**, 295 (1921).

[164] *Arch. Internal Med.*, **24**, 116 (1919).

[165] *J. Biol. Chem.*, **76**, 319 (1928).

[166] *Am. J. Physiol.*, **80**, 230 (1928).

[167] The student is referred to the classical paper of E. H. Starling, *J. Physiol.*, **16**, 224 (1894), and to E. M. Landis, *Am. J. Physiol.*, **82**, 217 (1927).

A series of important papers on lymph have appeared from C. K. Drinker's laboratory at Harvard: *Am. J. Physiol.*, **97**, 52; **98**, 66, 70, 378 (1931); **100**, 642; **101**, 223, 232, 612 (1932); **103**, 34, 533 (1933).

The question of definition has been brought up. Certain students of the subject hold the view that the term " lymph " should be restricted to the fluid within the lymph channels and should not be employed in designating the fluid which fills the intracellular spaces and in which the tissues are virtually bathed or "soaked." In line with the present conception that the lymphatics constitute a more or less closed system, it may be inferred that lymphatic lymph differs in chemical composition from tissue lymph. In truth, however, there is no evidence for this assumption. The peripheral lymphatics are relatively permeable and permit the free interchange of material, including protein, so that it is probably accurate to consider the two fluids to be similar in composition. Accordingly, in this brief discussion of the subject, the tissue fluid, as well as the contents of the lymphatics, will be referred to as lymph.

Lymph collected from different regions of the body varies in composition. Thus, the fluid from the lower extremity contains 2 to 3 per cent protein; the lymph from the intestines 4 to 6 per cent, and that from the liver 6 to 8 per cent. These differences have been associated with variations in capillary permeability, rate of reabsorption, and other factors.

Considering the high concentrations of protein in lymph, it may be expected to exert an appreciable colloid osmotic pressure. Field and Drinker obtained values of 131 to 195 mm. H_2O for cervical lymph (dogs) and 138 to 344 mm. for thoracic duct lymph, the latter often containing a large amount of protein. In the same group of animals the values obtained for blood varied between 334 and 466 mm. H_2O. Drinker and associates hold the view that blood capillaries normally " leak " protein; this does not re-enter the blood vessels unless delivered by the lymphatics.

The colloid osmotic pressure per gram of protein is higher for lymph than for blood. This accords with the relatively greater proportion of albumin in the former. It is the difference between the colloid osmotic pressure of the blood and lymph in a given area which determines the " effective " osmotic pressure of the blood and the return of fluid from the tissues.

A comparative study of the chemical composition of blood serum and thoracic lymph of the dog has been made by Arnold and Mendel,[168] whose results show that both normally and abnormally there is an interrelationship between the composition of the lymph and plasma. An interchange of material is continually taking place, and whenever any

[168] *J. Biol. Chem.*, **72**, 189 (1927).

fluctuations in the concentrations occur, the diffusible constituents pass easily and rapidly between the blood, lymph, and the tissues. The normal relations are indicated in the following table:

TABLE XLIII

	Total Solids	Chlorides	Calcium	Phos-phorus	Sugar	Non-protein Nitrogen	Protein Nitrogen
	G. per 100 cc.	Mg. per 100 cc.	Mg. per 100 cc.	Mg. per 100 cc.	Mg. per 100 cc.	Mg. per 100 cc.	G. per 100 cc.
Serum........	8.3	392	10.4	4.3	123	27.2	0.9
Lymph........	5.2	413	9.2	3.6	124	27.0	0.57

The relation of the composition of cervical lymph to that of the blood is indicated by the data in Table XLIV, obtained by Heim.[169]

TABLE XLIV

COMPARISON OF THE CONCENTRATIONS OF SOME OF THE CONSTITUENTS IN PERIPHERAL (CERVICAL) LYMPH AND BLOOD PLASMA OF THE DOG UNDER NORMAL CONDITIONS (Nembutal anesthesia)

	Pro-tein (Kjel-dahl)	N. P. N.	Urea	Uric Acid	Crea-tinine	Sugar	Amino Acids	Chlor-ides as NaCl	Phosphorus		Cal-cium
									Total	Inorg.	
	Per cent	Mg. per 100 cc.	Mg. per 100 cc.	Mg. per 100 cc.	Mg. per 100 cc.	Mg. per 100 cc.	Mg. per 100 cc.	Mg. per 100 cc.	Mg. per 100 cc.	Mg. per 100 cc.	Mg. per 100 cc.
Plasma: Average........	6.18	32.6	21.7	Trace	1.37	123.0	4.90	678	22.0	5.6	11.70
Lymph: Average........	3.32	34.8	23.5	Trace	1.40	132.2	4.84	711	11.8	5.9	9.84
Ratio: Lymph/plasma...	0.54	1.07	1.07		1.03	1.08	0.99	1.05	0.54	1.05	0.84
Number of animals.	(16)	(10)	(7)	(3)	(7)	(16)	(1)	(7)	(6)	(3)	(11)

The lymph as it flows away from the lacteals is rich in fat and other absorbed material. As the fat is in a highly emulsified condition, the

[169] *Am. J. Physiol.*, **103**, 553 (1933); see also A. M. Walker, *J. Biol. Chem.*, **101**, 269 (1933).

fluid has a milky appearance, and for this reason was called, by the earlier physiologists, "lacteal fluid," a name later replaced more or less generally by the term *chyle*. Except for a higher solid content, the chyle is very similar in composition to the lymph in other parts of the body.

Transudates and Exudates. The movement of fluid through the capillary wall is influenced by many factors. It has been shown, for example, that above a venous pressure of 12 cm. H_2O, the rate of filtration is directly proportional to the increase in venous pressure, and when this reaches 15 to 20 cm., fluid tends to accumulate in the tissue spaces.[170] However, as the tissue pressure rises through the accumulation of fluid, it tends to diminish the filtration rate. The temperature of the part is also a factor, the rate of filtration through the capillary wall being greater at higher than at lower temperatures. Other factors have been considered elsewhere.

It must also be recognized that the permeability of the capillary endothelium is subject to change as a result of noxious influences, anoxemia, bacterial toxins, etc. Thus it is that the physical process of filtration associated with the normal exchange of fluid and other substances between the tissues and the blood may become modified particularly in the direction of increased accumulation of fluid in the tissues and body cavities (pleural, pericardial, peritoneal, etc.). When the process is non-inflammatory in origin, the product is called a transudate. Disturbance in circulation, with passive congestion, is a common cause. Inflammatory processes, on the other hand, give rise to exudates. As has been stated by Wells,[171] it is often very difficult to decide whether a given fluid is an exudate or a transudate, there being no definite line of demarcation either etiologically or chemically. The differentiation is usually based on the following properties: (1) the specific gravity of transudates is below 1.015, that of exudates above 1.018; (2) exudates contain much more protein (3 per cent or above) than transudates; (3) transudates coagulate slowly, if at all, whereas exudates, because they contain much more fibrinogen, coagulate readily; (4) transudates are sterile, whereas exudates contain specific organisms; (5) exudates, in acute infections, contain pus cells (polymorphonuclear leukocytes); in chronic infections lymphocytes predominate; in transudates few cells are ordinarily present.

These differential points reveal a qualitative difference between exudates and transudates. We may consider first the condition in

---

[170] A. Krogh, E. M. Landis, and A. H. Turner, *J. Clin. Investigation*, **11**, 63 (1932); Landis and J. H. Gibbon, *ibid.*, **12**, 105 (1933).

[171] H. G. Wells, "Chemical Pathology," 5th edition, 1925, Chap. XVI.

which the capillary endothelium is impermeable to protein. The resulting product is a protein-free filtrate, or ultrafiltrate, in short a transudate. The other extreme is the condition in which the membrane has become so altered as to permit the free passage of protein, so that the concentration of this constituent in the effusion is the same as in the blood. In general, exudates approach this condition. Transudates, on the other hand, represent a state in which the integrity of the capillary endothelium has not been reduced to the same extent and is therefore still capable of preventing to a greater or lesser degree the diffusion of protein, particularly the globulin and fibrinogen fractions.

The composition of a transudate while in equilibrium with the blood is determined by known physicochemical laws. In studies of ascitic fluid[172] and edema fluid, the work of several investigators has established that the distribution of ions between the plasma and the transudate is governed by the Donnan equilibrium in the same manner as if the equilibration were established on the two sides of a collodion membrane. The protein content of ascitic fluid is variable. Loeb, Atchley, and Palmer[173] have recorded values of 0.8 to 0.9 per cent in three cases of hepatic cirrhosis, whereas, in a case of cardiac decompensation, as much as 4.5 per cent was found. As the amount of protein increases, the inequalities in ionic distribution between the plasma and transudate become less pronounced, but even in exudates, the Donnan effect is demonstrable.

According to the analyses of Greene and associates,[173] the total cation concentration is greater in ascitic fluid than in serum, whereas the reverse holds for the anions. The accompanying data (Table XLV) are the averages obtained in a group of 10 patients. These values are expressed in milli-equivalents per kg. of water.

The water content of the ascitic fluid was, on an average, 96.74 per cent. The protein varied from 0.56 to 5.0 per cent; average 3.09 per cent.

Synovial Fluid. This is a viscid, transparent, alkaline fluid, contained in joint cavities, bursae, and tendon sheaths. Lubrication and the protection of the structures involved in movement are its principal

---

[172] Ascitis is an accumulation of serous fluid in the peritoneal cavity. Heart disease, cirrhosis of the liver, and kidney disease are the important general causes. Ascitis may also result from local causes, such as inflammation of the peritoneum, abdominal tumors, or obstruction to the portal circulation or of the inferior vena cava.

[173] Loeb, Atchley, and Palmer, *J. Gen. Physiol.*, 4, 591 (1921–22); see also Hastings, Salvesen, Sendroy, and Van Slyke, *ibid.*, 8, 701 (1927). Greene, Bollman, Keith, and Wakefield, *J. Biol. Chem.*, 91, 203 (1931); Muntwyler, Way, and Pomerene, *ibid.*, 92, 733 (1931).

functions. Motion is a physiological stimulus for increased production; inflammation, irritation, and trauma are pathological stimuli. Because of its accessibility, the fluid from the knee joint has been the most frequently studied.

TABLE XLV

COMPOSITION OF BLOOD SERUM AND TRANSUDATES (ASCITIC FLUID)

Na		K		Ca		Mg		Cl	
Serum	Fluid	Serum	Fluid	Serum	Fluid	Serum	Fluid	Serum	Fluid
150.1	144	4.7	3.4	5	4	2.1	2.0	102.4	105.8

HCO$_3$		P		Total cations		Total anions	
Serum	Fluid	Serum	Fluid	Serum	Fluid	Serum	Fluid
29.5	28.7	2.2	2.1	161.9	153.4	136	138.8

Cajori and Pemberton[174] have compared the composition of blood plasma with that of synovial fluid in cases of arthritis with joint effusion and found almost identical values for non-protein nitrogen, urea nitrogen, and amino-acid nitrogen. The concentration of non-electrolytes in synovial fluid may be changed by inducing corresponding changes in the blood. Less protein was present in the synovial fluid than in the plasma, and the albumin-globulin ratio was slightly higher in the synovial fluid than in the plasma. The sodium chloride content was somewhat higher in the synovial fluid. As pointed out by Fremont-Smith and Dailey,[175]

TABLE XLVI

CONCENTRATION OF DIFFUSIBLE CONSTITUENTS OF SYNOVIAL FLUID AND PLASMA IN CASES OF JOINT EFFUSION, IN MILLIGRAMS PER 100 CC. (AVERAGE OF 9 CASES)

Non-protein N		Urea N		Amino Acid N		Sodium chloride	
Plasma	Fluid	Plasma	Fluid	Plasma	Fluid	Plasma	Fluid
26.2	26.1	15.8	15.8	5.6	5.9	565	595

[174] *J. Biol. Chem.*, **76**, 471 (1928).   [175] *J. Biol. Chem.*, **70**, 779 (1926).

in a similar study, these results may be explained by assuming that a simple membrane equilibrium exists between blood plasma and synovial fluid. In tables XLVI and XLVII are tabulated the average results of Cajori and Pemberton.

TABLE XLVII

ALBUMIN AND GLOBULIN CONTENT OF SYNOVIAL FLUID AND PLASMA IN CASES OF JOINT EFFUSION, IN PERCENTAGE (AVERAGE OF 10 CASES)

Total Proteins		Albumin		Globulin		Albumin/Globulin	
Plasma	Fluid	Plasma	Fluid	Plasma	Fluid	Plasma	Fluid
7.00	4.97	3.76	3.00	1.97	1.47	1.9	2.0

Cerebrospinal Fluid. Normal cerebrospinal fluid is a clear, colorless, alkaline fluid with a specific gravity of about 1.006 to 1.008. The protein content is very low, being 0.02 per cent, or less.

Fremont-Smith and co-workers[176] have compared the electrolyte distribution in serum and cerebrospinal fluid and concluded from their results that the formation of spinal fluid is analogous to the production of intracellular fluid. The concentration of calcium in the fluid is approximately equivalent to the amount of diffusible calcium in the plasma and is normally about 5 mg. per 100 cc. (Greenberg).[177] Additional evidence in support of the idea that spinal fluid is a simple dialyzate and that its formation is governed by the factors outlined for the Donnan equilibrium has been offered by Muntwyler and associates,[178] Dailey,[179] and others. The evidence includes data for the distribution of the sodium, chloride, and bicarbonate ions. A complete analysis of the total electrolyte system is still lacking.

Certain facts, however, oppose the theory that the spinal fluid is solely an ultrafiltrate. Although it is true that the glucose concentration runs more or less parallel in the plasma and the spinal fluid, the amount in the latter is normally considerably lower (about 65 mg. on the average). The point has been made that the tissues which are bathed by the cerebrospinal fluid utilize the dextrose more rapidly than it is

[176] F. Fremont-Smith, *Arch. Neurol. Psychiatry*, **17**, 317 (1927); Fremont-Smith, M. E. Dailey, *et al., ibid.*, **25**, 1271, 1290 (1931).
[177] *Proc. Soc. Exp. Biol. Med.*, **27**, 514 (1929–30); see also S. Morgulis and A. M. Perley, *J. Biol. Chem.*, **88**, 169 (1930); A. T. Cameron and V. H. K. Moorhouse, *ibid.*, **63**, 687 (1925).
[178] E. Muntwyler, C. T. Way, and E. Pomerene, *J. Biol. Chem.*, **92**, 733 (1931).
[179] M. E. Dailey, *ibid.*, **93**, 5 (1931).

restored by the blood. However, Cockrill[180] has definitely shown that this inequality is not limited to glucose. Creatinine, urea, and uric acid are likewise unequally distributed between the water of the plasma and that of the cerebrospinal fluid. When plasma is dialyzed *in vitro* against cerebrospinal fluid, this unequal distribution of non-electrolytes is not obtained.

In experiments on frogs, Walker[181] has shown that the cerebrospinal fluid contains 30 per cent less of reducing substances than the plasma. The fluid also contained less phosphate. In depancreatized dogs with blood sugar values of 351 to 520 mg. per 100 cc., the cerebrospinal fluid contained from 220 to 292 mg. Walker has therefore concluded that the cerebrospinal fluid is not formed by a simple process of filtration or dialysis, but that the choroidal epithelium possesses selective properties, not exhibited by the capillary epithelium, or by the glomerular membrane.

Intraocular Fluid. Closely resembling the cerebrospinal fluid in composition is the aqueous humor, a clear fluid which fills the anterior and posterior chambers of the eye and which permeates the gel-like vitreous humor and the intracellular spaces of the various ocular coats.

Duke-Elder[182] gives the following figures for comparison between the composition of the blood serum and the aqueous and vitreous humors:

TABLE XLVIII

	Quantities of Various Constituents in Grams per 100 cc.		
	Aqueous	Vitreous	Serum
Water..........................	99.6921	99.6813	93.3238
Total protein......................	0.0201	0.0403	7.3692
Urea.............................	0.028	0.029	0.027
Reducing substances estimated as glucose	0.0983	0.0973	0.091
Na..............................	0.2787*	0.2731	0.3351‡
Cl..............................	0.4371†	0.4168	0.3664§

* 121 millimols per liter. ‡ 145.6 millimols per liter.
† 123 millimols per liter. § 103 millimols per liter.

[180] *Arch. Neurol. Psychiatry*, **25**, 1297 (1931).
[181] *J. Biol. Chem.*, **101**, 269 (1933).
[182] W. S. Duke-Elder, *Biochem. J.*, **21**, 66 (1927); *J. Physiol.*, **62**, 315 (1927); **68**, 155 (1929–30). *Brit. J. Ophthal.*, Monograph series, iii, 1927; and particularly "Recent Advances in Ophthalmology," Blakiston's Son & Co., Philadelphia, 1929, p. 189–212. The student is also referred to Adler's "Clinical Physiology of the Eye," Macmillan Co., New York, 1933, Chap. XIII, for a good discussion of the chemical and physical properties of normal aqueous humor.

These data indicate that the intraocular fluid is formed by a process of dialysis and that its composition can be explained on the basis of Donnan's theory of membrane equilibria. Considering the distribution of the sodium and chloride ions between the blood and the aqueous humor, the theoretical relationship is:

$$[Na^+]_{aqueous} \times [Cl^-]_{aqueous} = [Na^+]_{serum} \times [Cl^-]_{serum}$$

Substituting the respective values for these concentrations, in terms of millimolar equivalents, the relationship becomes:

$$121 \times 123 = 145 \times 103$$

$$14,883 = 14,935$$

Duke-Elder has pointed out that the close agreement in these results forms a strong argument that the formation of the aqueous humor is by a process of dialysis, a view supported by the data of other investigators.[183]

Stary and Winternitz[184] have shown that the concentration of calcium in the aqueous (horse) is equivalent to the diffusible calcium content of the serum. They obtained the following values: serum calcium, 12.1 mg.; aqueous humor, 7.4 mg.; serum ultrafiltrate, 7.4 mg.

Walker,[181] on the other hand, has reported differences in the composition of the aqueous and the serum of various animals (frog, fowl, rabbit, cat, dog, and man). As in the case of cerebrospinal fluid, he found the non-electrolytes (urea, uric acid, sugar) to be present in lower concentration than in the serum, or in ultrafiltrates derived from serum. He therefore contends that the ciliary epithelium, like the choroidal epithelium, exhibits selective qualities not possessed by the capillary endothelium, or glomerular membrane, and that the intraocular fluids are not simple dialyzates.

These opposing views cannot be reconciled on the basis of the meager and conflicting data available at present. It will be necessary to obtain more adequate and consistent values for the various constituents before the theoretical implications can be properly evaluated.

[183] A. C. Krause and A. M. Yudkin, *J. Biol. Chem.*, **88**, 471 (1930).
[184] *Z. physiol. Chem.*, **212**, 215 (1932).

CHAPTER IX

PHYSIOLOGICAL OXIDATIONS

In terms of the electronic conception, oxidation is defined as the loss of electrons by an atom or ion, and reduction as the reverse. Thus Fe^{++} is oxidized to Fe^{+++} through the loss of an electron, whereas, by the addition of an electron, the ferric ion is reduced to the ferrous state, as represented by the following electrochemical equation:

$$Fe^{++} \rightleftharpoons Fe^{+++} + e$$

The symbol e in this equation represents a definite quantum of energy, namely 1 faraday, or 96,500 coulombs of negative electricity.

It will be observed that oxidation is always accompanied by reduction, the substance oxidized (*oxidant*) giving up negative electrons; the substance reduced (*reductant*) absorbing them. In the well-known Cannizzaro reaction, in which acetaldehyde is simultaneously oxidized to acetic acid and reduced to ethyl alcohol,

$$2CH_3CHO \rightarrow CH_3COOH + CH_3CH_2OH$$

there is merely a transfer of electrons. The chemical energy derived from the oxidation of one molecule of acetaldehyde is utilized in the reduction of the second molecule. The total process is therefore accompanied by no liberation of energy; nor is any energy added from the outside. But in many oxidation reactions the products formed contain less energy than the original substance and hence the process is accompanied by the liberation of energy. To illustrate, the oxidation of glucose to lactic acid, and of the latter to simpler substances, is associated with the release of energy. This is electronic or chemical energy, capable of being transformed into heat, kinetic, or work energy, light, as in the firefly, electricity, as in the electric eel or torpedo ray.[1] Ultimately all forms of energy are degraded to heat energy.

The inertness of molecular hydrogen and oxygen is well illustrated

---

[1] These have special organs which are said to generate an electromotive force of several hundred volts. But apart from such special cases, all living cells produce some electrical energy, which though of small magnitude is nevertheless of considerable physiological significance.

by the fact that at ordinary temperatures these do not react with measurable velocity. The reaction is greatly accelerated, however, in the presence of a suitable catalyst, such as colloidal platinum, or palladium, the first stage of the reaction consisting in the formation of hydrogen peroxide:

$$H_2 + O_2 \rightarrow H_2O_2$$

In the second stage, the hydrogen peroxide is decomposed as follows:

$$2H_2O_2 \rightarrow O_2 + 2H_2O$$

The contrast between the non-reactivity of molecular oxygen and hydrogen in the absence of catalysts and the readiness with which they react in the presence of inorganic catalysts and in biological oxidations has naturally drawn attention to the problem of their activation. The objective of students of the subject has been to determine whether these catalyzed reactions depend fundamentally on the activation of the hydrogen of the oxidizable substance, or of the oxygen in the oxidizing agent.

Warburg's Theory. In various forms, the theory has been propounded that activation of oxygen is the essential factor. Warburg formerly advocated the view that inorganic iron is concerned in this activation, but since the discovery of the significance of the heme compounds this conception has been modified. He now considers the function of hemin to be that of a " respiratory ferment." Presumably the oxygen combines with the respiratory ferment $(X \cdot Fe)$ as follows:

$$X \cdot Fe + O_2 \rightleftharpoons X \cdot FeO_2$$

The resulting compound in turn oxidizes organic substances, as represented by the equation:

$$X \cdot FeO_2 + 2A \rightleftharpoons X \cdot Fe + 2AO$$

It has been shown that substances which combine with iron, such as HCN, inhibit the respiratory process. [2]

[2] O. Warburg, *Science*, **61**, 575 (1925).

In addition to hemin and iron salts, the salts of other metals have been described as activators of oxygen. Thus, the oxidation of sugars may be accelerated by adding small amounts of copper or manganese. In a weakly alkaline solution, Meyerhof (cited by Warburg) found that 1–100 mg. of copper, when added to 100 mg. of fructose, accelerated the oxidation 140 per cent. A similar amount of iron caused an increase of 70 per cent.

It has been demonstrated by Warburg that charcoal shaken in aqueous solutions of amino acids causes chemical changes resembling reactions of metabolism. In an approximately neutral solution, at body temperature, leucine yields ammonia,

Bach-Engler Theory.—Bach[3] and Engler[4] independently advanced an hypothesis for tissue oxidation, according to which molecular oxygen is believed to react with some constituent of the protoplasm (*oxygenase*) to form a peroxide. The latter is broken down by an enzyme, *peroxidase*, yielding active oxygen which is capable of oxidizing the metabolites in the tissues.

The formation of peroxides as intermediate products of oxidation is a familiar phenomenon. For example, in the oxidation of benzaldehyde to benzoic acid, there is first formed benzoyl-hydrogen peroxide

$$C_6H_5 \cdot CHO + O_2 = C_6H_5 \cdot CO \cdot O \cdot OH$$

This substance is a powerful oxidizing agent and reacts with another molecule of benzaldehyde to form two molecules of benzoic acid

$$C_6H_5 \cdot CO \cdot O \cdot OH + C_6H_5 \cdot CHO = 2C_6H_5 \cdot COOH$$

In the presence of substances that are readily oxidized, such as indigo, the oxygen of the peroxide is taken up by the indigo and there are formed but one molecule of benzoic acid and the oxidation products of the indigo.

Proponents of the peroxide theory of oxidation have pointed out various analogies between the reactions just cited and the changes involved in biochemical oxidations and reductions.

Wieland's Theory of Oxidation. According to this theory, oxidation depends on the " activation " of hydrogen, and in the case of biological reactions this is believed to be due to enzymes, which Wieland described as "dehydrases" and which Thunberg has designated by the term " dehydrogenases." Before describing these enzymes, it is appropriate to consider first the mechanism of some simple non-enzymic reactions. The oxidation of hydroquinone may be selected for illustration. It has been shown that in the presence of suitable catalysts, such as palladium

---

carbon dioxide, and valeric acid. From cystine are formed ammonia, carbon dioxide, and sulfuric acid, in addition to some undetermined products of incomplete combustion. It has been suggested by Warburg that these substances are oxidized at the surface of the charcoal and that iron present in the charcoal possibly as an iron-nitrogen carbon complex plays an essential part in the reactions involved by facilitating the transference of oxygen. Iron-free charcoal, such as may be prepared from pure sucrose, does not have this effect, but if impregnated with iron salts, or with organic compounds containing iron and heated to glowing, it becomes activated.

Warburg's so-called charcoal model is inhibited by cyanides. If sufficient cyanide is added to combine with all of the iron contained in the charcoal, the latter completely loses its capacity to oxidize amino acids. *Arch. ges. Physiol.*, **148**, 295 (1912); *Ergebnisse Physiol.*, **14**, 253 (1914).

[3] *Compt. rend.*, **124**, 951 (1897).

[4] *Ber.*, **30**, 1669 (1897).

black, this reaction may be brought about in the complete absence of oxygen:

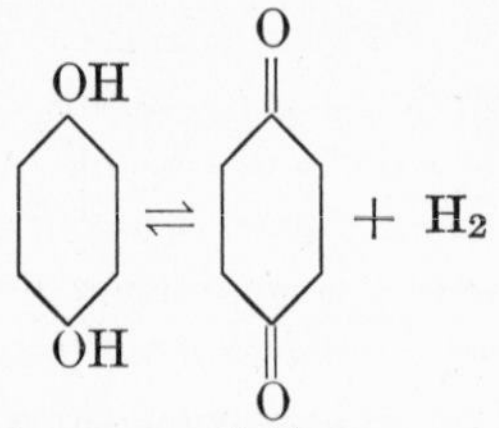

Hydroquinone   Quinone

The activated hydrogen is taken up to some extent by the palladium, but the reaction soon comes to a standstill unless some other *hydrogen acceptor* (oxygen, methylene blue,[5] etc.) is present. In short, the conversion of hydroquinone to quinone illustrates the oxidation of an organic compound by a process which has been termed " dehydrogenation."

Taking as another example, the simple reaction in which carbon monoxide is oxidized to carbon dioxide, it can be shown that the first step is a reaction with water, yielding formic acid. This and the succeeding steps may be represented as follows:

$$CO + H_2O = HCOOH$$
$$HCOOH = CO_2 + H_2$$
$$H_2 + O_2 = H_2O_2$$
$$H_2O_2 = H_2O + \tfrac{1}{2}O_2$$

[5] Methylene blue is a quinoid dyestuff which is reduced by hydrogen to the colorless leuco-methylene blue. Only "activated" hydrogen is supposed to be effective, inasmuch as no change occurs when molecular hydrogen is passed through a solution of methylene blue. The reaction has been represented as follows (Thunberg [7]):

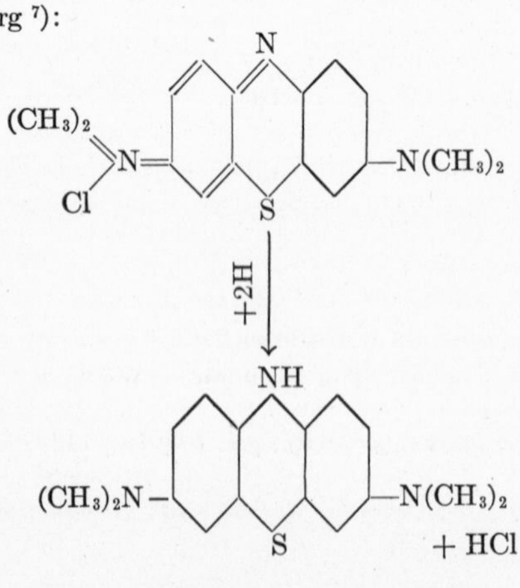

Methylene blue (chloride)

Leuco-methylene blue

The second stage in the reaction involves the decomposition of the formic acid into carbon dioxide and hydrogen. This reaction proceeds as indicated in the above scheme because of the presence of oxygen. The oxygen acts as a hydrogen acceptor; the hydrogen peroxide which is formed is then decomposed to water and oxygen. As Dakin[6] has pointed out, the above scheme for the burning of carbon monoxide is not a figment of the chemist's imagination but is based on the actual isolation, under suitable experimental conditions, of formic acid, hydrogen, and hydrogen peroxide as intermediate products.

It is a matter of much significance that the oxidation of carbon monoxide will take place in the absence of oxygen but not in the absence of water. In the above equations, the hydrogen which is split off unites with, or is " accepted " by, free oxygen, to form a peroxide. In the presence of colloidal platinum or palladium, each of which is capable of taking up a certain amount of hydrogen, the reaction occurs even in the absence of oxygen.

To summarize, the conversion of carbon monoxide into carbon dioxide illustrates the type of oxidation reaction in which the successive steps are: *hydration* and *dehydrogenation*.

The oxidation of acetaldehyde to acetic acid may be represented as follows:

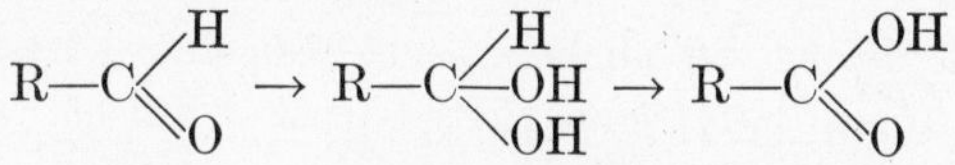

$$R-C\overset{H}{\underset{O}{\diagdown}} \rightarrow R-C\overset{H}{\underset{OH}{\diagup}}OH \rightarrow R-C\overset{OH}{\underset{O}{\diagdown}}$$

$$\text{Aldehyde} \qquad \text{Aldehyde-hydrate} \qquad \text{Acid}$$

Here, as in the case of carbon monoxide, the first step in the oxidation is hydration; the second step is one of dehydrogenation.

Hydration and dehydrogenation doubtless constitute the stages in the oxidation of many metabolites. It is customary to represent the combustion of glucose in the animal organism by the following equation:

$$C_6H_{12}O_6 + 6O_2 = 6CO_2 + 6H_2O$$

and to take it for granted that the oxygen for the reaction is supplied through respiration and that the carbon dioxide is eliminated in the same way. In reality, however, the equation does not represent the facts, except in so far as the end-products of the reaction and the stoichiometric relations of the various components are concerned. As has been emphasized by Thunberg,[7] the oxygen consumed during

---

[6] "Oxidations and Reductions in the Animal Body," 1922 edition, p. 4.

[7] *Quart. Rev. Biol.*, **5**, 318 (1930). This is a brief review on hydrogen-activating enzymes of the cells, and contains a bibliography to the work of Thunberg and others.

respiration does not react with carbon atoms, but is transformed into water. The participation of the water in the reaction may be represented by amplifying the above equation as follows:

$$\underset{\downarrow\ \ \ \ \ \ \ \ \downarrow \ \ \ \ \ \ \ \ \ \ \ \ \ \ \ \ \uparrow}{C_6H_{12}O_6 + 6H_2O + 6O_2 = 6CO_2 + 12H_2O}$$

Dehydrogenases. The participation of these enzymes in biological oxidations was first suggested by Wieland and has since been the subject of investigation of a number of workers, notably Thunberg. From a study of the so-called Schardinger reaction, Wieland concluded that milk contained a dehydrogenase. Formaldehyde, added to milk containing methylene blue, causes rapid decolorization of the dye. Through the transfer of hydrogen to the methylene blue, the aldehyde hydrate is oxidized to formic acid. Formaldehyde thus functions as the " hydrogen donator " and the methylene blue as the " hydrogen acceptor." This reaction is not obtained with boiled milk, owing to the destruction of the enzyme.

Tissues seem to contain a variety of dehydrogenases, each more or less specific in its action. Thunberg demonstrated the presence in muscle of one acting on succinic acid—succino-dehydrogenase. He introduced into suitably constructed tubes muscle substance and methylene blue. To some of the tubes the potassium salt of succinic acid was added. All the tubes were evacuated to remove the oxygen. Inasmuch as muscle contains organic substances which under the influence of appropriate dehydrogenases yield hydrogen, the methylene blue was slowly decolorized. As contrasted with the slow rate of formation of the leuco base in the control tubes was the very rapid decolorization of the dye in the tubes containing succinic acid. Since only " activated " hydrogen is capable of reducing methylene blue, Thunberg concluded that muscle contained an enzyme capable of rendering active the succinic acid molecule, resulting in the transfer of hydrogen to the dye and the oxidation of succinic to fumaric acid:

$$\underset{\text{Succinic acid}}{COOH \cdot CH_2 \cdot CH_2 \cdot COOH} \xrightarrow{-2H} \underset{\text{Fumaric acid}}{COOH \cdot CH{=}CH \cdot COOH}$$

Employing this and similar methods, the enzymic dehydrogenation of a large variety of substances has been studied. These include various acids, such as malic, fumaric, lactic, hydroxybutyric, tartaric, glutaric, and a number of amino acids. The dehydrogenases of *Bacillus coli*, according to Quastel,[8] activate fifty-six different organic compounds. It is inconceivable that a single bacterium should contain such a large number of specific enzymes for the activation and dehydrogenation of as many organic compounds. The problem of the specificity of the dehydrogenases has therefore attracted some attention, and though it appears that the specificity is not always sharply defined (for example, the dehydrogenase acting on lactic acid also activates α-oxybutyric acid), it is nevertheless true in many cases that the action of a certain dehydrogenase is restricted to a given compound.

From the liver of various animals, Harrison[9] has extracted a dehydrogenase (glucose dehydrogenase) which oxidizes glucose to gluconic acid. A group of bacterial enzymes (*hydrogenylases*) has been described by Stephenson and Stickland which liberate molecular hydrogen.[10] Finally Stickland and Stephenson[11] have found an enzyme in *B. coli* which activates molecular hydrogen.

Catalase. Catalase is widely distributed both in plants and in animals. It has the property of decomposing hydrogen peroxide into water and oxygen, the latter being given off as a gas.

$$2H_2O_2 = 2H_2O + O_2$$

Numerous attempts have been made to show that catalase is directly concerned in the oxidative processes of the tissues, but we are still uncertain of its full significance. Its chief function may be the decomposition of hydrogen peroxide that is formed as a by-product in physiological oxidations. Dixon[12] has shown that, when purine bases are oxidized by molecular oxygen in the presence of xanthine-oxidase as a catalyst, the oxidase is progressively destroyed during the course of the reaction by the hydrogen peroxide that is formed. Dixon found that he could prevent destruction of the oxidase by the addition of catalase. Thus, catalase seems to have a protective function in animal tissues.

The active group of catalase appears to be an iron-porphyrin complex.[13]

Peroxidases. The function of peroxidases in biological oxidations is believed to be the transfer of oxygen, linked as a peroxide, to oxidizable substances. They differ from the catalases in that they do not decom-

[8] *Biochem. J.*, **20**, 166 (1926).
[9] *Ibid.*, **25**, 1016 (1931); **27**, 496 (1933).
[10] *Ibid.*, **26**, 712 (1932).
[11] *Ibid.*, **25**, 205 (1931).
[12] *Biochem, J.*, **19**, 507 (1925).
[13] K. Zeile and H. Hellström, *Z. physiol. Chem.*, **192**, 171 (1930); Zeile, *ibid.*, **195**, 39 (1931).

pose hydrogen peroxide in the absence of an oxidizable substance, the oxygenase of the Bach-Engler theory. The peroxidases are widely distributed, being especially abundant in the roots and seedling sprouts of the higher plants. A good source for experimental purposes is the horseradish.

Gum guaiac or its constituent, guaiaconic acid, when mixed with potato scrapings, turns blue. The change in color is due to the oxidation of the guaiaconic acid by active oxygen. Taken by itself, this observation is of little significance; but when considered in conjunction with certain observations of Bach and Chodat and of Bach,[14] it offers a clue to the mechanism involved in the oxidation of the guaiaconic acid.

Bach and Chodat approached the peroxidase problem by studying extracts prepared from the roots of the horseradish. These extracts, when treated with guaiaconic acid, did not give a blue reaction; but when hydrogen peroxide was also added, the guaiaconic acid was oxidized, with the production of the blue color characteristic of the test. It is to be noted that the addition of hydrogen peroxide to the horseradish extracts did not result in the liberation of oxygen gas. Moreover, hydrogen peroxide alone did not produce any effect on the gum guaiac. Bach and Chodat therefore concluded that the horseradish extracts contained a substance capable of activating hydrogen peroxide, and as this constituent showed the properties of an enzyme (it was destroyed by heating, precipitated by alcohol, etc.), it was called " peroxidase." The guaiac reaction is not specific, however, for peroxidase. Alsberg[15] has shown, for example, that a large variety of substances, including hemoglobin, hemocyanin, ferrous sulfate, the chlorides of cobalt, nickel, and copper, give the guaiac test.

As is well known, the cut surface of a potato blackens on exposure to air. This is usually attributed to the oxidation of the amino acid tyrosine, and possibly of compounds related to it, for it has been shown by Bach that fresh potato juice oxidizes tyrosine rapidly and that it therefore contains *tyrosinase*. When the juice is treated with alcohol, a precipitate is formed which no longer exhibits this property unless hydrogen peroxide is also added. As the hydrogen peroxide, by itself, has no effect on tyrosine, we may assume that the added peroxide serves merely to replace a similar substance which was present in the cell and in the fresh potato juice, but which was not precipitated by the alcohol.

What is the significance of these observations? According to Bach's theory, the oxidation of guaiaconic acid by potato scrapings, and of tyrosine by potato juice, may be explained on the following basis.

[14] Various papers in the *Berichte*, beginning in 1903.
[15] *Arch. exp. Path. Pharmakol.*, Supplement-Band, 39 (1908).

In the first case, we have the enzyme peroxidase; in the second, we have as one of the constituents of the tissues an auto-oxidizable substance (Bach's oxygenase). The splitting of the peroxides, and hence the transfer of oxygen from the peroxides to the substrate (guaiaconic acid and tyrosine in the above examples), is accelerated by the enzyme peroxidase. In the presence of free oxygen, the auto-oxidizable constituent may be reoxidized to the peroxide form.

Certain inorganic salts behave like "peroxidases." The oxidation of lactic acid by hydrogen peroxide is an extremely slow process. This reaction may be accelerated, however, by the addition of a peroxidase (extract of horseradish) or a trace of ferrous sulfate. Not only the salts of iron but also the salts of copper and manganese, metals which are capable of existing in two different states of valence are effective in this regard.

It has been reported by Kuhn, Hand, and Florkin[16] that, as with the catalases, the active group of the peroxydases is an iron-porphyrin complex.

Oxidases; Specific Oxidizing Enzymes. The oxidases are presumably enzymes which activate oxidizing substances, rendering them more susceptible to reduction. One of these, indophenol oxidase, is believed to oxidize cytochrome.[17] Another is the enzyme tyrosinase, which is of widespread occurrence both in plants and in animals and is obtained especially from certain mushrooms, such as *Russula delica* and *Russula nigricans*. Bertrand[18] found that on broken mushrooms (*R. nigricans*) the red coloration turns black, a change which he has attributed to the action of the oxidizing enzyme tyrosinase. The oxidation and coloration of the juice of the beet, of potatoes, and of dahlias are among the familiar examples of the action of this enzyme. The oxidation of tyrosine to melanin by the action of tyrosinase has been studied by Raper and his associates.[19] Uric acid is oxidized by uricase.

Tyrosinase is said to be activated by peroxidase. Xanthine-oxidase, hitherto considered an oxidase, is in reality a dehydrogenase.

As stated elsewhere, the activation of oxygen has been stressed by Warburg, who has described the catalyst of cell respiration as the "Atmungsferment" and showed its relation to hemin. In many respects this is the most clearly defined "oxidase," but even its indi-

[16] *Z. physiol. Chem.*, **202**, 255 (1931).

[17] D. Keilin, *Proc. Roy. Soc. (London)*, B, **104**, 206 (1928–29).

[18] See Effront-Prescott, "Biochemical Catalysts in Life and Industry," John Wiley & Sons, 1917, p. 299.

[19] H. S. Raper and A. Wormall, *Biochem., J.*, **17**, 454 (1923); **19**, 84 (1925); **19**, 92 (1925); **20**, 69, 735 (1926); **21**, 89, 1370 (1927); see also H. S. Raper, "The Aerobic Oxidases," *Physiol. Rev.*, **8**, 245 (1928).

viduality is in question. According to Kuhn,[16] the "Atmungsferment" of Warburg constitutes a system of which peroxidase, catalase, and oxygenase are among the component parts. In a brief discussion of the subject, Keilin[20] has expressed his opinion that indophenol oxidase forms with cytochrome an intracellular catalytic system which can be recognized as Warburg's oxidation system of the cell.

Luciferase. Certain fungi, bacteria, protozoa, medusae, insects, molluscs, and fish are capable of emitting light by a process of chemiluminescence. This is due to oxidative changes in which the chemical energy is converted directly into light energy. The process differs widely, therefore, from that involved in artificial light production, where most of the energy formed is lost as heat. One of the constituents concerned in the production of light is an oxidizable substance, luciferin, which is thermostable. The other constituent is thermolabile and is believed to be an enzyme, hence the name luciferase.

The indications are, according to recent work of Harvey,[21] that luciferase catalyzes the oxidation of luciferin. In turn the energy of oxidation of the luciferin excites the luciferase. The excited molecules of luciferase emit light on returning to the normal state.

The Rôle of Cytochrome in Physiological Oxidations. Keilin has stated that the main respiratory system of the cell comprises the following components: (1) dehydrogenases, (2) metabolites, (3) cytochrome, (4) oxidase, and (5) molecular oxygen.

As has been remarked, elsewhere, cytochrome is an intracellular pigment widely distributed in nature. Its presence has been established in aerobic bacteria, yeasts, and in the higher plants and animals. Cytochrome is not a single substance, but is composed of three hemochromogens, which Keilin[22] has provisionally designated *a*, *b*, *c*. These substances originate from heme, the first step being the formation of a hemochromogen from the free intracellular heme, which is contained in all aerobic cells, and some undetermined nitrogen compound. Component *b* of cytochrome somewhat resembles this hemochromogen. In some cells (*B. coli* and other facultative aerobes) the latter is the only visible heme compound. This hemochromogen, then, is the precursor of all three components of cytochrome, being converted into these presumably as a result of repeated oxidations and reductions.

[20] *Proc. Roy. Soc. (London), B.*, **111**, 291 (1932).

[21] *J. Biol. Chem.*, **78**, 369 (1928); see also E. N. Harvey, "The Nature of Animal Light," Lippincott, Philadelphia and London, 1920; Harvey and P. A. Snell, *Proc. Am. Phil. Soc.*, **69**, 303 (1930); *J. Gen. Physiol.*, **14**, 529 (1930–31).

[22] D. Keilin, *Proc. Roy. Soc. (London), B*, **98**, 312 (1925); **100**, 129 (1926); **104**, 206 (1928–29).

Keilin has shown that the heme constituents of the cell are responsible for the thermostable peroxidase reaction. The test for peroxidase is shown by the oxidation of benzidine, guaiacum, paraphenylenediamine and other chromogens, in the presence of hydrogen peroxide. A large variety of animal tissues have been shown to give this reaction before, and particularly after, boiling, and the intensity of the reaction has been found to be proportional to the cytochrome and free hemin content of the tissues.

Of the three components of cytochrome, a and c are not auto-oxidizable. On the contrary, component b, the free heme, and the hemochromogen precursor of cytochrome are auto-oxidizable.. The oxidation of cytochrome in the tissues, particularly of components a and c, is brought about by a specific oxidizing enzyme, *indophenol oxidase* (oxidizes "Nadi" reagent, consisting of dimethyl-paraphenylene-diamine-hydrochloride and α-naphthol, to indophenol blue). Anything which inhibits or destroys this enzyme, such as KCN, H₂S, CO at high partial pressure in the dark, acetone, alcohol, heat (when the cells are warmed above 70° C., or dried in air), inhibits or abolishes the oxidation of cytochrome. Thus, indophenol oxidase is intimately connected with cytochrome in the processes of cellular respiration.

The reduction of cytochrome (the oxidized form) is brought about as follows, according to the views of Keilin: The organic constituents of the tissues, subject to the reactions of metabolism, are activated by *dehydrases* and thus become hydrogen donators. Any factors which inhibit or destroy these enzymes, such as cold (below $-2°$ C.), heat (above 52° C.), narcotics, such as alcohol and ethyl urethane, also inhibit or prevent the reduction of oxidized cytochrome. The a component of cytochrome is most unstable, decomposing readily above 55° C.; b is likewise unstable but not to the same degree as a; c is heat stable and otherwise very resistant.

On the basis of a careful study, Keilin has reached the conclusion that, in addition to the peroxidase effect that has been mentioned, cytochrome acts as a carrier between two types of activating mechanisms in the cell: (1) the dehydrases, activating the hydrogen of organic molecules; and (2) the indophenol oxidase, activating oxygen. Cytochrome thus acts as a hydrogen acceptor which is specifically oxidized by the indophenol oxidase.

Component b of cytochrome shares with components a and c the functions that have just been described, but in addition, being an auto-oxidizable substance, it may act more directly as a carrier between the hydrogen donators and molecular oxygen, without the intervention of an oxidase. The hemochromogen precursor of cytochrome and the free heme have similar properties. All three (heme, hemochromogen, cytochrome component *b*), in addition, are presumably capable of acting as direct catalysts, promoting the oxidation of substances which are not activated by dehydrases.

Glutathione. In 1921, Hopkins[23] isolated from yeast, muscle, and mammalian liver a substance which he named glutathione. At first it was thought to be a dipeptide of cystine and glutamic acid, but later work by other investigators,[24] as well as in Hopkins' laboratory,[25] showed it to be a tripeptide, containing glycine, in addition to the amino acids just mentioned. The reduced form of glutathione is a glutamic acid-cysteine-glycine complex:

$$\underset{\displaystyle \underset{\text{NH}_2}{|}}{\text{COOH}\cdot\text{CH}}\cdot\text{CH}_2\cdot\text{CH}_2\cdot\text{CO—NH}\cdot\underset{\displaystyle \underset{\text{CH}_2\cdot\text{SH}}{|}}{\text{CH}}\cdot\text{CO—NH}\cdot\text{CH}_2\cdot\text{COOH}$$

Glutamyl-cysteinyl-glycine

It has been known for a long time that cysteine may be readily oxidized to cystine. In fact, this conversion occurs spontaneously in slightly alkaline solutions of cysteine exposed to the air, as shown by Mathews and Walker.[26] And, in turn, the reverse process, the reduction of cystine, occurs almost as readily in the presence of even mild reducing agents. Accordingly, a system composed of cysteine and cystine may be regarded as an auto-oxidizable system, the cysteine being oxidizable by molecular oxygen, the cystine being reducible by hydrogen. Such a system could conceivably play a part in tissue oxidations. The reactions involved would be essentially as represented by the equation:

$$O + \begin{array}{l} \text{COOH}\cdot\text{CHNH}_2\cdot\text{CH}_2\text{SH} \\ \\ \text{COOH}\cdot\text{CHNH}_2\cdot\text{CH}_2\text{SH} \end{array} \underset{\text{Reduction}}{\overset{\text{Oxidation}}{\rightleftharpoons}} \left. \begin{array}{l} \text{COOH}\cdot\text{CHNH}_2\cdot\text{CH}_2\text{S} \\ \\ \text{COOH}\cdot\text{CHNH}_2\cdot\text{CH}_2\text{S} \end{array} \right| + \text{H}_2\text{O}$$

Cysteine   Cystine

As to the precise rôle of glutathione in physiological oxidations, there is at present considerable uncertainty, though it is evident that the oxidized form, which for convenience may be represented as G—S—S—G, is capable of acting as an hydrogen acceptor. It is thus converted to the reduced form, G—SH, which is in turn readily oxidized by transferring the hydrogen to some other hydrogen acceptor, including

[23] *Biochem. J.*, **15**, 286 (1921).

[24] G. Hunter and B. A. Eagles, *J. Biol. Chem.*, **72**, 133, 147 (1927); E. C. Kendall, B. F. McKenzie, H. L. Mason, *ibid.*, **84**, 657 (1929); **88**, 409 (1930); B. H. Nicolet, *ibid.*, **88**, 389 (1930).

[25] *Ibid.*, **84**, 269 (1929); see also Pirie and Pinhey, *ibid.*, **84**, 321 (1929).

[26] *Ibid.*, **6**, 21 (1909).

oxygen. Methylene blue is, however, a much more efficient hydrogen acceptor and has been employed in the experimental studies of the properties of glutathione. The changes which glutathione undergoes may be represented as follows:

$$G—SH \qquad HS—G$$
$$+ O_2$$
$$\downarrow$$
$$G—S————S—G + H_2O_2$$
$$+ H_2$$
$$\downarrow$$
$$G—SH \qquad HS—G$$

Tissues have a marked capacity to reduce glutathione. Presumably the metabolites of the tissues are thus oxidized. In a recent statement, Hopkins and Elliott[27] have expressed the view that the transfer of hydrogen to molecular oxygen by this path, though representing but a small part of the total respiration, may prove to represent a specialized and significant aspect of tissue oxidations.

Lohmann[28] has shown that glutathione acts as a coenzyme for glyoxalase, a tissue enzyme which converts methyl-glyoxal into lactic acid. According to Jowett and Quastel,[29] the behavior of glutathione in this respect depends on a course of reactions which may be represented as follows:

$$CH_3 \cdot CO \cdot CHO + G \cdot SH \rightleftharpoons$$
$$CH_3 \cdot CO \cdot CHOH \cdot S \cdot G \xrightarrow{+ H_2O} CH_3 \cdot CHOH \cdot COOH + G \cdot SH$$

Human red corpuscles show a high glyoxalase activity. They also contain glutathione.[30]

Hexuronic, or Ascorbic Acid. Recent research seems to have established the identity of this substance to vitamin C (p. 585). It is referred to in this connection because of its marked reducing properties and its widespread distribution in plant and animal tissues. Szent-Györgyi[31] has presented evidence to show that the cabbage leaf contains an enzyme which in the presence of oxygen rapidly oxidizes ascorbic acid. The oxidation product thus formed in turn acts as an hydrogen acceptor. In short, the inference is that ascorbic acid, or vitamin C, is capable of undergoing alternate oxidation and reduction in the tissues and that it may therefore represent another mechanism in biological oxidations.

[27] *Proc. Roy. Soc. (London), B,* **109,** 58 (1931–32).
[28] *Biochem. Z.,* **254,** 332 (1932).
[29] *Biochem. J.,* **27,** 486 (1933).
[30] S. R. Benedict and G. Gottschall, *J. Biol. Chem.,* **99,** 729 (1932–33).
[31] *J. Biol. Chem.,* **90,** 385 (1931).

Behavior of Dyes. Dyes which can be reversibly oxidized and reduced act as catalysts for some of the oxidative processes taking place in living cells, as is manifested by an increased oxygen consumption. Barron and Hoffman[32] have shown that this behavior depends on whether the normal consumption of oxygen by the cell is slower or quicker than the oxidation activated by the dye. If either the speed at which the dye is reduced by the cell, or the speed at which the leuco-dye (colorless form) is oxidized by atmospheric oxygen is slower than the normal process, the dye cannot increase the rate of oxygen consumption. Methylene blue, cresyl blue, toluylene blue chloride, cresyl violet are effective catalysts. Safranin and neutral red on the contrary are reduced with difficulty and are hence without catalytic effect.

Among the earlier attempts to measure the oxidation-reduction intensities of tissues by means of indicators were the experiments of Ehrlich. He injected intravenously, into living animals, suspensions of alizarin blue and indophenol blue, and subsequently examined the organs for the presence of these dyes, either in the colorless or reduced form, or in the oxidized or blue form. Of the two dyes, indophenol blue is more easily reduced. Ehrlich[33] found that certain organs (heart, gray matter of the brain) which presumably have a high oxygen potential, did not reduce either dye. Most of the tissues reduced indophenol blue but had no effect on alizarin blue. The reduction potential of still other organs (lungs, liver, fatty tissue) is apparently very high as even alizarin blue was reduced by these organs in Ehrlich's experiments.

Within the last few years, interest in this problem has been revived and its scope greatly extended by a group of active workers, the most prominent of whom is W. Mansfield Clark.[34] He and his associates have developed a theoretical basis for the measurement of oxidation-reduction potentials in organic systems, and some progress has been made in studying the significance of the reduction intensity and capacity of living cells.[35] The further development of knowledge in this direction will probably increase our comprehension of many physiological and pathological processes.

[32] *J. Gen. Physiol.*, **13**, 483 (1929–30).

[33] P. Ehrlich, "Das Sauerstoffbedürfniss des Organismus," Berlin, 1885.

[34] "Recent Studies on Reversible Oxidation-Reduction in Organic Systems," *Chem. Rev.*, **2**, 127 (1925).

[35] Cannan, Cohen, and Clark, United States Health Service Publications, Supp. **55A**, 1009 (1926); Needham and Needham, *Proc. Roy. Soc. (London)*, B, **99**, 173 (1926); Cohen, Chambers, and Reznikoff, *J. Gen. Physiol.*, **11**, 585 (1928).

For a review of recent literature on the subject of biological oxidations and reductions, the student is referred to R. Wurmser, *Ann. Rev. Biochem*, **1**, 55 (1932); **2**, 15 (1933).

CHAPTER X

INTERMEDIARY METABOLISM OF CARBOHYDRATES

In tracing the fate of carbohydrates in metabolism, we are primarily concerned with the chemical changes which glucose undergoes after absorption.[1] The carbohydrates of the diet do not constitute the only source of glucose, for certain of the amino acids and glycerol are convertible into sugar and glycogen. In 100 grams of protein there is a sufficient amount of the so-called sugar-forming amino acids to yield about 58 grams of glucose.[1a] As we shall see in a later chapter the stages in the intermediary metabolism of these amino acids are in part similar to those encountered in carbohydrate metabolism. The actual formation of glucose from protein can be demonstrated when little or no carbohydrate is fed, during starvation, in pancreatic diabetes, and in phlorhizin diabetes. The last is a severe form of renal glycosuria produced by injecting phlorhizin (p. 66) into animals. Dogs made "diabetic" in this way may excrete large amounts of sugar even after the glycogen of the liver has been depleted. In these animals the proteins of the food and of the tissues are partly converted to glucose, and, if the disturbance is severe enough, for each gram of nitrogen excreted in the urine, 3.65 grams of glucose are simultaneously eliminated. Each gram of nitrogen in the urine represents the metabolism of about 6.25 grams of protein.

A certain amount of glucose is derived from the glycerol part of the

[1] Magee and Reid, *J. Physiol.*, **73**, 181 (1933), have reported that the rate of intestinal absorption of glucose is increased in the presence of phosphate. It has been further shown by A. Bodansky, *J. Biol. Chem.*, **104**, 473 (1934), that an increase in serum phosphatase occurs after carbohydrate ingestion, suggesting that the transitional formation of hexose-phosphate is a factor in intestinal absorption. Indeed, Wilbrandt and Laszt, *Biochem. Z.*, **259**, 398 (1933), have explained the difference in the rates of absorption of hexoses and pentoses (p. 197) on the basis that the former are esterified with phosphoric acid, while the latter are not. Moreover, E. Lundsgaard, *Biochem. Z.*, **264**, 221 (1933), has shown that phlorhizin introduced into the intestine inhibits the action of phosphatase on the one hand, and the absorption of glucose from the intestine, on the other.

[1a] The amount of sugar obtainable from protein varies somewhat with different proteins, depending on the relative proportion of sugar-producing amino acids. For details see D. Rapport, "The Interconversion of the Major Foodstuffs," *Physiol. Rev.*, **10**, 349–472, and especially p. 392 (1930).

fat molecule. Chambers and Deuel[2] have shown a practically complete conversion of glycerol to glucose in phlorhizinized dogs. Ordinarily, glycerol is oxidized to carbon dioxide and water. The weight of experimental evidence at present opposes the view that the fatty acids are converted into carbohydrate (compare p. 369).

Glycogen Synthesis. The sugar entering the portal circulation is largely deposited in the liver as glycogen. Normally the liver also removes glucose from the systemic blood when its concentration exceeds a certain level (about 70 to 90 mg. per cent). The process of glycogen formation, or *glycogenesis*, in the liver, in addition to conserving food material for subsequent utilization, thus also serves in the regulation of the sugar concentration in the blood.

Fructose is converted into glucose and glycogen in the liver, the rate of glycogen formation being even greater than that for glucose, while galactose is stored more slowly, or less completely, so that when a large amount of this sugar is fed, a considerable proportion is excreted in the urine. In man, the pentose sugars are not utilized, and when fed are excreted unchanged. It has also been shown (in the rat) that xylose does not form glycogen.[3] After its oral administration, a certain amount is retained in the liver, blood, and kidney, but it is probable that the pentose is only temporarily stored and is eventually excreted unchanged.

Herbivorous animals obtain a certain amount of their energy from pentosans. These polysaccharides are acted upon by bacteria in the alimentary tract. By this action a variety of substances, such as organic acids, are produced which the animal is able to utilize. The synthesis of lactose from the fermentation-digestion products of the pentosans has also been suggested. However, in man, the pentosans are not utilized at all, and if pentose sugars are fed, they are excreted unchanged in the urine.

The following amino acids are considered to be potential sources of glycogen in the animal organism: glycine, alanine, serine, cystine, aspartic acid, glutamic acid, hydroxyglutamic acid, arginine, and proline. In experiments with white rats that had been previously fasted for 24 hours, Wilson and Lewis[4] demonstrated the deposition of glycogen as a result of the oral administration of *d*- and *dl*-alanine. Contrary results were obtained with two other sugar-forming amino acids, glycine and *d*-glutamic acid, which yielded only small amounts of glycogen, as determined by comparing the composition of the livers of the fed animals and those of suitable controls.

[2] *J. Biol. Chem.*, **65**, 21 (1925).
[3] M. M. Miller and H. B. Lewis, *J. Biol. Chem.*, **98**, 133, 141 (1932).
[4] *J. Biol. Chem.*, **84**, 511 (1929).

In the fasting animal about 10 per cent of the fat, representing the glycerol moiety, is a potential source of glucose and glycogen. Catron and Lewis[5] fed rats that had been fasted for 24 hours 1 gram of glycerol. This was followed during the next 2–3 hours of observation by an increase in the glycogen content of the liver, comparable to that obtained on feeding an equivalent amount of glucose.

As will be described later, lactic acid is another source of liver glycogen. The conversion in the liver of d-lactic acid (as the sodium salt) into glycogen has been observed by Cori and Cori[6] in experiments conducted on the white rat. In contrast, l-lactic acid, though absorbed at the same rate, formed practically no liver glycogen and about 30 per cent was excreted in the urine. In the opinion of these investigators, l-lactic acid is utilized, but only about one-fourth as readily as the dextro isomer.

Glycogenesis in Muscle. Muscle glycogen is formed principally from the glucose of the blood. It is stated that the glucose concentration is usually greater in arterial than in venous blood, owing to the withdrawal by the tissues of some of the sugar.[7] This is especially evident after a carbohydrate-rich meal.

Although the ingestion of fructose leads to an increase in muscle glycogen, this is not due to its conversion in the muscle tissue itself. Inasmuch as the liver is capable of transforming fructose into glucose, it is conceivable that muscle glycogen owes its origin to the glucose thus formed. However, even when the liver is completely extirpated, injected fructose leads to the deposition of glycogen in muscle. This would be convincing proof of a fructose → glycogen synthesis, but for certain facts reported by Bollman and Mann.[8]

These investigators found that, in hepatectomized dogs, the injection of fructose was followed by a rise in the glucose content of the blood, but if, of all the remaining viscera, the intestines alone were also removed, this rise did not occur. Nor was any muscle glycogen formed under these conditions. Bollman and Mann have shown further that in animals which had intact livers, but from which the stomach and intestines had been removed, the process of conversion of fructose to glucose is apparently possible.

In short, fructose is not utilized directly by muscle in the synthesis

[5] *Ibid.*, **84**, 553 (1929).

[6] *Ibid.*, **81**, 389 (1929); compare with Abramson, Eggleton, and Eggleton, *ibid.*, **75**, 763 (1927).

[7] M. Friedenson, M. K. Rosenbaum, E. J. Thalheimer, and J. Peters, *J. Biol. Chem.*, **80**, 269 (1928).

[8] *Am. J. Physiol.*, **96**, 683 (1931).

of glycogen.   It is first converted into glucose, either in the intestines or liver, but not, to any appreciable extent, in the other tissues of the body.

The synthesis and accumulation of glycogen in the liver are believed to be regulated by insulin, the pancreatic hormone (p. 468), but the underlying mechanism is obscure.   It is not even known whether the primary effect is to promote the synthesis, or to inhibit the reverse process of *glycogenolysis*.   Still less is known of the rôle of insulin in the glycogen metabolism of muscle.   Indeed, there is no convincing evidence, according to certain authorities, that it has anything to do either with the synthesis or storage of muscle glycogen.   Nor has it been conclusively shown that the hydrolysis of muscle glycogen is increased in the absence of insulin, as is the case with liver glycogen.

Glycogenolysis.   To meet the requirements of the tissues when no carbohydrate is being absorbed, the glycogen of the liver is converted into glucose, a process termed *glycogenolysis*.   The importance of the liver as a constant source of supply of blood sugar is shown by the fact that, when this organ is extirpated, the blood-sugar concentration diminishes rapidly and the animal dies.   No other organ or tissue of the body seems capable of supplying carbohydrate, and even the glycogen of the muscle is not directly convertible into glucose.

The conversion of liver glycogen into glucose is believed to be due to an enzyme, *glycogenase*.   In the extirpated liver, the conversion occurs very rapidly, but *in vivo* the conditions normally are apparently such that the amount of either substrate or enzyme available at any time is limited.   It has been stated (Cori[9]) that, when insulin is lacking, the enzymic hydrolysis of liver glycogen is unchecked.   This leads to the disappearance of the glycogen.   A continuous supply of insulin by the pancreas is therefore essential for the preservation of hepatic glycogen.   Opposed to this inhibition to glycogenolysis is the accelerating effect of epinephrin, the hormone of the adrenal medulla (p. 487).   How epinephrin exerts this effect on the glycogenase in the hepatic cells of the living organism is not understood.

The fate of muscle glycogen will be considered in detail presently. Suffice it to state at this point that whereas liver glycogen yields glucose, glycogen breakdown in muscle yields lactic acid, as first shown by Fletcher and Hopkins.[10]   This has been particularly well brought out in a recent experiment by Simpson and Macleod.[11]   They confined their studies to rabbit's liver and muscle.   After freezing in liquid air these tissues were ground to a fine powder, and determinations were made of the changes in glycogen, glucose, and lactic acid.   In the pow-

[9] *Physiol. Rev.*, **11**, 143 (1931).   [10] *J. Physiol.*, **35**, 247 (1907).
[11] *Ibid.*, **64**, 255 (1927).

dered liver preparations, as the glycogen disappeared, the free sugar increased, while the lactic acid content remained unchanged. The muscle preparations, on the contrary, showed no change in the free sugar, but an increase in lactic acid, as the glycogen diminished.

The administration of epinephrin causes a decrease in the glycogen content of muscle. [12]

Blood Sugar. This refers primarily to d-glucose. In addition, the blood, but particularly the corpuscles, contain an appreciable amount of non-sugar-reducing [13] substances which represented a part of the blood-sugar values as determined by the older methods of analysis, but which are more or less excluded by employing certain of the newer procedures. Mention should also be made of the presence of a small amount of hydrolyzable sugar in blood. [14]

In the postabsorptive state the normal concentration of glucose varies between 70 and 90 mg. per cent. Slight deviations from this range are not uncommon. As will be seen shortly, even during the absorption of large amounts of glucose, the concentration in the blood is not elevated above a certain point. There is accordingly a relatively constant level, the maintenance of which presupposes an adequate mechanism tending to create a balance between the inflow and outflow of sugar.

The principal sources of blood sugar have been considered. A rise in the sugar level may be caused by:

(1) The absorption of carbohydrate (glucose) from the alimentary canal,

(2) Sugar formation in the liver, principally from glycogen (glycogenolysis).

However, the increase in blood sugar, which is usually associated with carbohydrate absorption, promptly stimulates the secretion of insulin, which in turn promotes the storage of glycogen in the liver, with the result that the blood sugar is returned to its normal level.

Liver glycogen formation may thus be considered as one of the factors causing the disappearance of sugar from the blood and comes into play when the concentration is elevated above normal.

Glucose also disappears from the blood through its conversion into

---

[12] C. F. Cori and G. T. Cori, *J. Biol. Chem.*, **79**, 321 (1928).

[13] Glutathione is the most abundant non-sugar-reducing substance. V. Schelling (*J. Biol. Chem.*, **96**, 17 [1932]) obtained values of 14.7–38.8 mg. per 100 cc. of blood in 21 normal subjects. See also S. R. Benedict and G. Gottschall, *ibid.*, **99**, 729 (1932–33). Thioneine is another non-sugar-reducing substance in mammalian blood (*J. Biol. Chem.*, **83**, 361 [1929]).

[14] M. R. Everett, H. A. Shoemaker, and F. Sheppard, *J. Biol. Chem.*, **74**, 739 (1927); Everett and Sheppard, *ibid.*, **80**, 255 (1928).

muscle and tissue glycogen. As it is continually used up in tissue oxidation, a constant demand for replenishment is set up which is met by the removal of glucose from the circulation at a rate determined by several factors, but principally by the degree of tissue activity. The utilization of sugar for this purpose, however, produces no pronounced depletion in the blood, for even a slight fall in the sugar level causes a discharge of epinephrin from the adrenals, which in turn accelerates liver glycogenolysis, thus playing a very important rôle in the regulation of the blood-sugar level.

Finally there remains to be considered the participation of the kidneys in blood-sugar regulation. Normally, the amount of reducing substance in the urine is very small, and of this the greater part is not glucose for it is non-fermentable. West and Peterson[15] examined 24-hour specimens of urine of 55 normal subjects and found the daily excretion of glucose to average only 0.142 gram. This shows that ordinarily very little glucose escapes through the kidneys. However, when the glucose concentration of the blood reaches a certain value, which varies somewhat in different individuals but which is usually between 0.15 and 0.18 per cent, large amounts of sugar are excreted. The concentration in the blood at which this occurs is called the "renal threshold."

Not uncommonly individuals are encountered whose renal thresholds are low. In such cases marked glycosuria is observed even though there is little or no rise in the blood sugar. During pregnancy renal glycosuria of this type is not uncommon. In extreme cases, the permeability of the kidney to sugar appears to be so great that glucose is excreted even when the concentration in the blood is subnormal. Individuals exhibiting this peculiarity may be quite normal otherwise. Finally, the renal threshold may be higher than 0.18 per cent. Especially in diabetics of long standing, the kidneys may be relatively impermeable to glucose even when the concentration in the blood reaches values as high as 0.25 per cent.

The various points bearing on the subject of the regulation of the sugar concentration of the blood that have been considered in the preceding paragraphs are represented in the following diagram (Fig. 28), drawn by Ringer and Baumann and modified somewhat to conform to the facts as they are known at present.

Carbohydrate Tolerance. The capacity of the body to assimilate carbohydrates has long been the subject of intensive study. Prior to the advent of modern methods of blood analysis, this was measured by

---

[15] *Biochem. J.*, **26**, 1720, 1728, 1742 (1932).

determining the amount of sugar which it was necessary to feed an individual before sugar appeared in the urine. A healthy person can tolerate 100–200 grams of glucose at a single dose without developing glycosuria. This was taken to indicate the efficiency of the tissues in removing the absorbed sugar from the blood. It must be borne in mind, however, that individual variations in renal threshold may introduce an error in this method, for in the case of a high threshold no sugar will appear in the urine even though the accumulation of sugar in the blood may be

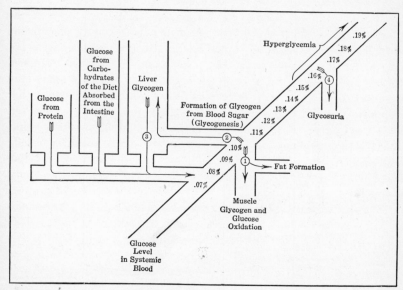

FIG. 28.—Schematic illustration of some of the factors which regulate the sugar concentration of the blood. ① and ② under control of pancreatic hormone; ③ under control of sympathetic nervous system and adrenalin; ④ regulated by renal threshold. (After Ringer and Baumann, with modifications, "Endocrinology and Metabolism," edited by L. F. Barker, Appleton, 1922, vol. 3, p. 252). Reproduced by permission.

considerable, whereas in an individual with a low renal threshold marked glycosuria may develop even with a moderate increase in the sugar content of the blood.

With the introduction of simple methods for the quantitative measurement of blood sugar, the changes in the concentration of this constituent have been taken as the basis for determining carbohydrate tolerance. The blood is analyzed before and at certain intervals after giving a definite amount of glucose, usually 100 grams. Normally, the blood sugar rises to a maximum during the first half-hour or hour and returns to normal levels by the end of the second hour.   The analytical data obtained may be plotted on coordinate paper as ordinates, and the time intervals as abscissas.   The maximum height of the curve, the time at which this maximum occurs, and the time required for the curve to return to normal levels are all taken into account in interpreting the results.   Variations in the rate of absorption and the previous state of nutrition may have a modifying effect on the sugar-tolerance curve.

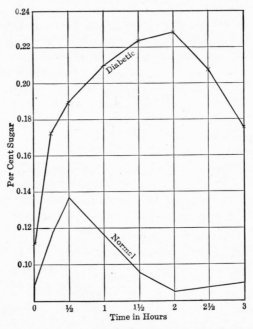

Fig. 29.—Glucose tolerance curve in the case of a normal and a diabetic individual. Ordinates = per cent sugar; abscissas = time after the ingestion of 100 grams of glucose.

Carbohydrate tolerance is reduced in diabetes, in conditions where the liver is injured (phosphorus and chloroform poisoning), and to a less extent in acute infections and other pathological conditions.   It is increased in hypopituitarism.   Variations in galactose tolerance in females have been associated with their sexual status by Rowe.[16]

The Degradation of Glucose in Vitro. Presumably because of the formation of salts, the sugars are much more reactive in alkaline solution, undergoing many transformations both in the presence and absence of

[16] A. W. Rowe, "The Differential Diagnosis of Endocrine Disorders," William Wood & Co., Baltimore, 1932, Chap. XIII.

oxygen and yielding a large variety of degradation products (p. 50).[17]
These changes have been carefully studied for many years partly because
it was hoped that in this way some knowledge might be gained regarding
the changes of glucose in metabolism.   In a weak alkaline solution
α, d-glucose readily changes to β, d-glucose.   Even more remarkable than
this change are the intramolecular rearrangements of the glucose molecule, resulting in the formation of six isomeric hexose sugars, including
d-mannose and d-fructose.[18, 19]   It has been suggested that the instability of sugars in alkaline solution is primarily due to the formation of salts
of the sugars, the sugars acting as weak acids.   The instability of d-glucose is increased with an increase in the concentration of alkali, the
glucose breaking up according to Nef into 116 different compounds,
many of which are sugars containing 2, 3, 4, and 5 carbon atoms.   In
the absence of oxygen these dissociation products form lactic acid and
other substances.   These reactions have an important bearing here
because they yield products similar to those encountered in the intermediary metabolism of glucose in the tissues.   The weakness of the
glucose molecule is believed to be due to the formation of di-enols (Nef)
as intermediate products.   These substances decompose almost spontaneously.   The di-enols may be named according to the position of the
double bond—the weak point in the molecule—as represented by the
following formulas:

$$
\begin{array}{ccc}
\text{HCOH} & \text{H}_2\text{COH} & \text{CH}_2\text{OH} \\
\parallel & | & | \\
\text{COH} & \text{COH} & \text{HCOH} \\
| & \parallel & | \\
\text{HOCH} & \text{HOC} & \text{HOC} \\
| & | & \parallel \\
\text{HCOH} & \text{HCOH} & \text{COH} \\
| & | & | \\
\text{HCOH} & \text{HCOH} & \text{HCOH} \\
| & | & | \\
\text{CH}_2\text{OH} & \text{CH}_2\text{OH} & \text{CH}_2\text{OH} \\
1\text{--}2 & 2\text{--}3 & 3\text{--}4
\end{array}
$$

d-Glucose di-enols

A quantitative study of the formation of lactic and other acids
has been made by Shaffer and Friedemann.[20]   From their work it
appears that in 0.5 N alkali and in the absence of oxygen, glucose is

[17] P. A. Shaffer and T. E. Friedemann, *J. Biol. Chem.*, **86**, 345 (1930).

[18] J. U. Nef, *Liebig's Ann.*, **403**, 204 (1913).

[19] J. W. E. Glattfeld, *Am. Chem. J.*, **50**, 135 (1913).

[20] *J. Biol. Chem.*, **61**, 585 (1924).   P. A. Shaffer, "Intermediary Metabolism of
Carbohydrates," *Physiol. Rev.*, **3**, 394 (1923).

mainly converted into 3–4 di-enol, which in turn is decomposed to glyceric aldehyde, methyl glyoxal, and lactic acid. The intermediate
formation of dihydroxyacetone as a result of the splitting of 3–4 di-enol
is also likely.

$$
\begin{array}{ccccc}
\text{HCO} & \text{CH}_2\text{OH} & \text{CH}_2\text{OH} & \text{CH}_3 & \text{CH}_3 \\
| & | & | & | & | \\
\text{HCOH} & \text{HCOH} & \text{HCOH} & \text{CO} & \text{CHOH} \\
| & | & | & | & | \\
\text{HOCH} & \text{HOC} & \text{HCO} & \text{HCO} & \text{COOH} \\
| & \| & \cdots\cdots & & \\
\text{HCOH} & \text{COH} & \text{HCO} & \text{Methyl} & \text{Lactic} \\
| & | & | & \text{glyoxal} & \text{acid} \\
\text{HCOH} & \text{HCOH} & \text{HCOH} & & + \\
| & | & | & & \\
\text{CH}_2\text{OH} & \text{CH}_2\text{OH} & \text{CH}_2\text{OH} & & \\
\text{Glucose} & \text{3–4 Di-Enol} & \text{Glyceric} & & \\
& & \text{aldehyde} & &
\end{array}
$$

Other saccharinic acids
and resins

The above, according to Shaffer, is an outline of the main reactions
which occur when glucose is decomposed in half-normal alkali in the
absence of oxygen. However, the oxidation of glucose in an alkaline
solution seems to follow a different path. In the presence of oxygen,
glucose is not broken down by way of lactic acid. According to Shaffer
and Friedemann, 1 molecule of glucose, when oxidized by hydrogen
peroxide in an alkaline solution, yields 4 molecules of formic acid and
1 molecule of glycolic acid. Moreover, if glucose is first decomposed
in the absence of oxygen, the lactic acid which is formed cannot be
oxidized by subsequent treatment with hydrogen peroxide.

This seems to rule out lactic acid formation as an intermediate step in
the oxidation of glucose in an alkaline solution. Nor does it appear that
methyl glyoxal is formed in the process. Shaffer points out that the
production of lactic acid is not limited by the rate of formation of
methyl glyoxal. What determines the rate of glucose decomposition
is the presence of oxygen. It seems that oxidation of glucose begins
even before the production of glyceric aldehyde. Evidence for this
may be found in Friedemann's observations, which show that the
products of the simultaneous oxidation and dissociation of glucose
and glyceric aldehyde are different. Glyceric aldehyde yields more
formic acid and little or no glycolic acid, whereas a considerable amount
of glycolic acid is formed from glucose. In the absence of oxygen,
where we have merely the dissociation of the substance by the alkali,
glucose and glyceric aldehyde yield the same products.[21]

[21] A recent review of the mechanism of carbohydrate oxidation is that of W. L.
Evans, *Chem. Rev.*, **6**, 281 (1929); compare with E. F. Degering and F. W. Upson,
J. Biol. Chem., **94**, 423 (1931–32).

The products of glucose decomposition obtained *in vitro* are not unrelated to those arising in biological systems. Indeed, many of the compounds thus formed will be encountered repeatedly in our discussion of the intermediary metabolism of carbohydrates.

The First Stages in the Metabolism of Carbohydrate. A starting-point in the discussion of carbohydrate metabolism is glycogen. Its decomposition into lactic acid is a familiar phenomenon, having been studied in frog muscle by Fletcher and Hopkins[22] nearly a generation ago. More recently Meyerhof[23] has prepared cell-free extracts of muscle which are capable of rapidly transforming added glycogen into lactic acid. The action of these extracts, which reflects the process in muscle, depends on a relatively complex enzyme system. This may be separated into the enzyme proper, and a co-enzyme fraction composed of several constituents which seem to be essential to at least one stage of the process. These are, according to Lohmann,[24] adenylic acid pyrophosphate, free phosphate, and magnesium ions.

It is of interest to observe that, in alcoholic fermentation, a similar co-enzyme system activates the yeast enzymes, and indeed Lohmann has stated that the co-ferment preparations derived from yeast and muscle are in a measure replaceable. Such differences as occur have been attributed to the difference in the adenylic acids from the two sources.

Muscle extracts contain an amylase or *glycogenase*, hence the inference that glycogen is first changed to glucose.[25] This enzyme is some-

[22] *J. Physiol.*, **35**, 247 (1907).
[23] O. Meyerhof, "Die chemischen Vorgänge im Muskel," Berlin, 1930, p. 150.
[24] *Biochem. Z.*, **237**, 445 (1931); *Naturwissenschaften*, **19**, 180 (1931).

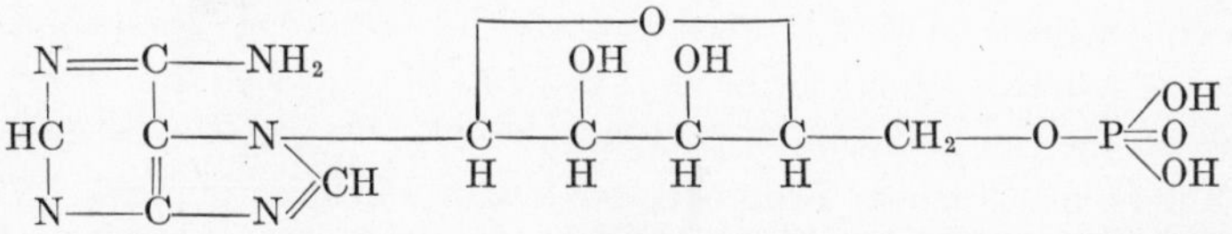

Adenylic acid

There is some difference of opinion as to whether adenylic acid exists as the pyrophosphate, or as a triphosphate. Pyrophosphoric acid ($H_4P_2O_7$) has the following formula:

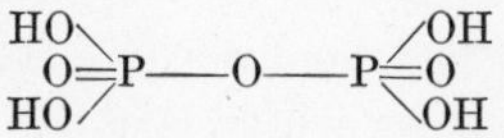

[25] It is not certain that all of this is glucose. Indeed, Barbour states that the sole product of the hydrolysis of glycogen by muscle extract appears to be a trisaccharide. *J. Biol. Chem.*, **85**, 29 (1929–30); see also H. Pringsheim, *Ber.*, **57**, 1581 (1924); K. Lohmann, *Bioch. Z.*, **178**, 444 (1926); E. M. Case, *Biochem. J.*, **25**, 561 (1931).

what more heat-stable than other enzymes, for if muscle extracts are heated for a time to 38° C., they lose their capacity for transforming glycogen to lactic acid, but retain their power of forming reducing sugar. Such partially inactivated extracts are also capable of converting hexosediphosphoric acid into lactic acid. This suggests that the component affected must be one related to the esterification of glucose with phosphoric acid.

If the formation of glucose represents an intermediate stage in the metabolism of muscle glycogen, the reaction

$$\text{Glucose} \xrightarrow{\text{(muscle extract)}} \text{lactic acid}$$

should occur very readily, in fact more readily than the reaction

$$\text{Glycogen} \xrightarrow{\text{(muscle extract)}} \text{lactic acid}$$

However, this is not the case. Lactic acid is produced from glucose or fructose much more slowly than from glycogen when added to muscle extract. Is it possible, therefore, that the conversion of glycogen to lactic acid does not include in its path the formation of a hexose sugar?

Meyerhof found that the conversion of glucose to lactic acid by muscle extract could be greatly accelerated by the addition of an activator derived from yeast, to which the term " hexokinase " has been given. It is a water-soluble, thermolabile substance, and is presumably present in greater abundance in yeast than in muscle. Hexokinase seems to be concerned with the esterification of certain hexoses with orthophosphoric acid. It activates the formation of phosphoric acid esters of fructose about twice as rapidly as of glucose, while exerting no effect on the esterification of galactose.

Esters of Glucose, Fructose, etc., with Phosphoric Acid. *Hexose-Diphosphoric Acid.* Ever since Harden and Young[26] showed that phosphates accelerate the fermentation of sugars by yeast and discovered hexose-diphosphoric acid in the products resulting from such fermentation, the relation of phosphates to carbohydrate metabolism has been the subject of intensive study. Hexose-diphosphoric acid, according to Morgan and Robison,[27] and confirmed by Levene and Raymond,[28] is α-frustose-1 : 6-diphosphoric acid:

[26] *Biochem. Z.*, **32**, 173 (1911); *Proc. Roy. Soc. (London)*, B., **81**, 528 (1909).
[27] *Biochem. J.*, **22**, 1270 (1928).
[28] *J. Biol. Chem.*, **80**, 633 (1928).

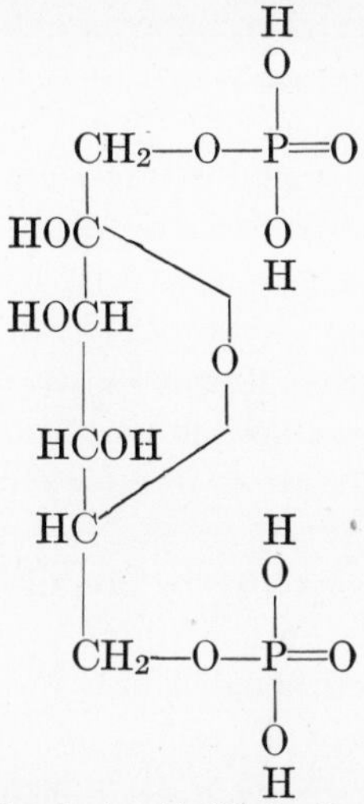

$$
\begin{array}{c}
\overset{\displaystyle H}{\underset{\displaystyle |}{O}} \\
CH_2\!-\!O\!-\!P\!=\!O \\
HOC \qquad\quad O \\
| \qquad\qquad H \\
HOCH \\
\qquad\qquad O \\
HCOH \\
HC \qquad\quad \overset{\displaystyle H}{\underset{\displaystyle O}{}} \\
CH_2\!-\!O\!-\!P\!=\!O \\
O \\
H
\end{array}
$$

Fructose-diphosphoric acid (Harden-Young ester)

Hexose-diphosphoric acid ester may be designated as the Harden-Young ester, after its discoverers.

Hexose-Monophosphoric Acid of Neuberg. The hexose-diphosphoric acid of Harden-Young may be partially hydrolyzed to yield hexose-monophosphoric acid, as first shown by Neuberg.[29] This is believed to be α-fructose-6-monophosphoric acid and may be designated as the Neuberg ester.

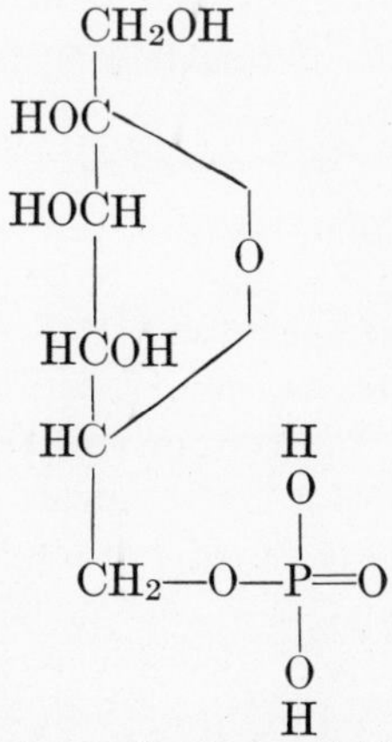

$$
\begin{array}{c}
CH_2OH \\
HOC \\
HOCH \\
\qquad\qquad O \\
HCOH \\
HC \qquad\quad \overset{\displaystyle H}{\underset{\displaystyle O}{}} \\
CH_2\!-\!O\!-\!P\!=\!O \\
O \\
H
\end{array}
$$

α-Fructose-6-monophosphoric acid (Neuberg ester)

The Robison-Embden Ester. The formation of hexose-monophosphoric acid, along with the diphosphoric ester of Harden and Young, was suspected by Harden and Robison[30] in 1914. In 1922 it was iso-

[29] *Biochem. Z.*, **88**, 432 (1918).   [30] *Proc. Chem. Soc.*, **30**, 16 (1914).

lated by Robison[31] and found to differ from the Neuberg ester. Independently Embden and associates[32] discovered in muscle press juice an ester identical with the Harden-Young ester. Because it was thought to be the precursor of lactic acid it was named " lactacidogen." This designation was later transferred to a hexose-monophosphoric acid which Embden and Zimmermann[33] isolated from muscle. In time, evidence accumulated to show that this ester and the Robison ester were identical and that it was in reality an equilibrium mixture consisting of 70 per cent glucose-monophosphoric acid and 30 per cent fructose-monophosphoric acid. The equilibrium mixture is formed very rapidly from either the pure glucose or fructose ester, in the presence of an enzyme. The Robison-Embden ester is, moreover, a product of the enzymatic (muscle extract) hydrolysis of the Harden-Young ester, magnesium ions being required in the process. Although it was formerly considered that the Neuberg ester is exclusively a product of the acid hydrolysis of the Harden-Young ester, more recent work indicates its presence among the products of yeast fermentation (Robison).[34]

It should be noted in particular that the aldose and ketose monophosphates are interconvertible and that the reaction Harden-Young ester $\rightleftharpoons$ Robison-Embden ester is reversible.

The aldose component of the Robison-Embden ester is believed to be glucose-6-monophosphoric acid:[35]

$$
\begin{array}{l}
\text{HC——OH} \\
\quad| \\
\text{HCOH} \\
\quad| \\
\text{HOCH} \quad \text{O} \\
\quad| \\
\text{HCOH} \\
\quad| \\
\text{HC} \\
\quad| \\
\text{CH}_2\text{—O—P=O} \\
\end{array}
$$

Robison-Embden ester (glucose component)

[31] Biochem. J., 16, 809 (1922).   [33] Ibid., 141, 225 (1924).
[32] Z. physiol. Chem., 93, 124 (1914).   [34] Biochem. J., 26, 2191 (1932).
[35] E. J. King, R. R. McLaughlin, and W. T. J. Morgan, Biochem. J., 25, 310 (1931); R. Robison and E. J. King, ibid., 25, 323 (1931); P. A. Levene and A. L. Raymond, J. Biol. Chem., 89, 479 (1930); 91, 751 (1931).
The subject has been recently reviewed by Robison, "The Significance of Phosphoric Esters in Metabolism," New York University Press, 1932.

Other Esters. Robison and Morgan[36] have found that, in the fermentation of either glucose or fructose with dried yeast, trehalose-monophosphoric acid is one of the products formed. More recently Robison[34] has also discovered the presence of mannose-monophosphoric acid.

Lohmann[37] found two more esters, which at first appeared to be diphosphates, differing from the Harden-Young ester. These new forms accumulated when muscle " brei " was treated with either fluoride or iodoacetic acid. It was later shown by Embden[38] that under the conditions defined by Lohmann, glyceric-acid-monophosphoric acid (abbreviated phosphoglyceric acid) and α-glycero-phosphoric acid were formed. The " Lohmann ester " may therefore be considered to be a mixture of the two compounds. The importance of these observations in contributing to our knowledge of carbohydrate metabolism will now be considered.

Relation of Hexose-phosphates to Carbohydrate Metabolism. The discovery that glyceric-acid-monophosphoric acid and glycero-phosphoric acid are products of enzymatic hydrolysis of fructose-diphosphoric acid (Harden-Young ester) at once brought the latter compound into prominence in relation to carbohydrate metabolism. Notwithstanding its formation from glycogen in muscle extracts and in muscle under various experimental conditions, it had not been isolated from normal muscle, and hence its significance was left in doubt. On the other hand, hexose-monophosphoric acid (Robison-Embden ester), because of its occurrence in muscle, was definitely linked with normal sugar metabolism, having been regarded by Meyerhof as the stabilization product of a much more labile ester, which as a rule did not accumulate, but was transformed *status nascendi* to lactic acid. The present position has in no sense minimized the importance of the equilibrium mixture of hexose-monophosphates, but has brought to the fore fructose-diphosphoric acid as the probable intermediate product in the transformation of the former into lactic acid. The stages have been represented by Embden as follows:

First phase: Synthesis of hexose-diphosphoric acid from 1 molecule of hexose and 2 molecules of H_3PO_4, or from 1 molecule of hexose-monophosphoric acid and 1 molecule of H_3PO_4.

Second phase: Decomposition of the hexose-diphosphoric acid (Harden-Young ester) into 1 molecule of dioxyacetone-phosphoric acid and 1 molecule of glyceric-aldehyde-phosphoric acid, as indicated by the following formulas:

[36] *Biochem. J.*, **22**, 1277 (1928).

[37] *Naturwissenschaften*, **19**, 180 (1931); F. Lipmann and K. Lohmann, *Biochem. Z.*, **222**, 389 (1930).

[38] G. Embden, H. J. Deuticke, and G. Kraft, *Klin. Wochenschr.*, **12**, 213 (1933).

$$
\begin{array}{ccc}
\begin{array}{l}
CH_2\!\!-\!\!O\!\!-\!\!P\!\!\lessgtr^{O}_{OH} \\
C\!=\!O \\
CHOH \\
CHOH \\
CHOH \\
CH_2\!\!-\!\!O\!\!-\!\!P\!\!\lessgtr^{O}_{OH}
\end{array}
& = &
\begin{array}{l}
CH_2\!\!-\!\!O\!\!-\!\!P\!\!\lessgtr^{O}_{OH} \\
C\!=\!O \\
CH_2OH \\
\text{Dioxyacetone-phosphoric acid} \\
+\ CHO \\
CHOH \\
CH_2\!\!-\!\!O\!\!-\!\!P\!\!\lessgtr^{O}_{OH}
\end{array}
\end{array}
$$

Fructose-diphosphoric acid   Glyceric-aldehyde-phosphoric acid

Third phase: Dismutation of the 2 molecules of triose-phosphoric acid formed in the preceding stage into 1 molecule of phosphoglyceric acid and 1 molecule of glycerophosphoric acid (α or β-glycerophosphoric acid is formed depending on whether the hexose-diphosphoric acid produced in the first stage was a ketose or an aldose).

$$
\begin{array}{l}
CH_2\!\!-\!\!O\!\!-\!\!P\!\!\lessgtr^{O}_{OH} \\
C\!=\!O \\
CH_2OH
\end{array}
+
\begin{array}{l}
CH_2\!\!-\!\!O\!\!-\!\!P\!\!\lessgtr^{O}_{OH} \\
CHOH \\
CHO
\end{array}
+\ H_2O =
\begin{array}{l}
CH_2\!\!-\!\!O\!\!-\!\!P\!\!\lessgtr^{O}_{OH} \\
CHOH \\
CH_2OH
\end{array}
+
\begin{array}{l}
CH_2\!\!-\!\!O\!\!-\!\!P\!\!\lessgtr^{O}_{OH} \\
CHOH \\
COOH
\end{array}
$$

Dioxyacetone-phos- Glyceric-aldehyde- Glycerophosphoric Phosphoglyceric
phoric acid phosphoric acid   acid   acid

Fourth phase: Cleavage of the phosphoglyceric acid into pyruvic acid and phosphoric acid, as follows:

$$
\begin{array}{l}
CH_2\!\!-\!\!O\!\!-\!\!P\!\!\lessgtr^{O}_{OH} \\
CHOH \\
COOH
\end{array}
=
\begin{array}{l}
CH_3 \\
C\!=\!O \\
COOH
\end{array}
+\ H_3PO_4
$$

Phosphoglyceric acid Pyruvic
       acid

Fifth phase: Reduction of the pyruvic acid into lactic acid at the expense of the oxidation of the glycerophosphoric acid to triose-phosphoric acid.

$$
\begin{array}{l}
CH_3 \\
C\!=\!O \\
COOH
\end{array}
+
\begin{array}{l}
CH_2\!\!-\!\!O\!\!-\!\!P\!\!\lessgtr^{O}_{OH} \\
CHOH \\
CH_2OH
\end{array}
=
\begin{array}{l}
CH_3 \\
CHOH \\
COOH
\end{array}
+
\begin{array}{l}
CH_2\!\!-\!\!O\!\!-\!\!P\!\!\lessgtr^{O}_{OH} \\
CHOH \\
CHO
\end{array}
$$

Pyruvic acid α-Glycerophosphoric Lactic acid Triose-phosphoric
     acid   acid

It is assumed that the triose-phosphoric acid undergoes intramolecular rearrangement with the formation, as before, of phosphoglyceric acid and glycerophosphoric acid. The former yields pyruvic acid, which combines with the latter to produce lactic acid. Ultimately, therefore, all of the triose-phosphoric acid is converted into lactic acid.

Embden's scheme has been accepted by Meyerhof.[39]

Up to a certain point the process of lactic acid formation in muscle and the process of alcoholic fermentation by yeast have a common path. The juice expressed from macerated yeast converts hexose-diphosphoric acid into α-glycerophosphoric and phosphoglyceric acids. As in the case of muscle these products accumulate in the presence of fluoride, which inhibits further change. When phosphoglyceric acid is added to fresh yeast it decomposes to acetaldehyde, carbon dioxide, and phosphoric acid. The α-glycerophosphoric acid, on the contrary, is not acted on further. Nor is it responsible for the reduction of aldehyde to alcohol. Hence it cannot be considered as an intermediate product in fermentation. It has been noted, however, that hexose-diphosphoric acid, or glyceric-aldehyde-phosphoric acid, promotes the reduction of acetaldehyde. Meyerhof [39, 40] has separated the fermentation process into two phases, the initial phase and the stationary phase, or condition. Whereas in muscle extract, pyruvic acid is converted by the glycerophosphoric acid, in yeast it is split up to acetaldehyde, carbon dioxide, and phosphoric acid, without the intermediation of the glycerophosphoric acid. Some precursor of the latter, presumably glyceric-aldehyde-phosphoric acid (a triose phosphoric acid), reduces the acetaldehyde to ethyl alcohol. The new fermentation scheme has been represented by Meyerhof, as follows:

Initial Phase:

A. 1 Hexose-diphosphoric acid = 4 triose phosphoric acid = 2 α-glycerophos-
  + 1 glucose   phoric acid
  + 2 phosphoric acid   +2 phosphogly-
                                                              ceric acid

B. 2 Phosphoglyceric acid   = 2 pyruvic acid   = 2 acetaldehyde
                               + 2 phosphoric acid   + 2 carbon dioxide
                                                      + 2 phosphoric
                                                        acid

Stationary Condition:

C. 2 Acetaldehyde   = 2 triose phosphoric   = 2 alcohol + 2 phos-
  + 1 glucose   acid + 2 acetalde-   phoglyceric acid
  + 2 phosphoric acid   hyde

Reaction B is inhibited by fluoride; reactions A and C are inhibited by iodoacetic acid; reaction C is catalyzed by hexose-diphosphoric acid.

The Position of Methylglyoxal in Intermediary Carbohydrate Metabolism. Prior to the appearance of Meyerhof's recent paper, it was almost generally conceded by students of the subject, including

[39] *Nature*, **132**, 337, 373 (1933).
[40] O. Meyerhof and W. Kiessling, *Biochem. Z.*, **264**, 40; **267**, 313 (1933).

Meyerhof, that *methylglyoxal* was the common intermediary in the anaerobic breakdown of carbohydrate to lactic acid in muscle and in alcoholic fermentation. Cori,[41] writing on carbohydrate metabolism in 1931, states: " Methylglyoxal is now accepted as an intermediary in the anaerobic breakdown, and in the schemes of most authors it also appears in the aerobic breakdown." It will be noted that in the discussion in the preceding paragraphs methylglyoxal has been excluded, and indeed Meyerhof has now taken the position that on the basis of the new experimental results " the assumption of the rôle of methylglyoxal as an intermediate product in the splitting of carbohydrates becomes superfluous."

Without questioning Meyerhof's present position, it must be recognized, nevertheless, that the acceptance of methylglyoxal as an intermediate was based on a considerable body of experimental evidence. Interest in this compound was first stimulated through the discovery by Dakin and Dudley[42] and by Neuberg[43] in tissues, including muscle, of an enzyme, " glyoxalase " (or *methyl-glyoxalase*), capable of converting methylglyoxal into lactic acid. As represented in the following equation, this change is an internal Cannizzaro reaction, part of the molecule (aldehyde group) being oxidized while another part (carbonyl group) is reduced. For this reason Neuberg described the enzyme involved in this reaction as " keto-aldehyde mutase."

$$
\begin{array}{c}
CH_3 \\
| \\
CO \\
| \\
CHO
\end{array}
\; + \;
\begin{array}{c}
H_2 \\
\| \\
O
\end{array}
\; \rightleftarrows \;
\begin{array}{c}
CH_3 \\
| \\
CHOH \\
| \\
COOH
\end{array}
$$

Methyl glyoxal   Lactic acid

Leukocytes contain glyoxalase and are hence capable of transforming methylglyoxal into lactic acid. In fact, all tissues known to produce lactic acid from glucose or glycogen have been found capable of forming methylglyoxal and of transforming added methylglyoxal into lactic acid as readily as, or more readily than, carbohydrate. In summing up this evidence, Case[44] states that " these two circumstances, taken in conjunction with the widespread occurrence of glyoxalase in nearly all tissues, make the probability strong that methylglyoxal is indeed a normal precursor of lactic acid."

Other interesting observations may be cited. When the action of

[41] *Physiol. Rev.*, **11**, 143, especially 191 (1931).
[42] *J. Biol. Chem.*, **14**, 155, 423 (1913).
[43] *Biochem. Z.*, **51**, 484 (1913).
[44] *Biochem. J.*, **26**, 759 (1932).

methylglyoxal is inhibited in tissue preparations (liver, muscle) to which hexose-diphosphate has been added, methylglyoxal accumulates. Neuberg and Kobel[45] have shown that yeast, lactic acid bacteria, or mammalian tissue extracts, when freed from co-enzyme, produce large amounts of methylglyoxal from hexose-monophosphoric acid.

Compared with the ready formation of lactic acid from methylglyoxal is the slow production of pyruvic acid ($CH_3 \cdot CO \cdot COOH$). It is to be noted that the formation of lactic acid involves intramolecular rearrangement, while the reaction methylglyoxal → pyruvic acid is the result of direct dehydrogenation. The slow production of pyruvic acid has been explained by the supposition that the methylglyoxal which participates in fermentation is structurally not identical with extraneously added methylglyoxal. It is also possible, as suggested by Case, that pyruvic acid is not an intermediate in lactic acid formation. Nor does Case consider it to be a product of the direct oxidation of lactic acid. Pyruvic acid is formed, however, when muscle extract is incubated with starch or hexose-diphosphate, the rate being in fact increased in the presence of antiglyoxalase, suggesting, as Meyerhof now believes, that the path of pyruvic acid formation does not lie through methylglyoxal.

Meyerhof contends partly on the basis of Lohmann's work that the formation of methylglyoxal is not essential to the transformation of glucose into lactic acid. Glutathione is a true co-enzyme for glyoxalase, as shown by Lohmann.[46, 47] Muscle extract from which the glutathione has been removed by dialysis is no longer capable of acting on methylglyoxal. In the process of dialysis, adenylpyrophosphoric acid and magnesium ion are also lost to the extract, but even when these are restored, the capacity to convert methylglyoxal into lactic acid is not regained. However, such partially reactivated extracts are able to transform glycogen into lactic acid, evidently without the intermediate formation of methylglyoxal. Under the same conditions, but in the presence of sulfite which fixes the pyruvic acid, it can be shown that pyruvic acid is formed. Its relation to lactic acid, into which it is presumably converted by an oxidation-reduction process, has been indicated (p. 324).

[45] *Biochem. Z.*, **203**, 463 (1928); **207**, 232; **216**, 493 (1929).

[46] *Biochem. Z.*, **254**, 332 (1932).

[47] According to M. Jowett and J. H. Quastel, *Biochem. J.*, **27**, 486 (1933), glutathione reacts with methylglyoxal to form an addition compound. This is acted upon by glyoxalase, with the production of lactic acid and the regeneration of glutathione. See also M. E. Platt and E. F. Schroeder, *J. Biol. Chem.*, **104**, 281 (1934).

Products of Carbohydrate Metabolism. Thus far we have considered mainly the anaerobic formation of lactic acid. While this constitutes an important phase of muscle metabolism, the question of the oxidation of glucose remains to be considered, as well as the fate of the lactic acid. It was long supposed that the latter was an intermediate product in the oxidation of carbohydrate to its end-products, namely carbon dioxide and water. In recent years, however, the trend of opinion has changed and considerable evidence has been offered in support of the idea that lactic acid itself is not oxidized in the body, but that to be utilized it must first be reconverted to hexose.

If this is granted, it must follow that either glucose or some other intermediate formed from glucose is the precursor of carbon dioxide and water. Accordingly, attention has been centered on methylglyoxal as the probable precursor, not only of lactic acid in muscle and of alcohol in alcoholic fermentation, but of carbon dioxide as well. Its alleged relation to lactic acid has been considered. For alcoholic fermentation the scheme of Neuberg[48] has been widely accepted (Meyerhof [23], p. 167), but opposed to this is Meyerhof's new scheme (p. 325). Lusk[49] considered the following reactions to be the most probable in the formation of carbon dioxide:

$$CH_3CO \cdot CHO + H_2O \rightarrow CH_3 \cdot CHO + HCOOH \xrightarrow{\;+O\;} CO_2 + H_2O$$
$$\Big\downarrow {+O}$$
$$CH_3COOH \xrightarrow{\;+2O_2\;} 2CO_2 + 2H_2O$$

Certain facts are thought to contribute to the probability of this scheme. Formic acid is a normal constituent of urine. It diminishes during fasting and increases on a potato or meat diet. Acetaldehyde has likewise been detected in urine and also in blood. When fed to animals, even in large amounts, acetic acid disappears. However, the path of its oxidation has not been determined.

---

[48] Neuberg's scheme for alcoholic fermentation:

1. $C_6H_{12}O_6 = 2CH_3 \cdot CO \cdot CHO + 2H_2O$
   (Methylglyoxal)

2. $\begin{array}{ll} CH_3 \cdot CO \cdot CHO + H_2O\ H_2 & CH_2OH \cdot CHOH \cdot CH_2OH \\ \qquad\qquad | \;\;=\;\; & \qquad + \text{(Glycerol)} \\ CH_3 \cdot CO \cdot CHO \quad + \quad O & CH_3 \cdot CO \cdot COOH \\ & \qquad\text{(Pyruvic acid)} \end{array}$

3. $CH_3 \cdot CO \cdot COOH = CH_3 \cdot CHO + CO_2$

4. $\begin{array}{ll} CH_3 \cdot CO \cdot CHO \quad O & CH_3 \cdot CO \cdot COOH \\ \qquad\qquad | \;\;=\;\; & \\ CH_3 \cdot CHO \qquad H_2 & CH_3 \cdot CH_2OH \\ & \qquad\text{Alcohol} \end{array}$

[49] G. Lusk, "Science of Nutrition," Saunders, Philadelphia, 4th edition, p. 349.

The doctrine has been followed that if a given substance by perfusion through liver forms glycogen, or if it gives rise to an extra excretion of glucose in the urine of severely diabetic or phlorhizinized animals, it constitutes a satisfactory criterion for considering it to be an intermediate product of carbohydrate metabolism. This has been based on the assumption that the reactions involving the oxidation of the glucose molecule are entirely reversible.

A few examples will be cited for illustration. Sansum and Woodyatt,[50] and Ringer and Frankel,[51] have shown that when glyceric aldehyde is given to phlorhizinized dogs, it is almost completely converted into glucose. This is also true of dihydroxyacetone. Perfusion of dog liver with dl-glyceric aldehyde yields both d-sorbose and d-glucose, according to Embden, Schmitz, and Wittenberg.[52] The formation of glycogen by perfusing tortoise livers with glyceric aldehyde has been observed by Parnas.[53] As shown by Dakin and Dudley,[54] methylglyoxal is almost quantitatively converted into glucose in the phlorhizinized dog. Dakin[55] holds that in the conversion of l-lactic acid into d-glucose there must be some intervening reaction which involves the loss of asymmetry and hence of optical activity of the lactic acid. Methylglyoxal or dihydroxyacetone, being optically inactive, might fulfill this requirement.

Although the synthesis of glucose and glycogen from the substances just mentioned is unquestioned, considerable doubt has arisen regarding the validity of the assumption that the reactions of carbohydrate metabolism are necessarily reversible. Indeed, such authorities of the subject as Shaffer[56] and Cori[42] lean toward the view that such substances as lactic acid, pyruvic acid, and glyceric aldehyde are not themselves oxidized, but that their normal path in metabolism lies via glucose.

At the present stage in the development of the problem it would be well-nigh futile to attempt to reconcile the divergent opinions or to explain the accumulated data in terms of a given hypothesis. Admittedly the situation is at present obscured by many inconsistencies. So far as these are due, not to faulty information but to the misinterpretation of experimental data, the inconsistencies are more apparent than real and will no doubt be cleared away in time. The newer develop-

[50] *J. Biol. Chem.*, **24**, 327, 343 (1916).
[51] *Ibid.*, **18**, 233 (1914).
[52] *Z. physiol. Chem.*, **88**, 210 (1913).
[53] *Zentr. Physiol.*, **26**, 671 (1912).
[54] *J. Biol. Chem.*, **15**, 127 (1913).
[55] "Oxidations and Reductions in the Animal Body," 2d edition (1922), Chap. IV.
[56] *Physiol. Rev.*, **3**, 419 (1923).

ments have particularly unsettled our former comprehension of the last stages of carbohydrate decomposition. Although these chemical changes had never been precisely defined, the idea had become more or less fixed that methylglyoxal was the starting-point in these reactions, particularly in view of lack of evidence of the direct oxidation of either lactic or pyruvic acids. In the Embden-Meyerhof scheme, methylglyoxal does not fit in. Is there another precursor? The question is obviously an open one, but in view of the circumstances that have been outlined, the observations of Toenniessen and Brinkmann[57] appear significant.

These investigators perfused the muscles of eviscerated rabbits with incompletely oxygenated blood containing pyruvate. Succinic acid and formic acid appeared in the perfusate, but there was no increase in lactic acid. These results suggest that the pyruvic acid may undergo polymerization and dehydration, this resulting in the formation of a molecule of succinic acid and two molecules of formic acid. The latter is oxidized, while the succinic acid changes in turn to fumaric, malonic, oxalacetic, and pyruvic acids. The whole cycle then repeats itself.

In the absence of any other adequate explanation this hypothesis appears very attractive, especially so in anticipation that the theory proposed by Embden and Meyerhof may prevail.

Carbohydrate Metabolism in Relation to Muscular Activity. Our knowledge of the chemical changes which accompany muscle activity has been drastically revised and considerably amplified in the last few years. The former conception was that, in the initial process of contraction, glycogen (or some product of glycogen) is changed " explosively " into lactic acid, the energy for the contraction being derived from this reaction. In the recovery process the lactic acid disappeared, four-fifths being resynthesized into glycogen, while the remaining fifth (or its equivalent) was oxidized. Part of the energy thus derived was obviously used in restoring the muscle to its original condition of readiness for further muscular activity, the remainder of the energy appearing as heat.

Meyerhof determined that for each gram of lactic acid appearing in muscle, 390 calories (small) of heat were produced. One gram of lactic acid is derived from 0.9 gram of glycogen + 0.1 gram H_2O. The difference between the calorific value of this amount of glycogen and its equivalent of lactic acid was estimated to be $3790 - 3602 = 188$ calories. This is approximately one-half the heat actually produced. It was then shown that an additional 105 calories result from the neutralization of

1 gram of lactic acid. Thus there remained approximately 80 calories unaccounted for. (As a result of later studies, the calorific value of glycogen was found to be somewhat higher [3836 calories] and the heat of neutralization somewhat lower.) In short, the interesting question arose as to the source of this extra heat.

The explanation was found in the fact that the formation of lactic acid is not the primary chemical change in muscular contraction, but that it is preceded by the hydrolysis of creatine-phosphoric acid (phosphocreatine, creatine phosphate, see p. 423), this reaction being accompanied by the development of heat. This is the primary change which occurs when muscle is stimulated, the energy liberated being equivalent to 120 calories per 1 gram of H_3PO_4.

In 1927 Embden and Zimmermann[58] discovered the presence in muscle of adenosine phosphate, or adenylic acid (p. 433). At about the same time, Parnas and Mozolowski [59] discovered the formation of ammonia in muscle. It was subsequently shown that the ammonia was derived from the adenylic acid. Then followed the isolation by Lohmann[60] in 1929 of a compound which on hydrolysis, in neutral solution or with acid, yielded adenylic acid and pyrophosphoric acid. This suggested that the adenylic acid was present in combination as pyrophosphate. Lohmann then showed that adenylic acid pyrophosphate (or adenylpyrophosphate) was essential in the breakdown of glycogen into lactic acid, its rôle in glycolysis being that of a co-enzyme. The presence of magnesium ion was also found to be essential. Yeast likewise contains adenylpyrophosphate, this being presumably somewhat different from the compound in muscle. It plays an analogous rôle as a co-zymase in yeast fermentation, as shown by Euler and his associates.[61]

It was shown by Meyerhof and Lohmann[62] that, in the breakdown of adenylpyrophosphoric acid to orthophosphate, ammonia, and inosinic acid, energy is set free—170 calories per 1 gram of H_3PO_4.

Another important discovery which contributed to the elucidation of the problem of muscle metabolism was the observation of Lundsgaard[63] that in muscle poisoned with iodoacetic acid (sodium salt), energy was produced without the formation of lactic acid, but at the expense of creatine phosphate. That muscular contraction could

---

[58] Z. physiol. Chem., **167**, 137 (1927).

[59] Biochem. Z., **184**, 399 (1927).

[60] Naturwissenschaften, **17**, 624 (1924).

[61] Z. physiol. Chem., **165**, 140 (1927); **168**, 177 (1927); **177**, 237 (1928); **184**, 163 (1929).

[62] Biochem. Z., **253**, 431 (1932).

[63] Ibid., **217**, 162 (1930).

occur and energy could be produced in the absence of lactic acid formation was indeed remarkable and an important step leading to the revision of our conception of the sequence of events in muscular activity.

Stated briefly, the chain of events as understood at present is approximately as follows. Creatine phosphate is hydrolyzed to provide the energy for contraction. This is a reversible reaction, the synthesis being at the expense of the energy derived from the breakdown of adenylpyrophosphoric acid (or adenosine triphosphate, according to some investigators). Part of this energy results from the liberation of pyrophosphoric acid (or of two molecules of phosphoric acid) and part from the splitting off of ammonia. The phosphoric acid liberated from the creatine phosphate and probably also from the adenylpyrophosphoric acid is utilized in part in the esterification of hexose derived from the enzymic hydrolysis of the glycogen. The phosphoric acid is again set free in the later stages of the contraction process. The resynthesis of the adenylic acid-pyrophosphate depends on energy obtained from the breakdown of glycogen to lactic acid.[64] Four-fifths (according to some, three-fourths) of the lactic acid thus formed is resynthesized into glycogen, the energy for this endothermic reaction being derived from the oxidation of the remaining one-fifth (or fourth) of the lactic acid (?), or its equivalent.

The changes occurring during the stage of oxidative recovery restore the muscle to its original status. The resynthesis of phosphocreatine and adenylpyrophosphoric acid (adenosine triphosphate) is brought to completion. According to Parnas, the deaminized molecule is restored, the amino group being derived from amino acids by a process of oxidation-deamination. The changes during contraction and recovery are represented on p. 416.

With a sufficient oxygen supply the lactic acid formed in the contraction process is removed largely through resynthesis into glycogen, so

[64] In a recent review Parnas[65] states that for the synthesis of phosphocreatine in muscle extracts, the reaction being alkaline, 12 Calories (large) per mol are required. These are supplied by the breakdown of adenosine-triphosphoric acid, or by lactic acid. In the decomposition of the former, 25 large calories are liberated when the two phosphate groups are split off and an additional 8 when the compound is deaminized. The reconstitution of the adenosine-triphosphoric acid is dependent on the energy derived from glycolysis, i.e., the conversion of glycogen to lactic acid.

[65] The student is referred to the following reviews of the subject of muscle metabolism: P. Eggleton, "The Position of Phosphorus in the Chemical Mechanism of Muscular Contraction," *Physiol. Rev.*, 9, 432 (1929); O. Meyerhof, "Die chemischen Vorgänge im Muskel," Berlin, 1930; T. H. Milroy, "The Present Status of the Chemistry of Skeletal Muscular Contraction," *Physiol. Rev.*, 11, 515 (1931); A. V. Hill, "The Revolution in Muscle Physiology," *ibid.*, 12, 56 (1932); D. M. Needham, "The Biochemistry of Muscle," Methuen & Co., Ltd., London, 1932; J. K. Parnas, "The Chemistry of Muscle," *Ann. Rev. Biochem.*, 1, 431 (1932); 2, 317 (1933).

that the amount of carbohydrate in the muscle after recovery is the same as before the contraction minus the lactic acid equivalent that has been oxidized.

Thus it is that muscular activity depends on the coordination of a number of chemical reactions, some of which are endothermic, others exothermic.

Further Observations on the Interrelationship of Glycogen, Glucose, and Lactic Acid. After the ingestion of sugar there is a decrease in the elimination of phosphates in the urine, as well as a fall in the inorganic phosphates of the blood. This relation of glucose ingestion to decreased phosphate elimination is observed in normal individuals; but in diabetes, when carbohydrate metabolism is impaired, the relation is not observed. In completely depancreatized dogs, there is no appreciable fall in phosphates unless insulin is administered.

The reduction of blood inorganic phosphate has been explained by assuming that it was accompanied by an accumulation of hexosephosphate in the tissues. Direct evidence of such an increase has been obtained by Cori and Cori[66] and by Kerr and Blish[67] after insulin or epinephrin administration. Glucose feeding does not in itself affect the hexosephosphate content of muscle.

The process glycogen $\rightleftarrows$ glucose occurs in the liver, and the sugar thus formed is liberated into the systemic circulation. Reconversion of this sugar into glycogen occurs in the muscles, where, as we have seen, the reaction glycogen $\rightleftarrows$ lactic acid takes place. The lactic acid formed during muscular contraction is for the most part reconverted into glycogen during the recovery phase, but a small amount of lactic acid escapes into the blood. Even in a state of rest, the blood contains lactic acid, which has been estimated to vary between 5 and 20 mg. per 100 cc. of blood.[68] In moderate exercise the blood lactic acid increases. For example, walking at a rate of 3.5 miles per hour was found by Hill, Long, and Lupton[69] to cause the lactic acid content of the blood to increase from 20.9 mg. (the concentration before the period of exercise) to 36.6 mg. per 100 cc. Somewhat more strenuous exercise, namely walking at the rate of 4.1 miles per hour, produced an increase of from 21.4 mg., the initial value, to 58.9 mg. per 100 cc. Quite obviously,

---

[66] *J. Biol. Chem.*, **94**, 581 (1931). Cori and Cori analyzed muscle removed from the living animal under ether anesthesia and determined the average hexosephosphate content to be 53.3 mg. per cent as hexose (equivalent to 8.9 mg. per cent of phosphorus).

[67] *Ibid.*, **97**, 11 (1932).

[68] Compare A. V. Bock, D. B. Dill, and H. T. Edwards, *J. Clin. Investigation*, **11** 775 (1932).

[69] *Proc. Roy. Soc. (London)*, B, **96**, 438; **97**, 84, 155 (1924).

during muscular exercise, there is an increased production of lactic acid and a somewhat greater amount escapes into the blood. If the exercise is moderate, the lactic acid, after reaching a certain level, does not continue to accumulate either in the muscles or in the blood. There is sufficient respiratory stimulation to provide an adequate extra supply of oxygen to keep pace with the increased lactic acid formation and in this way a balanced condition is reached which has been referred to as the *steady state*. This means that there is a steady rate of oxygen utilization, and that the lactic acid content of the muscle, though above normal, is nevertheless maintained at a constant level.

The situation is different when the exercise is more violent in character. First, with regard to the lactic acid in the blood, there is a marked increase. In an experiment of Hill and his associates, the subject ran in a standing position for 4 minutes (breathing pure oxygen). At rest, the lactic acid content was 20 mg. per 100 cc., whereas immediately after the exercise it was 86 mg. In another experiment, the subject ran in place at 239 steps per minute for 9.5 minutes, breathing air. The lactic acid rose from 8.5 to 204 mg. per 100 cc. A similar effect was observed by Barr, Himwich, and Green.[70] In a series of experiments they subjected a number of individuals to approximately 3500 kilogram-meters of work, performed in a period of 3.5 minutes, and determined, among other things, the change in lactic acid in the blood. Invariably there was an increase. The difference between the lactic acid concentration at rest and at the end of the exercise ranged between 31.7 mg. and 85.8 mg.

The essential difference between moderate and violent exercise is that in the latter there is a considerable accumulation of lactic acid in the muscle. This is because the supply of oxygen, after reaching a limiting value, cannot be increased any further and does not keep pace with the lactic acid production. When light or moderate exercise is stopped, there is a prompt return to normal of the gaseous exchange, and the lactic acid concentration in the blood begins to fall. Not so when violent exercise is suddenly terminated. For some minutes thereafter the lactic acid content of the blood continues to increase (see for example Barr and Himwich[71]), before the drop sets in, and the oxygen utilization continues at a high level for a considerable period. During violent exercise when the oxygen supply is inadequate, the tissues go into " oxygen debt," and a long period of recovery, during which the oxygen utilization continues at a high level, is required before the debt is paid. Thus, in the experiments of Hill, Long, and Lupton, a subject, after running 3 meters

70 *J. Biol. Chem.*, **55**, 495 (1923).   71 *Ibid.*, **55**, 539 (1923).

per second for 5 minutes, took 9.5 minutes to recover (i.e., before his oxygen intake returned to normal) and his oxygen debt was 1.7 liters. After running in place for 20 seconds as violently as possible, he went into debt 5.5 liters of oxygen and took 14 minutes to recover. A quarter of a mile run, followed by severe gymnastic exercise, resulted in an oxygen debt of 12.4 liters, the subject taking 44 minutes to recover.

Margaria, Edwards and Dill [71a] have presented evidence to show that an oxygen debt is incurred in muscular activity even before there is evidence of a lactic acid increase. This so-called *alactacid* oxygen debt has been related to the oxidation of substances (ordinary fuel) furnishing the energy for the resynthesis of phosphagen.

Now, what we are primarily interested in here is the fate of the lactic acid which escapes into the blood, for, it is seen, this occurs to some extent even in the resting condition and is much increased during exercise. A small portion of the lactic acid is excreted in the urine and the amount lost in this way may be considerable during violent exercise, but the larger proportion is returned to the liver, there to be resynthesized into glycogen. Thus, as Cori and Cori [72] have pointed out, a sugar molecule can go through a complete cycle in the body; it can in turn be liver glycogen, blood sugar, muscle glycogen, blood lactic acid, and again liver glycogen. This cycle may be represented as in the diagram to the left.

An abundance of evidence has accumulated in support of this idea, but only a small portion of the literature can be referred to here. For example, the question as to whether muscle glycogen is converted directly into glucose has been virtually settled. When the liver is removed, the blood sugar rapidly

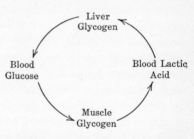

falls to very low levels, as shown by the work of Bollman, Mann, and Magath. [73] As the muscle contains considerable amounts of glycogen and as this does not prevent the hypoglycemia and does not disappear to any great extent, it is concluded that muscle glycogen is not readily converted into glucose.

It is well known that epinephrin, ether anesthesia, and asphyxia produce hyperglycemia. But, as has been shown by Soskin, [74] if the abdominal viscera, including the liver, are removed, hyperglycemia does not

[71a] *Am. J. Physiol.*, **106**, 689 (1933).
[72] *Ibid.*, **81**, 389 (1929); see also *Physiol. Rev.*, **11**, 143 (1932).
[73] *Am. J. Physiol.*, **74**, 238 (1925).
[74] *Ibid.*, **81**, 382 (1927).

develop under these conditions despite the fact that there is glycogen in the muscles.

There remains to be considered some of the evidence for the transformation of lactic acid into glycogen in the liver. It is to be supposed than in severe liver damage, as in phosphorus poisoning, the liver would lose its ability to convert lactic acid into glycogen and that there would be an increased excretion of lactic acid in the urine. This is actually the case. Parnas and Baer[75] observed glycogen synthesis in the turtle liver, perfused with sodium lactate. Abramson, Eggleton, and Eggleton,[76] however, were unable to demonstrate the synthesis of glycogen in the liver from racemic sodium lactate in dogs under amytal anesthesia. On the other hand, Izume and Lewis[77] observed glycogen deposition in the liver of fasting rabbits injected subcutaneously with sodium lactate, and more recently Cori and Cori,[72] working with rats, found that if sodium d-lactate is fed by mouth or injected subcutaneously, glycogen is deposited in the liver. Sodium l-lactate, though absorbed from the intestine at the same rate as the d-isomer, hardly formed any liver glycogen. Cori and Cori state that of the d-lactate absorbed in three hours, 40–95 per cent was retained as liver glycogen and none was excreted in the urine, whereas 30 per cent of the l-lactate absorbed was recovered in the urine.[78]

Direct evidence of the operation of the lactic acid-glycogen-glucose cycle is to be found in the work of Himwich and co-workers,[79] who determined the changes in the composition of the blood on passage through muscle and liver. Comparing the blood of the femoral artery and vein they found less glucose and more lactic acid in the venous blood, indicating the removal of glucose and the addition of lactic acid by the tissues (muscle) of the lower extremity. On the contrary, the hepatic vein blood contained, almost invariably, more glucose and less lactic acid than arterial blood, or the blood of the portal vein, showing that in passing through the liver, the blood discharged lactic acid and acquired glucose.

Previously fasted animals subjected to prolonged and strenuous exercise may show marked depletion of body glycogen without any change in liver glycogen, the latter being readily synthesized from lactic acid. As shown by the experiments of Long and Grant,[80] the restora-

---

[75] Biochem. Z., 41, 414 (1912).

[76] J. Biol. Chem., 75, 763 (1927).

[77] Ibid., 71, 51 (1926–27).

[78] For a more extensive review refer to C. F. Cori, "The Harvey Lectures, 1927–1928," p. 76 (1929).

[79] J. Biol. Chem., 85, 571 (1929–30); 90, 417 (1931).

[80] Ibid., 89, 553 (1930).

tion of body (muscle) glycogen, under these circumstances, occurs much more slowly, requiring about 12 hours for its completion.

During exercise in the undernourished animal the increase in fixed acids (chiefly lactic) in the blood is in excess of the amounts present in normally fed, exercised animals. Moreover, the return to the initial state is a much slower process, suggesting, according to Schlutz, Hastings, and Morse,[81] a disturbance in the mechanism for delivering oxygen to, and removing metabolic products from, the tissues.

The altered capacity of the tissues to oxidize carbohydrate, as a result of starvation, has been studied by Dann and Chambers.[82] They found that the oxidation of glucose fed to dogs that had been fasted for a period of three weeks is completely suppressed for about four hours following its ingestion. Carbohydrate metabolism was not restored to normal if only glucose were fed, suggesting that a fundamental change had been produced in the sugar-oxidizing mechanism, the return of which to normal depends on factors not yet determined.

The Metabolism of Nerve. The significant contributions to our knowledge of nerve metabolism are of very recent origin. It has been established that activity in nerve is accompanied by an increased consumption of oxygen and production of carbon dioxide, and the development of a small amount of heat. The respiratory quotient of resting nerve varies between 0.75 and 0.80. Such values would be consistent with the utilization of a mixture of fat, protein, and carbohydrate. During activity, the respiratory quotient of nerve rises. If the respiratory quotient of the extra metabolism is computed, it is found to vary between 0.95 and 1.0. This corresponds to the values which would be obtained if only carbohydrate were being oxidized, or if protein were being utilized in such a way as to form ammonia, rather than urea, as the end-product of the nitrogenous metabolism.

Himwich and Nahum[83] studied the respiratory metabolism of the brain of dogs and concluded from their results that carbohydrate was used exclusively as the source of energy. They found, moreover, that the venous blood from the brain contained less dextrose and lactic acid than the blood going to the brain. Even in diabetes, the utilization of carbohydrate seemed unimpaired.

According to Gerard,[84] when normal oxidations are prevented by oxygen lack or respiratory poisons, the familiar glycolysis appears.

[31] *Am. J. Physiol.*, **104**, 669 (1933).

[82] *J. Biol. Chem.*, **89**, 675 (1930); **95**, 413 (1932); **100**, 493 (1933).

[83] *Am. J. Physiol.*, **90**, 389 (1929).

[84] The subject of nerve metabolism has been comprehensively discussed in an admirable review by R. W. Gerard, *Physiol. Rev.*, **12**, 469 (1932).

Lactic acid, once formed, however, cannot be rebuilt into carbohydrate or even burned when oxygen is again available. On the other hand, Holmes[85] considers lactic acid to be utilized by the brain as a source of energy.

During tetanization of nerve, phosphocreatine is hydrolyzed. The formation of ammonia which attends activity, as well as other evidence, suggests the possible existence of an adenylpyrophosphoric acid mechanism.

The Conversion of Carbohydrate to Fat.[86]   The synthesis of fat from carbohydrate in the animal organism is an established fact and a matter of common knowledge and experience. It involves the formation from glucose of both glycerol and fatty acids. From their chemical relationship, the origin of glycerol from glyceric aldehyde or some other 3-carbon intermediate of carbohydrate metabolism, seems probable. The origin of the fatty acids on the contrary is a somewhat more debatable point. These are probably formed from acetic aldehyde by aldol condensation, as originally suggested by Nencki. This may be represented as follows:

$$
\begin{array}{ccc}
\begin{array}{c} CH_3 \\ | \\ CHO \\ | \\ CH_3 \\ | \\ CHO \\ \text{2 Acetaldehyde} \end{array}
& \rightarrow &
\begin{array}{c} CH_3 \\ | \\ CHOH \\ | \\ CH_2 \\ | \\ CHO \\ \text{Aldol} \end{array}
\end{array}
$$

Through the reduction of the hydroxyl group and oxidation of the aldehyde group, butyric acid would be obtained. Or by repeated aldol condensation, the higher fatty acid homologues would be derived.

This general view has been adopted by Leathes and Raper,[87] who consider that the process may involve the primary synthesis of longer chains of unsaturated fatty acids, as indicated by the following formulas:

$$4CH_3 \cdot CHO \rightarrow CH_3 \cdot CH : CH \cdot CH : CH \cdot CH : CH \cdot CHO$$

Reduction followed by oxidation of the aldehyde group would yield an 8-carbon saturated fatty acid, $CH_3(CH_2)_6COOH$. It is assumed that the higher fatty acids may be formed in a similar manner.

[85] *Biochem. J.*, **24**, 914, 1119 (1930).

[86] The subject has been comprehensively reviewed by D. Rapport, "The Interconversion of the Major Foodstuffs," *Physiol. Rev.*, **10**, 349 (1930).

[87] J. B. Leathes and H. S. Raper, "The Fats," London, 1925.

Smedley and Lubrzynska[88] have suggested that the mechanism of fatty acid synthesis from carbohydrate may involve the condensation of acetic aldehyde with pyruvic acid, $CH_3 \cdot CO \cdot COOH$, derived by the oxidation of methylglyoxal (pyruvic aldehyde), yielding a ketonic acid which is converted by the splitting off of carbon dioxide into an aldehyde having one carbon atom less than the ketonic acid. The aldehyde then condenses with another molecule of pyruvic acid and again gives off a molecule of carbon dioxide. By the repetition of this process, long carbon chains may be built up. This type of synthesis has been observed *in vitro* in the case of butyl aldehyde and pyruvic acid. When the fatty acid chain is built up, it very likely undergoes a certain amount of oxidation yielding intermediate compounds containing unsaturated linkages. One stage in the synthesis may be represented as follows:

$$CH_3CHO + CH_3CO \cdot COOH \rightarrow CH_3CH : CH \cdot CO \cdot COOH + H_2O$$

$$CH_3CH : CH \cdot CO \cdot COOH \rightarrow CH_3CH : CH \cdot CHO + CO_2$$

Glycuronic Acid. The formation of this compound in the animal organism reveals a path of glucose oxidation unlike any considered hitherto. Glycuronic acid was first isolated from the urine of animals that had been fed camphor, but it has been detected since, though in small amounts, in normal urine.

$$
\begin{array}{c}
\overset{H\quad OH}{\underset{\diagdown\diagup}{}} \\
C \\
| \\
HCOH \\
| \\
HOCH \qquad O \\
| \\
HCOH \\
| \\
HC \\
| \\
COOH
\end{array}
$$

Glycuronic acid

Glycuronic acid does not exist in the urine in the free form, but in combination, chiefly with compounds of the aromatic series. Two kinds of linkage occur—the glucosidic type, as in phenol-, or menthol-glycuronic acid; and the ester type, as in glycuronic acid-monobenzoate.

[88] *Biochem. J.*, **7**, 364, 375 (1913).

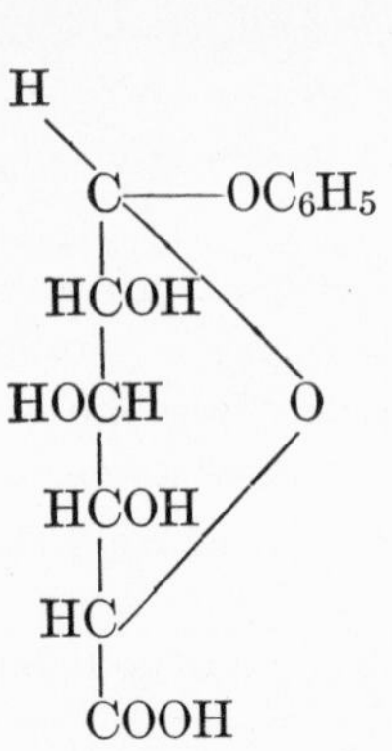

Phenylglycuronate

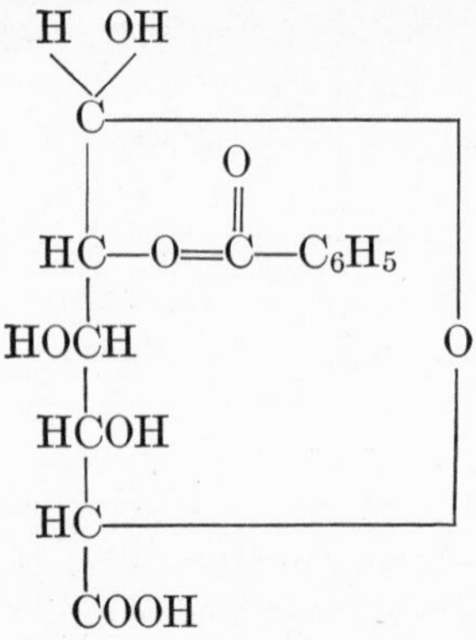

Glycuronic-acid-monobenzoate

When hydroxybenzoic acid is fed to dogs, it is conjugated with two molecules of glycuronic acid, forming an ester linkage with one and a glucoside linkage with the other, as indicated by the following formula:

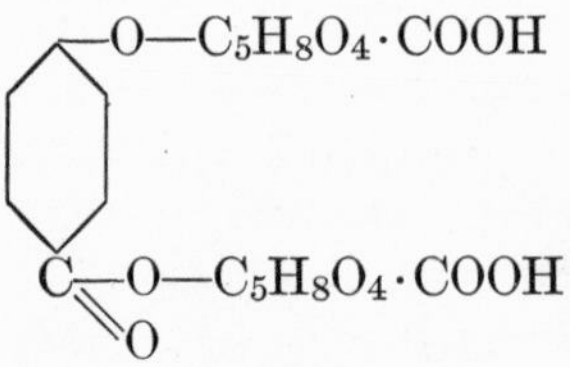

Administered in small amounts (about 3 grams), glycuronic acid disappears completely.   Given in larger amounts, a portion is recovered in the urine.   Although in general it appears that the organism possesses only a limited capacity to oxidize this substance, it is interesting to note that in dogs menthol-glycuronic acid is oxidized almost completely.   In man, the administration of glycuronic-acid-imonobenzoate leads to an excretion of hippuric acid (benzoyl-glycine), suggesting the cleavage and possible oxidation of the glycuronic acid residue.

In the past, glycuronic acid was considered chiefly from the standpoint of a detoxicating agent, it being assumed that the process of conjugation consisted in rendering a toxic substance less toxic, or non-toxic. Quick [89] to whose work we owe much of our present knowledge of glycuronic acid metabolism, has recently pointed out the interesting fact that conjugation with glycuronic acid yields products which are much stronger acids than the original substances which were presumably

---

[89] A. J. Quick, *J. Biol. Chem.*, **61**, 667, 679 (1924); **67**, 477; **70**, 59, 397 (1926); **74**, 331 (1927); **80**, 535 (1928); **92**, 65 (1931); **95**, 189; **96**, S3; **97**, 403 (1932); **99**, 119 (1932–33); **100**, 441 (1933).

detoxified. He has therefore suggested that a fundamental factor in conjugation is the conversion of a weak acid, which the body apparently cannot excrete, to a strong acid which it can eliminate through the kidney.

It is conceivable that the physiological significance of glycuronic acid is not restricted to its function in forming conjugation products. As has been emphasized by Quick, it stands to reason that any substance which the human organism can synthesize at the rate of nearly 1 gram per hour cannot be ignored without incurring the danger of overlooking perhaps an important metabolic process.

Tissue Constituents Containing Sugars. It should now be pointed out that certain amounts of sugar and other foodstuffs are used in the construction and repair of tissue and that these processes also constitute a phase of metabolism, called anabolism. The reverse process, which is the dissimilation of tissue constituents, is called catabolism. The metabolism of tissue constituents proceeds at a rather constant rate, because tissue breakdown in health is usually constant, and may be broadly referred to as endogenous metabolism, in contradistinction to the direct metabolism of foodstuffs, which is called exogenous metabolism. However, these terms are customarily used in a more restricted sense, as we shall see later in considering purine and creatine metabolism.

The conversion in the body of glucose into galactose is indicated by the synthesis of lactose in the mammary glands of lactating mammals. Pentose (d-ribose and d-ribodesose) enter into the synthesis of nucleic acids and of closely related constituents of cells. Galactosamine has been reported present along with glucosamine in various protein combinations. Moreover, galactose exists in combination with lipids in nervous tissue (galactolipids or cerebrosides), and together with glucose in the mucroproteins. Glucose and mannose are also known to occur in other proteins.

Cartilage, bone, tendons, and fascia contain chondroitin, an amino polysaccharide, conjugated with sulfuric acid.

These are among the better-known tissue constituents containing carbohydrate in combination. Their synthesis in the body must therefore be considered as part of the carbohydrate metabolism. What becomes of these substances in catabolism is uncertain. Perhaps a certain amount of these carbohydrates is reconverted into glucose and shares its fate in metabolism. There is also a strong likelihood that the small amounts of pentose, galactosamine, and glucosamine, etc., which may be formed in tissue catabolism are excreted in the urine unchanged.

Glycosuria. The presence of sugar in the urine is termed glycosuria (glucosuria) or mellituria. It may be entirely physiological, but is often a symptom of diabetes, a disease in which the metabolism of carbohydrates is impaired.

When sugar is found in the urine, it is nearly always glucose. Rarely, fructose and pentose may be present. During the last stages of pregnancy, particularly during the last few days before delivery, as well as during lactation, excretion of lactose is not uncommon. Following the injection or rapid absorption of disaccharides (sucrose, maltose), these may appear in the urine.

Sugar appears in the urine either when its concentration in the blood is high and exceeds the renal threshold, or when the kidneys are unusually permeable to this substance. The concentration of glucose in the blood may increase as a result of insufficient glycogenesis or because of an excessive amount of glycogenolysis. When large amounts of carbohydrate are being absorbed and the rate of conversion into glycogen does not keep pace with the rate of absorption, there is a piling up of sugar in the blood (hyperglycemia) and the excretion of part of it in the urine. When the appearance of sugar in the urine is due to the ingestion of excessive amounts of carbohydrate, the condition is termed *alimentary glycosuria*. This is purely a physiological phenomenon and may be produced in normal individuals.

In a considerable proportion of normal individuals there is a tendency to glycosuria in the afternoon, as recently shown by Harding, Selby, and Armstrong.[90] It has been assumed by these authors that "afternoon glycosuria" may be due to a lowering in the renal threshold at that time of the day.

Deficient glycogenesis occurs in conditions of acidosis and of liver injury (alcoholism, cirrhosis, phosphorus poisoning) and is associated with the excretion of sugar in the urine.

Glycosuria and hyperglycemia occur in mechanical asphyxia and in carbon monoxide poisoning, obviously as a result of increased glycogenolysis, for it has been shown that no hyperglycemia or glycosuria develops in animals in which the circulation through the liver is excluded by means of an Eck fistula. Hyperglycemia and glycosuria occur in ether and chloroform anesthesia and in morphine and strychnine poisoning.

Puncture Glycosuria. In a classical experiment, Claude Bernard discovered that puncturing the medulla of the brain in the region of the floor of the fourth ventricle resulted in glycosuria. This form of experimental glycosuria has been named *la piqûre* or puncture diabetes. It is important to bear in mind that the intensity and duration of the

90 *Biochem. J.*, **26**, 957 (1932).

glycosuria produced in this way depend on the amount of glycogen present in the liver at the beginning of the experiment. If the glycogen has been removed by previous starvation, glycosuria does not occur, or is very slight.

A similar effect may be obtained by stimulating the sympathetic nerve supply to the liver (electrical stimulation or injection of adrenalin or epinephrin). These forms of glycosuria are believed to result from increased glycogenolysis.

Possibly related to these conditions are various forms of transitory glycosuria due to nervous disturbances. It is well known that a blow on the head may lead to glycosuria (traumatic glycosuria). Fright, agitation, or struggling causes hyperglycemia and the consequent excretion of sugar in the urine (psychic or emotional glycosuria). Folin[91] examined students before and after a difficult examination and found sugar in the urine of over 15 per cent. Hyperglycemia and glycosuria are uncommon in exercise with little or no emotional stress, but common in exercise with emotional stress, as on the football field.[92] Similar observations on the relation of emotion to glycosuria were made by Cannon, but others have been unable to confirm his results. Some clinicians have attempted to establish a relationship between nerve strain and the incidence of diabetes. Although the importance of nervous factors in the etiology of diabetes has probably been exaggerated, nevertheless Macleod points out the frequent occurrence of diabetes in those predisposed to neurotic conditions, or in those whose daily habits entail much nerve strain.

Renal Glycosuria and Phlorhizin Diabetes. Glycosuria due to increased renal permeability is perhaps more frequent than was imagined before it became possible to analyze the blood for its sugar content. Errors in diagnosis were no doubt frequent when the clinician was forced to rely solely on urine analyses. Renal diabetes is distinguished by the low concentration of sugar in the blood. The experimental production of a somewhat similar condition was accomplished in 1886 by von Mering[93] upon injecting into animals phlorhizin, a glucoside which is found in the root bark of the cherry, apple, pear, and plum trees. Just as in renal diabetes, the sugar concentration of the blood in phlorhizin diabetes frequently falls to 0.07–0.08 per cent. The animal organism, in attempting to maintain the sugar concentration of its blood within normal levels, uses up a large proportion of its stored glycogen, and when this is depleted the proteins of the tissues are called upon to supply the

[91] Folin, Denis, and Smillie, *J. Biol. Chem.*, **17**, 519 (1914).

[92] Edwards, Richards, and Dill, *Am. J. Physiol.*, **98**, 352 (1931).

[93] Verhandl. V. Congr. inn. Med., 1886, p. 185.

needed sugar. The sugar-forming amino acids are converted into glucose, but no sooner is it formed than it is excreted by the kidneys. Thus, in severe phlorhizin diabetes, after the glycogen has been used up, 3.65 grams of glucose are excreted for every gram of nitrogen. The ratio between glucose and nitrogen excretion is called the D : N or G : N ratio and has been found to be a most valuable criterion in determining the severity of the condition both in phlorhizin diabetes and in true pancreatic diabetes. When no food is taken, a D : N ratio of 3.65 is called the fatal ratio, for it indicates a complete failure in the utilization of glucose.

A plausible explanation of the mechanism of phlorhizin glycosuria has been lacking until recently when Lundsgaard [94] showed that in phlorhizin diabetes the kidney contains sufficient of the poison to inhibit the action of phosphatase. He has suggested that phlorhizin glycosuria may be due to the inability of the kidney to effect the synthesis of hexosephosphates, which is assumed to be a stage in the reabsorption of glucose from the kidney tubules.

As an experimental method, phlorhizin diabetes has proved itself most useful. In the hands of the distinguished American physiologist Graham Lusk, his numerous students, and a number of others, this was developed into a powerful tool by means of which many difficult problems in intermediary metabolism were solved. The quantitative character of these studies enhances their value considerably. The author will again have occasion to refer to these investigations in discussing the intermediary metabolism of the proteins. [95]

It is important to bear in mind that the various forms of glycosuria described in the preceding paragraphs are usually transitory and, moreover, are not true forms of diabetes.

Pancreatic Diabetes. From a clinical standpoint this is the most common and important cause of glycosuria. Impairment in the utilization of carbohydrate is the characteristic defect in pancreatic diabetes. The tendency to hyperglycemia is very pronounced and is accompanied, when the renal threshold is exceeded, by the excretion of large quantities of glucose. Carbohydrate metabolism has been considered in relation to diabetes in other connections and will be referred to again, especially in the discussion of insulin, the hormone of the pancreas (p. 468).

---

[94] *Biochem. Z.*, **264**, 209 (1933).

[95] An excellent review of the subject of phlorhizin diabetes has been written by T. P. Nash, *Physiol. Rev.*, **7**. 385 (1927).

CHAPTER XI

INTERMEDIARY FAT METABOLISM

The changes which fats undergo while in transport to the tissues constitute the starting-point in our discussion of intermediary fat metabolism. As has been stated elsewhere, the greater part of the fat absorbed from the intestine is taken up by the lymphatics and enters the blood by way of the thoracic duct. However, a considerable portion enters the blood directly, as shown by the fact that the blood of the portal vein contains more fat than is present in the general circulation, a difference which tends to disappear in the post-absorptive state.[1] During short periods of starvation, the mobilization of fat from the region drained by the portal vein also raises the fat content of the portal blood, which in passing through the liver discharges some of the fat, as demonstrated by the results of analyses of the blood taken simultaneously from the portal and hepatic veins (Himwich).[2] Moreover, it is probable that the liver may also remove fat reaching it by way of the hepatic artery. Under certain conditions, notably in depancreatized, fasting animals, the situation may be reversed; i.e., the fat content of the blood of the hepatic vein may rise above that in the portal vein, indicating the withdrawal of fat from the liver.

The " lipemia," or increase in blood lipids which results from the entrance of fat into the blood, may persist for several hours. In individuals at rest the administration of 1 gram of fat per kilogram of body weight is followed by a slow rise in the blood-fat concentration, reaching a maximum value in 4 hours, then rapidly diminishing, with a return to the normal level in 6–7 hours. A somewhat different lipemia curve is obtained in individuals not at rest. The rise occurs more rapidly, attaining a maximum value in about 3 hours, which is somewhat below the maximum obtained in the resting individual.[3]

During fat absorption there is a definite increase in the concentration

---

[1] O. Cantoni, *Boll. soc. ital. biol. sper.*, **3**. 1278 (1928).

[2] H. E. Himwich, W. H. Chambers, A. L. Hunter, and M. A. Spiers, *Am. J. Physiol.*, **99**, 619 (1931–32).

[3] N. I. Nissen, *Acta Med. Scand.*, **74**, 566 (1931); cited by W. R. Bloor, *Ann. Rev. Biochem.*, **2**, 149 (1933).

of phospholipids (lecithin, etc.) and cholesterol esters.[4]   In human subjects, Man and Gildea[5] observed that within 4 to 6 hours after the ingestion of 3.54 grams of fat per kilogram of body weight, the fatty acids in the serum increased to 30 to 90 per cent above the initial level.   The average increase in phospholipid fatty acids was 18 per cent.   The ingestion of a balanced meal, which included fat, resulted in an average rise of 21 per cent in total fatty acids, of which from 5 to 24 per cent was combined as phospholipid.[6]

A special significance has been attached to the cholesterol esters and the phospholipids of the blood.   It has been assumed that, in these combinations, the transport and interchange of the fatty acids between the tissues are facilitated.   It has also been suggested that the formation of these compounds represents an early stage in the intermediary metabolism of the fatty acids.   This question will be considered in more detail shortly.

Following a fat-containing meal, there is a marked increase in the number of the so-called " chylomicrons,"[7] which is more or less proportional to the increase in fat content.   The chylomicrons are very small fat droplets, 1 micron, or less, in diameter, and are invisible to the naked eye.   Not infrequently, during absorption, as well as in certain pathological conditions (anemia, nephrosis, etc.), the plasma assumes a milky appearance due to the presence of much larger fat globules than the chylomicrons.   Generally this is associated with an unusually high

---

[4] W. R. Bloor, *J. Biol. Chem.*, **23**, 317 (1915); *Physiol. Rev.*, **2**, 92 (1922); *Ann. Rev. Biochem.*, **1**, 267 (1932); A. Knudson, *J. Biol. Chem.*, **32**, 337 (1917); M. Bodansky, *Proc. Soc. Exp. Biol. Med.*, **28**, 628, 630 (1931); S. M. Ling, *Chinese J. Physiol.*, **5**, 381 (1931); I. H. Page, L. Pasternack, and M. L. Burt, *Biochem. Z.*, **223**, 445 (1930).

[5] E. B. Man and E. F. Gildea, *J. Biol. Chem.*, **99**, 61 (1932–33).

[6] Channon and Collinson have analyzed beef blood obtained at a fasting level. The principal components were phosphatide, cholesterol, cholesterol esters, and an unsaponifiable fraction.   Only a small fraction of the total was found to be in combination as neutral fat (*Biochem. J.*, **23**, 666, 1212 [1929]).   Compare with Bloor's analyses (*J. Biol. Chem.*, **59**, 543 [1924]).

The data of Man and Gildea[5] are also of interest in this connection.   Human serum obtained before breakfast shows the following distribution of fatty acids:

Subject No.	I	II	III	IV	V	VI	VII	VIII	IX
Phospholipid fatty acids, m.eq.	4.6	6.5	6.5	5.6	5.2	5.8	5.0	5.1	5.8
Non phospholipid fatty acids, m.eq.	5.8	8.3	9.4	7.8	5.0	7.6	5.2	7.2	7.2

Assuming the cholesterol content to be 160–200 mg. per 100 cc., or approximately 4–5 m.eq., and that of this 2–4 m.eq. is present as esters, it follows that the fatty acids in serum present in combination as fat constitute about 30 per cent of the total.

[7] S. H. Gage and P. A. Fish, *Am. J. Anat.*, **34**, 1 (1924).

lipid content, but the correlation is inconstant and it is therefore probable that other factors are involved which affect the degree of dispersion of the lipids.

Storage of Fat. The storage of fat may occur in many regions of the body, but especially in the superficial fascia under the skin where it may be present as a layer an inch or more in thickness. This layer of fat is called the *panniculus adiposus.* Large amounts of fat occur, likewise, in the intermuscular connective tissue, omentum and mesentery, and in association with the internal organs, such as the lungs, heart, kidneys, ovaries, testes, and liver. The fat in the adipose tissue of any given species is normally characteristic of that species, but the deposition of fat foreign to an animal may occur under certain conditions. A classical experiment showing this is that of Lebedeff,[8] who starved two dogs until their reserve fat was nearly used up. One dog was then fed mutton tallow and the other linseed oil, with the result that the fat deposited in the adipose tissue of the first dog resembled mutton fat, whereas the fat laid down in the second animal was liquid at 0° C. and contained larger amounts of unsaturated fatty acids than is normal for dog fat. In a similar experiment, Munk[9] fed a previously starved dog rape-seed oil and was able to demonstrate the deposition of the triglyceride of erucic acid ($C_{22}H_{42}O_2$). Eckstein[10] has also shown that the nature of the fat deposited is influenced by the fats of the diet, and he has been able to demonstrate the deposition of the myristyl radical both in the hides and carcasses of rats fed with myristic acid. However, the fat deposited on diets containing tributyrin or tricaproin did not contain the butyryl or caproyl radical, although it differed from the fat synthesized from fat-free precursors, namely protein and carbohydrate. The difference was in the degree of unsaturation rather than in the saponification numbers, as might be supposed. On a practically fat-free diet Eckstein's rats deposited fat having on an average an iodine number of 68 and a saponification number of 194, whereas on the tricaproin diet these values were 59 and 191, respectively. Brominized and iodized fats, obtained by treating fats containing unsaturated fatty acids with iodine or bromine, have been fed previously starved animals and later recovered in their bodies.

In a series of similar experiments, Powell[11] fed tricaprylin to rats. Only traces of caprylic acid were deposited, but as in the case of feeding butyric and caproic acids, there was a distinct lowering of the iodine

[8] *Arch. ges. Physiol.,* **31**, 11 (1883).
[9] *Arch. path. Anat. Physiol.,* **95**, 407 (1884).
[10] *J. Biol. Chem.,* **81**, 613 (1929); **84**, 353 (1929).
[11] *J. Biol. Chem.,* **89**, 547 (1930); **95**, 43 (1932).

number and very little change in the saponification number. However, when tricaprin was fed, capric acid comprised 15 per cent of the fatty acids of the depot fat, which was characterized by a high saponification number (216 as compared with 198 in the controls) and an even lower iodine number (47.7 as compared with 63.3 in the controls). Similar results were obtained with trilaurin; lauric acid comprised as much as 25 per cent of the depot fat. The iodine number was 44.8 and the saponification number 218.

These facts have an important bearing in relation to stock-raising. In certain parts of this country, the diet of hogs is composed largely of meal prepared from cottonseed or peanuts. This food may so modify the consistency of the fat laid down by these animals as to affect the marketability of the lard and other products. Ellis and co-workers[12] have shown that corn, peanut and soybean oils, when fed to hogs to the extent of 4 per cent of the ration, have a distinct softening effect on the body fat, whereas a similar amount of cottonseed oil produces a hard fat. Increasing the cottonseed oil to 8 and 12 per cent levels results in the deposition of a softer, more unsaturated fat, containing a much greater proportion of linoleic acid. The rate of fat storage in hogs is not altered even on rations practically devoid of fat, but the fat deposited under these conditions is hard and the linoleic acid content is conspicuously low.

This problem has also been studied in rats by Anderson and Mendel.[13] In their experiments, the diet was very carefully controlled and only the fat, or other nutrients available for fat formation, were

---

[12] *J. Biol. Chem.*, **69**, 219, 239 (1926); see also N. R. Ellis and O. G. Hankins, *ibid.*, **66**, 101 (1925); Ellis and J. H. Zeller, *ibid.*, **89**, 185 (1930); Ellis, C. S. Rothwell, and W. O. Pool, *ibid.*, **92**, 385 (1931).

One hog kept on a basal corn diet and a 4 per cent level of cottonseed oil deposited a back fat having the following characteristics: iodine number, 64; melting-point, 46.2; saponification number, 196.3. The fatty acid distribution in per cent was: oleic acid, 34.5; linoleic, 16.4; total saturated, 44.5. In contrast are the following data for the fat deposited on the 12 per cent level: iodine number, 83.8; melting-point, 35.5; saponification number, 195.6. Fatty acids: oleic, 32.3; linoleic, 28.2; total saturated, 34.9.

One hog kept on a low fat ration for 257 days attained a weight of 282 lb. The body fat had an iodine number of 55.1, a melting-point of 37.6° C., and a saponification number of 195. The distribution of the fatty acids was as follows: oleic, 58.9; linoleic, 1.3; arachidonic, 0.02; palmitic, 24.3; stearic, 10.3; myristic, 0.7 per cent.

Bhattacharya and Hilditch have pointed out that, in the deposition of hog fat under various circumstances, there is a marked tendency to approximate constancy in the molar content of the C_{18} acids in spite of variation in the total proportion of saturated to unsaturated acids (*Biochem. J.*, **25**, 1954 [1931]).

[13] *J. Biol. Chem.*, **76**, 729 (1928).

varied. They found that when soybean oil, cottonseed oil, or peanut oil was fed, the resulting body fat resembled the food fat. When butter fat or coconut oil were fed, the deposited fat differed from the food fat, having a lower iodine number. Anderson and Mendel point out that even after a particular type of " soft " body fat has been developed, it. is possible to alter its chemical make-up by changing to a " hardening " diet rich in carbohydrate. This process is apparently due first to the gradual depletion of the soft fat and the subsequent deposition in its place of the harder variety. This process is relatively slow, but it may be materially hastened if prior to changing the diet the fat reserves are partly used up by a short period of fasting.

Over twenty years ago, Henriques and Hansen[14] made similar, though not as extensive, observations on hogs. In one of their experiments, they fed a hog on barley and another on maize. The fat laid down in the connective tissue of the former had an iodine number of 57.7 and a melting-point of 27.4°, whereas the fat of the corn-fed hog had an iodine value of 75.6 and a melting-point of 23°. Despite the profound effect which diet has on the nature of the fat deposited, it is nevertheless true that the fat in any given species is fairly constant in composition. This is due in large part, no doubt, to the similarity in the type of food consumed by animals of the same species.

The composition of adipose-tissue fat varies in different parts of the body. In their experiments on hogs, Henriques and Hansen showed that subcutaneous fat has a higher iodine number and a lower melting-point than perirenal fat, which in turn has a higher iodine number and a lower melting-point than omental fat. These differences may be due to temperature, for these workers have shown that the temperature of subcutaneous tissue in the hog, 1 cm. from the surface, is 33.7°; at 2 cm., it is 34.8°; and at 4 cm., 39° C. The composition of fat has been modified by altering the temperature of the environment. In one experiment, Henriques and Hansen kept three pigs from the same litter at different temperatures; the first was kept at 30–35° C. and the second at 0°; the third was also kept at 0° but was covered and kept warm with a sheepskin coat. After two months, the pigs were killed and the fat analyzed. It was found that the fat of the pig kept at 0° C. without any cover showed the highest iodine number (72.3). The pig kept at 30–35° had deposited fat having an iodine number of 69.4, whereas the clothed pig, kept at 0° C., had fat which showed the lowest iodine number of the series (67.0). There is, as yet, no satisfactory explanation which accounts for these variations. One can readily see, however, the

[14] *Skand. Arch. Physiol.*, **11**, 151 (1901); also described in the monograph by Leathes and Raper, p. 100.

advantage of having a relatively solid fat, of high melting-point, in the region of the back of some animals, which is so often exposed to the relatively high temperatures of the sun's rays.

Distribution of Adipose Tissue. A detailed study of the distribution and character of the fat deposited in the organism has been reported from Mendel's laboratory.[15] The following factors have been considered: diet, weight, sex, undernutrition, fasting, exercise, ovariectomy, the administration of thyroxin. The normal distribution of fat in the various depots in the female rat was approximately as follows (in per cent): subcutaneous 50, genital 20, perirenal 12, mesenteric 10, intermuscular 5, omental 3. This distribution was independent of the type of diet fed; however, the greatest amount of fat was deposited on a diet rich in fat. The degree of saturation (iodine number) of the stored fat was independent of the distribution, but was markedly influenced by the type of fat in the diet.[16] In young rats, the proportion of subcutaneous fat was larger than in the older animals. With increase in weight, the rate of storage was found to be increased. The female rats stored more fat in the genital depots, whereas male rats accumulated a greater proportion of fat in the perirenal fat depots. Undernutrition or forced activity in animals kept on a starch diet resulted in a decreased proportion of the genital fat. Intermuscular fat increased in proportion as a result of physical activity, but even on an *ad libitum* diet, the exercised animals became thin. Neither weight, sex, undernutrition, fasting, nor exercise influenced the iodine number of the fat deposited. As compared with non-spayed controls, ovariectomized rats stored less fat in the genital depots, but more in the subcutaneous tissues. Daily doses of thyroxin markedly diminished the total fat deposited. The distribution was approximately the same as in the controls, but the fat deposited was considerably more unsaturated.

It is probable that not all the fat in the body has the same physio-

---

[15] L. L. Reed, F. Yamaguchi, W. E. Anderson, and L. B. Mendel, *J. Biol. Chem.*, **87**, 147 (1930); Reed, Anderson, and Mendel, *ibid.*, **96**, 313 (1932).

[16] Thus, in rats kept inactive and given an unlimited amount of food, the following differences in the iodine number were observed (average values for 6 animals in each group).

	Inter-muscular	Genital	Subcuta-neous	Perire-nal	Mesen-teric	Omen-tal
I. Starch diet	57.1	55.4	56.6	53.8	50.2	
II. Soybean oil	105.1	114.0	111.3	118.3	110.0	100.9
III. Coconut oil	29.7	28.2	29.4	28.6	25.8	26.2

logical significance. An apparently clear-cut and sound distinction has been made by a number of workers (Mayer, Schaeffer,[17] Terroine,[18] and others) between the so-called *élément constant* and *élément variable*. The tissues of animals that have starved to death still contain a certain amount of fat, which seems to be fairly constant for any given species. In the mouse, for example, about 23 per cent of the dry weight of the animal consists of fatty acids, whereas in the chicken the fatty acids constitute about 25 per cent of the dry weight. It is believed that a certain amount of fat is an essential component of protoplasm, and that this cannot be reduced without causing death. This is the *élément constant*. On the other hand, the reserve fat is variable in amount, depending on the state of nutrition and other factors. The fatty acids in reserve or storage fat are present in combination with glycerol as neutral fat. Such fat, because it varies in amount, has been called the *élément variable* by the group of workers mentioned above.

It appears that the kidney, spleen, lung, and heart contain no *élément variable* or storage fat but only the *élément constant*, or indispensable fat. This is demonstrated by comparing the composition of these organs in overfed, normal, and starved animals. Leathes cites data for the kidney, in which 11.1, 11.9, and 13.4 per cent of fatty acids were found in overfed, normally fed, and starved animals, respectively. If anything, these data, instead of showing that fat is stored on a high-fat diet, indicate that there is a greater migration of fat to this organ during starvation than normally. In muscle, the figures obtained in the conditions just mentioned were 17.6, 11.3, and 4.6 per cent, showing unmistakably the possibility of the storage of fat in muscle tissue. Finally, the values given for the liver are 12.9, 10.5, and 11.3 per cent. Thus, the liver does not seem to play as important a part in fat storage as is often supposed. Occasionally, the amount of fat in the liver may increase considerably, usually as a result of sudden fat mobilization, but even then the storage of fat in this organ is believed to be transitory.[19]

Blatherwick[20] has made the interesting observation that rats fed diets containing whole liver develop livers containing large amounts of fat and cholesterol esters. The effect seems to be related to the cholesterol contained in liver and indeed it was found possible to reproduce

---

[17] *J. physiol. path. gén.*, **15**, 510, 535, 773, 984 (1913); **16**, 1, 23 (1914).

[18] E. F. Terroine, *J. physiol. path. gén.*, **16**, 384, 212 (1914); "Physiologie des substances grasses," Paris (1919).

[19] Monaghan (*J. Biol. Chem.*, **98**, 21 [1932]) reduced the phospholipid content of the tissues in fasting rats to a value 60 per cent below normal and accordingly has raised a question as to the validity of the conception of the *élément constant*.

[20] *J. Biol. Chem.*, **97**, Proc. xxxiii (1932); **100**, xviii (1933); **103**, 93 (1933).

the condition of "fatty liver" by feeding cholesterol. This has been confirmed by Chanutin and Ludewig,[21] who have shown, moreover, that other tissues (kidney, heart, brain, etc.) are practically unaffected.

Relation of Lecithin and Choline to Fat Deposition in the Liver. Depancreatized dogs receiving insulin, but kept on a diet of cane sugar and lean beef develop, after a variable period, failure of liver function, characterized by fatty infiltration and degeneration. The alleviation of this critical condition may be brought about by the addition of lecithin to the diet. Stimulated by this interesting observation, Best and associates demonstrated that normal rats when fed a diet containing a fairly saturated fat showed an abnormal accumulation of fat in the liver. This was not observed in control animals receiving a similar diet together with lecithin. A difference in the composition of the fat deposited was indicated by the iodine number (average of 100 in the experimental group, as contrasted with an average of approximately 132 in the control group). Further investigation revealed that the effect of lecithin was due to the choline component of the molecule. Betaine was found to exert a similar effect, while amino-ethyl alcohol, the nitrogenous base of kephalin, was without action. Choline and betaine have been shown to prevent, likewise, the abnormal deposition of fat in the liver (rat), produced by feeding cholesterol.[21a]

Human Fat. Cathcart and Cuthbertson[22] have analyzed the abdominal fat of a normal subject and obtained an average iodine value of 68.4. Similar analyses of fat from two stout women yielded an average iodine value of 71. The liver fat was freed from other lipids. In the normal individual, the iodine number was 127. Marked fatty change was visible in the livers of the obese women, but the iodine number of the fat was only 73. The average iodine number of normal muscle fat was 74.

Obesity. Obesity is usually the result of overnutrition, lack of exercise, or both. It is a matter of common observation, however, that certain individuals increase in weight despite an *apparently* moderate diet, while others remain thin in spite of all efforts to gain weight by overeating. Then there is the average individual who seems to make

---

[21] *Ibid.*, **102**, 57 (1933).

[21a] J. M. Hershey, and S. Soskin, *Am. J. Physiol.*, **98**, 74 (1931); C. H. Best and Hershey, *J. Physiol.*, **75**, 49 (1932); Best, Hershey and M. E. Huntsman, *ibid.*, **75**, 56 (1932); Best and Huntsman, *ibid.*, **75**, 405 (1932); Best and Ridout, *ibid.*, **78**, 415 (1933); Best, G. C. Ferguson and Hershey, *ibid.*, **79**, 94 (1933).

[22] *J. Physiol.*, **72**, 349 (1931); see also A. J. McAmis and W. E. Anderson, *Proc. Soc. Exp. Biol. Med.*, **28**, 749 (1930–31), and H. C. Eckstein, *J. Biol. Chem.*, **64**, 797 (1925).

no conscious attempt to control his diet but whose weight remains fairly constant over a period of many years.

Grafe[23] advanced the view that in normal individuals the intake of excessive amounts of food results in an increased metabolism, so that the extra energy is not stored and the weight is therefore maintained relatively constant. Accordingly he attributed obesity to the failure of this alleged metabolism-stimulating mechanism, whereas leanness he considered to be due to an over-response to a normal stimulus. A distinction was drawn by Grafe between so-called *exogenous obesity* and the *endogenous* or *constitutional* type, the former being due presumably to inactivity and overnutrition, whereas the latter he believed to be in some way associated with intrinsic factors such as endocrine derangement. Disease of the hypophysis, castration, the menopause, myxedema, and other physiological and pathological disturbances are usually, but not invariably, accompanied by the deposition of an abnormal amount of fat.

Grafe's so-called *Luxuskonsumption* hypothesis has been challenged by Wiley and Newburgh.[24] They overfed an unusually thin subject, but observed no increase in metabolism above that due to the specific dynamic action of the extra food (p. 521). Moreover, the subject gained weight rapidly. Newburgh is of the opinion that obesity is never directly caused by an abnormal metabolism, but that it is always due to food habits not adjusted to the metabolic requirement. Either more food is eaten than is normally needed, or the intake is not sufficiently reduced in response to a lowered requirement, from whatever cause.

Diabetes occurs not infrequently in obese individuals past middle age, and it has often been suggested that obesity may be regarded in many cases as a precursor and possibly even a cause of diabetes.[25]

Relation of Phospholipids to Fat Metabolism. The phospholipids have been associated with two important physiological functions, one related to their occurrence as essential components of the cell, and particularly of the cell membrane, the other related to intermediary fat metabolism. Loew[26] was probably the first to suggest that lecithin served as a conveying mechanism in the interchange of fat in the body,

[23] E. Grafe and D. Graham, *Z. physiol. Chem.*, **73**, 1 (1911); Grafe, *Ergebnisse Physiol.*, **21**, part 2, 197, 282 (1923).

[24] *J. Clin. Investigation*, **10**, 733 (1931); L. H. Newburgh and M. W. Johnston, *ibid.*, **8**, 197 (1929–30).

[25] The student is referred to the editorial entitled "Obesity and Diabetes," *J. Am. Med. Assoc.*, **95**, 202 (1930); see also S. F. Adams, *J. Nutrition*, **1**, 339 (1929); E. P. Joslin, New England, *J. Med.*, **209**, 519 (1933).

[26] O. Loew, *Biol. Zentr.*, **11**, 269 (1891).

a view which received much support from the later observation of Bloor[27] that the phospholipid concentration increased markedly during alimentary lipemia. With the demonstration that cholesterol esters likewise increased during fat absorption, the formation of these esters has also been accepted as a possible mechanism in the transportation of fatty acids.

It has been shown repeatedly, in feeding experiments with various fats, that as a result of fat absorption, the fatty acids of the liver always have a higher iodine number than the fatty acids of the ingested fat. Particularly does this affect the phospholipid fraction, which though usually unchanged in percentage is altered chemically by becoming more unsaturated. This occurs even on feeding so unsaturated a fat as cod-liver oil. After absorption, the iodine number of the liver phospholipid is higher than that of the cod-liver oil and much higher than that of the liver phospholipid, in the fasting state.

Such facts have led to the view, first advanced by Leathes,[28] that the liver participates in fat metabolism, its function being that of converting the fatty acids (in the form of phospholipids, etc.) which it absorbs into more highly unsaturated fatty acids, by a process of dehydrogenation. It may be supposed that the fats are thus rendered more useful to other tissues because the ease with which fatty acid chains are broken up and oxidized is presumably determined by the number of double linkages.

Storage or depot fat, which is relatively resistant to oxidation, consists almost entirely of the triglycerides of fatty acids, only a small proportion of which are highly unsaturated. The amount of phospholipid is small and the iodine number varies between 60 and 70, being usually about 65.[29] In contrast to this is the composition of the lipids present in the liver. Bloor,[30] who has made a detailed study of the tissues of the beef, gives 87 for the average iodine number of the mixed fatty acids of the fat (acetone-soluble) fraction of the liver. The mixed fatty acids of the kephalin and lecithin fractions have higher iodine numbers, these being 119 and 108, respectively. Somewhat higher values are given by Theis,[31] whose results show a constant

[27] W. R. Bloor, *J. Biol. Chem.*, **24**, 447 (1916).

[28] J. B. Leathes and L. Meyer-Wedell, *J. Physiol.*, **38**, xxxviii (1909); E. L. Kennaway and Leathes, *Proc. Roy. Soc. Med., Pathol. Sect.*, **2**, 136 (1909); Leathes and H. S. Raper, "The Fats," London, 1925.

[29] H. C. Eckstein, *J. Biol. Chem.*, **64**, 797 (1925).

[30] *Ibid.*, **56**, 711 (1923); **59**, 543 (1924); **68**, 33 (1926); **72**, 327 (1927); **80**, 443 (1928).

[31] *Ibid.*, **76**, 107 (1928); **77**, 75 (1928); **82**, 327 (1929).

relation of phospholipid to neutral fat in the liver, as indicated by the following figures:

	Phospholipid, Per Cent	Neutral Fat, Per Cent
Beef liver.................	55	45
Rabbit liver..............	55–65	35–45
Human liver..............	60	40

However, if the liver is damaged or diseased, this relation is altered; the proportion of phospholipid is greatly diminished apparently because of failure to convert neutral fat to phospholipid. In liver injury the desaturation of the fatty acids is not carried as far as normally, for according to the data given by Theis the iodine number of the various lipid fractions is markedly diminished.

The difference in the degree of unsaturation of the liver and depot lipids is not due solely to the predominance of the phospholipid fraction in the former. Bloor and Snider[32] have shown that the neutral fat of the liver is itself relatively unsaturated, having a higher iodine number than the fat of the depots, or of any other organ examined (heart, kidney, lung). Although this finding is in harmony with Leathes' conception of the liver as a desaturating organ, Bloor[33] has nevertheless emphasized the possibility, recently, in view of the direct absorption of fat into the portal system (p. 345), that changes in the degree of unsaturation of the liver lipids may be due to the removal, by the liver, from the portal blood which reaches it, of those fatty acids of a very high iodine number.[34]

Diet is an important factor influencing the composition of phospholipids in animal tissues. Thus, Sinclair,[35] in feeding experiments on cats, compared the effect of an exclusive diet of either beef kidney or beef muscle.[36] As regards the phospholipid content in the various

[32] *Ibid.*, **87**, 399 (1930).

[33] *Ann. Rev. Biochem.*, **1**, 272 (1933).

[34] A similar objection to Leathes' hypothesis was voiced by some of the earlier students of the subject. To answer it, Raper fed cats coconut oil, a very unsaturated fat (iodine number of about 8) containing a high percentage of volatile fatty acids. Raper recovered from the liver volatile fatty acids which were more unsaturated than those contained in the coconut oil.

[35] *J. Biol. Chem.*, **86**, 579 (1930).

[36] The iodine number of beef kidney phospholipid is about 98 and of beef muscle phospholipid 82. Beef kidney contains about 7 times as much phospholipid as beef muscle.

tissues no difference was observed except in the liver, more phospholipid being present in the livers of the animals on the kidney diet than in the livers of those maintained on the muscle diet. However, with the exception of the brain there was a marked difference in the degree of unsaturation of the phospholipids of the various tissues in the two groups, as shown by the following data[37] for the iodine number:

	Beef Kidney	Beef Muscle
Brain..................	105 ± 2.4	100 ± 1.8
Liver..................	145 ± 2.5	124 ± 8
Kidney................	112 ± 1.9	95 ± 3.8
Heart..................	140 ± 3.6	121 ± 3.2
Striated muscle.........	131 ± 6.3	108 ± 2.7

In a comparison of the composition (iodine number) of the phospholipids and neutral fats in the tissues of rats maintained on various diets, Sinclair[38] found the most saturated phospholipids (iodine number of about 100) in rats kept on a fat-free or fat-poor diet. The most unsaturated phospholipids were observed in animals receiving cod liver oil. But it seemed that any fat, including coconut oil, produced more unsaturated phospholipids than those synthesized on the "fat-free" diet. There was a rough parallelism between the iodine number of the neutral fat stored by the animal and that of the food fat, but no such relation was demonstrable for the tissue phospholipids.

Growth is another important factor, according to Sinclair.[39] It appears from his studies on rats that the phospholipid content, in relation to the tissue solids, decreases rapidly after birth, the period of most rapid decline coinciding with the period of most rapid growth.[40]

Activity. In comparing various muscles of the beef, Bloor found that the more active the muscle, the higher its per cent content of phospholipid and unsaponifiable substance. A similar relation can be made out for different organs (kidney, pancreas, lung, brain), for according to Bloor, the arrangement of the organs in the order of their phospholipid

[37]Compare with E. F. Terroine, and P. Belin, *Bull. soc. chim. biol.*, **9**, 12 (1927); Terroine and C. Hatterer, *ibid.*, **12**, 674 (1930).

[38] *J. Biol. Chem.*, **92**, 245 (1931).

[39] *Ibid.*, **88**, 575 (1930).

[40] On the contrary, Monaghan (*ibid.*, **98**, 21 [1932]) found that there is a constant value for the phospholipid fatty acids in a given tissue of rats which are growing normally on an adequate diet. However, any type of dietary deficiency associated with a falling off in the rate of growth is also accompanied by a decrease of the phospholipid fatty acid content of the tissues.

content gives a series which represents also the order of their functional activity.

In the corpus luteum of the pig the phospholipid content was about three times as great during its active state in ovulation and pregnancy as in the resting state. Mammary glands (rabbit) at the end of pregnancy had twice the phospholipid content of the resting glands. Malignant tumors had about three times the content of phospholipid and twice the amount of cholesterol as benign tumors.[41]

Metabolic Significance. The question of the metabolic significance of the phospholipids has been reopened recently by Sinclair.[42] He observed that if rats, previously kept on a fat-poor diet, are fed cod-liver oil, the degree of unsaturation of the constituent fatty acids of the phospholipids in the liver and muscle is markedly increased. The change is rapid, particularly in the liver, where the replacement of the more saturated by the more unsaturated fatty acids is essentially complete within three days. The rate of turnover in the rest of the carcass is slower, only about 50 per cent replacement occurring in the same period. Moreover, the rate of turnover is not increased by reducing the temperature of the environment, as might be expected from the fact that metabolism is intensified at low temperatures. In contrast to the rapid rate with which the degree of unsaturation was increased from a lower to a higher level, the reverse process, namely the decrease from a high level of unsaturation to a low level, was found to be very slow.[43] This was attempted by fasting or by changing to a fat-free diet or to one containing coconut oil.

It seems therefore that the tissue phospholipids have a marked tendency to attain, and having once attained to maintain, a high degree of unsaturation.

From such observations, Sinclair has been led to conclude: (1) that the phospholipids in muscle, in liver, and presumably in other tissues as well should no longer be regarded as intermediary products in the metabolism of fat; (2) that food fat may exert an influence on the

---

[41] W. R. Bloor, *Proc. Soc. Exp. Biol. Med.*, **27**, 294 (1929–30).

[42] *J. Biol. Chem.*, **95**, 393 (1932); **100**, lxxxvii (1933).

[43] This effect seems to be independent of the amount of cod-liver oil fed. Indeed, if either a fat-free or fat-poor diet is supplemented by one drop of cod-liver oil per day, it results in a marked increase in the iodine number of the phospholipids, particularly in the liver, where it almost attains the maximum value. These small fat supplements do not, however, influence the degree of unsaturation of the neutral fat. Now, it has been observed that, on a fat-free diet, growth is retarded. Sinclair accordingly raises the question of a possible causal relationship between the low degree of unsaturation of the tissue phospholipids and the subnormal growth of rats on a fat-free diet (*J. Biol. Chem.*, **96**, 103 [1932]).

degree of unsaturation of the tissue phospholipids which is quite apart from that which may be due to the utilization of food fat for the repair of " wear and tear " of the tissues.

Sinclair's view is a radical departure from the conception developed by Leathes, which has been so generally accepted during the last twenty years. To summarize: according to this conception, the fatty acids of depot or ingested fat are built up into phospholipids and desaturated in the liver, whence they are carried by the blood to the muscle and other tissues and organs of the body for utilization either in providing energy or for tissue repair. This formulation of the initial stages of fat metabolism has been useful as a starting-point in the consideration of the subsequent stages in the combustion of the fatty acids.

The evidence for either view is essentially inferential, and it will require a comprehensive re-examination of the problem before a clear statement of the significance of the phospholipids will be possible. Until adequate information is available, final judgment is necessarily reserved.

Oxidation of Fatty Acids. Normally, the fatty acids are completely oxidized to carbon dioxide and water. Of the intermediate steps in the process, little was known until Knoop[44] published the results of his investigations in 1904. Earlier attempts had been made to trace the fate of fatty acids in metabolism, by feeding the lower members to animals and then examining the urine for end-products. These experiments were unsuccessful because the fatty acids were either completely oxidized or partly excreted unchanged. Knoop, however, conceived the idea of feeding phenyl derivatives of the lower fatty acids.

Benzoic acid is not oxidized in the body, and when fed, is excreted in the urine in combination, partly with glycine as hippuric acid. The reaction is represented by the following equation:

$$C_6H_5 \cdot COOH + CH_2NH_2 \cdot COOH = C_6H_5CONHCH_2COOH + H_2O$$

Phenylacetic acid is likewise resistant to oxidation and is detoxified to form phenaceturic acid, in which form it is excreted. In man, according to Thierfelder and Sherwin,[45] phenylacetic acid is conjugated to form phenacetyl-glutamine. The formation of phenaceturic acid may be written:

$$C_6H_5CH_2COOH + CH_2NH_2 \cdot COOH$$
$$= C_6H_5CH_2CO \cdot NH \cdot CH_2COOH + H_2O$$

[44] *Beitr. chem. Physiol. Path.*, **6**, 150 (1904).
[45] *Ber.*, **47**, 2630 (1914).

However, on feeding phenylpropionic acid, Knoop found hippuric acid in the urine, showing that two carbon atoms of the side chain had been removed by oxidation. Phenylbutyric acid yielded phenaceturic acid, and phenylvaleric acid gave rise in the body to benzoic acid, which was in turn converted into hippuric acid and excreted. Knoop therefore concluded that the oxidation of a fatty-acid chain occurs at the β-carbon atom. The oxidation of phenylvaleric acid may be represented as follows:

Phenylvaleric acid · Phenylpropionic acid · Benzoic acid

Other evidence is available in support of Knoop's hypothesis of β-oxidation. In diabetes, the oxidation of fat is incomplete, with the result that products of incomplete oxidation are found in the urine. These are β-hydroxybutyric acid and acetoacetic acid. In normal metabolism, these are further oxidized to carbon dioxide and water; but in diabetes, or more correctly, in disturbed of glucose metabolism, they are partly converted into acetone, the remainder being excreted unchanged. Collectively, they are called the "acetone bodies." A better term would be "acetone substances" or "acetone compounds." Both hydroxybutyric and acetoacetic acids are excreted partly as salts. This accounts for the loss of fixed base from the body when these substances are formed in metabolism. The prevailing opinion is that the formation of acetone bodies cannot be explained otherwise than by assuming that the long-chain fatty acids, of an even number of carbon atoms, are oxidized successively at the β-carbon atom.

Ringer[46] has shown that, when propionic acid is given to phlorhizinized dogs, it is completely converted into glucose. When valeric acid is given, oxidation apparently occurs at the β-carbon atom, yielding two fragments, one of which is propionic acid. This in turn is converted

[46] *J. Biol. Chem.*, **12**, 511 (1912): **14**, 43 (1913).

into glucose, so that three-fifths of the carbon of valeric acid may be accounted for in the extra sugar of the urine.

Further evidence in support of Knoop's theory is to be found in the work of Dakin, who, after administering phenylpropionic acid, isolated in the urine not only hippuric acid but also a number of other substances, including β-phenyl-β-hydroxypropionic acid, benzoylacetic acid, and acetophenone, these being obviously intermediate products of the oxidation of phenylpropionic acid and analogous to the acetone bodies. Dakin[47] extended his studies to phenyl derivatives of other fatty acids and obtained results pointing, likewise, to oxidation at the β-carbon atom. No less important are his experiments *in vitro*, in which he treated ammonium salts of fatty acids with hydrogen peroxide and found that oxidation occurred at the β-carbon atom, with the partial formation of ketones having one carbon atom less than the original acids.

Knoop's theory, while it postulates the removal of successive pairs of carbon atoms, does not throw any light on the mechanism by which it is accomplished. In a more recent study Dakin[48] perfused a surviving liver with caproic acid ($CH_3 \cdot CH_2 \cdot CH_2 \cdot CH_2 \cdot CH_2 \cdot COOH$) as well as with the following derivatives: $\alpha\beta$-hexenic acid ($CH_3 \cdot CH_2 \cdot CH_2 \cdot CH{=}CH \cdot COOH$), β-hydroxycaproic acid ($CH_3 \cdot CH_2 \cdot CH_2 \cdot CHOH \cdot CH_2 \cdot COOH$), and β-ketocaproic (butyrylacetic) acid ($CH_3 \cdot CH_2 \cdot CH_2 \cdot CO \cdot CH_2 \cdot COOH$).

The results with caproic acid showed a pronounced formation of acetoacetic acid and β-hydroxybutyric acid, but the intermediate formation of β-hydroxycaproic acid could not be definitely established.

Perfusion with $\alpha\beta$-hexenic acid resulted in the formation of acetoacetic acid and probably β-hydroxybutyric acid. There were also indications for the intermediate formation of some β-hydroxycaproic acid, but not of β-ketocaproic acid.

Perfusion with β-hydroxycaproic acid gave rise to both acetoacetic acid and β-hydroxybutyric acid, with indications of the possible intermediate formation of β-ketocaproic acid.

Perfusion with β-ketocaproic acid resulted in the production of considerable amounts of acetoacetic and β-hydroxybutyric acids, with indications of the reduction of the β-ketocaproic acid to β-hydroxycaproic acid.

Dakin states that no definite answer can be given to the question whether an unsaturated, β-hydroxy, or β-ketonic acid is formed first in the oxidation of caproic acid. He suggests the probability that all these

[47] *Ibid.*, **4**, 77, 227, 419 (1908); **5**, 173, 303 (1908); **6**, 203, 221 (1909).
[48] *Ibid.*, **56**, 43 (1923).

acids are in a readily shifting equilibrium with one another and are easily interconvertible.

Quick[49] has made a careful study of the metabolism of the phenyl derivatives of the fatty acids and his results also support the theory of β-oxidation. He finds, however, that the benzoic acid formed from phenylpropionic acid in the dog is not excreted solely in combination with glycine. In fact, a much larger proportion is conjugated with glycuronic acid, the ratio in the dog being about 3 : 1. Similarly phenylacetic acid, irrespective of its source in metabolism, combines with glycuronic acid and glycine in the ratio of 1 : 2. Quick does not regard the intermediate formation of hydroxy compounds as a likely step in the oxidation of fatty acids. For example, the administration of phenyl-β-hydroxypropionic acid results in the excretion of about 75 per cent, unchanged.

We cannot be certain, therefore, that the oxidation of butyric acid occurs by way of β-hydroxybutyric acid, acetoacetic acid, and acetic acid, in the order named. When either butyric acid or β-hydroxybutyric acid is administered to diabetic animals, acetoacetic acid is formed. Yet there is equally valid evidence that the reverse transformation, namely, that of acetoacetic acid to β-hydroxybutyric acid, may occur. This question may also be considered in the light of Wieland's theory of oxidation. We may assume dehydrogenation to be the first step in the oxidation of butyric acid, and hydration the second step. The third step is again dehydrogenation. The acetoacetic acid thus formed may then react with water to yield two molecules of acetic acid. Another possible decomposition is suggested by the work of Dakin, who treated sodium acetoacetate with hydrogen peroxide at room temperature and obtained acetic, glyoxylic, and formic acids and carbon dioxide. The reactions may be represented as follows:

$$
\begin{array}{ccc}
CH_3 & CH_3 & \\
| & | & \\
CO & COOH & \\
| & \rightarrow & \\
CH_2 & CHO & \\
| & | & \rightarrow H \cdot COOH + CO_2 \\
COOH & COOH &
\end{array}
$$

There is perhaps a somewhat greater amount of evidence that either the unsaturated acids or the β-ketonic acids, rather than the β-hydroxy acids, are the initial products of the oxidation of fatty acids. Nevertheless, the following diagram (after Dakin)[50] is a fairly accurate representa-

[49] Ibid., 77, 581; 80, 515, 527, 535 (1928); 98, 537 (1932).

[50] H. D. Dakin, "Oxidations and Reductions in the Animal Body," Longmans, Green & Co., 1922 edition, p. 42.

tion of our present knowledge of the relations that have been considered thus far:

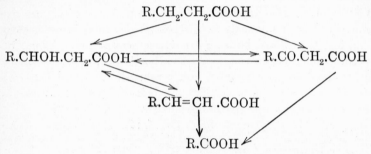

From the foregoing evidence it would appear that β-oxidation is the predominant reaction of fatty acids in metabolism. The question, however, has been raised whether this is the only mode of oxidation. Clutterbuck and Raper[51] treated the ammonium salts of various fatty acids, from caproic to stearic, with hydrogen peroxide and obtained evidence of oxidation occurring at the α- and δ-carbon atoms. In a later study, Raper and Wayne[52] administered normal phenylpropionic, phenylbutyric, phenylvaleric, and phenylcaproic acids to dogs, and the results of their analyses showed that the fatty-acid side chains were oxidized in accordance with the theory of β-oxidation. Under the same conditions, phenylnonoic (9 carbon atoms in the side chain) and phenyldecoic (10 carbon atoms in side chain) acids yielded smaller amounts of benzoic acid and phenylacetic acid, respectively, than would be expected if there were quantitative β-oxidation of the side chain. They suggested therefore, that in addition to β-oxidation, some other mode of oxidation takes place.

Data presented by Smedley-Maclean and Pearce[53] lend weight to this suggestion. These investigators studied the oxidation of oleic acid by hydrogen peroxide in an alkaline solution. On the addition of a small amount of a cupric salt as a catalyst, oxidation was definitely increased. There was, moreover, a partial replacement of β-oxidation by oxidation in the γ- and δ-positions. A considerable amount of succinic acid was present among the products of oxidation.

The shifting of double bonds is not an unfamiliar phenomenon. Quick[54] has shown that phenylisocrotonic acid, $C_6H_5 \cdot CH{=}CH \cdot CH_2 \cdot COOH$, is handled by the organism exactly like phenylbutyric acid. Although the double bond is between the β- and γ-carbon atoms, the split occurs between the α- and β-positions. This observation is signifi-

[51] Biochem. J., 19, 385 (1925).   [53] Ibid., 25, 1252 (1931).
[52] Ibid., 22, 188 (1928).   [54] J. Biol. Chem., 77, 581 (1928).

cant in showing that the oxidation does not necessarily occur at the point of unsaturation.

Witzemann[55] has investigated the oxidation by potassium permanganate of the sodium salts of a series of α-hydroxy-straight-chain-fatty acids. It has been known for a long time that α-hydroxybutyric acid is partly oxidized with the loss of 1 carbon atom and partly with the loss of 2 carbon atoms. This has been confirmed by Witzemann, who found, moreover, that the two types of breakdown occur almost equally. These may be summarized as follows:

A. $CH_3CH_2CHOHCOOH + O_2 \rightarrow CH_3CH_2COOH + CO_2 + H_2O$

B. $CH_3CH_2CHOHCOOH + 5O \rightarrow CH_3COOH + 2CO_2 + 2H_2O$

It is pointed out that α-hydroxybutyric acid occupies a pivotal position between lactic acid (α-hydroxy-propionic acid) which is oxidized exclusively by the loss of 1 carbon atom, and the higher α-hydroxy homologues, in which the loss of 2 carbon atoms at a time occurs readily. Particularly remarkable is the fact that, in the presence of an excess of alkali (1 molecule of alkali per molecule of the sodium salt of the fatty acid), the point of rupture of the fatty-acid chain shifts from a loss of 1 carbon atom largely to a loss of 2 carbon atoms at a time. This result was obtained even with lactic acid. According to Witzemann, the loss of 1 carbon atom is due to the oxidation of the α-keto acid, while the loss of 2 carbons follows the oxidation of its enol isomer. This may be represented by the following formulas:

$$
\begin{array}{ccc}
 & & R \\
 & & | \\
 & & CH_2 \\
 & & | \\
R & & C{=}O \\
| & \nearrow & \cdots | \cdots \\
CH_2 & & COOH \\
| & & \\
CHOH & & \\
| & & R \\
COOH & & | \\
 & \searrow & CH \\
 & & \cdots , \cdots \| \cdots \\
 & & C{-}OH \\
 & & | \\
 & & COOH \\
\end{array}
$$

In short, the work of Witzemann indicates that the exclusion of α-oxidation in fat metabolism is not necessarily justified, inasmuch as α-hydroxy-fatty acids may lose more than one carbon atom on oxidation.

[55] *J. Biol. Chem.*, **95**, 219, 247 (1932).

Ketogenesis. Reference has been made to the formation of acetone bodies (*ketogenesis* or *ketosis*) and their excretion in the urine (*ketonuria* or *acetonuria*) in conditions of faulty fat metabolism. Small amounts of these substances appear normally in the urine, particularly acetone, which may be regarded as the product of a side reaction.[56] It has its origin in acetoacetic acid as represented by the following equation:

$$
\begin{array}{ccc}
CH_3 & & CH_3 \\
| & & | \\
C{=}O & & C{=}O \\
| & \rightarrow & | \\
CH_2 & & CH_3 \\
| & & + \\
COOH & & CO_2
\end{array}
$$

Ketosis occurs in diabetes,[57] in starvation, during the early stages of phosphorus poisoning, during anesthesia, in children during infections, and in other conditions. Acetone bodies increase in the blood and are not only excreted in the urine but appear on the breath as well. When the problem of ketogenesis is examined carefully, it becomes obvious at once that the complete oxidation of fatty acids is in some way dependent on carbohydrate metabolism. In diabetes, the failure to oxidize the fatty acids completely can be related directly to faulty carbohydrate metabolism. When carbohydrate utilization is improved, as by the administration of insulin, the formation of acetone bodies ceases. Similarly, during fasting, as long as glycogen is present, fat metabolism is essentially normal; but just as soon as the reserve carbohydrate is depleted and the starving animal has only fat and protein to draw on for its metabolic needs, the products of incomplete fatty-acid oxidation appear. This does not continue indefinitely, however, for a point may be reached in starvation when, perhaps as a result of some metabolic adjustment, the process of utilizing fat becomes more efficient. The interrelationship between carbohydrate and fat metabolism is

---

[56] For a quantitative study of ketone-body excretion in normal individuals the reader is referred to J. A. Behre (*J. Biol. Chem.*, **92**, 679 [1931]). In 12 subjects, the daily excretion of total acetone bodies (calculated as acetone) varied from 14.5 to 23.5 mg. (average 19.4 mg.), of which 12.2 to 20.5 mg. (average 16.2 mg.) was present as β-hydroxybutyric acid. The maximum excretion during the day occurred in the afternoon or evening and was to a certain extent correlated with an increased urinary volume. Even so short a period of fasting as 6 to 12 hours was accompanied by a small, though unmistakable, rise in the excretion of ketone bodies.

[57] In severe diabetes the daily excretion of acetone bodies may exceed 50 grams. See: G. Lusk, "The Science of Nutrition," 4th edition, 1928, p. 677; P. A. Shaffer, "Antiketogenesis," Harvey Lecture, 1922–23, p. 105.

indicated by the oft-repeated aphorism, "fats burn in the flame of carbohydrates," and by the following statement of Macleod:

If the carbohydrate fires do not burn briskly enough, the fat is incompletely consumed; it smokes, as it were, and the smoke is represented in metabolism by the ketones and derived acids.

In addition to the fatty acids certain of the amino acids constitute another potential source of acetone bodies. In conditions of carbohydrate deprivation or in severe diabetes, these substances are ketogenic (that is, give rise to ketones), as we shall see when we study their metabolism in the next chapter.[58]

Anti-ketogenesis. In 1921, Shaffer[59] described certain experiments in which he demonstrated that the velocity of oxidation of acetoacetic acid by hydrogen peroxide in an alkaline solution is greatly accelerated in the presence of glucose. The accelerating effect of glucose, thus demonstrated *in vitro*, was accepted as analogous to the well-known fact that, in the body, the oxidation of glucose facilitates the oxidation of fatty acids. This effect, according to Shaffer, may perhaps be explained by assuming the formation of a highly oxidizable compound from acetoacetic acid and some intermediate product of glucose metabolism.[60]

Shaffer's results show that the oxidation of acetoacetic acid occurs only when there is oxidized simultaneously 1 molecule of glucose for each 2 molecules of the acid. The inference is that 2 molecules of acetoacetic acid react with 1 molecule of glucose. It is assumed that 1 fatty-acid molecule gives rise to 1 molecule of acetoacetic acid, and that therefore, in the body, the metabolism of 1 glucose molecule insures the complete oxidation of 2 molecules of fatty acid. Glucose may be replaced by other anti-ketogenic substances. For example, the anti-ketogenic value of one glycerol molecule is one-half of that of a glucose molecule; from this it follows that a molecule of fat, to burn completely, requires but 1 molecule of glucose. The latter takes

---

[58] The liver is believed to be the chief site of the formation of acetone bodies. In part this may be due to this organ's large energy requirement, which is probably satisfied by fat in the diabetic organism and by fat and glucose in the normal individual. The observations of Goldfarb and Himwich indicate that no fat is oxidized by the cerebral cortex, nor does this tissue remove acetone bodies from the blood, as does the testicle, which apparently oxidizes fat quite readily. See H. E. Himwich, W. Goldfarb, and A. Weller, *J. Biol. Chem.*, **93**, 337 (1931); Goldfarb and Himwich, *ibid.*, **101**, 441 (1933).

[59] *J. Biol. Chem.*, **47**, 433 (1921).

[60] P. A. Shaffer and T. E. Friedemann, *ibid.*, **61**, 585 (1924); Friedemann, *ibid.*, **63**, p. xxi (1925); E. S. West, *ibid.*, **66**, 63 (1925); **74**, p. xlii (1927); see also Hynd, *Proc. Roy. Soc. (London), B*, **101**, 244 (1927).

care of two fatty acids, while the glycerol makes possible the oxidation of the third fatty acid. Although in the body the anti-ketogenic or ketolytic value of 1 molecule of glycerol or glyceric aldehyde appears to be equivalent to one-half that of glucose, the behavior *in vitro* is such as to indicate that the ketolytic value of glycerol, glyceric aldehyde, glycol aldehyde, and glyoxal is the same as that of glucose; that is, *in vitro*, a single molecule of any one of these substances will make possible the oxidation of 2 molecules of acetoacetic acid.

The Ketogenic: Anti-ketogenic Balance in Man. The problem was further extended by Shaffer[61] to the consideration of the relations involved in the ketogenic: anti-ketogenic balance in man. The substances that may give rise to acetone bodies in metabolism are the fatty acids and certain of the amino acids (leucine, phenylalanine, tyrosine, probably histidine, and possibly others). The substances that have the opposite effect, i.e., the anti-ketogenic substances, are the carbohydrates, the sugar-forming amino acids, and glycerol.

Considering first the ketogenic factors, it has been estimated that 1 gram of fat (average molecular weight taken as 874) corresponds to 3.43 millimols of ketogenic material.[62] This is based on the assumption that each molecule of fatty acid gives rise to 1 molecule of acetoacetic acid. Shaffer has estimated the ketogenic equivalent of 1 gram of urinary nitrogen (this represents the metabolism of 6.25 grams of protein) to be 15 millimols. Accordingly, 1 gram of protein may be expected to yield 2.4 millimols of acetoacetic acid.

Of the anti-ketogenic substances, the carbohydrates are most important. One gram of glucose is equal to 5.56 millimols. For other carbohydrates, it is necessary to calculate first the glucose equivalent. The glucose equivalent of 1 gram of urinary nitrogen (representing the metabolism of 6.25 grams of protein) is 3.6 grams, corresponding to 20 millimols. Accordingly, 1 gram of protein is equivalent to 3.2 anti-ketogenic milli-equivalents of glucose. One gram of fat contains 1.14 millimols of glycerol ($1/874 \times 1000$). Since 2 molecules of glycerol are equivalent to 1 molecule of glucose, it follows that the glucose equivalent of 1 gram of fat is 0.57 millimol.

These values are necessary in the calculation of the ketogenic : anti-ketogenic ratio, R.

$$R = \frac{2.4P + 3.43F}{3.2P + 0.57F + 5.56G}$$

[61] *J. Biol. Chem.*, **47**, 449 (1921); **49**, 143 (1921); **54**, 399 (1922).

[62] $\dfrac{3 \times 1000}{874} = 3.43.$

In this equation, P is the grams of protein metabolized; F, the grams of fat; G, the grams of glucose. The quantities of these substances burned may be determined either by direct or indirect calorimetry (Chapter XVI). The ratio may also be calculated by substituting, for P, F, and G, the quantities of protein, fat, and carbohydrate, respectively, which are fed. Obviously, this would give, at best, only a rough approximation, owing to the difference between the food fed and the food metabolized. Nevertheless such calculations have been found practically useful in planning dietaries, with the object of either avoiding ketosis, as in the treatment of diabetes, or of producing it, as in the treatment of epilepsy, in which condition beneficial results have been obtained from a keto-genic diet.

In a clinical study of the problem, Woodyatt[63] found that for the complete oxidation of 1.5 grams of fatty acid, 1 gram of glucose must be utilized. The fatty acid : glucose ratio (FA/G), according to Woodyatt, is therefore 1.5. On a molecular basis, this ratio signifies that 1 mole-cule of glucose is anti-ketogenic or ketolytic for 1 molecule of fatty acid. Woodyatt considered this ratio the threshold for ketosis which, when exceeded, would result in acetonuria. Although this observation has been confirmed by others, a close study of the problem has disclosed that between FA/G ratios (on a molecular basis) of 1 : 1 and 2 : 1 relatively small amounts of acetone are produced. It is only when the 2 : 1 ratio is exceeded that the production of ketone bodies is significant and in general it then corresponds to the excess of fatty acids. This is a remark-able confirmation of Shaffer's theory, based originally on *in vitro* experi-ments, that the combustion of 1 molecule of glucose permits the simul-taneous oxidation of 2 molecules of fatty acid.

Individual variations in susceptibility to ketosis occur. McClellan and associates[63a] have observed in the case of an obese individual that the threshold for ketosis was definitely above normal (about 1 : 2.4). This observation has been interpreted as indicative of a greater efficiency in the utilization of fats than in normal men. Perhaps the Eskimos are also better able to utilize fat, as suggested by Heinbecker,[64] who showed that Eskimos excrete but very small amounts of acetone bodies during starvation.[65]

---

[63] *Arch. Internal Med.*, **28**, 125 (1921).

[63a] *J. Biol. Chem.*, **80**, 639 (1928).

[64] *Ibid.*, **80**, 461 (1928); **93**, 327 (1931).

[65] Deuel and Gulick (*J. Biol. Chem.*, **96**, 25 [1932]) have made the remarkable observation in human subjects that women develop a much greater ketosis than males during fasting. They suggest that this may be due to either a greater glycogen store in the male or a more economical utilization of the glycogen during the early days

The interdependence of fat and carbohydrate metabolism shows fundamental differences in different animals. In primates the relation is in agreement with Shaffer's theory. The cat and dog, on the contrary, have a high tolerance for ketones, do not develop a starvation ketosis, and dispose of large amounts of acetoacetic acid administered intravenously.

Ketogenesis and Acid-base Balance. The relation of acetone bodies to the acid-base balance of the blood has already been referred to. The acetone bodies are excreted partly in combination with fixed base and partly in combination with ammonia. This accounts both for the depletion of the alkali reserve of the body and for the increased excretion of ammonia in the urine.

The most pronounced manifestations of ketosis are observed in severe diabetes. Values in excess of 300 mg. of acetone bodies per 100 cc. of blood and daily urinary excretions of acetone bodies of 50 grams, or more, have been encountered not infrequently. The acidosis is correspondingly severe. An individual in diabetic coma may have a CO_2-combining power of 15 volumes per cent or even less. Both the ketosis and acidosis may be relieved by insulin, or by insulin and glucose, the response being remarkably rapid.

Acidosis accompanies ketosis in starvation. However, neither is very pronounced in male adults; but in women and particularly in children these manifestations may be severe. In carbohydrate deprivation, if the ketogenic : anti-ketogenic ratio exceeds 2 : 1, ketosis and acidosis develop. The greater tendency of pregnant women to develop ketosis as a result of carbohydrate deprivation has been associated with a lowered glycogen content of the liver.

The ketosis which results from vomiting is essentially of the same type as that occurring in starvation, being due to food deprivation. Accordingly, it is usually most pronounced in children. The formation and excretion of acetone bodies tend to produce acidosis by diminishing the alkali reserve. However, as has been stated elsewhere, if large amounts of gastric contents are vomited, the loss of Cl^- and the corresponding bicarbonate excess tend to produce an alkalosis. In adults,

---

of the fast. From a control value of 0.02 gram of acetone bodies, the excretion rose in the male subjects to an average of 1.9 grams on the third day and 2.66 grams on the fourth day. In the females, the initial value was likewise 0.02 gram; it rose to 8.47 grams on the third day, and diminished somewhat on the fourth day to 6.56 grams. Accompanying these changes in the female was a marked acidosis; in one case the CO_2-combining power diminished from 53.6 on the first day to 26.9 volumes per cent on the fourth day of the fast. In a male subject, the change was much less; 52.1 to 46.6 volumes per cent.

the latter may outweigh the tendency to acidosis, so that it is not uncommon in such cases to find ketosis accompanied by an alkalosis. On the other hand, in children, and especially in infants, the onset of ketosis may be so rapid that it will be accompanied by acidosis. In the toxemias of pregnancy ketosis is very marked. Usually it is associated with acidosis, which may be of only moderate degree, owing to the opposing tendency toward alkalosis resulting from the loss of gastric contents.[66]

Cause of Ketogenesis. We may now turn to a brief consideration of the cause of ketogenesis. It is obvious, of course, that when carbohydrate is not available for metabolism, whether from an insufficient exogenous carbohydrate supply, a deficiency in endogenous reserve, or through the impairment or loss of the ability to oxidize glucose, the organism is forced to burn fat in much larger amounts than normally. The oxidation of fat under these altered conditions becomes the most prominent reaction of metabolism and, as Leathes has expressed it, there is a flooding of the "metabolic mill" with fat. This may conceivably result in the incomplete oxidation of the fat and the production of acetone bodies. There are many examples of chemical reactions in which the intermediate stages can be detected only when one part of a given reaction is exaggerated. For instance, in severe muscular exercise, the formation of lactic acid is more rapid than its removal (either by oxidation or resynthesis into glycogen). The result is that lactic acid accumulates in the blood and a certain amount of it escapes in the urine. Many circumstances suggest a close parallelism between this and ketogenesis, the latter probably being the result of a one-sided metabolism in which excessive amounts of fat are burned. According to this view, the anti-ketogenic effect of glucose would be due to its fat-sparing action.

Fat as a Source of Carbohydrate. The conversion of glycerol into glucose is well established. In the diabetic animal this conversion has been demonstrated by Chambers and Deuel,[67] who administered glycerol to a phlorhizinized dog and recovered 97 to 98 per cent as extra glucose in the urine.

While the conversion of carbohydrate into fatty acids is unquestioned, the reverse transformation of fatty acids into glucose and glycogen is one of the most controversial subjects in physiological chemistry. The opposing points of view have been presented by the late Professor

[66] An excellent summary of the clinical aspects of ketosis is to be found in J. P. Peters and D. D. Van Slyke, "Quantitative Clinical Chemistry," Vol. 1, pp. 485–509. A comprehensive bibliography is included.

[67] J. Biol. Chem., **65**, 21 (1925).

Lusk,[68] who catégorically denied the conversion of fat into glucose, and by Macleod,[69] who is perhaps the leading exponent of the concept that, under certain conditions, if not always, fatty acids serve as a source of carbohydrate. The liver has been discussed as the probable site of this conversion.[70]

The transformation of fatty acids into carbohydrate is believed to occur in the plant during germination. The formation of carbohydrate at the expense of fatty acids in the silkworm has also been described. Considering some of the more direct experimental work in mammals, reference may be made to the study of Chaikoff and Weber,[71] who injected repeated doses of epinephrin into depancreatized dogs and found an extra excretion of glucose in the urine, which they could not account for as being derived from either the glycogen store of the liver, glycerol, or tissue protein. According to these investigators, the epinephrin did not produce an increase in the lactic acid of the blood. This point has been disputed, however, by Cori and Cori,[72] and others, who have observed the formation of lactic acid under similar experimental conditions. It has therefore been contended that Chaikoff and Weber did not give due consideration to the muscle glycogen as the indirect source of the extra glucose.

In phlorhizinized dogs, Wertheimer[73] observed an increase in liver glycogen following insulin injection. The more fat contained in the liver, the more resistant did the animals seem to the development of insulin hypoglycemia and the more quickly did the sugar level return to normal. These observations Wertheimer interpreted as evidence for the transformation of fat to glucose and for the idea that insulin accelerates this reaction. These experiments have been repeated by Hawley,[74] whose results in no way indicated that conversion of fat into carbohydrate occurred under these conditions.

Soskin[75] fed depancreatized dogs fat and observed an extra excretion of glucose, the source of which could not be accounted for on the basis of the known precursors from the body. The gluconeogenesis was therefore attributed to fatty acids. This type of experiment has obvious physiological limitations, a fact not unrecognized by Soskin.

[68] "Science of Nutrition," 4th edition, Saunders, Philadelphia, 1928, pp. 209, 405, 639–643.

[69] "Carbohydrate Metabolism and Insulin," London, 1926, p. 130.

[70] H. Jost, Z. physiol. Chem., 197, 90 (1931).

[71] J. Biol. Chem., 76, 813 (1928).

[72] Ibid., 85, 275 (1929).

[73] Arch. ges. Physiol., 213, 298 (1926).

[74] Am. J. Physiol., 101, 185 (1932).

[75] Biochem. J., 23, 1385 (1929).

Low respiratory quotients, below 0.7, have been frequently reported for animals during hibernation. It is stated that during this period of winter sleep the glycogen does not disappear completely and that the nitrogen excretion is too low to make it seem probable that protein is the exclusive source of carbohydrate. The only remaining source of the carbohydrate would appear to be the fat reserves. Many of these observations have been criticized on the ground of the faulty methods employed in the determination of the respiratory quotient.

Rapport,[76] in his masterly review on the subject of the interconversion of the major foodstuffs, summarizes the data that have been offered in support of the fatty acid → carbohydrate transformation and concludes that "no convincing proof exists for the production of carbohydrate from fatty acids in the animal, and that on the contrary, the weight of evidence is at present against it." He nevertheless recognizes that the case cannot be considered as closed.

The Utilization of Fat in the Production of Energy. There can be no doubt of the utilization of fat by the animal body in the production of energy. The evidence for the utilization of fat by muscles is afforded by the experiments of Zuntz,[77] Benedict and Cathcart,[78] Krogh and Lindhard,[79] and others. If muscular work is accomplished at the expense of carbohydrates, the respiratory quotient is high, whereas if fats are burned, the quotient is low. Calorimetry will be considered later in greater detail; for the time being, it is sufficient to state that, by measuring the respiratory quotient of animals during muscular exercise, a fair idea may be had regarding the kind of material which is being burned. This is therefore one method of studying the problem in question.

The results of Zuntz and those of Benedict and Cathcart show that fats and carbohydrates are about equally well utilized in the production of muscular work. Krogh and Lindhard, on the contrary, were unable to account for about 11 per cent of the potential energy of fat. No satisfactory explanation has been offered to account for this discrepancy. Attempts have been made to correlate it with the transformation of fat to carbohydrate, the assumption being that fat, *per se*, is not utilized in muscular work, but only after its conversion into carbohydrate. This assumption is unwarranted on the basis of available experimental evidence.

[76] *Physiol. Rev.*, **10**, 349 (1930).

[77] N. Zuntz, "Die Quellen der Muskelkraft," "Oppenheimer's Handbuch Biochem.," **4**, Part I, 826 (1911).

[78] F. G. Benedict and E. P. Cathcart, "Muscular Work," Carnegie Inst. Publ. (1913).

[79] *Biochem. J.*, **14**, 290 (1920).

Blood leaving a working muscle contains less fat than the blood entering it (Lafon).[80] Himwich[81] found a similar relation on comparing the venous and arterial blood of the lower extremity in phlorhizinized or depancreatized dogs. These observations taken in conjunction with the data that have been obtained in determinations of the gaseous exchange of muscle *in situ*[82] and *ex situ*[83] add materially to the chain of evidence that fat oxidation occurs in muscle.

Further Observations on the Interchange of Fat in the Animal Body. *Muscular exercise* produces in fasting individuals an increase in the blood lipids, confined largely to the glyceride fraction, suggesting a mobilization of this source of energy from the adipose tissue in response to the demands of the working muscles.[84] In a recent study by Stewart[85] normal men performed muscular work on an ergometer bicycle at rates varying from about 800 to 1200 kg-m. per minute. The blood fat usually rose after about 8000 kg-m. of work had been done. With greater rates of work the increase in blood fat occurred earlier. Continuance of muscular exercise led in time to a return of the blood fat toward normal and later to a second rise. After recovery from a first period of work, a second period produced a rise in the blood fat more easily than usual. When the initial blood fat was abnormally high, as was the case in some of the diabetic, as well as normal, subjects, work produced a preliminary fall. On the other hand, in individuals with an abnormally low fasting blood fat, the response was more conspicuous than otherwise and occurred even as a result of relatively light muscular exertion. The increase in blood fat could be abolished by the administration of 100 grams of glucose *per os* prior to the muscular exertion.

The following data illustrate the effect of muscular exercise:

Subject	Work Kg.-m.	Blood Sample	Fat mg. per 100 cc.	Cholesterol mg. per 100 cc.	Lipid P. mg. per 100 cc.
REI..........	33,000	Before work	511	118	18.8
		After work	674	118	16.5
		After partial recovery	467	.....	19.0
		After complete recovery	425	.....	15.0

---

[80] *Compt. rend. Acad. Sci.*, **156**, 1248 (1913).
[81] H. E. Himwich, W. H. Chambers, A. L. Hunter, and M. A. Spiers, *Am. J. Physiol.*, **99**, 619 (1931–32).
[82] Himwich and W. B. Castle, *ibid.*, **83**, 92 (1927); Himwich and M. I. Rose, *ibid.*, **88**, 663 (1929).
[83] H. B. Richardson, E. Schorr, and R. O. Loebel, *J. Biol. Chem.*, **86**, 551 (1930).
[84] J. W. T. Patterson, *Biochem. J.*, **21**, 958 (1927).
[85] C. P. Stewart, R. Gaddie, and D. M. Dunlop, *ibid.*, **25**, 733 (1931).

Lymph in the Transportation of Fat. In considering the transportation of fat in the body and particularly the mobilization of fat from the depots, attention in the past has been primarily directed toward the changes produced in the blood, the lymph having been principally associated with the transportation of fat absorbed from the intestine. It now appears from the work of Ivy and associates[86] on fasting, normal and phlorhizinized dogs that the lymph also participates in the transportation of reserve fat to the tissues.

Pregnancy. As regards fat metabolism, the embryo is in a large measure independent of the maternal organism. There does not appear to be a free interchange of fat through the placental barrier, as indicated by the difference in the lipid content of the maternal and fetal blood. Slemons and Stander[87] found the blood fat of the mother (human) at term to be higher than that of the new-born. This is shown by the following average data obtained in six normal cases of labor without anesthesia:

	Total Fat Mg. per 100 cc.	
	Whole Blood	Plasma
Maternal................	908	942
Fetal...................	707	737

Hofbauer[88] fed coconut oil to pregnant dogs and reported finding lauric acid, a constituent of the oil, in the fat of the fetus, indicating its placental transmission. On the other hand, Mendel and Daniels[89] in feeding experiments with fats treated with fat-soluble stains (Sudan III, Biebrich Scarlet, etc.) found that the placental membrane was impermeable to the ingested fats.

Wesson[90] fed pregnant rats diets containing 5 per cent of either butterfat or cod-liver oil and compared the composition of the maternal and fetal tissues with respect to their content of the highly unsaturated fatty acids, giving insoluble bromine addition compounds. The maternal tissues were markedly affected by the two diets. In proportion to

[86] H. R. Rony, B. Mortimer, and A. C. Ivy, *J. Biol. Chem.*, **96**, 737 (1932).

[87] *Bull. Johns Hopkins Hosp.*, **34**, 7 (1923); see also J. R. Murlin, *Am. J. Obstet. Gynecol.*, **75**, 913 (1917).

[88] Cited by J. Needham, "Chemical Embryology," Vol. II, p. 1192. The student is referred to this work for a detailed discussion of fat metabolism in the embryo.

[89] *J. Biol. Chem.*, **13**, 71 (1912–13).

[90] *Bull. Johns Hopkins Hosp.*, **38**, 237 (1926).

the total fat present, the unsaturated fatty acids on the cod-liver oil rations were nearly four times as abundant as on the butterfat diet. In contrast was the close similarity in the ratios of unsaturated fatty acids : total fat in the fetuses of the two groups of rats. Of several possible explanations, Wesson considered the most likely to be that the fetal organism possessed the capacity of synthesizing its own particular type of fat.

In a more extensive study, Chaikoff and Robinson[91] compared the effects of coconut oil, butter, Crisco, peanut oil, cottonseed oil, corn oil, and linseed oil, fats having iodine numbers ranging from 8 to 179. The fats constituted 40 per cent of the weight of the diet. The result of feeding these different rations was a marked variation in the composition of the maternal fat, as indicated by the data in Table XLIX. In the fetuses, the quality of the fat was not influenced to the same degree, being modified only about one-fifth as much as the maternal fat. The extent to which the fetal fat was thus modified was more closely related to the degree of unsaturation of the fat of the mother than that of her diet.

TABLE XLIX

EFFECT OF FOOD FAT ON FETAL AND MATERNAL FAT

Diet	Average Iodine Number		
	Diet	Maternal Fat	Fetal Fat
Coconut oil....................	8.0	41.1	68.0
Butter........................	33.0	57.8	70.5
Crisco........................	75.0	79.0	76.8
Peanut oil	95.0	94.0	80.0
Cottonseed oil.................	107.0	102.0	81.8
Corn oil......................	124.0	117.0	81.6
Linseed oil...................	179.0	139.0	88.2
Starch (fat-poor diet)...........	.....	65.0	72.5
Protein (fat-poor diet)..........	.....	66.7	74.1

During pregnancy, and particularly in the later stages, the fat, lecithin, and cholesterol concentrations in the blood are conspicuously increased. The total lipid content of the blood at term in human individuals is frequently 50 per cent above the normal, non-pregnant level, and 30 per cent higher than the value at 3 months (Tyler and Underhill).[92] It has been suggested that the greater mobilization of fat

[91] J. Biol. Chem., **100**, 13 (1933).   [92] J. Biol. Chem., **66**, 1 (1925).

during pregnancy may be due to the increased activity of the pituitary gland.

Lactation. It is possible that the fat mobilized at term by the maternal organism not only provides the fetus with an extra supply as evidenced by an extra deposit in the fetal livers, but that a portion is also utilized by the mother in the production of colostrum. After parturition, the concentrations of the various blood lipids continue to be high. In cattle, Maynard and associates[93] have observed a sharp rise after delivery, the increase being maintained for a considerable part (140 days) of the lactation period. Meigs, Blatherwick, and Cary[94] considered the milk fat to be derived from the phospholipids of the blood. However, from the work of Maynard it appears that the rise in concentration is parallel for all of the blood lipids. The total fatty acids, as well as the phospholipids, increase to about twice the non-lactating level (Schaible).[95] A striking correlation exists between the amount of blood lipids and the quantity of milk secreted. Late in lactation, accompanying the reduction in blood lipids is a marked diminution of milk production, and hence of the total fat secreted, but the concentration of the fat in the milk remains relatively unchanged. In cattle maintained on rations low in fat the same correlation has been observed, namely low blood lipids and diminished milk formation, but no change in the fat content of the milk. Such information as is available at present indicates that the fat of the diet, as well as the reserve fat of the tissues and the fat which the maternal organism is capable of synthesizing, are the precursors of the milk fat. That the mammary gland does not merely secrete the fat of the maternal blood, but also plays a definite rôle in the production of a more or less characteristic fat from these precursors is indicated by the work of Petersen, Palmer, and Eckles.[96]

Products of Fat Anabolism and Catabolism. As in the case of the other foodstuffs, the fats have a dual fate in metabolism. In addition to their utilization in the production of energy, a portion is used in the synthesis of essential tissue constituents many of which have been considered in an earlier chapter. The phospholipids and cerebrosides are synthesized *de novo* in the body, and it appears probable that the organism is also capable of producing cholesterol and perhaps other sterols. It is to some of these constituents that the permeability and other physical properties of cells are partly attributed. The part played by

[93] L. A. Maynard, E. S. Harrison, and C. M. McCay, *ibid.*, **92**, 263 (1931); McCay and Maynard., *ibid.*, **92**, 273 (1931); *J. Nutrition*, **2**, 67 (1929–30).

[94] *J. Biol. Chem.*, **37**, 1 (1919).

[95] *Ibid.*, **95**, 79 (1932).

[96] *Am. J. Physiol.*, **90**, 573 (1929).

fats and fat-like substances in the life of the cell has been reviewed by Leathes.[97]

The lipids secreted by the sebaceous glands (sebum) enable certain animals, particularly the fur- and feather-bearing ones, to shed water. The secretions on the skin also serve to diminish heat radiation. Sebum is a mixture of a number of fatty substances and is secreted by the sebaceous glands of the skin. A similar substance is cerumen, which is formed in the sebaceous and sweat glands of the cartilaginous part of the outer ear.

Lipoproteins are present in the blood as well as in many tissues. Taylor[98] has stated that, if a gland like the kidney which is rich in lipoproteins be completely extracted with fat solvents and then digested with trypsin, a subsequent extraction will yield a goodly amount of fatty substance. Some of this will be found to consist of phosphatides and sterols and the remainder of neutral fat.

Lipoproteins are very probably broken down into their respective lipid and protein residues. It is assumed that these follow the usual paths of protein and fat metabolism. The lecithin is presumably broken down to glycerol, fatty acids, phosphoric acid, and choline. The last-named substance is believed to give rise to trimethylamine, small amounts of which occur in urine. The formation of trimethylamine is represented by the following equation:

$$
\begin{array}{c}
CH_3 \\
CH_3 \\
CH_3
\end{array}
\Big\rangle N \Big\langle
\begin{array}{l}
CH_2CH_2OH \\
\\
OH
\end{array}
\quad \rightarrow \quad
\begin{array}{c}
CH_3 \\
CH_3 \\
CH_3
\end{array}
\Big\rangle N \; + \; CH_2OH \cdot CH_2OH
$$

Choline   Trimethylamine   Glycol

The galactose of the cerebrosides follows the usual path of carbohydrate metabolism. The fate of cholesterol in metabolism is obscure. A portion is excreted unchanged in the bile. Cholic acid may have its origin in cholesterol, there being a close chemical relationship between the two compounds.

[97] J. B. Leathes and H. S. Raper, "The Fats," Chap. X, 1925 edition; also Leathes in *Lancet*, **1**, pp. 803, 853, 957, 1019 (1925).

[98] A. E. Taylor, "Digestion and Metabolism," 1912, p. 347.

Summary. The main facts of fat metabolism may be outlined as follows:

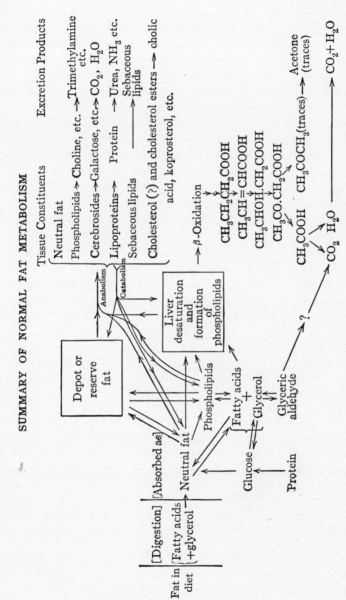

SUMMARY OF NORMAL FAT METABOLISM

CHAPTER XII

INTERMEDIARY METABOLISM OF PROTEIN

There is a continuous and relatively uniform degradation of protein in the animal body, which is often referred to as the "wear and tear" of the tissues. It is obvious that this loss must be made up, for otherwise the animal would gradually waste away. The formation of proteins characteristic of a particular tissue clearly depends on the availability in sufficient amounts of the necessary amino acids. Such indeed is the destiny of a considerable proportion of the amino acids derived from the proteins of the diet. A second fate of amino acids in metabolism is their utilization for some specific purpose, such as the formation of hormones, bile salts, catalysts, purines, pigments, etc. As has been pointed out by McCance,[1] the number of reactions in this class is large, and each one is a law unto itself. Inasmuch as there is ordinarily no storage of protein in the body of an adult animal, the actual protein needs are not in excess of the amount required to replace the protein lost and for the specific reactions just mentioned. However, if the protein intake is limited to these requirements and if the supply of carbohydrate and fat is inadequate to meet the caloric needs of the animal, the body may be forced to depend on the protein of its own tissues for the supply of energy. At such times an excessive amount of tissue breakdown occurs.

It is evident that if the amino acids of the proteins of the diet are not present in the same proportions as in the proteins of the animal, there must be an excess of some amino acids which are not utilized in protein synthesis and hence must be disposed of in some other way. Moreover, the protein intake is usually in excess of the anabolic needs of the organism. Consequently, a certain amount of the amino acids derived from the diet is burned directly or converted into sugar and fat. *Exogenous metabolism* is the metabolism of all protein ingested in excess of that required by the tissues for maintenance and growth. *Endogenous metabolism*, on the other hand, usually refers to the metab-

---

[1] R. A. McCance, "The Chemistry of the Degradation of Protein Nitrogen," *Physiol. Rev.*, **10**, 1 (1930).

olism which produces as end-products creatinine, neutral sulfur, and the part of the urea and uric acid not derived from the food.[2]

Nitrogen Equilibrium. By comparing the intake of nitrogen as protein with the total elimination of nitrogen (in the urine, feces, and perspiration), it is possible to determine whether the body is gaining or losing protein. If such studies are carried on over a short period, such as 24 hours, there may appear to be a retention of nitrogen. This is more often due to a lag in the elimination of the nitrogenous end-products of protein-metabolism than to a synthesis of protein. For accurate work, studies in nitrogen equilibrium should be carried on over a period of several days, separate analyses being made of the food and excreta of each day. In the adult, there is ordinarily no retention of nitrogen; that is, the nitrogen intake as protein is equivalent to the nitrogen elimination. This is a condition of *nitrogen equilibrium*, or *nitrogen balance*.

The statement that in the adult individual there is no retention of nitrogen needs to be qualified. It is well known that muscular development and a gain in weight result when an individual performs muscular work over a period of several weeks or months, provided he is supplied during this time with an adequate amount of food, especially protein. Bornstein[3] investigated this question and found that nitrogen retention occurred (positive nitrogen balance) when the increase in muscular activity was accompanied by an increase in the protein intake.

Negative nitrogen balance occurs when the endogenous protein metabolism exceeds the protein intake. This occurs in malnutrition, starvation, fevers, and other wasting diseases. In fevers, the patient is often given large amounts of sugar for the purpose of sparing the tissue proteins as much as possible. The more essential organs, such as the heart and brain, are spared even in prolonged starvation. During convalescence there is regeneration of the tissues and hence a retention of nitrogen.

In growing animals the excretion of nitrogen is less than the corresponding protein intake, a portion of the amino acids of the diet being used in the synthesis of new tissue protein.

Anabolism. To meet the anabolic needs of the body a certain minimum of protein is required. This question will be considered in somewhat greater detail elsewhere, but for the purpose of the present discussion it is sufficient to state that the actual needs of the body seem

---

[2] For an excellent summary of the theories of endogenous and exogenous protein metabolism the student is referred to H. H. Mitchell and T. S. Hamilton, "The Biochemistry of Amino Acids," Chemical Catalog Co., New York, 1929, Chap. IX.

[3] *Arch. ges. Physiol.*, **83**, 540 (1901).

to be far less than the amount formerly considered necessary. The older physiologists believed that an adequate diet should contain about 120 grams of protein, a value which was based on German statistical data and which also corresponded closely to the statistical data for the average daily protein intake in the United States. Chittenden, on the other hand, showed in a long series of experiments on individuals engaged in various occupations, including athletes and soldiers, that one-half this amount is adequate and that even less may be sufficient. There are observations on record to show that nitrogen equilibrium may be maintained under special conditions on as little as 2.2 grams of nitrogen per day, or about 15 grams of protein, provided sufficient carbohydrate is given at the same time.

Catabolism. When the tissues break down, the protein molecules are apparently hydrolyzed, probably with the aid of tissue enzymes, yielding mainly amino acids. There is no reason for assuming that the metabolism of these differs from that of the amino acids derived directly from the diet.

The study of intermediary protein metabolism is essentially the study of the fate of the individual amino acids. This is the main purpose of the present chapter.

Metabolism of Glycine. The metabolism of this amino acid may be considered from several angles, the first being that of its breakdown to NH_3, CO_2, and H_2O in normal metabolism. Its conjugation with benzoic acid and other aromatic acids to form hippuric acid and related compounds is to be considered as a phase of its metabolism, as is also the formation of glycocholic acid by conjugation with cholic acid. We also have to include the synthesis of sugar from glycine in the diabetic animal as well as its possible formation in the normal individual. Finally it has been reported that glycine is a precursor of creatine, an important constituent of muscle (p. 417).

The steps in the breakdown of glycine in the course of normal metabolism are not definitely known. However, the following changes seem possible:

$$\begin{matrix} CH_2NH_2 \\ | \\ COOH \end{matrix} \rightarrow \begin{matrix} CH{=}NH \\ | \\ COOH \end{matrix} \rightarrow \begin{matrix} C{\diagup}^{OH}_{\diagdown NH_2} \\ | \diagdown H \\ COOH \end{matrix} \rightarrow \rightarrow NH_3 + 2CO_2 + H_2O$$

In liver perfusion experiments with glycine ammonia is formed.[4]

---

[4] A. Bornstein, *Biochem Z.*, **212**, 137 (1929); **214**, 374 (1929); R. Kohn, *Z. physiol. Chem.*, **200**, 191 (1931).

Small amounts of methylamine are also produced, probably by simple decarboxylation:

$$\begin{array}{c} CH_2NH_2 \\ | \\ COOH \end{array} \rightarrow CH_3NH_2 + CO_2$$

Evidence for the synthesis of glycine in the body is to be found in the numerous experiments in which benzoic acid or benzoates have been fed to animals and hippuric acid found in the urine.[5] Hippuric acid (benzoyl-glycine) is a normal constituent of the urine of horses, cattle, and other herbivorous animals. In small amounts, it is likewise present in human urine. Not only does the body use any preformed glycine that may be present either in the diet or in the tissues, but it is at times forced to synthesize this amino acid in large amount for the purposes of detoxication. Quick[6] has estimated that the maximum synthesis of glycine in man is 9 mg. per kg., per hour. Although there is no doubt that this occurs, we do not know how it is brought about. Knoop as well as Dakin[7] have suggested that the formation of glycine in the body may result from the oxidation at the β-carbon atom of α-amino β-hydroxy acids such as serine. Dakin has shown that phenylserine does not behave like phenylalanine in the body, for it yields benzoic acid. Thus, it appears to be oxidized at the β-carbon atom as represented in the equation:

$$C_6H_5 \cdot CHOH \cdot CHNH_2 \cdot COOH + O \rightarrow C_6H_5 \cdot COOH + CH_2NH_2 \cdot COOH$$

The conversion of glycine into sugar in the animal body has been definitely established. The relationship between amino acids and glucose has been studied, especially by Lusk and his pupils, the general procedure consisting in feeding phlorhizinized dogs with these amino acids and analyzing the urine for nitrogen and glucose. To bring out the significance of these experiments, it may be well to describe them in some detail.

Suppose that we have a dog which has been rendered completely " diabetic " with phlorhizin. We collect the urine of the animal for a given period and analyze it for glucose and nitrogen. This gives us the necessary data for calculating the glucose : nitrogen or D : N ratio.

[5] See, for example, the recent papers of W. H. Griffith and H. B. Lewis, *J. Biol. Chem.*, **57**, 1 (1923); Griffith, *ibid.*, **69**, 197 (1926); **82**, 415 (1929).

[6] *Ibid.*, **92**, 65 (1931).

[7] H. D. Dakin, "Oxidations and Reductions in the Animal Body," 1922 edition, Chap. III.

Let us assume that it is found to be 3.65, which means that the dog is completely diabetic and is unable to utilize any sugar, no matter what its source may be. Now suppose we give the dog 16 grams of glucose and set out to determine whether any or all of it may be recovered in the urine as extra glucose. The urine is therefore collected a second time for a sufficient period to assure complete excretion of the glucose and again analyzed for glucose and nitrogen. Suppose we now find the urine to contain 2.87 grams of nitrogen and 25.92 grams of glucose. Assuming that the D : N ratio had not changed in the meantime, there should have been excreted 3.65 grams of glucose for every gram of nitrogen, both having had their origin in the tissue proteins which were broken down during this interval. $3.65 \times 2.87 = 10.49$. The difference between this value and the total sugar elimination, $25.92 - 10.49 = 15.43$ grams, is the amount of extra sugar excreted. In short, practically all of the sugar that was given to the dog has been recovered in the urine.

We may now analyze the results obtained on feeding glycine. For this purpose an experiment described by Lusk[8] may be selected. A phlorhizinized dog, having a D : N ratio of 3.38, was given 20 grams of glycine, and the urine collected during the next 14 hours was analyzed and found to contain 47.42 grams of glucose and 12.84 grams of nitrogen. Since 20 grams of glycine contain 3.73 grams of nitrogen, the difference between 12.84 and 3.73, or 9.11 grams, represents the protein metabolism during this interval. Therefore, $9.11 \times 3.38 = 30.79$ grams of glucose had its origin in the protein metabolized. The difference between 47.42 grams, the total sugar excreted, and 30.79 grams, that is, 16.63 grams, must have been formed, therefore, from the ingested glycine. This accords well with the calculated yield (16 grams) based on the assumption that all of the carbon of glycine is converted into glucose. This conversion may be represented as follows, though actually the path of conversion of glycine into glucose is still obscure:

$$3 \; \begin{array}{c} CH_2NH_2 \\ | \\ COOH \end{array} \quad \rightarrow 3 \; \begin{array}{c} CH_2OH \\ | \\ COOH \end{array} \quad \rightarrow 3 \; \begin{array}{c} CH_2OH \\ | \\ CHO \end{array} \quad \rightarrow C_6H_{12}O_6$$

$$\text{Glycine} \qquad\qquad \text{Glycolic} \qquad\qquad \text{Glycolic} \qquad \text{Glucose}$$
$$\text{acid} \qquad\qquad\quad \text{aldehyde}$$

If this represents the sequence of events, glycolic acid and aldehyde should yield glucose when given to diabetic animals. Sansum and Woodyatt[9] showed that this occurs. As much as 75 per cent of the

[8] G. Lusk, "The Science of Nutrition," 4th edition, 1928, p. 228; Ringer and Lusk, Z. physiol. Chem., **66**, 106 (1910).

[9] J. Biol. Chem., **17**, 521 (1914).

glycolic acid which they had administered slowly to a phlorhizinized dog escaped oxidation and appeared in the urine as extra glucose.

In contrast to the ready transformation of glycine into glucose in the diabetic animal is the inconspicuous effect in the normal animal, judging from the results of Wilson and Lewis.[10] On feeding glycine to rats they found no change in the glycogen content of the liver or other tissues. A similar administration of d- or dl-alanine, on the other hand, produced a definite increase in the glycogen reserves of the body.

Metabolism of Alanine; General Course of Amino-acid Metabolism. The opinion generally held is that oxidation of amino acids occurs in the α position and is accompanied by the removal of the amino group. Much attention has been devoted to the problem in an attempt to determine the intermediate steps of the process.

Neuberg and Langstein[11] fed a starving rabbit alanine and obtained lactic acid in the urine. Embden[12] perfused a surviving liver with alanine and likewise obtained lactic acid. It was therefore supposed that the formation of α-hydroxy acids was the immediate result of hydrolysis as represented by the following equation:

$$
\begin{array}{ccc}
\text{R} & & \text{R} \\
| & & | \\
\text{CH}_2 & & \text{CH}_2 \\
| & & | \\
\text{CH·NH}_2 + \text{HOH} & = & \text{CH·OH} + \text{NH}_3 \\
| & & | \\
\text{COOH} & & \text{COOH}
\end{array}
$$

This view is not generally accepted, however, the weight of evidence pointing to an oxidative deamination with the intermediate formation of α-ketonic acids. In general, α-amino acids and the corresponding α-ketonic acids share the same fate in metabolism and are oxidized with approximately the same rapidity, whereas the α-hydroxy acids are oxidized less readily. It is considered that the α-hydroxy acids are not formed directly from amino acids, but from the corresponding ketonic acids or aldehydes.

Dakin[13] has suggested that, in the conversion of amino acids into ketonic acids, the corresponding glyoxals are formed as intermediate

---

[10] Ibid., **85**, 559 (1929–30).

[11] Arch. Anat. Physiol., Physiol. Abt., 514 (1903).

[12] Cited by Dakin in "Oxidations and Reductions in the Animal Body," 1922 edition, p. 67.

[13] Ibid., Chap. III.

products. Taking alanine as the example, these ideas may be represented as follows:

Lactic acid

$$CH_3CHOH.COOH$$

$$\begin{array}{cccccc}
CH_3 & CH_3 & & CH_3 & CH_3 & \\
| & | & & | & | & \\
CHNH_2 \rightarrow & C=O & \xrightarrow{\;O\;} & C=O \longrightarrow & CHO \longrightarrow \cdots\cdots\rightarrow & CO_2+H_2O \\
| & | & & | & + & \\
COOH & CHO & & COOH & CO_2 & \\
\text{Alanine} & \text{Pyruvic aldehyde} & & \text{Pyruvic acid} & & \\
& \text{(Methyl glyoxal)} & & & & \\
& +NH_3 & & & &
\end{array}$$

According to Knoop,[14] hydrates of imino acids are formed in the process of deamination of amino acids. This is very suggestive, for we may then assume the following sequence of events: The first step in the metabolism of an amino acid may be taken to be one involving the loss of hydrogen by dehydrogenation, resulting in the formation of the corresponding imino acid. Presumably the next step is one of hydration; the hydrate thus formed, because of its instability, parts with its ammonia, yielding a ketonic acid. These changes are represented as follows:

$$\begin{array}{cccccccc}
R & & R & & R & & R & \\
| & & | & & | & & | & \\
CH_2 & & CH_2 & & CH_2 & & CH_2 & \\
| \quad H & -H_2 & | & +H_2O & | \quad OH & \longrightarrow & | & +NH_3 \\
C & \longrightarrow & C=NH & \longrightarrow & C & & C=O & \\
| \quad NH_2 & & | & & | \quad NH_2 & & | & \\
COOH & & COOH & & COOH & & COOH & \\
\text{Amino acid} & & \text{Imino acid} & & \text{Hydrate} & & \text{Ketonic} & \\
& & & & \text{of imino} & & \text{acid} & \\
& & & & \text{acid} & & &
\end{array}$$

Fate of Ammonia. The formation of urea and its physiological significance will be considered in detail later. For the present it is sufficient to state that in mammals, and particularly in man, the ammonia which is formed in the deamination of the amino acids is converted almost quantitatively into urea. This is the principal end-product of protein metabolism, the quantity present in the urine being determined largely by the amount of protein ingested. The utilization of ammonia in neutralizing acid will be considered in a later section.

Conversion into Glucose. Alanine may be completely converted, carbon for carbon, into glucose in phlorhizin diabetes, as shown by

[14] *Z. physiol. Chem.*, **67**, 489 (1910); **148**, 294 (1925).

Ringer and Lusk[8] and by Dakin and Dudley.[15] Mandel and Lusk[16] proved the transformation of lactic acid into glucose, and Dakin and Dudley[17] recovered the methyl glyoxal which they administered to a diabetic dog, as urinary glucose. The evidence for the complete conversion of pyruvic acid, on the other hand, is not very striking. Dakin has suggested the possibility that only such pyruvic acid as undergoes reduction to lactic acid is converted into glucose.

Synthesis of Alanine. Embden and Schmitz[18] have demonstrated the synthesis of alanine in a series of experiments in which ammonium pyruvate was perfused through the liver. Alanine was recovered in the perfusate. Glycogen may likewise serve as a source of alanine, as reported by Fellner,[19] who perfused salts of ammonia through glycogen-rich and glycogen-poor livers and observed a greater amount of alanine synthesis in the former than in the latter.

Metabolism of Serine. The one definitely known fact concerning the metabolism of *l*-serine is its quantitative conversion into glucose in the completely diabetic animal. The intermediary metabolism of this amino acid may be represented as follows:

$$
\begin{array}{ccccl}
CH_2OH & CH_2OH & CH_2OH & & \text{Glucose (in diabetes)} \\
| & | & | & \nearrow & \\
CHNH_2 \rightarrow & C{=}O \rightarrow & CHOH & \Big< & \\
| & | & | & \searrow & \\
COOH & CHO & CHO & & CO_2 + H_2O \text{ (normal oxidation)} \\
\text{Serine} & \substack{\alpha\text{-keto, }\beta\text{-oxypro-}\\ \text{pionic alde-}\\ \text{hyde}} & \substack{\text{Glyceric}\\ \text{aldehyde}} & &
\end{array}
$$

The close chemical relationship of serine and alanine suggests that these amino acids may be interchangeable in metabolism, and, as has been stated elsewhere, there is some evidence for the view that serine may serve as a source of glycine in metabolic processes.

Metabolism of Valine. The fate of valine in metabolism is not definitely known. Oxidation at the α-carbon atom should yield isobutyric acid, but Dakin[20] was not able to demonstrate this in phlorhizinized dogs. Moreover, isobutyric acid is readily converted into glucose in diabetic animals, whereas valine does not yield sugar. Nor does this amino acid give rise to acetone bodies when perfused through the liver (Embden, Salomon, and Schmidt).[21]

Metabolism of Leucine. By oxidative deamination, leucine yields the corresponding ketonic acid, which is in turn oxidized to isovaleric

[15] *J. Biol. Chem.*, **17**, 451 (1914).
[16] *Am. J. Physiol.*, **16**, 129 (1906).
[17] *J. Biol. Chem.*, **15**, 127 (1913).
[18] *Biochem. Z.*, **38**, 393 (1912).

[19] *Ibid.*, **38**, 414 (1912).
[20] *J. Biol. Chem.*, **14**, 321 (1913).
[21] *Hofmeister's Beiträge*, **8**, 129 (1906).

acid. This is believed to undergo demethylation, forming β-hydroxy-butyric acid. From this point, its fate is presumably identical with that of all other fatty acids, oxidation occurring at the β-carbon atom (see Fat Metabolism). Hence, leucine may be a source of acetone bodies in the diabetic animal. A certain amount of acetone may be formed directly by the oxidation of isovaleric acid. These reactions are represented below:

$$
\begin{array}{ccc}
CH_3 \quad CH_3 \rightarrow & CH_3 & \longrightarrow CO_2 \\
\diagdown \diagup & | & + \\
CO & COOH & H_2O \\
\nearrow & & \uparrow \\
\end{array}
$$

$$
\begin{array}{cccccccc}
CH_3 \quad CH_3 & CH_3 \quad CH_3 & CH_3 \quad CH_3 & CH_3 & CH_3 & & \\
\diagdown \diagup & \diagdown \diagup & \diagdown \diagup & | & | & & \\
CH & CH & CH & CHOH & C=O & CH_3 & \\
| \quad \longrightarrow & | \quad \longrightarrow & | \rightarrow & | \rightarrow & | \rightarrow 2| & & \\
CH_2 & CH_2 & CH_2 & CH_2 & CH_2 & COOH & \\
| & | & | & | & | & & \\
CHNH_2 & C=O & COOH & COOH & COOH & & \\
| & | & \text{Isovaleric Acid} & & & & \\
COOH & COOH & & & & & \\
\text{Leucine} & + & & & & & \\
& NH_3 & & & & & \\
& \downarrow & & & & & \\
& \text{Urea} & & & & &
\end{array}
$$

Leucine is present in all proteins. Therefore, even if it were not synthesized in the body, it would probably be supplied in adequate amounts in the diet. When acted upon by bacteria it yields isovaleric acid and isoamylamine. Yeast fermentation produces isoamyl alcohol.

Metabolism of Isoleucine. Not much information is available concerning the metabolism of this amino acid. It does not give rise to glucose, and its conversion into acetone bodies is not definitely established (Dakin, p. 75).

Metabolism of Aspartic Acid. The intermediary steps in the metabolism of aspartic acid are not definitely known. If oxidation occurred at the carbon atom attached to the amino group, keto-succinic acid would be formed. This compound is known to be converted into pyruvic acid when treated with macerated liver or muscle tissue. A different view is held by Ringer and Lusk,[22] who believe that aspartic acid is converted into malic acid and subsequently into β-lactic acid. Ackerman[23] found that aspartic acid, incubated with putrefying pan-

[22] G. Lusk, "The Science of Nutrition," 1928 edition, p. 242.
[23] Z. Biol., **56**, 87 (1911).

creas, produces β-alanine. This cannot, however, be the normal path of aspartic acid metabolism, for Corley[24] has shown that β-alanine is not converted into glucose in the completely phlorhizinized animal. The student will note, however, that whatever the intermediate products may be, they are in part sugar-forming. Indeed, it has been shown by Ringer and Lusk that in phlorhizinized dogs the equivalent of three carbon atoms of the four in aspartic acid can be accounted for in the form of extra glucose in the urine. Although the paths of metabolism of this amino acid in normal oxidation have not been precisely formulated, its transformation into glucose, on the basis of available knowledge, may be represented as follows:

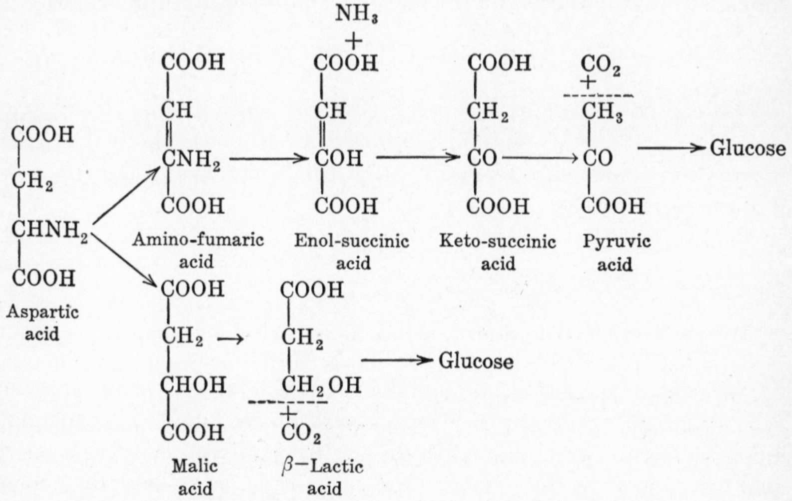

Aspartic acid when added to minced muscle under anaerobic conditions gives rise to succinic, fumaric, and malic acids, according to recent observations of Needham.[25]

The removal of aspartic acid, together with the other dicarboxylic amino acids (glutamic and hydroxyglutamic), from hydrolyzed casein does not alter the nutritive value of the resulting material (St. Julian and Rose).[26] With this as the substitute for protein, young rats have been found to grow normally, indicating that the organism is capable of synthesizing the dibasic amino acids, including aspartic.

Metabolism of Glutamic Acid. Only three carbon atoms of the five in glutamic acid are converted into glucose in the completely diabetic

[24] *J. Biol. Chem.*, **81**, 545 (1929).
[25] D. M. Needham, *Biochem. J.*, **24**, 208 (1930).
[26] *J. Biol. Chem.*, **98**, 439 (1932).

animal (Lusk).[27] As in the case of aspartic acid, the formation of sugar has been explained in more than one way. Deamination at the α-carbon atom and subsequent oxidation at the β-carbon atom would yield glyceric acid. This, in turn, would be oxidized completely in the normal animal, or it would be converted into sugar, carbon for carbon, in the completely diabetic animal. On the other hand, it is possible to conceive that ketoglutaric acid is formed first, and that this is converted into either malic or succinic acid. Needham[25] has shown that under anaerobic conditions, succinic acid is formed from glutamic acid when the latter is added to minced muscle. Both malic and succinic acids are non-toxic and presumably are oxidized in the body. It would be much more difficult to postulate the intermediary formation of glutaric acid,

$$(COOH \cdot CH_2 \cdot CH_2 \cdot CH_2 \cdot COOH)$$

for this compound, when injected, is severely nephropathic (Rose).[28]

The probability of glutamic acid synthesis in the body has been referred to. It will also be recalled that this amino acid is a component of glutathione (p. 306).

Relatively little is known of the metabolism of hydroxyglutamic acid, but it may be assumed to be more or less similar to that of glutamic acid.

Metabolism of Arginine. Mammalian liver contains an enzyme, *arginase*, capable of hydrolyzing arginine with the production of urea and ornithine (Kossel and Dakin).[29] Inasmuch as this enzyme is absent from the liver of birds, Clementi[30] proposed the generalization that arginase is present in the livers of all animals which form urea as the end-product of nitrogen metabolism and absent in those in which uric acid is the end-product.

There is conflicting opinion concerning the occurrence of this enzyme in other tissues; however, the situation has been considerably clarified by Hunter and Dauphinee[31] in their splendid survey of its distribution in various species of animals. In mammals, arginase was not found in any organs except the liver and kidney, and the latter contained a relatively small amount. On the contrary, in birds, which contain no arginase in the liver, the kidneys were found to have more than any other kidney studied save the dogfish's. The distribution in the

[27] *Am. J. Physiol.*, **22**, 174 (1908).

[28] *J. Pharmacol. Exp. Therap.*, **24**, 123, 147 (1924).

[29] *Z. physiol. Chem.*, **41**, 321 (1904); **42**, 181 (1904).

[30] A. Clementi, *Atti accad. Lincei, Rendic.*, Series 5, **23**, 612 (1915); **25**, 483 (1918); **27**, 299 (1922);

[31] *Proc. Roy. Soc. (London)*, B, **97**, 227 (1925).

remaining tissues was variable in different species. In herring and dogfish, and possibly in fishes at large, the organ next in activity to the liver was the heart.

Arginase is said to be present in certain bacteria and fungi.

Both ornithine and arginine yield sugar in phlorhizin diabetes, in amounts sufficient to account for three carbon atoms, or one-half the total number in arginine (Dakin).[32]

The steps in the metabolism of this amino acid are not fully understood, but it is believed that succinic acid is an intermediate product, as represented by the following scheme:

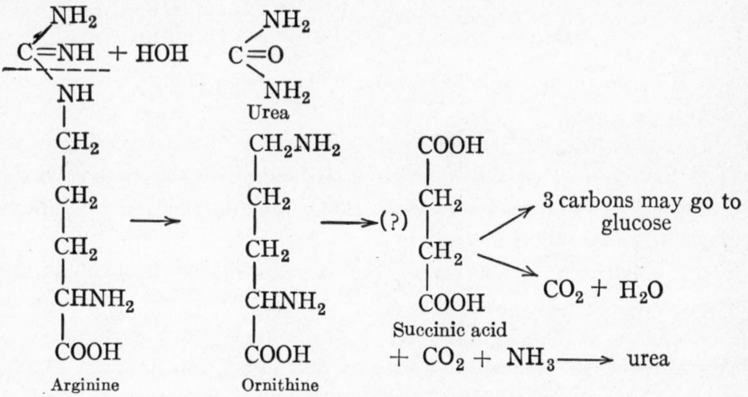

Another pathway of metabolism has been suggested, namely one involving the conversion of arginine into guanidine-butyric acid, $(NH_2 \cdot \overset{NH}{\overset{\|}{C}} \cdot NH \cdot CH_2 \cdot CH_2 \cdot CH_2 \cdot COOH)$, which by β-oxidation would yield guanidine acetic acid $(NH_2 \cdot \overset{NH}{\overset{\|}{C}} \cdot NH \cdot CH_2 \cdot COOH)$. By methylation, the latter would yield creatine $(NH_2 \cdot \overset{NH}{\overset{\|}{C}} \cdot NCH_3 \cdot CH_2 \cdot COOH)$. There is, however, no experimental evidence in support of this idea.[33] The conversion of guanidine-acetic acid into creatine seems to be established,[34] but arginine itself is not known to be a precursor of either

[32] H. D. Dakin, "Oxidations and Reductions in the Animal Body," 1922 edition, p. 81.

[33] K. Thomas and M. G. H. Goerne, Z. physiol. Chem., **92**, 163 (1914); **104**, 73 (1918–19).

[34] L. Baumann and H. M. Hines, J. Biol. Chem., **31**, 549 (1917).

creatine or creatinine.[35]   In experiments with rats, Rose and Cook[36] could find no relationship between the arginine content of the diet and the total creatinine elimination in the urine.   Nor does arginine affect the storage of creatine in the tissues (Meyer and Rose).[36]   Hyde and Rose[37] fed daily an amount of arginine equivalent to 1 gram of creatine to a male and a female subject, and although the experiment was continued for six and eight weeks, respectively, there was no evidence of an increased output of either creatine or creatinine.   A similar result was obtained in dogs by Grant, Christman, and Lewis.[38]   The problem of creatine metabolism will be considered more fully in the following chapter.

The production of urea in liver autolysis is believed to be the result of the action of arginase on the arginine contained in the tissue.   However, Krebs and Henseleit[39] have recently described the formation of urea from ammonia through the participation of ornithine.   As will be seen presently (p. 411), ornithine is supposed to react with CO_2 and NH_3 to form *citrulline*, which in turn adds another molecule of NH_3 to form arginine.   The latter is then hydrolyzed to urea and ornithine, thus making possible a repetition of the cycle.

Convincing evidence of the synthesis of arginine in the body has been obtained in Rose's laboratory.   Bunney and Rose[40] found that rats grew normally on a diet deficient in arginine.   Moreover, Scull and Rose[41] determined that the tissues of animals maintained on an arginine-poor diet accumulated during the experimental period 2 to 3 times as much arginine as could be accounted for by the total arginine consumed in the diet.

Metabolism of Lysine.   Since Dakin has shown that lysine yields neither glucose nor acetone bodies in phlorhizin diabetes, all pathways of metabolism that would give rise to either ketogenic or anti-ketogenic substances must be excluded.   Corley[42] states that ϵ-aminocaproic acid is also not a sugar-former in the completely phlorhizinized dog.

Lysine is not synthesized in the body and must therefore be provided

---

[35] Compare W. H. Thompson, *J. Physiol.*, **51**, 111 (1917).   For an excellent review of the subject the student is advised to consult H. H. Mitchell and T. S. Hamilton, "Biochemistry of Amino Acids" (1929), p. 333.

[36] *J. Biol. Chem.*, **64**, 325 (1925);   see also C. E. Meyer and W. C. Rose, *ibid.*, **102**, 461 (1933).

[37] *Ibid.*, **84**, 535 (1929).

[38] *Proc. Soc. Exp. Biol. Med.*, **27**, 231 (1929).

[39] *Z. physiol. Chem.*, **210**, 33 (1932).

[40] *J. Biol. Chem.*, **76**, 521 (1928).

[41] *Ibid.*, **89**, 109 (1930).

[42] J. Biol. Chem., **81**, 545 (1929).

in the diet. Its metabolism in embryonic development has been considered by Calvery.[43]

Metabolism of Cystine. The first step in the normal metabolic degradation of cystine is believed to be its reduction to form two molecules of cysteine.[44] The next step is probably an oxidative deamination, the ammonia being presumably converted to urea. The sulfur is for the most part oxidized to sulfate and is eliminated in the urine mainly as inorganic sulfate. A smaller amount is excreted as ethereal sulfates, conjugated substances formed in the detoxication of absorbed products of intestinal putrefaction, such as phenol and indoxyl. In addition, the urine contains a certain amount of unoxidized sulfur. It is probable that most of the inorganic sulfate is derived from exogenous metabolism, for the amount varies with the total nitrogen and particularly with the urea elimination. The significance of these urinary constituents will be further considered in other connections.

Cystine is a constituent of glutathione (p. 306) and insulin and is the precursor of taurine. The last occurs in combination with cholic and choleic acids in taurocholic and taurocholeic acids, respectively (p. 468). The formation of taurine from cysteine may be brought about by oxidizing the latter with bromine. The reactions are represented as follows:

$$
\begin{array}{ccccc}
\mathrm{CH_2SH} & & \mathrm{CH_2(SO_3H)} & & \mathrm{CH_2(SO_3H)} \\
| & \rightarrow & | & \rightarrow & | & + \ \mathrm{CO_2} \\
\mathrm{CHNH_2} & & \mathrm{CHNH_2} & & \mathrm{CH_2 \cdot NH_2} \\
| & & | & & \text{Taurine} \\
\mathrm{COOH} & & \mathrm{COOH} & & \\
\text{Cysteine} & & \text{Cysteic Acid} & &
\end{array}
$$

It is possible, however, that in the body conjugation of the cholic acid occurs with cysteine and that the conjugated product is then oxidized to taurocholic acid. Taurine and cysteic acid are oxidized with difficulty, if at all (Schmidt and Clark),[45] though the latter is deaminized quite readily.

Cysteine is readily oxidized by iodine to cystine: $2R—SH + I_2 = R—S—S—R + 2HI$. The further action of iodine results in the slow oxidation of cystine to cysteic acid: $R—S—S—R + 5I_2 + 6H_2O = 2R—SO_3H + 10HI$.[46] In acid solution (HCl or H_2SO_4), cystine is

[43] *Ibid.*, **83**, 649 (1929); **95**, 297 (1932).

[44] Lewis and McGinty and Lewis, Updegraff and McGinty have shown that the administration of phenyluraminocystine and dibenzoylcystine results in the excretion of phenyluraminocysteine and dibenzoylcysteine, respectively (*J. Biol. Chem.*, **53**, 349 [1922]; **59**, 59 [1924]).

[45] *J. Biol. Chem.*, **53**, 193 (1922).

[46] K. Shinohara, *J. Biol. Chem.*, **96**, 285 (1932).

similarly oxidized by free oxygen, but much more slowly (Andrews).[47] However, in the presence of copper salts this reaction is greatly accelerated, provided the cystine is dissolved in hydrochloric acid.

In unusual intoxications with foreign organic compounds, cystine may be used by the organism as the detoxicating agent. Thus the monohalogen derivatives of benzene are converted into the corresponding mercapturic acid derivatives and excreted.[48]

Cysteine is quantitatively converted into glucose (carbon for carbon) in phlorhizin diabetes (Dakin),[49] probably with the intermediate formation of serine.

A large proportion of the cystine derived from the food is required for the synthesis of various types of keratins, found in hair, wool, feathers, and other epidermal structures. Wilson and Lewis,[50] using the method of Folin and Looney[51] for the determination of cystine, found human hair to contain between 15.6 and 21.2 per cent of this amino acid. It appears, however, that the demands for protein (and cystine) for the growth of the body with its essential tissues and organs take precedence over the demands for the growth of hair. Lightbody and Lewis[52] have shown that when diets of low cystine content are fed to rats, the growth of hair is much more markedly diminished than the general growth of the body. Similarly, the availability of cystine in the diet of sheep is apparently a factor which determines the cystine content of their wool.

Cystine accounts for practically all the sulfur in human hair, in wool, and in rabbit fur, but not in camel's hair.[53]

Experiments conducted in Mitchell's laboratory[54] have shown that on a cystine-deficient diet the growth of hair in rats is small and the cystine content is lower than normal. Some of the hair also shows structural abnormalities, possessing a thinner cortex, which presumably represents the completely keratinized part of the hair.

Diets deficient in cystine are inadequate for growth, which indicates that this amino acid is not synthesized in the body. Indeed even such

---

[47] J. C. Andrews, *ibid.*, **97**, 657 (1932); **102**, 263 (1933).

[48] For further details and references to the literature consult C. P. Sherwin, "The Fate of Organic Compounds in the Animal Body," *Physiol. Rev.*, **2**, 264 (1922); A. M. Ambrose and C. P. Sherwin, "Detoxication Mechanisms," *Ann. Rev. Biochem.*, **2**, 377 (1933).

[49] *J. Biol. Chem.*, **14**, 321 (1913).

[50] *J. Biol. Chem.*, **73**, 543 (1927).

[51] *Ibid.*, **51**, 421 (1922).

[52] *Ibid.*, **82**, 485 (1929).

[53] C. Rimington, *Biochem. J.*, **23**, 726 (1929); **25**, 71 (1931); J. Barritt and Rimington, *ibid.*, **25**, 1072 (1931).

[54] D. B. Smuts, H. H. Mitchell, and T. S. Hamilton, *J. Biol. Chem.*, **95**, 283 (1932).

closely related compounds as taurine, cysteic acid, dithiodiglycollic acid,

$$(COOH \cdot CH_2 \cdot S \cdot S \cdot CH_2 \cdot COOH)$$

β-dithiodipropionic acid

$$(COOH \cdot CH_2 \cdot CH_2 \cdot S \cdot S \cdot CH_2 \cdot CH_2 \cdot COOH)$$

and α-dihydroxy-β-dithiodipropionic acid

$$(COOH \cdot CHOH \cdot CH_2 \cdot S \cdot S \cdot CH_2 \cdot CHOH \cdot COOH)$$

are apparently not changed to cystine or cysteine, for it has been demonstrated that diets deficient in cystine and supplemented with these substances are inadequate for growth. It may be observed that dithiodiglycollic acid, β-dithiodipropionic acid, and α-dihydroxy-β-dithiodipropionic acid, administered orally or subcutaneously to rabbits, are all readily oxidized (Westerman and Rose).[55]

Moreover, only the natural *l*-cystine is utilized for growth, the *d*-cystine being ineffective.[56] In view of this remarkable physiological specificity it is therefore of interest to note that methionine is capable of replacing cystine in nutrition.[57] Another substance which apparently yields cystine in metabolism is homocystine, a derivative of methionine (see p. 398).[58]

Cystinuria. Cystinuria is an abnormal condition in which cystine is present in the urine, apparently because of some failure in its metabolism. It seems to be hereditary and is said to occur somewhat oftener in males than in females. Garrod[59] has described cystinuria as an inborn error of metabolism.

Robson[60] has investigated the genealogical tree of a patient with pronounced cystinuria. There was a definite family history of this abnormality as shown by the accompanying diagram. It is to be regretted that no information was available concerning many members of this family. These are indicated by crosses. Despite these gaps, however, this family tree illustrates very clearly the hereditary nature of the disease.

[55] *J. Biol. Chem.*, **79**, 423 (1928).
[56] V. du Vigneaud, R. Dorfmann and H. S. Loring, *ibid.*, **98**, 577 (1932).
[57] R. W. Jackson and R. J. Block, *ibid.*, **98**, 465 (1932); see also B. W. Chase and H. B. Lewis, *ibid.*, **101**, 735 (1933).
[58] Du Vigneaud, H. M. Dyer, and J. Harmon, *ibid.*, **101**, 719 (1933).
[59] Sir Archibald E. Garrod, "Inborn Errors of Metabolism," Oxford University Press, London, 2d edition, 1923.
[60] *Biochem. J.*, **23**, 138 (1929).

The nature of the metabolic derangement is somewhat obscure. It has been repeatedly demonstrated that the cystinuric can utilize completely considerable amounts of the free amino acid. For example, Robson fed his patient increasing amounts of cystine, starting with 2 grams and increasing the dose by 2 grams daily until 8 grams were given. For a four-day period a total of 20 grams of cystine were administered, 85 per cent of which was accounted for in the form of the extra inorganic

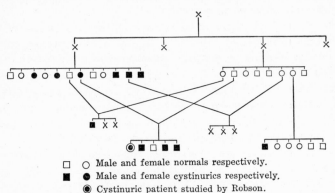

□   ○ Male and female normals respectively.
■   ● Male and female cystinurics respectively.
◉ Cystinuric patient studied by Robson.

FIG. 30.—Showing the family history of a patient with cystinuria.
(Courtesy of Dr. Robson.)

sulfate eliminated during that period. There was no elimination of extra cystine.

Cystinurics continue to excrete cystine even on a protein-free diet and during starvation, which would indicate that the cystine is at least partly endogenous in origin. It has also been known for some time that the excretion of cystine in cystinuria is definitely increased by increasing the quantity of protein in the diet. This would indicate an exogenous source for some of the cystine. However, Lewis and Lough[61] have made the remarkable observation that the increased excretion of cystine in cystinuria, on high-protein diets, is not related to their cystine content. They state that the excretion of cystine varies with the total nitrogen excretion (i.e., with the protein intake). It is therefore suggested that " the effect of high-protein diets in increasing the urinary output of cystine in cystinuria may be due . . . to a stimulation by the protein of some processes of endogenous metabolism, which results in the production of cystine, rather than to a failure to oxidize the exogenous cystine."

In a case of cystinuria recently studied by Brand, Harris, and

[61] J. Biol. Chem., **81**, 285 (1929).

Biloon,[62] the freshly voided urine did not contain free cystine but a cystine complex of undetermined constitution. When the urine was allowed to stand this compound gradually decomposed, liberating the free amino acid.

That the finding of cystine crystals in the urine is too rigid a criterion for the detection of cystinuria is shown by Lewis'[63] survey of about 11,000 urine specimens obtained from healthy young men and women. Although only four of these were found to excrete cystine crystals, fourteen others gave a strongly positive reaction for this amino acid.

The occurrence in the urine of cystinurics of other amino acids, such as lysine and tyrosine, and the diamines, putrescine and cadaverine, has been reported on several occasions. In 1911, Ackermann and Kutscher[64] isolated lysine from the urine of a cystinuric patient. The same patient was in 1927 under the observation of F. A. Hoppe-Seyler,[65] who isolated arginine. Results of this nature are suggestive of a more generalized metabolic disturbance than one involving cystine alone. However, in the case studied by Robson, there was no evidence of the presence in the urine of lysine, tyrosine, putrescine, or cadaverine.

Owing to its insolubility, the cystine may contribute to the formation of urinary concretions.[66] It is usually stated that there are no other well-defined pathological symptoms, and, indeed, cystinurics have been known to live to a ripe old age.[67] On the contrary, Robson, in referring to his patient's history, makes this statement: "Special interest was taken in the case because of the strong family history of the disease, several members having already died from the consequences of this disturbance."

Kaufmann[68] described a case of cystinuria in a 21-month-old boy which came to autopsy. There were chalky deposits of cystine in various internal organs such as the kidneys, walls of the intestines, mesenteric nodes, liver, and particularly in the spleen. Abderhalden,[69] to whom the tissues were sent for analysis, made a careful investigation of

---

[62] *J. Biol. Chem.*, **86**, 315 (1930).

[63] *Ann. Internal Med.*, **6**, 183 (1932).

[64] *Z. Biol.*, **57**, 354 (1911).

[65] *Deut. Arch. klin. Med.*, **154**, 97 (1927).

[66] Cystine calculi may attain a considerable size. Tennant (*J. Am. Med. Assoc.*, **80**, 305 [1923]) removed fourteen concretions, aggregating 73 g. in weight, from two kidneys and a ureter. One of these weighed 50 g. Mörner has also described a cystine stone weighing 50.2 g. (cited by H. B. Lewis, *Yale J. Biol. Med.*, **4**, 437 [1932]).

[67] E. Meyer (*Deut. Arch. klin. Med.*, **172**, 207 [1931]) has observed a case of cystinuria in a woman 87 years of age.

[68] E. Kaufmann, "Pathology," translated by Stanley P. Reimann, Philadelphia, 1929, Vol. II, p. 1413.

[69] *Z. physiol. Chem.*, **38**, 557 (1903).

the dead child's relatives.   There were two living brothers, one 14 months and the other $5\frac{1}{2}$ years old.   Both were cystinurics.   Another brother had died at 17 months and a sister at the age of $9\frac{1}{2}$ months under apparently similar circumstances.   It was established that the father of these children and the paternal grandfather had cystinuria.   Negative results were obtained in the case of the mother, although Abderhalden states that when the urine was treated with alkali and lead acetate and heated a blackening was obtained.   The nature of the sulfur-compound giving this test he was not able to determine.   The paternal grandmother was negative.

Equally interesting are the two cases of cystinuria described by Lignac,[70] one in a 3-year-old boy and the other in a boy 2 years old. Both children were markedly underweight, had never learned to walk, and the older had stopped growing at the age of 2 years.   On *post mortem* examination extensive deposits of cystine were found in all parts of the body, but especially in the kidneys.   That cystinuria, particularly in the young, may be associated with a very severe and extensive pathology is clearly shown by these cases.[71]

Metabolism of Methionine.   The close metabolic relationship of this amino acid to cystine has been brought out in two types of experiment.   In the first place it has been shown that albino rats kept on a cystine-deficient diet will resume growth when the deficiency is compensated by the addition to the diet of either cystine or methionine.[57]

The other evidence has been obtained through a study of the detoxication of monobrombenzene.   This compound is ordinarily converted in the organism into *p*-bromphenyl-mercapturic acid, in which form it is excreted in the urine.[72]

$$\text{S—CH}_2$$
$$\text{HC·NH·COCH}_3$$
$$\text{Br.}\quad\text{COOH}$$

p-Bromphenyl-mercapturic acid

[70] *Deut. Arch. klin. Med.*, **145**, 139 (1924).

[71] Various aspects of the problem of cystinuria are represented in the following papers: C. L. Alsberg and O. Folin, *Am. J. Physiol.*, **14**, 54 (1905); C. G. L. Wolf and P. A. Shaffer, *J. Biol. Chem.*, **4**, 439 (1908); J. M. Looney, H. Berglund, and C. R. Graves, *ibid.*, **57**, 515 (1923); A. Magnus-Levy, *Biochem. Z.*, **156**, 150 (1925); G. Rosenfeld, *Ergebnisse Physiol.*, **18**, 118 (1920).   The student is also referred to the discussion by Garrod and to the recent review on cystinuria by Lewis, *loc. cit.*[66]

[72] The reaction involves first oxidation to *p*-bromphenol and its subsequent conjugation with cysteine.   The resulting *p*-bromphenyl-cysteine then undergoes acetylation, as indicated.   Acetylation appears to be a fairly common reaction in the animal body.

It has been established by Karl Thomas[73] that the cystine for the detoxication of monobrombenzene is derived from the protein of the diet and not at the expense of the tissues. When dogs are given a high carbohydrate diet and just sufficient protein to maintain nitrogen equilibrium (or the " wear and tear " level) brombenzene is not converted into p-bromphenyl-mercapturic acid (Kapfhammer).[74] This fact has been utilized in Sherwin's laboratory[75] as a basis for studying the possible conversion of various sulfur-containing compounds into cystine. Dogs, maintained on a carbohydrate diet, were given brombenzene along with such substances as sodium sulfate, potassium sulfocyanide, taurine, ethyl-amino-mercaptan, and cystine. Only in the case of cystine was there any formation of mercapturic acid. In a more recent detailed investigation of the problem, White and Lewis[76] determined the distribution of the various sulfur fractions of the urine after the oral administration of monobrombenzene. They found that on a low-cystine diet this compound, after oxidation to bromphenol, was conjugated with sulfuric acid and excreted as an ethereal sulfate (p. 391). Accompanying the increase in the ethereal sulfate fraction there was a corresponding decrease in inorganic sulfate. A rise in neutral sulfur was also observed. However, when cystine was given, the path of detoxication was different and resulted, as other investigators had previously shown, in the formation of p-bromphenyl-mercapturic acid. Precisely the same results were obtained when the cystine-deficient diet was supplemented with methionine. From these observations, it may be concluded that the cystine used in the detoxication was derived from the methionine. However, White and Lewis have suggested that " cystine and methionine may have some common product of intermediary metabolism, which is essential for the normal function of the organism, and that, when methionine is supplied in the diet, the cystine present is thereby made available for the detoxication of the benzene derivatives."

When heated in sulfuric acid, methionine is converted into homocystine (Butz and du Vigneaud),[77] the next higher homologue of cystine. Its formation may be represented as follows:

[73] K. Thomas and H. Straczewski, *Arch. Anat. Physiol., Physiol. Abt.*, 249 (1919).

[74] *Z. physiol. Chem.*, **116**, 302 (1921).

[75] J. A. Muldoon, G. J. Shiple, and C. P. Sherwin, *J. Biol. Chem.*, **59**, 675 (1924); see also A. M. Ambrose and C. P. Sherwin, *Ann. Rev. Biochem.*, **2**, 377 (1933).

[76] *J. Biol. Chem.*, **98**, 607 (1932).

[77] *J. Biol. Chem.*, **99**, 135 (1932–33).

$$
\begin{array}{llll}
\text{CH}_3 & & & \\
| & & & \\
\text{S} & \text{SH} & & \\
| & | & & \\
\text{CH}_2 & \text{CH}_2 & \text{CH}_2\!-\!\text{S}\!-\!\text{S}\!-\!\text{CH}_2 & \\
| & | & | \qquad\qquad | & \\
\text{CH}_2 & \text{CH}_2 & \text{CH}_2 \qquad\quad \text{CH}_2 & \\
| \;\;\rightarrow & | \;\;\rightarrow & | \qquad\qquad | & \\
\text{CHNH}_2 & \text{CHNH}_2 & \text{CHNH}_2 \quad \text{CHNH}_2 & \\
| & | & | \qquad\qquad | & \\
\text{COOH} & \text{COOH} & \text{COOH} \quad\;\; \text{COOH} & \\
\text{Methionine} & \text{Homocysteine} & \text{Homocystine} &
\end{array}
$$

This compound when added to a cystine-deficient diet promotes growth, as has been shown by du Vigneaud and associates.[58] Whether homocystine is an intermediate in the metabolism of methionine remains to be determined.

Metabolism of Phenylalanine and Tyrosine. The first step in the metabolism of phenylalanine is believed to be its conversion into tyrosine (Embden and Baldes).[78] Dakin[79] tested this idea by injecting phenylalanine into rabbits, as a result of which the urine was found to contain phenylalanine but no tyrosine or other phenolic compounds. Para-substituted phenylalanines, such as p-methyl-phenylalanine, are broken down quite readily in the animal organism. According to Dakin, these observations argue against the supposition that phenylalanine is converted exclusively into tyrosine.

That a certain amount of phenylalanine escapes conversion to tyrosine, but is oxidized to phenylpyruvic acid, is also shown by certain results that have been reported from H. B. Lewis' laboratory.[80] Rabbits injected subcutaneously with phenylalanine were found to excrete significant amounts of phenylpyruvic acid. The same result was obtained when phenylpyruvic acid itself was injected, indicating that this compound is not easily oxidized in the body. In these experiments no evidence was obtained of the excretion of p-hydroxyphenylpyruvic acid. However, this compound was not recovered in the urine even after the administration of tyrosine, from which it may be concluded that, if p-hydroxyphenylpyruvic acid is formed, it readily undergoes further metabolic change. Accordingly, it is to be assumed, at least for the present, that a considerable part of the phenylalanine probably shares with tyrosine the same fate in metabolism. The two amino acids may therefore be studied together.

[78] *Biochem. Z.*, **55**, 301 (1913).

[79] H. D. Dakin, "Oxidations and Reductions in the Animal Body," 1922, p. 86.

[80] N. F. Shambaugh, H. B. Lewis, and D. Tourtellotte, *J. Biol. Chem.*, **92**, 499 (1931); J. P. Chandler and H. B. Lewis, *ibid.*, **96**, 619 (1932). Compare with Kotake, Masai, and Mori, *Z. physiol. Chem.*, **122**, 195 (1922).

Alcaptonuria   Before this is done, however, brief reference will be made to a peculiar and rare condition, called *alcaptonuria*, which appears to be hereditary, and in which there is obviously a derangement in the metabolism of these amino acids. Alcaptonuria occurs more frequently in males than in females. Its occurrence in a rabbit has been reported by J. Lewis.[81] The urine of alcaptonurics, when allowed to stand exposed to the air, absorbs oxygen and turns black, owing to the presence of homogentisic acid, which has the following formula:

$$HO - \underset{\underset{\displaystyle COOH}{|}}{\underset{\displaystyle CH_2}{|}} \overset{\displaystyle OH}{\bigcirc}$$

Homogentisic acid

It is important to note that phenylalanine and tyrosine, when given to an alcaptonuric, are converted into homogentisic acid and excreted as such, but when given to a normal individual are oxidized completely. Moreover, when homogentisic acid itself is administered to a normal individual it is apparently oxidized, but in the alcaptonuric this is not the case. Another observation which has strengthened the view that homogentisic acid represents an intermediate stage in the normal metabolism of phenylalanine and tyrosine is that of Embden, Salomon, and Schmidt,[78] who found that all three of these substances yield acetoacetic acid when perfused through a surviving liver.[82]

Alcaptonuric individuals who reach middle life may develop *ochronosis*, a condition in which the cartilages acquire a black pigmentation. Ochronosis has also been observed in persons who over a long period of

[81] *J. Biol. Chem.*, **70**, 659 (1926).

[82] Dakin, however, does not believe that homogentisic acid formation is a necessary step in the metabolism of tyrosine. According to this investigator, there is good evidence for believing that an immediate precursor of homogentisic acid is a compound having a quinonoid structure. Dakin (J. Biol. Chem., **9**, 151 [1911]) therefore administered *p*-methylphenylalanine and *p*-methoxyphenylalanine,

$$(CH_3 \cdot C_6H_4 \cdot CH_2 \cdot CHNH_2 \cdot COOH)$$

and

$$(CH_3O \cdot C_6H_4 \cdot CH_2 \cdot CHNH_2 \cdot COOH),$$

to alcaptonurics and showed that these substances were completely oxidized, presumably because of their inability to form quinonoid derivatives. Fromherz and Hermanns (Z. physiol. Chem., **91**, 194 [1914]) performed similar experiments with *m*-methyl-tyrosine and *p*- and *m*-methyl-phenylalanine. These substances do not undergo the quinonoid transformation and, hence, did not give rise to homogentisic acid in these experiments. Accordingly, Dakin has postulated that alcaptonuria represents a condition in which there is not only an abnormal formation of homogentisic acid but also an abnormal failure to catabolize it when formed.

years have applied carbolic acid dressings to ulcers of the legs. A detailed account of the chemical and clinical aspects of ochronosis is given by Sir Archibald E. Garrod in his monograph, " Inborn Errors of Metabolism."[83]

Tyrosinosis. A second abnormality in tyrosine metabolism has been described by Medes[84] under the term " tyrosinosis." Although only one case of this remarkable condition has been described thus far, its careful study by this investigator has given considerable information concerning several stages of the intermediary metabolism of tyrosine. Briefly stated, the condition described consists in a slowing up of the first steps of tyrosine metabolism and a complete stop at the stage of *p*-hydroxyphenylpyruvic acid. This was shown by the daily excretion from endogenous sources of about 1.6 grams of *p*-hydroxy-phenylpyruvic acid (enol form).

$$OH$$

$$CH_2$$

$$C{=}O$$

$$COOH$$

p-Hydroxyphenylpyruvic acid

Increasing the protein intake, or feeding tyrosine, resulted in an increased elimination of this compound, but tyrosine and *l-p*-hydroxyphenyl-lactic acid were likewise excreted. When the ingestion of tyrosine was increased still further, the urine also contained *l*-3 : 4-dihydroxyphenylalanine. The last two compounds Medes considers to be products of side reactions and not in the main path of metabolism.

Of particular interest from the standpoint of normal metabolism is the fact that when phenylalanine was fed it caused an increased excretion of tyrosine and of *p*-hydroxyphenylpyruvic acid. When the latter compound was administered, it was excreted in the urine partly unchanged and partly as *l-p*-hydroxyphenyl-lactic acid. The last compound, when fed, was excreted unchanged.

[83] For clinical studies of alcaptonuria the student is referred to the following recent papers: H. Reinwein, *Deut. Arch. klin. Med.*, **170**, 327 (1931); P. Sachs, *ibid.*, **170**, 344 (1931); K. Ballowitz, *Jahrb. Kinderheilk.*, **134**, 182 (1932).

Ochronosis in cattle has been described by H. Fink, *Z. physiol. Chem.*, **197**, 193 (1931).

Homogentisic acid has been detected in the serum and milk of a 26-year-old mother with alcaptonuria (F. Lanyar and H. Lieb, *Z. physiol. Chem.*, **203**, 135 (1931).

[84] *Biochem. J.*, **26**, 917 (1932).

According to Medes, these observations prove that the formation of
p-hydroxyphenylpyruvic acid is an early step in the normal metabolism
of tyrosine. In the case under consideration there was obviously a
failure in the transformation of the p-hydroxyphenylpyruvic acid into
2 : 5-dihydroxyphenylpyruvic acid, as well as failure in the conversion
of tyrosine into 2 : 5-dihydroxyphenylalanine. Especially striking was
the observation that homogentisic acid, when fed, was completely
oxidized. This strongly suggests that the 2 : 5 oxidation of tyrosine and
of p-hydroxyphenylpyruvic acid, which are steps in the normal metabolism of tyrosine, was impossible for the patient with tyrosinosis, whereas
a later step, namely the oxidation of homogentisic acid, is an impossi-
bility for the alcaptonuric.

Neubauer's Theory of Tyrosine Metabolism. These results are in
harmony with Neubauer's[85] theory of the intermediary metabolism of
tyrosine, according to which two paths of oxidation are open, one leading
through p-hydroxyphenylpyruvic acid, and the other through 2 : 5 dihydroxyphenylalanine. Both lead to 2 : 5 dihydroxyphenylpyruvic acid
and in turn to homogentisic acid. The next step involves cleavage of
the benzene ring with the formation of an open-chain compound.

These stages in the metabolism of tyrosine may be represented as
follows:

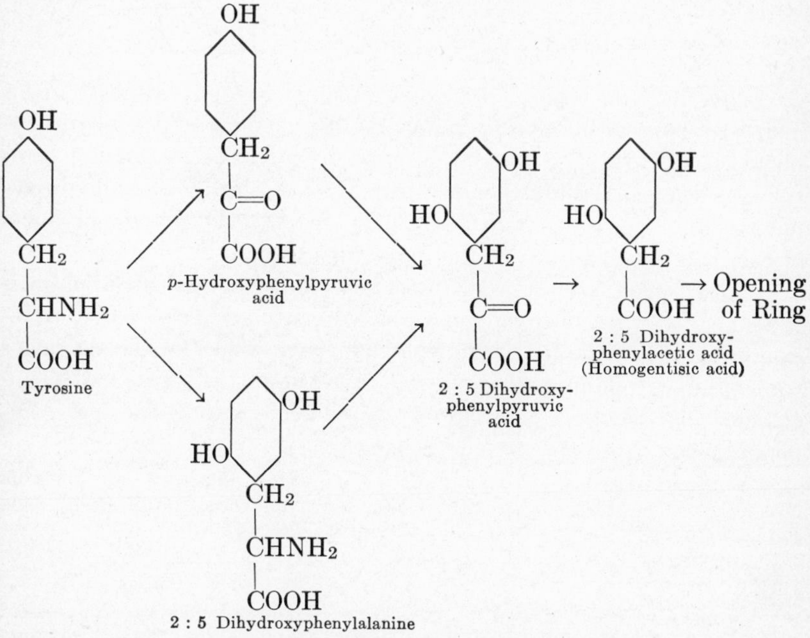

[85] O. Neubauer, "Intermediärer Eiweisstoffwechsel," in "Handbuch der nor-
malen und pathologischen Physiologie," Berlin, p. 862.

Opposed to Neubauer's theory is Dakin's conception,[86] according to which the path of oxidation of tyrosine lies only through p-hydroxy-phenylpyruvic acid, in which compound opening of the ring occurs normally. This would yield the following compound:

$$\overset{\|}{C}H-CH=COH-CH=CH-\overset{\|}{C}-CH_2-CO-COOH$$

On the other hand, if Neubauer's scheme is accepted, the latter stages of normal tyrosine metabolism may be indicated as follows:

Acetoacetic acid

From this scheme it is seen that tyrosine, and therefore phenylalanine, are ketogenic amino acids.

Synthesis. Phenylalanine and tyrosine may be formed in the body from the corresponding α-ketonic acids, as indicated from the perfusion experiments of Embden and Schmitz,[19] cited elsewhere.

This is, however, not a synthesis *de novo.* It has been the accepted opinion that either tyrosine or phenylalanine was essential in nutrition, because of the body's apparent inability to synthesize them. But the point of view has changed somewhat, since no absolute proof is available concerning the indispensability of these amino acids. Indeed, according to a recent statement of Scull and Rose,[87] only four amino acids have been thus far definitely established as indispensable dietary components, namely, *tryptophane, lysine, cystine,* and *histidine* (compare p. 561).

[86] H. D. Dakin, "Oxidations and Reductions in the Animal Body," pp. 84, et seq.
[37] *J. Biol. Chem.,* **89**, 109 (1930).

Melanin. Tyrosine is oxidized by the enzyme tyrosinase to the brownish black pigment melanin which occurs normally as the coloring matter of hair, in the choroid of the eye, and in the skin, particularly in the dark races. In the hereditary condition described as albinism, there is apparently a failure in the formation of melanin. Pathologically melanin occurs in large amounts in melanotic tumors (usually melanosarcomas). If there is extensive development of such a tumor, melanin may occur in the urine (melanuria). Cases of melanuria have, however, been reported in which a melanotic tumor was not demonstrable. The analyses of melanin that are to be found in the literature would seem to indicate a variable composition, but this is probably due to the presence of other cell constituents in the materials analyzed.[88]

The formation of melanin from tyrosine has been studied by Raper,[89] who has succeeded in isolating several of the intermediary products. The first product obtained in the oxidation of tyrosine ① is 3 : 4-dihydroxyphenylalanine ②, which is next oxidized to its corresponding quinone ③. This undergoes intramolecular change to form 5 : 6 dihydroxydihydroindole-2-carboxylic acid ④, which is oxidized to its corresponding quinone ⑤. This compound Raper believes to be the red substance which is the first visible product of the enzyme action. The enzyme tyrosinase is not necessary for the further stages of the reaction. The red substance is spontaneously decolorized, forming the base ⑥ or its carboxylic acid ⑦. These two compounds are believed to be the immediate precursors of melanin. The chemical constitution of melanin has not been definitely determined, but it has been suggested that it may be either $(C_5H_5O_3N)_n$ or $(C_8H_7O_3N)_n$, the supposition being that many molecules of the indole combine to form the amorphous melanin. The stages in the reaction resulting in the formation of the precursors of melanin are indicated by the following formulas:

---

[88] For an excellent review of the subject, the student is referred to H. G. Wells, "Chemical Pathology," 5th edition, Saunders, Philadelphia (1925), Chap. XX; see also H. Waelsch, "Zur Kentniss der natürlichen Melanine," *Z. physiol. Chem.*, **213**, 35 (1932).

[89] H. S. Raper, Biochem. J., **20**, 735 (1926), **21**, 89 (1927); *Physiol. Rev.*, **8**, 245 (1928); W. L. Duliere and Raper, Biochem. J., **24**, 239 (1930).

Tyrosine is closely related to, and together with phenylalanine is probably the precursor of, two additional substances of considerable physiological importance, epinephrin or adrenalin, the hormone of the medulla of the suprarenal (adrenal) gland, and thyroxin, the hormone of the thyroid gland. These hormones will be described in a later chapter.

Metabolism of Histidine. The fate of histidine in metabolism is obscure, and recent investigations have not elucidated the problem. It is not a sugar-forming amino acid (Rapport),[90] nor is it known to give rise to acetone bodies.[91]

Leiter[92] found that histidine injected intravenously into dogs was almost completely utilized. Even when as much as 5 grams were given, the increase in urinary imidazoles could account for only about 150 mg. of histidine. On the contrary, the injection of 1-gram quantities of methyl-imidazole and methyl-imidazole-lactic acid resulted in an excretion in the first 24 hours of approximately 30 and 40 per cent, respectively. Imidazole itself was not utilized appreciably, for 93 per cent of the 0.5 gram of this substance injected was recovered in the urine. Leiter states that in every case the increased urinary imidazole output was due entirely to the presence of the same imidazole as the one injected. These results indicate that the body has a high capacity for destroying the imidazole ring when attached to a side chain, particularly as in histidine, but that it does not have this capacity in the absence of the side chain. Leiter's conclusion was that none of the compounds which he used was an intermediary in the metabolism of any of the others. In considering Leiter's data in the light of later

[90] D. Rapport, *Physiol. Rev.*, **10**, 349, and especially 397 (1930).
[91] Compare H. D. Dakin and A. J. Wakeman, *J. Biol. Chem.*, **10**, 499 (1912); Dakin, *ibid.*, **14**, 321 (1913); M. Konishi, *Z. physiol. Chem.*, **122**, 237 (1922).
[92] *J. Biol. Chem.*, **64**, 125 (1925).

investigations, it seems that the possibility of partial conversion of imidazole-lactic acid to histidine, in his experiments, has not been ruled out.

It has been suggested that urocanic acid, β-imidazole-acrylic acid, may be an intermediate product of the metabolism of histidine. Its occurrence in dogs' urine (Jaffe),[93] especially after feeding large amounts of histidine (Kotake and Konishi),[94] and in the urine of the coyote (Swain)[95] has been reported. Others have failed to find this constituent in the urine.[95a]

Koessler and Hanke[96] estimated the daily urinary excretion of imidazole complexes in normal individuals to vary between 120 to 220 mg. Considerably higher values have been reported by Kauffmann and Engel[97] (150 to 600 mg.). The lowest concentrations have been encountered in nephritis; relatively high values have been obtained in diseases of the liver.

Histidine is one of the sources of purines in metabolism. Rats maintained on an histidine-free diet excrete less uric acid and allantoin than normal. With the addition of histidine to the deficient diet, there is an increased excretion of these constituents, as well as of creatinine (Rose and Cook).[98] The inability of the organism to synthesize histidine and hence its indispensability in nutrition seems to be well established. It has been shown, however, that both in metabolism and for growth histidine may be replaced by imidazole-lactic acid.[99]

It is to be noted here that histidine is not the only source of purines in metabolism. Further than this, no attempt will be made at this point to trace the fate of histidine in the body. The following formulas bring out the structural relationship between histidine, imidazole-lactic acid, allantoin, and uric acid:

[93] *Ber.*, **7**, 1669 (1874); **8**, 811 (1875).

[94] *Z. physiol. Chem.*, **122**, 230 (1920).

[95] *Am. J. Physiol.*, **13**, 30 (1905).

[95a] Compare: S. Edlbacher and J. Kraus, *Z. physiol. Chem.*, **191**, 225 (1930); **195**, 267 (1931); E. Abderhalden, *ibid.* **200**, 87 (1931); F. Kauffmann and E. Mislowitzer, *Biochem. Z.* **226**, 325 (1930). According to Edlbacher, the imidazole ring in histidine is disrupted by deamination, through the action of a specific enzyme, histidase, yielding glutamic acid. It is difficult to reconcile this with the fact that histidine does not form sugar in phlorhizin glycosuria.

[96] *J. Biol. Chem.*, **59**, 803 (1924).

[97] *Z. klin. Med.*, **114**, 405 (1930).

[98] *J. Biol. Chem.*, **64**, 325 (1925).

[99] G. J. Cox and W. C. Rose, *J. Biol. Chem.*, **68**, 781 (1926); see also B. Harrow and C. P. Sherwin, *ibid.*, **70**, 683 (1926).

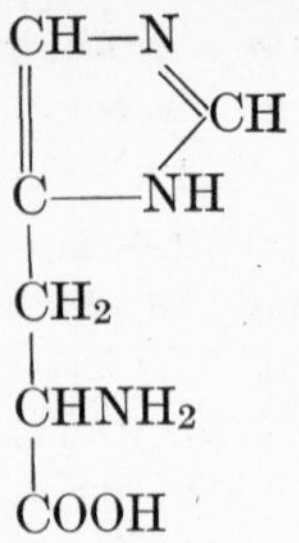

$$
\begin{array}{c}
\text{CH—N} \\
\ \ \| \qquad \text{>CH} \\
\text{C—NH} \\
| \\
\text{CH}_2 \\
| \\
\text{CHNH}_2 \\
| \\
\text{COOH}
\end{array}
$$

Histidine

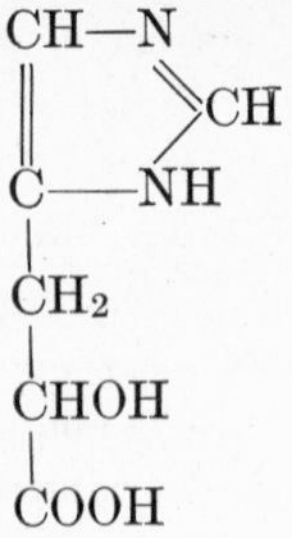

$$
\begin{array}{c}
\text{CH—N} \\
\ \ \| \qquad \text{>CH} \\
\text{C—NH} \\
| \\
\text{CH}_2 \\
| \\
\text{CHOH} \\
| \\
\text{COOH}
\end{array}
$$

Imidazole-lactic acid

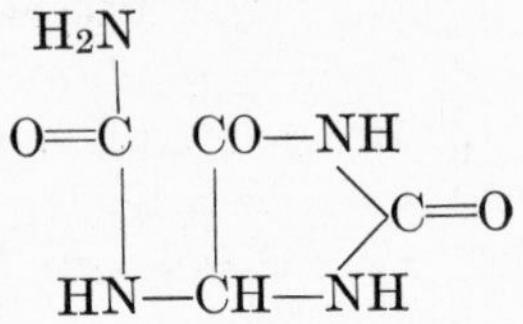

$$
\begin{array}{c}
\text{H}_2\text{N} \\
| \\
\text{O=C} \quad \text{CO—NH} \\
| \qquad\quad \text{>C=O} \\
\text{HN—CH—NH}
\end{array}
$$

Allantoin

$$
\begin{array}{c}
\text{HN—C=O} \\
| \qquad | \\
\text{O=C} \quad \text{C—NH} \\
| \qquad \| \qquad \text{>C=O} \\
\text{HN—C—NH}
\end{array}
$$

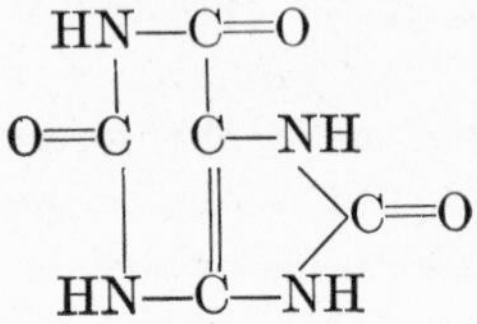

Uric acid

In 1909, Tanret[100] isolated a base from ergot, which Barger and Ewins[101] identified as the betaine of thiolhistidine, represented by the following structural formula:

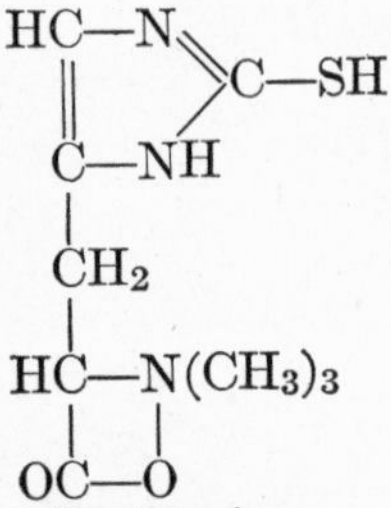

$$
\begin{array}{c}
\text{HC—N} \\
\ \ \| \qquad \text{>C—SH} \\
\text{C—NH} \\
| \\
\text{CH}_2 \\
| \\
\text{HC—N(CH}_3)_3 \\
|\qquad | \\
\text{OC—O}
\end{array}
$$

Ergothioneine
(Thioneine)

This substance was named ergothioneine. Several years ago it became apparent that the blood corpuscles contained a hitherto unknown sulfur compound. This was eventually shown to be identical with ergothioneine.[102, 103] Benedict and his associates have suggested that the term ergothioneine be contracted to *thioneine*. Human blood is reported to have 10–25 mg. per 100 cc. of this substance, and hog's blood,

---

[100] *J. pharm. chim.*, **30**, series 6, 145 (1909).

[101] *Trans. Chem. Soc.*, **99**, 2336 (1911).

[102] E. B. Newton, S. R. Benedict, and H. D. Dakin, *Science*, **64**, 602 (1926); *J. Biol. Chem.*, **72**, 367 (1927).

[103] B. A. Eagles and T. B. Johnson, *J. Am. Chem. Soc.*, **49**, 575 (1927); Hunter and Eagles, *J. Biol. Chem.*, **72**, 123 (1927).

14.5 mg. per 100 cc. However, considerable variations have been observed in the blood of pigs from different localities. Eagles and Vars[104] have reported certain experiments on pigs which they had fed protein hydrolyzates and suggest that the precursor of thioneine may be thiolhistidine. The physiological significance of thioneine remains to be determined.

Muscle contains a compound, carnosine, first isolated by Gulewitsch and Amiradzibi,[105] which has been shown to be β-alanyl-histidine. Closely related to this is anserine, or β-alanyl-methyl-carnosine, discovered in goose muscle and more recently in certain fishes by Ackermann and associates.[106]

Metabolism of Proline and Hydroxyproline. The structural relationship of proline, hydroxyproline, ornithine, derived from arginine, and glutamic acid, which is brought out by the following formulas, suggests the probability that these compounds share a common fate in metabolism.

$$
\begin{array}{cccc}
\text{COOH} & \text{CH}_2\text{NH}_2 & \text{CH}_2\text{---} & \text{CH}_2\text{---} \\
| & | & | & | \\
\text{CH}_2 & \text{CH}_2 & \text{CH}_2 & \text{CHOH} \\
| & | & | & | \\
\text{CH}_2 & \text{CH}_2 & \text{CH}_2 & \text{CH}_2 \\
| & | & | & | \\
\text{CHNH}_2 & \text{CHNH}_2 & \text{CH---NH} & \text{CH---NH} \\
| & | & | & | \\
\text{COOH} & \text{COOH} & \text{COOH} & \text{COOH} \\
\text{Glutamic} & \text{Ornithine} & \text{Proline} & \text{Hydroxyproline} \\
\text{acid} & & &
\end{array}
$$

In support of this idea may be mentioned the work of Dakin, who determined that the conversion of proline into glucose in phlorhizin glycosuria is sufficient to account for 3 of the 5 carbon atoms in proline. It will be recalled that only 3 carbon atoms of glutamic acid and of arginine are capable of conversion into glucose.

Moreover, there is some ground for the assumption that proline may be synthesized in the body from glutamic acid. Indeed, part of this transformation, namely the synthesis of pyrrolidone carboxylic acid ($\overline{\text{CO} \cdot \text{CH}_2 \cdot \text{CH}_2 \cdot \text{CHNH} \cdot \text{COOH}}$), has been accomplished in the laboratory (Abderhalden and Kautzsch).[107]

[104] *J. Biol. Chem.*, **80**, 615 (1928).

[105] *Ber.*, **33**, 1902 (1900); *Z. physiol. Chem.*, **30**, 565 (1900).

[106] D. Ackermann, O. Timpe, and K. Poller, *Z. physiol. Chem.*, **183**, 1 (1929); Ackermann and F. A. Hoppe-Seyler, *ibid.*, **197**, 135 (1931).

[107] *Z. physiol. Chem.*, **68**, 487 (1910).

Proline and hydroxyproline are oxidized by liver, apparently by a dehydrogenase,[108] but the end-products have not yet been determined.

From studies conducted by St. Julian and Rose[109] it appears that proline and probably hydroxyproline are non-essential dietary components. Indeed, even after removing the remaining 5-carbon amino acids (glutamic acid and arginine, which yields ornithine), as well as aspartic acid, the nutritive value of the resulting material was unaltered. In view of these results, it may be concluded that proline and hydroxyproline are formed in the body from other substances.

Tryptophane Metabolism. From the urine of certain animals (dog, rabbit, rat) there has been isolated a compound, *kynurenic acid*, which is obviously a product of tryptophane metabolism. Several theories for its formation have been proposed, one being that of Ellinger and Matsuoka,[110] according to which the first step is the formation of indole-pyruvic acid. When this substance is injected or fed to rabbits, it behaves like tryptophane in producing kynurenic acid. The various changes according to Ellinger's theory are indicated in the following scheme:

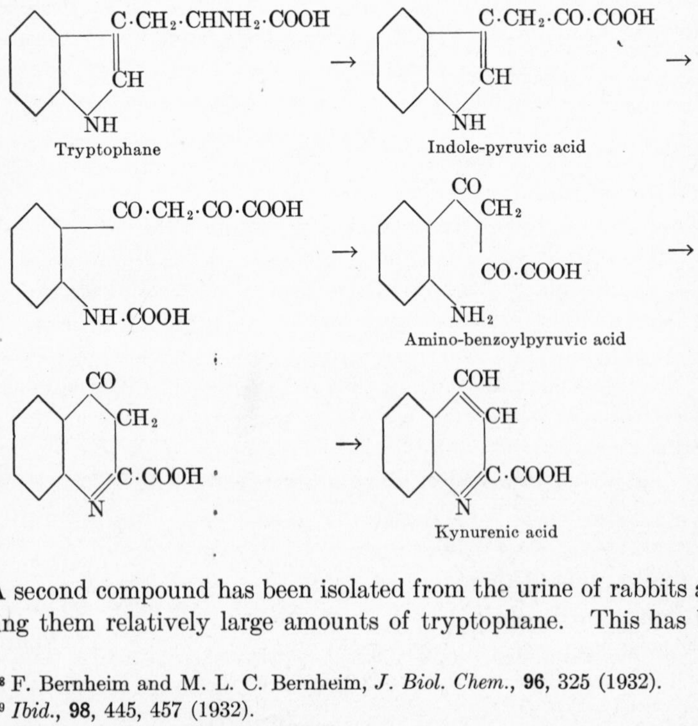

Tryptophane → Indole-pyruvic acid →

→ Amino-benzoylpyruvic acid →

→ Kynurenic acid

A second compound has been isolated from the urine of rabbits after feeding them relatively large amounts of tryptophane. This has been

---

[108] F. Bernheim and M. L. C. Bernheim, *J. Biol. Chem.*, **96**, 325 (1932).
[109] *Ibid.*, **98**, 445, 457 (1932).
[110] *Z. physiol. Chem.*, **109**, 259 (1920).

identified as *kynurenin* and is doubtless an intermediate between tryptophane and kynurenic acid.[111]

$$\underset{\text{Kynurenin}}{\bigcirc} \quad \overset{\text{COOH}}{\underset{\text{NH}_2}{\overset{|}{-C}}} = CH - CHNH_2 - COOH$$

Inasmuch as Ellinger and Matsuoka's theory makes no provision for the formation of kynurenin, Kotake has proposed a somewhat different hypothesis. This, however, makes no allowance for the production of indole-pyruvic acid.

There is evidence that kynurenic acid is formed in the liver, and that, at least in dogs, a considerable proportion is excreted in the bile. The prevailing conception is that kynurenic acid is not a link in the chain of normal tryptophane oxidation in the animal body, but rather that it is an end-product of a set of side reactions brought into play especially when tryptophane is administered in excess of ordinary metabolic requirements (Jackson and Jackson).[112] In view of this it is somewhat difficult to explain the disappearance of ingested kynurenic acid in man.[113]

Life cannot be maintained indefinitely on a diet lacking tryptophane, for the body cannot synthesize this amino acid *de novo*. However, it has been shown that indole-pyruvic acid can serve as a biological substitute for tryptophane,[114] suggesting the reversibility of the tryptophane → indole-pyruvic acid transformation. On the other hand, kynurenin is not available as a substitute for tryptophane. The rôle of this amino acid in nutrition will be discussed in a later chapter.

It has been reported that tryptophane and kynurenin give rise to the urinary pigment urochrome.[115]

Concerning the main path in the intermediary metabolism of tryptophane the one fact that seems to be fairly well established is the formation of indole-pyruvic acid. Much therefore remains to be done before the problem of the metabolism of this important amino acid is finally solved.

[111] Z. Matsuoka and N. Yoshimatsu, Z. *physiol. Chem.*, **143**, 206 (1925); Y. Kotake and associates, *ibid.*, **195**, 139 et seq. (1931); **214**, 1 (1933).

[112] J. *Biol. Chem.*, **96**, 697 (1932).

[113] The formation of kynurenic acid from various tryptophane derivatives has been investigated by C. P. Berg, J. *Biol. Chem.*, **91**, 513 (1931); L. C. Bauguess and Berg, *ibid.*, **104**, 691 (1934).

[114] R. W. Jackson, J. *Biol. Chem.*, **84**, 1 (1929); C. P. Berg, W. C. Rose, and C. S. Marvel, *ibid.*, **85**, 219 (1929).

[115] Y. Kotake and H. Sakata, Z. *physiol. Chem.*, **195**, 184 (1931).

CHAPTER XIII

INTERMEDIARY METABOLISM OF PROTEIN (Continued)

UREA

In mammals, amphibia, and most fishes, the chief end-product of protein metabolism is urea; in birds and reptiles, it is uric acid. The amount of urea formed depends on the diet, being greater on a high-protein diet than on a low one. A normal adult, on a protein intake of 100 to 120 grams, excretes about 30 grams of urea, which, expressed in terms of nitrogen, is equivalent to about 15 grams. The urea nitrogen excreted in twenty-four hours usually varies between 80 and 90 per cent of the total nitrogen, but when the total nitrogen is very low (4–7 grams), the percentage in the form of urea nitrogen is much lower (about 50 or 60 per cent of the total nitrogen).

A portion of the urea has its origin in arginine, but the major part is formed in the body from the ammonia which is split off in the deamination of amino acids. It has been supposed that the ammonia combines with carbon dioxide to form ammonium carbonate which, by the loss of one molecule of water, yields ammonium carbamate and, by the loss of a second molecule, yields urea. These reactions are indicated by the following formulas:

$$2NH_3 + CO_2 + H_2O \rightleftarrows C{<}^{ONH_4}_{ONH_4} \rightleftarrows C{<}^{ONH_4}_{NH_2} + H_2O \rightleftarrows C{<}^{NH_2}_{NH_2} + H_2O$$

$$\underset{\text{Ammonium}}{} \quad \underset{\text{carbonate}}{} \qquad \underset{\text{Ammonium}}{} \quad \underset{\text{carbamate}}{} \qquad \underset{\text{Urea}}{}$$

The conception of Fearon[1] that cyanic acid is an intermediate in the formation of urea as well as in its decomposition by urease has been definitely disproved by Sumner and associates.[2] In the enzymic

---

[1] *Biochem. J.*, **17**, 84, 800 (1917); *Physiol. Rev.*, **6**, 399 (1926).

[2] J. B. Sumner, *J. Biol. Chem.*, **68**, 101 (1926); Sumner, D. B. Hand, and R. G. Holloway, *ibid.*, **91**, 333 (1931). See also N. N. Iwanoff, *Biochem. Z.*, **150**, 108 (1924); H. D. Kay, *Biochem. J.*, **17**, 277 (1923).

hydrolysis of urea, Sumner considers ammonium carbamate to be the intermediate product.

A new theory has been recently advanced by Krebs and Henseleit,[3] based on a large number of determinations of the utilization of ammonia and carbon dioxide and the production of urea by slices of various organs kept in appropriate nutritive solutions. Of all the tissues studied, only the liver produced urea under these conditions. The rate of its formation from ammonia and carbon dioxide was greatly accelerated by the the addition of *ornithine*. In the presence of this substance, Krebs and Henseleit found the ratio of ammonia consumed to urea formed to be 1.81, as contrasted with the theoretical value of 2.0, indicating that some of the ammonia was derived from sources other than the added ammonia, presumably amino acids contained in the tissue. A large variety of amino acids and nitrogenous bases were tested, but none produced the acceleration characteristic of ornithine with the exception of *citrulline*, derived from ornithine by the addition of a molecule each of ammonia and carbon dioxide. In the presence of citrulline, the ratio 1.38 was obtained, which suggested it to be an intermediate—indeed, the first product in the conversion of ammonia into urea. The second step was considered to be a reaction between citrulline and a molecule of ammonia, resulting in the formation of arginine. In the presence of arginase, this decomposes to urea and ornithine. Thus the ornithine may be used over and over again, producing many times its molecular equivalent of urea. These reactions may be represented as follows:

$$
\begin{array}{cccc}
 & & & \begin{array}{c} NH_2 \\ | \\ O{=}C \\ \backslash \\ NH_2 \\ \text{Urea} \end{array} \\[2em]
 & \begin{array}{c} NH_2 \\ / \\ O{=}C \\ \backslash \\ NH \end{array} & \begin{array}{c} NH_2 \\ / \\ HN{=}C \\ \backslash \\ NH \end{array} & \\[2em]
\begin{array}{c} NH_2 \\ | \\ CH_2 \\ | \\ CH_2 \\ | \\ CH_2 \\ | \\ CHNH_2 \\ | \\ COOH \\ \text{Ornithine} \end{array}
& \xrightarrow[+\,NH_3]{+\,CO_2}
\begin{array}{c} NH \\ | \\ CH_2 \\ | \\ CH_2 \\ | \\ CH_2 \\ | \\ CHNH_2 \\ | \\ COOH \\ \text{Citrulline} \end{array}
\xrightarrow{+\,NH_3}
\begin{array}{c} NH \\ | \\ CH_2 \\ | \\ CH_2 \\ | \\ CH_2 \\ | \\ CHNH_2 \\ | \\ COOH \\ \text{Arginine} \end{array}
\xrightarrow{+\,H_2O}
\begin{array}{c} NH_2 \\ | \\ CH_2 \\ | \\ CH_2 \\ | \\ CH_2 \\ | \\ CHNH_2 \\ | \\ COOH \\ \text{Ornithine} \end{array}
\end{array}
$$

[3] *Z. physiol. Chem.*, **210**, 33 (1932).

Inasmuch as the third step depends on the presence of arginase, this theory explains the non-formation of urea in birds, in the livers of which this enzyme is lacking.

That the ammonia liberated in the deamination of amino acids and other substances such as taurine, sarcosine, and asparagine is available for urea production has been shown by Krebs[4] in a series of experiments in which these compounds were added to liver tissue (rat). With a few exceptions (d-isoleucine, l-aspartic acid, glutamic acid, cystine, phenylalanine), the addition of amino acids resulted in a measurable increase in urea formation.

Function of the Liver in the Production of Urea. The site of the formation of urea has been the subject of numerous investigations. All possible conclusions have been reached, namely (a) that urea is formed exclusively in the liver, (b) that urea is formed by all the tissues, but chiefly by the liver, (c) that all the tissues contribute to the formation of urea and that the liver plays no special rôle in this regard. The experimental evidence upon which these views are based has been reviewed by Bollman, Mann, and Magath.[5]

These investigators studied the effect of complete removal of the liver on urea formation in more than 90 dogs. In every case where urine was secreted after the operation, it was found to contain much less urea than normally. The urea content of the blood and tissues was likewise diminished very markedly. Assuming that no urea was being formed because of the absence of the liver, it was reasonable to argue that, if the excretion of urea were prevented in some way, the urea of the blood and tissues would neither increase nor decrease but remain constant. The correctness of this assumption Bollman and his associates were able to prove in a very satisfactory manner. From certain dogs they removed both kidneys and the liver simultaneously. Because of the removal of the kidneys and the resulting anuria, there would have followed a progressive accumulation of urea in the system if any were being manufactured. Their results showed very definitely, however, that the blood urea remained at a constant level after the operation. In other series of experiments, they removed both kidneys and, after a given interval, during which there occurred a progressive increase of urea in the blood, the liver as well. Immediately after the second operation, the increase in urea ceased and its concentration remained at a fairly constant level during the remainder of the experiment. It seemed obvious, therefore, that the production of urea in the body of

---

[4] Z. physiol. Chem., **217**, 191 (1933).
[5] Am. J. Physiol., **69**, 371 (1924); **92**, 92 (1930).

the dog is entirely dependent on the presence of the liver, since urea formation ceases completely as soon as the liver is removed.[6]

Kisch[7] has reported extra-hepatic urea production in selachians, part of the evidence being based on experiments with dehepatized torpedo rays. Inasmuch as arginase is widely distributed in fishes (and especially in selachians, of which the dogfish is the example most completely studied by Hunter and Dauphinee (see p. 388), this result is in harmony with Krebs and Henseleit's theory of urea formation (p. 411).

One may recall in this connection the classical experiment of Minkowski,[8] who, on extirpating the livers of geese, discovered that the uric acid content of the urine was markedly diminished, being replaced by ammonia. These observations indicated that the tissues contributed little if anything to the conversion of ammonia into uric acid. The formation of uric acid in birds, as has already been pointed out, is the analogue of urea formation in mammals.

Ammonia. The normal daily excretion of ammonia in the urine is quite appreciable, being usually in the neighborhood of 0.7 gram. As contrasted with this is the exceedingly low content of ammonia in the blood.[9] It is, of course, conceivable that the kidney may be able to

[6] Rabinowitch (*J. Biol. Chem.*, **83**, 333 [1929]) has reported an unusual case of acute yellow atrophy of unknown origin in which the involvement of the liver was so severe that on *post mortem* examination it looked as though all the glandular epithelium had disappeared, leaving the framework only. Microscopic study of many sections revealed only isolated liver cells, and the staining properties of even these were poor. Under these circumstances the liver must have been practically without function. The kidneys were likewise extensively damaged so that there was almost complete suppression of urine secretion. Before death this patient was in a condition not unlike that of the experimental animals, used by Bollman, Mann, and Magath, in which both the liver and kidneys had been removed. The biochemical findings were likewise similar. The amount of urea found in the urine was practically negligible both on account of the low concentration (0.07 per cent) and the exceedingly small volume (not more than 20 cc. per 24 hours, according to a personal communication). The blood-sugar concentration was 0.046 per cent before and 0.03 per cent after fermentation, which shows that only 16 mg. of glucose was present in 100 cc. of blood. There was no urea in the blood. On the contrary, the amino acid nitrogen concentration was very high, namely 216 mg. per 100 cc., which shows that there was marked retention of amino acids due to impaired renal function and practically no conversion of these into urea. These findings, unique in the literature, confirm the conclusions of Bollman, Mann, and Magath that the liver is the site of urea formation.

[7] *Biochem. Z.*, **225**, 197 (1930).

[8] *Arch. Exp. Path. Pharm.*, **21**, 41 (1886).

[9] The ammonia concentration of the blood has usually been given as less than 0.05 mg. per 100 cc. According to Folin, this low estimate is due to incomplete recovery and that approximately 0.1 mg. is the more nearly correct normal value (*J. Biol. Chem.*, **97**, 141 [1932]). See also Van Slyke and Hiller, *ibid.*, **102**, 499 (1933).

concentrate ammonium salts to a greater extent than other urinary constituents, but even granting this, there would still be many facts left unexplained. The ammonia elimination may be modified, especially by the intake of acids and fixed bases. The former causes an increase in ammonia elimination, the latter a decrease. Acidosis is characterized by a high ammonia output in the urine. The significance of these changes has been determined through the study of the acid-base equilibrium in conditions of acidosis. The organism can apparently afford to lose considerable quantities of ammonia much better than it can afford to lose fixed bases (K, Na, Ca). Therefore, any ammonia which may be formed for the purpose of neutralizing acid spares an equivalent amount of fixed base. However, inasmuch as there is so little ammonia in the circulation, it can hardly be considered to have a significant rôle in the neutralization of acids transported in the blood. Whatever part it does play in the neutralization of acid may therefore be related to the function of the kidney.

The doctrine that urinary ammonia originates in the kidney has been largely advanced by Nash and Benedict.[10] These investigators have contended that, if the kidneys functioned merely in excreting ammonia formed in other tissues, the effect of total nephrectomy or of tying off the ureters would be an accumulation of ammonia in the blood. Instead, Nash and Benedict found that these surgical manipulations produced no change in the ammonia content of the blood, although there was abundant evidence of retention of other non-protein nitrogenous constituents. They were also able to show that the blood collected from the renal vein in dogs contained on an average twice as much ammonia as was present in blood collected from other sources, such as the vena cava and carotid artery. It would appear, therefore, that the kidney, instead of excreting ammonia from the blood, actually forms the ammonia which it excretes, and in addition contributes a small amount of ammonia to the blood.

These observations have been confirmed by Loeb, Atchley, and E. M. Benedict,[11] who likewise observed that the blood from the renal vein of the dog contained more ammonia than blood from the vena cava or femoral artery. In rabbits the situation is somewhat different, as might be expected from the fact that these animals excrete an alkaline urine which contains only traces of ammonia. Accordingly, little ammonia should be formed in the kidney and hence its content in the

[10] J. Biol. Chem., 48, 463 (1921); 69, 381 (1926); Benedict and Nash, ibid., 82, 673 (1929); Nash and Williams, 94, 783 (1932); J. Pharmacol., 45, 487 (1932).
[11] J. Biol. Chem., 60, 491 (1924).

blood of the renal vein should not differ appreciably from the concentrations elsewhere in the circulation. This is precisely what Loeb and his associates found.

It is interesting to note that in uranium nephritis[12] (and this has also been observed in clinical nephritis), there is a marked reduction in the excretion of ammonia.

As to the precursors of urinary ammonia, the evidence is conflicting. It was the opinion of Wakeman and Dakin[13] that the reaction $NH_3 \rightarrow$ urea is irreversible. However, Nash and Benedict were led to the conclusion that urea was the most probable precursor of urinary ammonia, although they did not exclude the possibility that the ammonia may be derived from amino acids reaching the kidney. On the other hand, Mann and Bollman considered the source to be practically limited to urea. It will be recalled that in hepatectomized dogs there is a cessation of urea production. Mann and Bollman[14] observed that, when the urine of dehepatized dogs became extremely low in urea, the ammonia content was likewise diminished. If at this time urea was injected intravenously, there resulted a definite increase in ammonia excretion, an effect which was not produced by the injection of amino acids. It was therefore logical to conclude that urea is the precursor of urinary ammonia.

This view has been challenged, however. It has been shown, for example, in perfusion experiments with dog's kidney, that there is an increase in the ammonia content of the perfusate after the addition of glycine to the perfusion fluid.[15] According to Krebs,[16] amino acids are deaminized more rapidly by kidney than by liver. This investigator found no evidence for the conversion of urea into ammonia by slices of kidney. It is seen therefore that, although the site of urinary ammonia formation is well established, the question of its precursors is still unsettled.

[12] B. M. Hendrix and M. Bodansky, *ibid.*, **60**, 657 (1924).

[13] *Ibid.*, **9**, 327 (1911).

[14] *Am. J. Physiol.*, **85**, 390 (1928); **92**, 92 (1930).

[15] A. Bornstein and G. Budelmann, *Biochem. Z.*, **218**, 64 (1930); see also A. Patey and E. B. Holmes, *Biochem. J.*, **24**, 1564 (1930).

[16] *Z. physiol. Chem.*, **217**, 191 (1933); **218**, 157 (1933). Deamination occurred much more rapidly under aerobic than under anaerobic conditions. It may also be noted that according to Krebs' data the formation of ammonia at the expense of amino acids occurred, though in very small amounts, in tissues other than the liver and kidney (diaphragm, spleen, testicle, thyroid, pancreas, placenta, brain, retina, etc.). This is in conflict with the prevailing view of the non-ubiquitous formation of ammonia, with the possible exception of that derived from adenylic acid.

Ammonia from Adenylic Acid.   In 1927 Embden and Zimmermann[17] isolated from muscle a substance which proved to be adenosine-phosphoric acid (adenylic acid). As it exists in resting muscle, it is believed to be in combination with two additional labile molecules of phosphoric acid. The combination was first considered to be in the form of pyrophosphate, but the compound is now believed to be adenosine-triphosphoric acid. It is likely that deamination of adenylic acid and of the triphosphate proceed simultaneously and at about the same rate, the products formed being inosine-phosphate (inosinic acid) and inosine-triphosphate, respectively. The former compound (p. 433) has been known for a long time, having been discovered by Liebig in 1847, but its significance was unappreciated until the important researches of Embden[18] and of Parnas[19] and their associates made it clear that the deamination of adenylic acid is related to muscular activity.

Under anaerobic conditions adenylic acid is converted into inosinic acid, the latter accumulating in the muscle. However, when oxygen is available and muscle is working without fatigue, large amounts of ammonia may accumulate, but there is no decrease in adenylic acid. The restoration of the adenylic acid is apparently due to the re-amination of the inosinic acid. According to Parnas, the reaction adenylic acid $\rightarrow$ inosinic acid is irreversible, the ammonia being derived from amino acids. In accordance with this view, the changes during contraction and recovery may be represented as follows:

1. Contraction.

   Adenylic acid $\rightarrow$ inosinic acid $+$ NH_3

2. Recovery.

   Inosinic acid $+$ O_2 $+$ amino-acid X $\rightarrow$ adenylic acid $+$ deaminized X

Opposed to this conception is the view of Embden, who considered the process a reversible one, the ammonia previously liberated from the adenylic acid entering into the recovery reaction.

Since its discovery by Embden, the distribution of adenylic acid has been found to be widespread. Indeed, Parnas refers to its ubiquitous occurrence in animal tissues. It is also an important constituent of yeast, though it appears that the adenylic acid from this source differs somewhat in constitution from that contained in muscle.

[17] *Z. physiol. Chem.*, **167**, 137 (1927).

[18] *Ibid.*, **179**, 149 (1928).

[19] J. K. Parnas and W. Mozolowski, *Biochem. Z.*, **184**, 399 (1927); Parnas, *ibid.*, **206**, 16 (1929).

The rôle of this remarkable compound in glycolysis has been referred to elsewhere (p. 319) and has been studied especially by Euler and Myrbäck[20] and Meyerhof.[21] Its importance in muscular activity is related to the resynthesis of creatine-phosphate, an endothermic reaction the energy for which is supplied by the breakdown of adenosinephosphate or of lactic acid.[22]

The occurrence of adenylic acid in kidney necessitates its consideration as a possible precursor of urinary ammonia. However, inasmuch as it is present in relatively small amounts it is not likely to be an important source. Nor is there necessarily any relation between the ammonia formed in muscle and that which is excreted in the urine. In attempting, however, to associate the two, Bliss[23] has postulated that the ammonia is transported as an amide in combination with the blood proteins and that this complex is enzymically deaminized in the kidney, resulting in the liberation of ammonia which in turn combines with an acid radical (such as lactate) and is excreted in the urine. A criticism of this view is to be found in recent papers by Benedict and Nash, and Nash and Williams.[24]

CREATINE AND CREATININE

Creatine is methyl-guanidine acetic acid. It is widely distributed in animal tissues and is especially abundant in skeletal muscle. Calculations based on chemical analyses of the tissues indicate that the adult human body contains on an average about 100 grams of creatine, most of which is present in the muscles, where its concentration normally averages about 450 mg. per 100 grams. Heart muscle contains approximately 250 mg. per cent of creatine.

Creatinine is the anhydride of creatine and is a normal constituent of urine. From 1 to 2 grams of this substance are excreted daily by an adult man or woman, this amount being constant from day to day, espe-

[20] Z. physiol. Chem., **136**, 107 (1924); **138**, 1 (1924); **139**, 281 (1924).

[21] O. Meyerhof, "Die chemischen Vorgänge im Muskel," Berlin (1930).

[22] It has been estimated that the energy required for the resynthesis of phosphocreatine (when the reaction is alkaline) is equivalent to 12 large calories per mol. In the decomposition of adenosine-triphosphoric acid, 25 large calories are liberated when two phosphate groups are split off. An additional 8 calories are supplied when the substance is deaminized. For details the student is referred to O. Meyerhof, and K. Lohmann, Biochem. Z., **253**, 431 (1932). See also the reviews "The Chemistry of Muscle," by J. K. Parnas, Ann. Rev. Biochem., **1**, 431 (1932); **2**, 317 (1933), and T. H. Milroy's review, "The Present Status of the Chemistry of Skeletal Muscular Contraction," Physiol. Rev., **11**, 515 (1931).

[23] J. Biol. Chem., **81**, 137 (1929); J. Pharmacol., **40**, 171 (1930); **44**. 397 (1932).

[24] J. Biol. Chem., **82**, 673 (1929); **94**, 783 (1932); J. Pharmacol., **45**, 487 (1932).

cially in males. Normally, creatine is not found in the urine of male adults. It is occasionally found in the urine of females, and in that of children it is a normally occurring constituent. As first shown by Folin,[25] the elimination of creatinine is not influenced by the amount of protein in the diet, but is apparently a measure of endogenous protein metabolism.

When heated in acid solution, creatine is converted into creatinine; in an alkaline solution the reverse change takes place. The close chemical relationship between creatine and creatinine and the ease with which one is changed into the other in the laboratory would suggest that they are similarly affiliated physiologically. The subject of creatine and creatinine metabolism has engaged the efforts of numerous biochemists, and yet our knowledge of it is still incomplete.

The relation of creatine to creatinine is indicated by the following formulas:

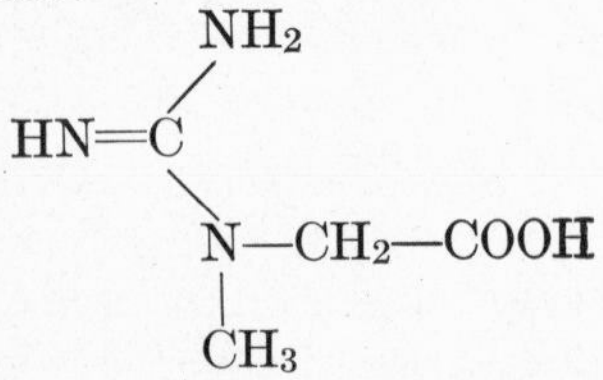

$$HN=C \begin{matrix} NH_2 \\ \diagup \\ \diagdown \\ N-CH_2-COOH \\ | \\ CH_3 \end{matrix}$$

Creatine

$$HN=C \begin{matrix} NH \\ \diagup & \diagdown \\ & C=O \\ N-CH_2 \\ | \\ CH_3 \end{matrix}$$

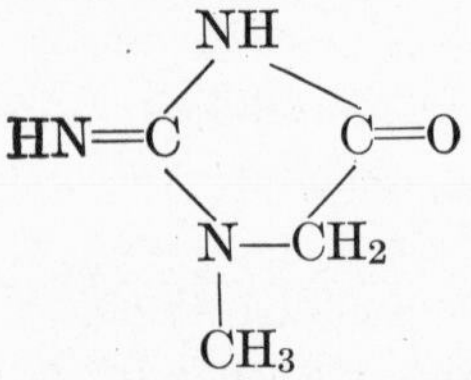

Creatinine

It is believed, however, that free creatine doubtless exists in the form of an internal salt, represented as follows:

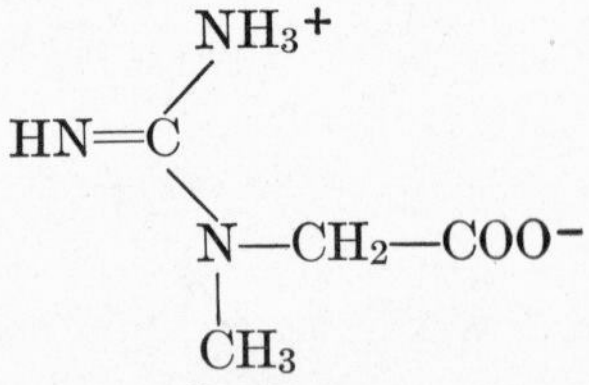

$$HN=C \begin{matrix} NH_3{}^+ \\ \diagup \\ \diagdown \\ N-CH_2-COO^- \\ | \\ CH_3 \end{matrix}$$

Creatine

Origin of Creatine. First we shall consider briefly the theories which have been proposed for the origin of creatine. According to Knoop[26] and Neubauer,[27] arginine may give rise in the body to γ-guanidine-butyric acid and in turn to guanidine-acetic acid, from which, by methylation, creatine would be formed. The conversion of guanidine-acetic acid into creatine has been reported by several investigators and seems to be fairly generally accepted, but on the other hand the metabolic relationship between arginine and creatine has not been established.

[25] *Am. J. Physiol.*, **13**, 66 (1905).
[26] *Z. physiol. Chem.*, **67**, 489 (1910).
[27] "Handlexikon d. Biochem.," **4**, 386 (1911).

In the pig, Gross and Steenbock[28] observed that arginine administered orally augments creatine excretion. Hyde and Rose,[29] on the contrary, after feeding arginine for as long as 8 weeks found no evidence of its conversion into creatine or creatinine in man. A similar result was obtained by Grant, Christman, and Lewis,[30] who fed arginine to a dog for 35 days and failed to influence the urinary excretion of either creatine or creatinine. That creatine formation is independent of the amount of protein fed,[31] or of arginine contained in the diet,[32] has also been demonstrated in rats. Nor is there any evidence for the transformation of phosphoarginine into phosphocreatine, creatine, or creatinine.[33] In reviewing the evidence for the origin of creatine from arginine, Hunter[34] states, "So large a body of almost purely negative evidence leads one rather forcibly to suspect that, if creatine is related to arginine at all, its mother substance must be not the free amino-acid, but the still combined arginine of the muscle or other tissue protein."

Because of their chemical relationship to creatine, guanidine and methylguanidine have been considered as its possible precursors. It probably would be reasonable to accept this hypothesis, if only there were proof of the formation of guanidine in metabolism.[35]

Choline and betaine have been likewise suggested as precursors of creatine. According to Riesser,[36] the formation of creatine from these substances may take place as represented by the following equations:

$$\underset{\text{Betaine}}{\overset{\displaystyle\text{COOH}}{\underset{\displaystyle\text{CH}_2\cdot\text{N(CH}_3)_3\text{OH}}{|}}} + \underset{\text{Urea}}{C\diagup\!\!\!\!\diagdown\overset{\text{NH}_2}{\underset{\text{NH}_2}{}}} = \underset{\text{Creatine}}{C\diagup\!\!\!\!\diagdown\overset{\text{NH}}{\underset{\text{N(CH}_3)\cdot\text{CH}_2\cdot\text{COOH}}{}}} + 2\text{CH}_3\text{OH}$$

$$\uparrow + O_2$$

$$\underset{\text{Choline}}{\overset{\displaystyle\text{CH}_2\text{OH}}{\underset{\displaystyle\text{CH}_2\text{N(CH}_3)_3\text{OH}}{|}}} + \underset{\text{Urea}}{C\diagup\!\!\!\!\diagdown\overset{\text{NH}_2}{\underset{\text{NH}_2}{}}} = C\diagup\!\!\!\!\diagdown\overset{\text{NH}}{\underset{\text{N(CH}_3)\cdot\text{CH}_2\cdot\text{CH}_2\text{OH}}{}} + 2\text{CH}_3\text{OH}$$

[28] J. Biol. Chem., **47**, 33 (1921).

[29] Ibid., **84**, 535 (1929).

[30] Proc. Soc. Exp. Biol. Med., **27**, 231 (1929).

[31] A. Chanutin, J. Biol. Chem., **89**, 765 (1930).

[32] C. E. Meyer and W. C. Rose, ibid., **102**, 461 (1933).

[33] D. M. Brown and J. M. Luck, Proc. Soc. Exp. Biol. Med., **29**, 723 (1932).

[34] A. Hunter, "Creatine and Creatinine," Longmans, Green & Co., London and New York, 1928, p. 227.

[35] The occurrence of guanidine and methylguanidine in vertebrate, and more rarely in invertebrate, tissues has been reported, but there has been some difficulty in proving that they are preformed constituents rather than the products of the chemical processes involved in their attempted isolation. See D. W. Wilson, Yale J. Biol. Med., **4**, 627 (1932); F. Kutscher and D. Ackermann, Ann. Rev. Biochem., **2**, 355 (1933).

[36] Z. physiol. Chem., **86**, 415 (1913); **90**, 221 (1914).

It is to be borne in mind that these reactions are entirely hypothetical. They are included here largely because they furnish an interesting working hypothesis and one that may perhaps prove to be fruitful. As to the precursor of betaine, it has been suggested by Barger[37] that this may be glycine.

The possibility that glycine is the source of creatine has been brought out by recent investigations. It has been known for several years that in progressive muscular dystrophy creatinuria is a constant manifestation and that when creatine is fed to individuals afflicted with this disease a considerable proportion, and not infrequently nearly all, is recovered in the urine as extra creatine. It is therefore reasonable to suppose that in such cases the ingestion of substances which are converted in the body into creatine would give rise to an extra excretion of this constituent.

With this in mind, Brand and associates[38] studied the effect of feeding patients suffering from progressive muscle dystrophy, in addition to their usual diet, various substances, such as amino acids, known proteins, urea, uric acid, guanidine-acetic acid, betaine, etc. Most of these were without effect. Guanidine-acetic acid, as others had previously shown, increased the creatine excretion. Betaine, however, produced only a temporary rise, followed by a drop below the control level. Slight increases resulted from the administration of alanine, arginine, and sarcosine, but the most conspicuous effect was obtained with glycine. The ingestion of this amino acid resulted at times in a 40 per cent rise in creatine excretion, above the control level. As there was no evidence of increased tissue disintegration, it was to be inferred that the creatine originated from the glycine. Moreover, it was shown that, on feeding benzoic acid, sufficient glycine was used in producing hippuric acid to cause a definite decrease in the creatine elimination. Gelatin being rich in glycine increased the creatinuria, whereas edestin or casein produced little or no effect.

The failure of histidine to form creatine is in conflict with the observations of Abderhalden and Buadze,[39] who consider this amino acid to be a precursor of creatine and creatinine. The negative or essentially negative results obtained in Brand's experiments with the amino acids other than glycine conflict also with the report of Beard and Barnes,[40]

[37] G. Barger, "The Simpler Natural Bases," London, 1914, p. 53.

[38] E. Brand, M. M. Harris, M. Sandberg, and A. I. Ringer, *Am. J. Physiol.*, **90**, 296 (1929); Brand, Harris, Sandberg, and M. M. Lasker, *J. Biol. Chem.*, **87**, ix (1930); Brand and Harris, *ibid.*, **92**, lix (1932); *J. Am. Med. Assoc.*, **101**, 1047 (1923).

[39] *Z. physiol. Chem.*, **200**, 87 (1931).

[40] *J. Biol. Chem.*, **94**, 49 (1931–32).

who have attempted to relate the increase of the muscle creatine in growing rats to the ingestion of a wide variety of substances, namely, arginine, histidine, valine, alanine, phenylalanine, choline, casein, edestin, etc.

Brand's results on the effect of glycine were soon confirmed by Thomas and associates.[41]   Incidentally it is to be noted that in progressive muscle dystrophy the capacity to synthesize this amino acid remains normal.[42]

Fate of Creatine and Its Conversion into Creatinine.   At the time when Folin[43] published his classical study on protein metabolism, the conversion of creatine into creatinine by the body was not questioned.   Folin observed, however, that feeding creatine had no effect on the excretion of creatinine.   Taken in small amounts, creatine was retained entirely; when larger quantities were ingested, only a part was retained, the remainder being excreted unchanged.   As a result of these observations, Folin came to the conclusion that the organism did not possess the power of converting creatine into creatinine and that these substances were independent of each other in metabolism.   Folin regarded creatine as a food and creatinine as a waste product.

Since their publication, Folin's results have been confirmed and denied by numerous workers.   In 1916, Rose and Dimmitt[44] furnished evidence in support of the view that creatine is convertible into creatinine.   These workers found that the ingestion of large doses of creatine in man caused an appreciable increase in the output of creatinine.   Thus, in certain of their experiments, the ingestion of 10 grams of creatine caused an increase of 0.26–0.34 gram of creatinine, whereas the increases observed after taking 20 grams of creatine were between 0.30 and 0.49 gram.   The greater part of the creatine, however, was excreted unchanged.   The ingestion of creatinine, on the contrary, was not followed by the appearance of creatine in the urine, from which it may be inferred that in the body the reaction creatine $\rightarrow$ creatinine is an irreversible one.

Benedict and Osterberg[45] studied the effects of prolonged feeding of creatine.   In one experiment they fed a dog a small quantity of creatine daily for a period of 70 days.   Thus a total amount of 32.9 grams of creatine (expressed as creatinine) was given.   The urine was

[41] K. Thomas, A. T. Milhorat, and F. Techner, *Proc. Soc. Exp. Biol. Med.*, **29**, 609 (1932); *Z. physiol. Chem.*, **205**, 93 (1932).

[42] I. K. Freiberg and E. S. West, *J. Biol. Chem.*, **101**, 449 (1933).

[43] "Hammarsten's Festschrift," Upsala, part 3 (1906).

[44] *J. Biol. Chem.*, **26**, 345 (1916).

[45] *Ibid.*, **56**, 229 (1923).

analyzed daily for a long period before creatine administration was begun to establish the dog's normal output of creatinine and creatine (in this case creatine was absent from the urine normally). The urine was analyzed daily during the experimental period and the analyses were continued for 7 weeks after the creatine feedings had been discontinued. Creatinuria was not observed until the tenth day after the administration of creatine was begun. From this time on, increasing amounts of creatine were present in the urine, the creatinuria continuing until the day after creatine feeding was stopped. Of the 32.9 grams of creatine fed during the 70 days, a total of 13 grams of creatine was recovered. Accordingly, 19.9 grams of creatine had been retained by the tissues. An increased daily excretion of creatinine became manifest about one week after the creatine administrations were instituted and this continued for the duration of the experiment, including the after period of 7 weeks. The extra creatinine eliminated was 5.8 grams, or 29.1 per cent of the creatine retained. The difference of 14.1 grams could not be accounted for either as extra urinary creatine or creatinine.

These results are of importance because they establish (1) that creatine is converted into creatinine, (2) that this conversion is not a direct process, but apparently involves a preliminary storage of the creatine in the tissues, (3) that creatinine is probably only one of the end-products of creatine metabolism, and that a proportion of the creatine may follow a different metabolic path.

Results similar to those of Benedict and Osterberg have been obtained in rats by Chanutin[46] and in man by Rose, Ellis, and Helming.[47] More recently, Chanutin and Silvette[48] have approached more directly the question of why administered creatine is not fully recovered in the urine either as extra creatine or creatinine. They injected creatine into completely nephrectomized rats and analyzed the various tissues for creatine. They showed that larger amounts were stored in the liver and muscles than elsewhere and moreover that not all of the creatine administered could be recovered in the tissues. In this way Chanutin and Silvette have demonstrated that creatine may be destroyed by the organism.

With the advance of knowledge it has become increasingly clear that creatine is probably the immediate precursor of creatinine, but that its metabolism is not restricted to this reaction. Creatinine is to be regarded

[46] *Ibid.*, **67**, 29 (1926).
[47] *Ibid.*, **77**, 171 (1928).
[48] *Ibid.*, **85**, 179 (1929); **89**, 765 (1930); see also **75**, 549 (1927); **80**, 589 (1928); Chanutin and H. H. Beard, *ibid.*, **78**, 167 (1928).

as an end-product, whereas creatine is doubtless an essential tissue constituent with a special function.[49]

Phosphocreatine. Eggleton and Eggleton,[50] on the basis of certain analyses of phosphate in muscle, reached the important conclusion that muscle contains a labile (easily hydrolyzable) organic phosphate, which they called *phosphagen.* At about the same time, Fiske and Sub-barow,[51] in this country, made a similar observation and showed that the substance in question was composed of creatine and phosphoric acid. Later studies confirmed these observations and indicated that phosphocreatine has the following constitution:

$$
\begin{array}{ccc}
 & H & OH \\
 & | & / \\
 & N-P=O \\
 & / & \backslash \\
HN = C & & OH \\
 & \backslash \\
 & N-CH_2-COOH \\
 & | \\
 & CH_3
\end{array}
$$

Stimulation of muscle is associated with the decomposition of phosphocreatine. This compound is so unstable that, in experiments involving its analysis, special precautions must be taken to prevent or minimize excitation of the muscle during removal. To avoid phosphocreatine hydrolysis after removal, the tissue is promptly frozen in liquid air. Freezing of tissue *in situ* before removal for analysis has also been employed.

Traumatic damage of muscles causes an unusually rapid cleavage of the phosphocreatine which is present. Rapid hydrolysis may be produced also by acid and alkali.

[49] Oxalyl-methyl-guanidine (creaton)

$$
HN=C \begin{array}{l} \diagup NH_2 \\ \diagdown N(CH_3) \cdot CO \cdot COOH \end{array}
$$

has been isolated from muscle by Gulewitsch (*Z. physiol. Chem.*, **217**, 63 [1933]). It had been previously described by Baumann and Ingvaldsen .(*J. Biol. Chem.*, **35**, 277 [1918]) and by Greenwald (*J. Am. Chem. Soc.*, **41**, 1109 [1919]) as an oxidation product of creatine. Its significance is obscure, though Gulewitsch has suggested that with creatine it may participate in oxidation-reduction reactions.

[50] *Biochem. J.*, **21**, 190 (1927); *J. Physiol.*, **63**, 155 (1927); *Physiol. Rev.*, **9**, 432 (1929).

[51] *Science*, **65**, 401 (1927); *J. Biol. Chem.*, **81**, 629 (1929).

In resting muscle the greater part of the creatine occurs as phosphocreatine; indeed, it has even been questioned whether free creatine is present in significant amounts. The molar concentration of the total free and labile phosphate in muscle (0.029–0.036) is greater than that of the creatine (0.025–0.03), so that there is the possibility of all the creatine being combined as phosphate. However, even in resting muscle a certain amount of the creatine is not combined with orthophosphoric acid (H_3PO_4) and is diffusible. Eggleton[52] found that resting frog sartorius immersed in saline solutions containing creatine loses creatine to the solution when the creatine in the latter is below a certain critical concentration (80 mg. per 100 cc. of solution, equivalent to 65 mg. per 100 grams of muscle). Fatigued muscle, on the other hand, was found to contain much more free creatine and to reach an equilibrium at a concentration of 200 to 300 mg. These observations, as well as other data obtained by direct chemical analysis, have shown that in resting muscle about 80 per cent of the creatine is probably present as phosphocreatine, the remainder being free creatine.

Soon after the discovery of phosphocreatine, it was shown by Meyerhof[53] that its hydrolysis either by acid or enzyme is accompanied by the liberation of considerable heat (11,000 to 12,500 calories per mol). Then followed the observation of Nachmansohn[54] that in muscular activity the phosphocreatine first broken down is rapidly restored even in the absence of oxygen. The source of the energy required for the resynthesis was at first obscure.

Two years later Lundsgaard[55] described an experiment in which it was shown that frog's muscle poisoned with iodoacetic acid may contract, but that no lactic acid is formed in the process. This was an astounding discovery, as it was contrary to the prevailing conception that the energy for contraction is obtained from the formation of lactic acid. Instead of the glycogen → lactic acid transformation, the contraction of the poisoned muscle was evidently associated with the breakdown of creatine phosphate. The theory was therefore advanced that the cleavage of phosphocreatine is the primary change and supplies the energy in the normal contraction of muscle. The energy for the resynthesis of phosphocreatine depends on the formation of lactic acid and the hydrolysis of two of the phosphate radicals of adenosinetriphosphoric acid and perhaps also the deamination of this compound as well as of adenylic acid (p. 332).

It has been determined that white muscle is richer in phospho-

[52] J. Physiol., 70, 294 (1930).
[53] Biochem. Z., 191, 106 (1927).
[54] Ibid., 196, 73 (1928).
[55] Ibid., 217, 162; 220, 1, 8; 227, 51 (1930); 230, 10; 233, 322 (1931).

creatine than red muscle.[56] The former is rapidly contractile; the latter contracts much more slowly. It has been inferred that in the slowly contracting red muscle there is more time for the restitution of the phosphagen, so that the amount of it can be less.

Phosphocreatine occurs in nerve tissue, where its properties are very similar to those in muscle.[57] When nerve is deprived of oxygen the phosphocreatine decomposes very rapidly. The rate of decomposition is further accelerated if the nerve is treated with a mono-halogen derivative of acetic acid. The electric organ of the torpedo ray contains phosphocreatine.[58]

In the muscle of crustaceans, Meyerhof and Lohmann[59] found phosphoarginine (arginine phosphate), the properties and functions of which appear to be analogous to those of phosphocreatine. The distribution of this phosphagen is not restricted however to the Crustacea, for it has been determined in coelenterates, platyhelminths, annelids, cephalopods, echinoderms, and urochords (*Ascidia*). In certain echinoderms and in the hemichords, both arginine-phosphate and creatine-phosphate are present, whereas in the cephalochords (*Amphioxus*) and Craniata (vertebrates) creatine phosphate alone has been found so far. In his monograph, Meyerhof refers to creatine-phosphoric acid as the vertebrate phosphagen (*Wirbeltierphosphagen*), whereas arginine-phosphoric acid is described as the invertebrate phosphagen (*Wirbellosenphosphagen*).[60]

$$
\begin{array}{c}
\text{H} \qquad \text{OH} \\
| \qquad / \\
\text{N—P=O} \\
/ \qquad \backslash \\
\text{HN=C} \qquad \text{OH} \\
\backslash \\
\text{NH} \\
| \\
(\text{CH}_2)_3 \\
| \\
\text{CHNH}_2 \\
| \\
\text{COOH}
\end{array}
$$

Phosphoarginine
(Arginine-phosphoric acid)

[56] D. Ferdmann and O. Feinschmidt, *Z. physiol. Chem.*, **178**, 173 (1928); A. Palladin, and S. Epplebaum, *ibid.*, **178**, 179 (1928).

[57] R. W. Gerard, "Nerve Metabolism," *Physiol. Rev.*, **12**, 469–492, especially 497 (1932).

[58] B. Kisch, *Biochem. Z.*, **225**, 183 (1930).

[59] *Naturwissenschaften*, **16**, 726 (1928).

[60] F. Kutscher and D. Ackermann, *Ann. Rev. Biochem.*, **2**, 355 (1933); A. Arnold and J. M. Luck, *J. Biol. Chem.*, **99**, 677 (1933). O. Meyerhof, "Die chemischen Vorgänge im Muskel," Berlin, 1930, p. 93.

Creatine occurs in the testes, liver, kidney, pancreas, spleen, thyroid, thymus, and brain.   It is of particular interest to note that in mammals the testes stand next to skeletal and cardiac muscle in creatine content. According to Greenwald,[61] the gonads of certain invertebrates, the tunicate *Boltinia, Echinurus*, the squid, and the sea-urchin *Arbacia pustulosa*, contain considerable amounts of creatine, much more being present in the male gonads than in those of the female.   Greenwald has suggested that creatine may have functions other than those related to muscular contraction.

Creatinuria.   Creatine is not present normally in the urine of the male adult but does occur as a normal constituent in the urine of children of both sexes before the age of puberty.   Creatinuria is likewise manifested in starvation, muscular diseases, exophthalmic goiter, eclampsia, and diabetes.   As we shall see, not all forms of creatinuria can be referred to the same fundamental cause, although it is evident that all are due either to incomplete storage of creatine or to incomplete conversion of creatine into creatinine.

Exogenous and Endogenous Creatinuria.   In the first place, it is important to consider whether all forms of creatinuria are endogenous in origin.   On this point there is much difference of opinion.   According to one group of workers, notably Denis,[62] the ingestion of large quantities of protein may cause creatinuria in cases where it is absent, or increase it where it already exists, whereas the reverse effect is obtained upon a minimum protein intake.

Rose,[63] on the other hand, was unable to induce creatinuria by feeding large quantities of protein to men and women.   In some of his experiments, the protein intake was so high as to result in a nitrogen excretion in the urine of as much as 35 grams.   Nevertheless, there was no evidence of creatinuria in these individuals.

Hunter[34] has pointed out that the excretion of creatine on a high protein intake need not necessarily be interpreted as proof of the exogenous origin of creatine.   The well-known effect of proteins in stimulating cellular metabolism (specific dyamic action) has been held responsible (Lewis, Dunn, and Doisy)[64] for the increased excretion of endogenous uric acid in experiments in which excessive amounts of proteins and amino acids were fed.   It may likewise have been the cause of the increased creatine formation in those cases where this has been observed.

---

[61] Proc. XIV International Physiological Congress, Rome, 1932.

[62] *J. Biol. Chem.*, **29**, 447 (1917); **30**, 47, 189 (1917); **31**, 561 (1917); **37**, 245 (1919).

[63] *Ibid.*, **34**, 601 (1918).

[64] *Ibid.*, **36**, 9 (1918).

Accordingly, creatine and creatinine metabolism is to be regarded as a phase of endogenous metabolism. The only obvious exception to this occurs when creatine as such is ingested.

Creatinuria in Children, Women, etc. Infants and children normally excrete creatine in addition to creatinine, as was first shown by Rose.[65] Several explanations have been offered for this phenomenon. It has been suggested that creatinuria in children may be due to the fact that they have less ability to retain creatine because their musculature is less developed and proportionately less abundant than in adults.

In women, after puberty, creatinuria is intermittent, except during pregnancy, when it is continuous. Whether creatinuria in women is to be related, as in children, to deficient muscular development or sex-glandular control, or to some other cause, is a matter that we are not able to decide at present, although the indications are that even muscularly well-developed women exhibit an occasional creatinuria. This indicates that sex is a probable factor, a view strengthened by the observations that creatinuria occurs in eunuchs[66] and, as in prepubescent boys, may be readily induced by the oral administration of small amounts of creatine in aged men and others with extinguished testicular function.[67]

Creatinuria in Starvation and Carbohydrate Deprivation. In every species of mammal, starvation is associated with the appearance or an increase of creatine in the urine. One of the more generally accepted explanations for this phenomenon is that the creatine of the urine is pre-existing creatine, released from disintegrating muscle, and excreted thereupon without change. Another view is that the excessive tissue protein breakdown which occurs during inanition leads to the production in the course of metabolism of more than a normal amount of creatine. That which is not converted into creatinine behaves like exogenous creatine, being partly retained in the body and partly excreted in the urine unchanged. Still another explanation is that the starving animal, or one deprived of carbohydrate, unlike the normal animal, is incapable of destroying the surplus creatine which it is constantly producing.[68]

Creatinuria disappears in the starving animal upon the administration of carbohydrate. It may be argued that this effect is due to the protein-sparing action of glucose, but it has also been suggested that glucose is specifically concerned in the conversion of creatine into cre-

[65] *Ibid.*, **10**, 265 (1911).

[66] B. Read, *ibid.*, **46**, 281 (1921).

[67] L. Remen, *Z. exp. Med.*, **80**, 238 (1931); F. Lasch, *ibid.*, **81**, 681 (1932).

[68] For a summary of the various theories the reader is referred to Hunter's monograph "Creatine and Creatinine," 1928, p. 197.

atinine, in a manner as yet unknown.   The fact that proteins are nearly as effective as carbohydrates in abolishing starvation creatinuria (Rose, Dimmitt, and Cheatham)[69] does not alter the situation as regards the dual explanation, for the protein may conceivably exert its effect either as a tissue sparer or by providing glucose precursors.

That a relationship exists between creatine-creatinine metabolism and carbohydrate metabolism is also indicated by the fact that creatinuria is characteristic of many conditions of deficient carbohydrate utilization (diabetes, phlorhizin glycosuria) as well as of conditions in which there is apparently a deficiency in glycogenic function.   In the latter group are included various forms of hepatic insufficiency, such as occur in eclampsia, phosphorus and chloroform poisoning, and carcinoma of the liver.   It is to be noted, however, that in none of these can we exclude entirely the factor of exaggerated endogenous or tissue metabolism.

Creatinuria Due to Excessive Tissue Catabolism; Hyperthyroidism. More clear-cut examples of the relation of endogenous protein metabolism to creatinuria are seen in fevers, in wasting diseases, following parturition, and in exophthalmic goiter.   In all of these an excessive amount of creatine is presumably liberated, and a portion of this is excreted into the urine unchanged.

The interesting observation has been reported by Abelin and Spichtin[70] that hyperthyroidism in rats induced by feeding thyroid substance results in a marked depletion of the creatine of the liver and muscle.   In some of their experiments they observed a reduction exceeding 60 per cent.

These observations are perhaps not unrelated to clinical hyperthyroidism (Graves' disease) in which creatinuria occurs not only after the administration of creatine or glycine, but also on a creatine-free diet.   This may be due to increased tissue protein destruction, but it is more likely related to a reduced ability of the muscle to retain the creatine formed in metabolism.   Whatever the explanation may be, the creatinuria is evidently associated with the heightened basal metabolism characteristic of the disease, for when this is reduced, as through the administration of iodine, the creatinuria is likewise diminished.   That the changes in the muscle, both anatomical and metabolic, occurring in hyperthyroidism resemble those in progressive muscular dystrophy has been recently emphasized by Shorr and associates.[71]   It is of par-

---

[69] *J. Biol. Chem.*, **26**, 339 (1916).

[70] *Biochem. Z.*, **228**, 250 (1930).

[71] E. Shorr, H. B. Richardson, and H. G. Wolff, *J. Clin. Investigation*, **12**, 966 (1933).

ticular interest to note that these investigators regard the muscular weakness in Graves' disease to be the result of a reparable impairment of the phosphocreatine mechanism.

Creatinuria in Diseases Affecting the Muscles. In his review of the subject, Hunter[72] refers to the following primary and secondary diseases of the muscular system in which creatinuria is known to occur: progressive muscular dystrophy, amyotonia congenita, progressive muscular atrophy, amyotrophic lateral sclerosis, myasthenia gravis, atrophies resulting from disuse, acute anterior poliomyelitis and other lesions of the spinal cord or motor nerves. In trichinosis, a condition associated with an inflammatory process in the muscles, there is marked creatinuria, as there is in generalized myositis fibrosa. In myotonia congenita there appears to be no abnormality of the creatine-creatinine metabolism. Although the literature on the subject of muscle disease is very extensive, fundamental knowledge is still lacking.

Goettsch and Brown[73] have described a nutritional form of muscular dystrophy in rabbits, characterized by a marked reduction of the creatine content of the muscles. It is of interest to note that low creatine values have been reported in myasthenia gravis[74] and particularly in generalized myositis fibrosa.[75]

The Significance of Creatinine. As we have seen, creatine is, under ordinary conditions, a product of endogenous protein metabolism. In the male adult it is converted completely into creatinine, in which form it is quantitatively excreted. Creatinine is present in exceedingly small amounts in the tissues. It is a true waste product and as such is promptly removed. In the reaction creatine → creatinine, carbohydrate oxidation is apparently essential, and if for any reason the available supply of carbohydrate is deficient, the transformation is incomplete, and some creatine appears in the urine. Under these conditions, the output of creatine + creatinine is equivalent to the amount of creatinine which would have been excreted if there were no creatine. Thus, creatine is present in the urine at the expense of creatinine.

In a given individual the elimination of creatinine is constant from day to day, provided the diet is free from creatine and creatinine present as such. Creatinine is therefore an end-product of endogenous protein and more particularly of muscle metabolism. The amount of creatinine excreted daily is independent of the volume of urine, the amount of

[72] *Loc. cit.*, p. 218.
[73] *J. Biol. Chem.*, **97**, 549 (1932).
[74] B. W. Williams and C. S. Dyke, *Quart. J. Med.*, **15**, 269 (1922).
[75] M. Bodansky, E. H. Schwab, and P. Brindley, *J. Biol. Chem.*, **85**, 307 (1929–30).

protein in the diet, and therefore of the total nitrogen metabolism. It is not influenced by the amount of ordinary muscular work (Shaffer).[76] What, then, is the cause of the variations in creatinine excretion in different individuals?

The Creatinine Coefficient. The number of milligrams of creatinine excreted in the urine in twenty-four hours per kilogram of body weight is called the creatinine coefficient. In men, the creatinine coefficient may vary between 18 and 32, with an average of about 24 or 25. In women, lower values are the rule, the average being about 18, with a normal range between 9 and 26. Children have even lower values, ranging between 9 and 17 at 5–13 years (Krause[77]). The more muscular an individual, the higher is his or her creatinine coefficient. Thus, obese or muscularly under-developed men may have a very low creatinine coefficient (as low as 15–18), whereas well-developed muscular women may have as high creatinine coefficients as normal men.[78]

In different animal species, according to Myers and Fine,[79] the creatinine coefficient is related not only to the amount of muscle, but to their creatine content as well. On the contrary, Chanutin and Kinard[80] could establish no such correlation from their experiments on dogs, rabbits, rats, and guinea-pigs.

PURINE AND PYRIMIDINE METABOLISM

Under purine and nucleic-acid metabolism, we have to consider (1) the fate of ingested nucleoproteins and nucleic acids and (2) the anabolism and catabolism of purines and pyrimidines in the body, whether derived from exogenous or endogenous sources.

Nucleic acids are present in the nuclei of cells. It is not known with certainty that they ever occur in the cytoplasm. According to the prevailing view, the nucleic acids are combined with protein, thus constituting the so-called nucleoproteins. On partial hydrolysis, nucleoproteins yield a protein residue and a protein-nucleic acid complex which has been called nuclein. If the cleavage is carried somewhat further, the nuclein yields protein and nucleic acid as cleavage products. These changes may be represented as follows:

---

[76] *Am. J. Physiol.*, **22**, 445 (1908); compare K. Kácl, *Biochem. Z.*, **245**, 453 (1932).
[77] *Quart. J. Exp. Physiol.*, **7**, 87, (1913).
[78] See for example the data of P. Hodgson and H. B. Lewis, *Am. J. Physiol.*, **87**, 288 (1928).
[79] *J. Biol. Chem.*, **14**, 9 (1913).
[80] *Ibid.*, **99**, 125 (1932–33).

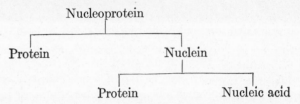

Nucleoprotein

Protein   Nuclein

Protein   Nucleic acid

Careful study of the nucleic acids obtained from a variety of sources has revealed the interesting fact that there are, perhaps, only two such compounds, one being characteristic of plant tissues, such as yeast, the other occurring in animal tissues. The difference between the two nucleic acids is indicated by the products which they yield on hydrolysis.

PRODUCTS OF HYDROLYSIS OF NUCLEIC ACIDS

Of Animal Origin	*Of Plant Origin*
Phosphoric acid	Phosphoric acid
Adenine	Adenine
Guanine	Guanine
Cytosine	Cytosine
Thymine	Uracil
Levulinic and formic acids	Pentose

Similar purines are present in both nucleic acids. One of the two pyrimidines is likewise common to both. The other pyrimidine is uracil in plant nucleic acid and thymine in animal nucleic acid. The carbohydrate component in nucleic acid of plant origin is d-ribose (Levene and Jacobs), whereas, in animal nucleic acid, it is believed to be d-2 ribodesose, a desoxypentose (Levene and London),[81]

$$\overset{\displaystyle O}{CHOH \cdot CH_2 \cdot CHOH \cdot CHOH \cdot CH_2,}$$

which during the process of hydrolysis is decomposed to levulinic and formic acids. With so many hydrolytic products, the complexity of the nucleic-acid molecule may be readily surmised.

Concerning the molecular configuration of the nucleic acids, certain details have been fairly well established, thanks to the labors of Levene, Jones, and others.[82] In yeast nucleic acid, for example, the purine or pyrimidine base is united directly to the sugar (d-ribose), the type of

[81] P. A. Levene and E. S. London, *J. Biol. Chem.*, **83**, 793 (1929); Levene and T. Mori, *ibid.*, **83**, 803 (1929); Levene, L. A. Mikeska, and Mori, *ibid.*, **85**, 785 (1929–30).

[82] Only the essential features of the subject can be dealt with here. For a more detailed discussion of the chemistry of nucleic acids, the student is referred to the monograph by Jones (W. Jones, "Nucleic Acids, Their Chemical Properties and Physiological Conduct," 2d edition, New York, 1920) and to the numerous papers by P. A. Levene and his associates. The distinction between plant and animal nucleic acids

linkage being that of a glucoside. Compounds of this type (sugar—purine or pyrimidine base) are called nucleosides. In turn, each nucleoside is united to a molecule of phosphoric acid (probably by an ester linkage), the point of union being between the sugar and the acid. The phosphoric acid-sugar-base compounds are called nucleotides or mono-nucleotides. Four such nucleotides constitute a tetranucleotide or nucleic-acid molecule. According to Levene,[83] yeast nucleic acid has the following molecular configuration:

$$\begin{array}{l} HO \\ O{=}P{-}O{-}C_5H_7O_2 \cdot C_5H_4N_5O \text{ (guanine)} \\ HO \\ \qquad\qquad | \\ \qquad\qquad O \\ \qquad\qquad | \\ \qquad O{=}P{-}O{-}C_5H_7O_2 \cdot C_4H_4N_3O \text{ (cytosine)} \\ \qquad HO \\ \qquad\qquad\qquad | \\ \qquad\qquad\qquad O \\ \qquad\qquad\qquad | \\ \qquad\qquad O{=}P{-}O{-}C_5H_7O_2 \cdot C_4H_3N_2O_2 \text{ (uracil)} \\ \qquad\qquad HO \\ \qquad\qquad\qquad\qquad | \\ \qquad\qquad\qquad\qquad O \\ \qquad\qquad\qquad\qquad | \\ \qquad\qquad\qquad O{=}P{-}O{-}C_5H_8O_3 \cdot C_5H_4N_5 \text{ (adenine)} \\ \qquad\qquad\qquad HO \end{array}$$

Yeast nucleic acid, according to Levene

Thymus nucleic acid has a formula analogous to that of yeast nucleic acid (Levene and London).[81]

$$\begin{array}{l} HO \\ O{=}P{-}O{-}C_5H_7O \cdot C_5H_4N_5 \text{ (adenine)} \\ HO \\ \qquad\qquad | \\ \qquad\qquad O \\ \qquad\qquad | \\ \qquad O{=}P{-}O{-}C_5H_7O \cdot C_5H_5N_2O_2 \text{ (thymine)} \\ \qquad HO \\ \qquad\qquad\qquad | \\ \qquad\qquad\qquad O \\ \qquad\qquad\qquad | \\ \qquad\qquad O{=}P{-}O{-}C_5H_7O \cdot C_4H_4N_3O \text{ (cytosine)} \\ \qquad\qquad\qquad\qquad | \\ \qquad\qquad\qquad\qquad O \\ \qquad\qquad\qquad\qquad | \\ \qquad\qquad\qquad O{=}P{-}O{-}C_5H_8O_2 \cdot C_5H_4N_5O \\ \qquad\qquad\qquad HO \qquad\qquad\qquad\qquad \text{ (guanine)} \end{array}$$

Thymonucleic acid (Levene and London)

is probably not as sharply drawn as has been supposed. Thus, Calvery, on hydrolyzing the β-nucleoprotein prepared from chicken embryos, obtained the same four pentose nucleotides that have been isolated from yeast nucleic acid (*J. Biol. Chem.*, **77**, 489 [1928]).

[83] *J. Biol. Chem.*, **41**, 19 (1920).

Inosinic, Guanylic and Adenylic Acids.   Three mononucleotides are present as such in animal tissues. Considered in the order of their discovery, these are inosinic, guanylic, and adenylic acids. The first was isolated from meat extract by Liebig; the second was discovered by Hammarsten in pancreatic tissue, and the third in muscle by Embden and Zimmermann.

On hydrolysis, inosinic acid yields phosphoric acid, hypoxanthine, and d-ribose.

$$\begin{array}{c} HO \\ \\ HO \end{array}\!\!\diagdown\!\!\!\!\!\!\!\diagup\,O\!\!=\!\!P\!-\!O\!-\!C_5H_8O_3\cdot C_5H_3N_4O \quad \text{(hypoxanthine)}$$
Inosinic acid

Guanylic acid is composed of phosphoric acid, guanine, and d-ribose.

$$\begin{array}{c} HO \\ \\ HO \end{array}\!\!\diagdown\!\!\!\!\!\!\!\diagup\,O\!\!=\!\!P\!-\!O\!-\!C_5H_8O_3\cdot C_5H_4N_5O \quad \text{(guanine)}$$
Guanylic acid

The component parts of adenylic acid are: adenine, d-ribose, and phosphoric acid.

$$\begin{array}{c} HO \\ \\ HO \end{array}\!\!\diagdown\!\!\!\!\!\!\!\diagup\,O\!\!=\!\!P\!-\!C_5H_8O_3\cdot C_5H_4N_5 \quad \text{(adenine)}$$
Adenylic acid

Adenylic acid is closely related to inosinic acid, the difference being that in the former the nitrogenous base is adenine whilst in the latter it is hypoxanthine. The discovery of adenylic acid together with the observation that ammonia is formed in muscular activity has given an unexpected significance to inosinic acid, the existence of which in muscle has been known since 1847.

Digestion of Nucleoproteins and Nucleic Acids.   The nucleoproteins of the food are converted by the proteolytic enzymes of the gastric and pancreatic secretions into protein and nucleic acids. These secretions take no part in the hydrolysis of the nucleic acids.

According to Levene, the foremost authority on the subject, the disintegration of nucleic acids, or *tetranucleotides*, is brought about by a specific enzyme present in the intestinal juice and also in the mucosa. It was originally described by Levene and Medigreceanu[84] as *nucleinase*. In a more recent contribution, Levene and Dillon[85] have reaffirmed the view of the specificity of this enzyme, which may also be designated as *polynucleotidase*, and have presented additional evidence to show that

[84] *J. Biol. Chem.*, **9**, 375, 389 (1911).   [85] *Ibid.*, **96**, 461 (1932).

it is distinct from *nucleotidase* or *nucleophosphatase,* another enzyme or group of enzymes of the intestinal juice and mucosa.

This second enzyme hydrolyzes *mononucleotides* to *nucleosides* and phosphoric acid, hence its designation as a *phosphatase.* However, its action is non-specific, inasmuch as it also hydrolyzes glycerophosphoric acid, hexosemonophosphate, and hexosediphosphate (Levene and Dillon).[86] It was formerly held that the nucleotidase of the intestinal juice decomposed only the purine nucleotides, whereas the pyrimidine nucleotides required for hydrolysis a nucleotidase present in the intestinal mucosa. This is evidently incorrect, for in Levene and Dillon's experiments, in which the nucleotidase used was derived from dog's intestinal juice, uridine-phosphoric acid (a pyrimidine nucleotide) was hydrolyzed even more readily than adenylic acid (a purine nucleotide).

Nucleosidase is concerned with the hydrolysis of the purine nucleosides, the products being a purine base and a reducing sugar (see p. 437). It has been shown by Levene and Dmochowski[87] that nucleosidase derived from pig intestinal wall is incapable of removing the base from nucleotides. Disintegration of the pyrimidine nucleosides apparently does not occur either in the intestinal wall or elsewhere in the body. The nucleinases and nucleotidases, on the other hand, occur not only in the intestinal juice and mucosa, but in other organs (liver, heart, muscle, kidney) as well.

Xanthylic acid, however, loses a considerable part of its purine base under certain conditions without the liberation of free phosphoric acid.

A very active enzyme preparation has been obtained by Klein[88] from calf intestinal mucosa which hydrolyzes thymus nucleic acid, yielding purine and pyrimidine nucleosides and phosphoric acid. Its action on yeast nucleic acid is considerably slower.

Chemistry of the Purines and Pyrimidines. The structural relationships of the purines and pyrimidines that are of special interest in metabolism are indicated below.

$$
\begin{array}{ccc}
1\ \text{N—C}\ 6 & \text{N=C—NH}_2 & \text{H—N—C=O} \\
| \quad | & | \quad | & | \quad | \\
2\ \text{C}\quad \text{C}\ 5\text{—N}\ 7 & \text{H—C}\quad \text{C—NH} & \text{H}_2\text{N—C}\quad \text{C—NH} \\
| \quad \| \quad \diagdown \text{C}\ 8 & \| \quad \| \quad \diagdown \text{CH} & \| \quad \| \quad \diagdown \text{CH} \\
3\ \text{N—C}\ 4\text{—N}\ 9 & \text{N—C—N} & \text{N—C—N}
\end{array}
$$

Purine "nucleus"   Adenine (6-amino-purine)   Guanine (2-amino-6-oxypurine)

[86] *Ibid.,* **88,** 753 (1930).

[87] *Ibid.,* **93,** 563 (1931).

[88] *Z. physiol. Chem.,* **207,** 125 (1932); F. Bielschowsky and W. Klein, *ibid.,* 202 (1932).

```
H—N—C=O              H—N—C=O              H—N—C=O
  |   |                |   |                |   |
H—C   C—NH          O=C   C—NH          O=C   C—NH
  ‖   ‖   \CH          |   ‖   \CH          |   ‖   \C=O
  N—C—N              H—N—C—N              H—N—C—NH

Hypoxanthine         Xanthine             Uric acid
(6-oxypurine)        (2-6-dioxypurine)    (2-6-8-trioxypurine)
```

```
1 N—C 6          N=C—NH2         H—N—C=O         H—N—C=O
  |   |           |   |            |   |            |   |
2 C   C 5       O=C   C—H        O=C   C—H        O=C   C—CH3
  |   ‖           |   ‖            |   ‖            |   ‖
3 N—C 4         H—N—C—H          H—N—C—H          H—N—C—H

Pyrimidine       Cytosine         Uracil           Thymine
"nucleus"        (2-oxy-6-amino-  (2-6-dioxy-      (2-6-dioxy-5-
                 pyrimidine)      pyrimidine)      methyl-pyrimidine)
```

Endogenous and Exogenous Sources of Purines.[89]   One of the best examples of nucleic-acid synthesis in the animal body is that first observed by Miescher,[90] who showed that the salmon, during its long migration from the sea to its spawning grounds, though abstaining from food, forms large amounts of nuclear material from its own tissues. Likewise, during the incubation of an egg, there is a progressive increase in the content of purine bases (Mendel and Leavenworth).[91]   It may be noted here that there is a similar formation of creatine during incubation.

Further evidence of purine synthesis is to be found in the experiments of Burian and Schur,[92] who compared the purine content of new-born rabbits and puppies with the concentrations in the tissues after varying periods of growth on a diet limited to the milk of the mother.   Much greater increases were found than could be accounted for on the basis of the purine content of the milk consumed during the periods of the experiments.   Somewhat similar were the observations of Kollmann,[93] who showed that human individuals, though kept on a very low purine diet, not only gained weight, but eliminated much larger quantities of uric acid than could be accounted for from the purine intake.

Benedict[94] has demonstrated the synthesis of purines in the Dal-

---

[89] For a detailed discussion of purine metabolism the student is referred to the review of the subject by W. C. Rose, *Physiol. Rev.*, **3**, 544 (1923).

[90] Cited by Rose, p. 555.

[91] *Am. J. Physiol.*, **21**, 77 (1908).

[92] *Z. physiol. Chem.*, **23**, 55 (1897).

[93] *Biochem. Z.*, **123**, 235 (1921).

[94] *J. Lab. Clin. Med.*, **2**, 1 (1916); Harvey Lectures, 1915–16, p. 346.

matian coach hound. In this species of dog, as in man, the end-product of purine metabolism is uric acid and not allantoin as in other dogs. Benedict kept a Dalmatian dog on a purine-free diet, and yet this animal continued to excrete uric acid.

Indeed, it has often been questioned whether exogenous purines and pyrimidines are ever anabolized into nucleic acids. A number of workers (Mendel and Brown,[95] Mendel and Lyman,[96] etc.), have shown that feeding purine bases or nucleic acids is followed very promptly by an increased elimination of either allantoin or uric acid. However, the excretion is not quantitative. Koehler[97] has observed that after the ingestion of uric acid, the concentration of this constituent in the blood does not increase and only about one-half of the amount administered is recovered in the urine. It is not known what happens to the retained purines. Koehler suggests that uric acid may be destroyed in the body. Another possibility is that a portion may be used for anabolic purposes. That the body may utilize the purines of its own tissues over and over again during starvation has been suggested by Rose.[98]

The conversion of histidine into purines has been referred to elsewhere (p. 405). Of other non-purine precursors there is no definite knowledge.

Of the foodstuffs, glandular tissues, such as thymus (sweetbreads), pancreas, liver, and kidney, are especially rich in purine bases. In the liver these are present to the extent of about $\frac{1}{2}$ gram in 100 grams of fresh tissue, whereas in the thymus gland the content is in the neighborhood of 1.5 per cent. Steak contains about 0.15–0.20 per cent. Milk contains about 15 mg. of uric acid per liter, and smaller quantities of adenine and guanine. Not all vegetables are devoid of purine bases. Peas, beans, and spinach contain appreciable amounts. Smaller quantities are present, likewise, in wheat, rye, and other grains.

Coffee, tea, and cocoa contain methyl-purine derivatives, as well as amino- and oxypurines, tea being especially rich in adenine. Calvery[99] has prepared both guanine nucleotide and cytosine nucleotide from dried tea leaves and is of the opinion that a pentose nucleic acid is a natural product of tea. It is unlikely that all of the methylated purines are converted into uric acid in metabolism. Some of these are probably excreted partly unchanged and partly after demethylation

[95] J. Am. Med. Assoc., **49**, 896 (1907).
[96] J. Biol. Chem., **8**, 115 (1910).
[97] Ibid., **60**, 721 (1924).
[98] Ibid., **48**, 575 (1921).
[99] Ibid., **72**, 549 (1927).

to mono-methyl-purine. Caffeine and theophylline, after ingestion, increase the elimination of uric acid.[94,100] Theobromine, on the other hand, does not seem to be converted into uric acid.

Metabolism of Guanine and Adenine; Origin of Uric Acid. Endogenous nuclear metabolism probably involves the preliminary hydrolysis of nucleic acids through the same stages as in digestion. It is not unlikely that the cleavage even of the purine nucleosides is incomplete so that in addition to the free purines considerable amounts of the corresponding nucleosides are liberated from the tissue nucleic acids or are absorbed from the intestine. That a portion may escape further change is indicated by the presence of adenosine[101] in human urine (Calvery).[102]

By hydrolysis, guanosine yields guanine, or, by deamination, it may be converted into xanthosine. Guanine, by the action of *guanase*, is changed into xanthine, whereas a nucleosidase acting on xanthosine would yield the same product.

Adenosine, on hydrolysis, yields adenine, or it may form inosine by deamination. The former is converted by *adenase* into hypoxanthine, whereas the same compound is formed from inosine by the action of a nucleosidase (inosine-hydrolase of Jones). Hypoxanthine is converted into xanthine by xanthine-oxidase, which is a dehydrogenase. In man, xanthine is finally converted into uric acid. These transformations and relations are outlined below and on p. 438.[103]

Guanosine → Xanthosine   Adenosine →   Inosine
    ↓   ↓   ↓   ↓
 Guanine   →   Xanthine   Adenine   → Hypoxanthine

[100] L. B. Mendel and E. L. Wardell, *J. Am. Med. Assoc.*, **68**, 1805 (1917); V. C. Myers and Wardell, *J. Biol. Chem.*, **77**, 697 (1928); see also R. F. Hanzal and V. C. Myers, *ibid.*, **97**, Proc. lxix (1932).

[101] The nucleosides are named after the purine or pyrimidine base which they contain. Thus the nucleoside of guanine is guanosine, of adenine, adenosine; of cytosine, cytidine; and of uracil, uridine.

[102] *J. Biol. Chem.*, **86**, 263 (1930).

[103] Compare Amberg and Jones, *Z. physiol. Chem.*, **73**, 408 (1911), and Rose, *Physiol. Rev.*, **3**, 564 (1923).

FATE OF ADENINE AND GUANINE

In a study of the deaminases of rabbit liver, Schmidt[104] found one enzyme which acted on guanine as well as guanosine. Guanylic acid was affected by a separate enzyme. Adenine, unlike guanine, was not deaminized, but the corresponding nucleoside was readily acted upon.

Allantoin.[105] In marsupials, rodents, carnivora, ungulates, and other animals, including monkeys, but excluding the anthropoid apes and man, allantoin is the chief end-product of purine metabolism, its formation from uric acid being indicated above. A most interesting exception, and one cited in an earlier connection, is the excretion of uric acid by the Dalmatian coach hound. This exception applies only to pure-bred animals, for a dog that is only part Dalmatian excretes both uric acid and allantoin.

---

[104] *Z. physiol. Chem.*, **208**, 185 (1932).

[105] The name is derived from the fact that it was first encountered in allantoic fluid (cow).

The conversion of uric acid into allantoin is attributed to the action of the enzyme *uricase*, which is evidently lacking in man.[106,107]

In a preliminary study of the fate of the purine nucleosides in the dog, Allen and Cerecedo[108] found that when fed in moderate amounts (2–3 grams) guanosine and adenosine were completely metabolized. About half of the guanosine nitrogen appeared as allantoin and one-third as urea. Adenosine yielded a similar proportion of allantoin, but there was no increase in urea nitrogen. From these observations it was concluded that purine metabolism in the dog does not end with allantoin, but that a portion of this is metabolized further, one of the products being urea. Guanine when fed to dogs in small amounts is partly converted into allantoin and partly into urea.

Bollman, Mann, and Magath[109] have shown that the destruction of uric acid and its conversion into allantoin in the dog is dependent on the liver, since complete extirpation of this organ results in the excretion of uric acid.

Metabolism of the Pyrimidines. Our knowledge of the fate of the pyrimidines in metabolism is less complete than that of the purines. Sweet and Levene[110] found that if they fed thymine to a dog, more than half could be recovered in the urine, but if the same amount of thymine was fed in the form of nucleic acid, none could be recovered in the urine. Wilson[111] performed similar experiments with uracil in rabbits and on a human subject. When administered as such, uracil was quantitatively excreted unchanged, but with uracil combined in the form of a nucleoside or nucleotide, very little of the uracil could be found in the urine. Nearly all of it had apparently undergone metabolism, the end-product of which was urea. On the basis of these and similar observations, Wilson suggested that the intermediary metabolism of nucleic

---

[106] The presence of allantoin in human urine, especially in pregnant women and nurslings, was claimed by some of the earlier investigators. Employing a recently developed technique, Larson (*J. Biol. Chem.*, **94**, 727 [1931–32]) found the daily excretion in man to be about 25–30 mg. This is a small fraction of the average uric acid excretion, and although it is conceivable that it represents a further stage in purine metabolism than uric acid, it is perhaps just as likely that it is exogenous in origin, representing the allantoin ingested with the food.

[107] Among recent contributions pertaining to the action and properties of uricase are the following: R. Truszkowski, *Biochem. J.*, **24**, 1340, 1349, 1359 (1930); **26**, 285 (1932); M. Z. Grynberg, *Biochem. Z.*, **236**, 138 (1931); W. Schuler, *Z. physiol. Chem.*, **208**, 237 (1932); K. Ro, *J. Biochem. (Japan)*, **14**, 361 (1931–32).

[108] *Proc. Soc. Exp. Biol. Med.*, **29**, 190 (1931–32); *J. Biol. Chem.*, **102**, 313 (1933).

[109] *Am. J. Physiol.*, **72**, 629 (1925); J. L. Bollman and F. C. Mann, *ibid.*, **104**, 242 (1933).

[110] *J. Exp. Med.*, **9**, 229 (1907).

[111] *J. Biol. Chem.*, **56**, 215 (1923).

acids involves radical changes in both the purine and pyrimidine groups before the relatively complex combinations (nucleosides and nucleotides) are broken up.

Deuel[112] has observed that when large quantities of thymine or uracil (1–3 grams) were given to dogs a considerable proportion appeared in the urine. However, when the same amounts were given in small divided doses over a period of days, the pyrimidines were apparently metabolized, for none could be detected in the urine. When a large amount (50 grams) of thymus nucleic acid was fed, the urine was found to contain free pyrimidines. Apparently, a sufficient amount of free pyrimidine had been liberated so that a portion escaped oxidation. This does not occur, under normal conditions, according to Deuel, who found it impossible to isolate even a trace of pyrimidine in 150 liters of human urine.

Results similar to those of Deuel were also obtained by Cerecedo.[113] When fed in small amount to dogs, uracil and thymine were metabolized, the predominant end-product being urea. Cytosine, on the other hand, escaped oxidation, being partly excreted unchanged and partly deaminized to uracil. In a later experiment, Emerson and Cercedo confirmed the observation that cytosine, administered as such, is not utilized directly, but that when given in combination as the nucleoside, is completely metabolized.

When the observations just recorded are summarized, the following conclusions seem justified: (1) uracil and thymine when present in small amount as the free base are readily utilized, (2) cytosine as such is not utilized directly, being partly excreted unchanged and partly converted into uracil, (3) pyrimidines in nucleoside combination, particularly cytosine nucleoside, are more readily and more completely metabolized than the free pyrimidines, (4) normally the urine contains little, if any, pyrimidines; possibly when large quantities of nucleoproteins are fed, the urine may contain a small amount of unchanged pyrimidines. The constituent pentose of the nucleosides appears to be completely utilized.

The metabolism of one of the pyrimidines, uracil, has been thoroughly investigated by Cerecedo.[114] Inasmuch as the *in vitro* oxidation of uracil yields isobarbituric acid and in turn isodialuric acid, these

[112] *Ibid.*, **60**, 749 (1924).

[113] *Ibid.*, **75**, 661 (1927); **87**, 453 (1930); *Proc. Soc. Exp. Biol. Med.*, **27**, 203 (1929).

[114] *J. Biol. Chem.*, **88**, 695 (1930); **93**, 269, 283 (1931); J. A. Stekol and L. R. Cerecedo, *ibid.*, **93**, 275 (1931); **100**, 653 (1933).

compounds were fed to dogs in small amounts. It was found that to a considerable extent they were metabolized to urea.

Isobarbituric acid is oxidized by potassium permanganate successively to formyloxaluric and oxaluric acids. When these compounds were fed to dogs they were likewise partly catabolized to urea. It was therefore assumed that the metabolism of uracil involves the following sequence of reactions:

$$
\begin{array}{ccc}
\text{NH—CO} & \text{NH—CO} & \text{NH—CO} \\
| \quad | & | \quad | & | \quad | \\
\text{CO} \quad \text{CH} \rightarrow & \text{CO} \quad \text{COH} \rightarrow & \text{CO} \quad \text{CO} \rightarrow \\
| \quad \| & | \quad \| & | \quad | \\
\text{NH—CH} & \text{NH—CH} & \text{NH—CHOH} \\
\text{Uracil} & \text{Isobarbituric} & \text{Isodialuric} \\
& \text{acid} & \text{acid}
\end{array}
$$

$$
\begin{array}{ccc}
\text{NH—CHO} & \text{NH}_2 & \text{NH}_2 \\
| & | & | \\
\text{CO} \rightarrow & \text{CO} \rightarrow & \text{CO} \quad + \quad \text{COOH} \\
| & | & | \quad\quad\quad | \\
\text{NH—CO—COOH} & \text{NH—CO—COOH} & \text{NH}_2 \quad\quad \text{COOH} \\
\text{Formyloxaluric acid} & \text{Oxaluric acid} & \text{Urea} \quad\quad \text{Oxalic} \\
& & \text{acid}
\end{array}
$$

It was noted that following the administration of isobarbituric, isodialuric, or formyloxaluric acid, the urinary output of inorganic sulfates diminished, while the ethereal sulfates increased correspondingly, suggesting that these derivatives of uracil were partly excreted as conjugated sulfates. This has been confirmed by Stekol and Cerecedo[114] in a recent experiment on human subjects. When isobarbituric acid was fed, it was partly catabolized to urea and partly excreted as an ethereal sulfate, the latter being formed at the expense of the inorganic sulfur fraction.

Less is known of the metabolism of thymine. According to Cerecedo, thymine glycol is an intermediate product in its conversion to urea.

$$
\begin{array}{ccc}
\text{NH—CO} & \text{NH—CO} & \text{NH}_2 \\
| \quad | & | \quad |\diagup\text{CH}_3 & | \\
\text{CO} \quad \text{C—CH}_3 \rightarrow & \text{CO} \quad \text{C} \rightarrow \cdots \rightarrow & \text{CO} \\
| \quad \| & | \quad |\diagdown\text{OH} & | \\
\text{NH—CH} & \text{NH—CHOH} & \text{NH}_2 \\
\text{Thymine} & \text{Thymine} & \text{Urea} \\
& \text{glycol}
\end{array}
$$

The partial conversion of cytosine, when fed as such, into uracil has been mentioned. Whether this represents an intermediate stage in the metabolism of cytidine, the corresponding nucleoside, remains to be determined.

Purine Metabolism in Birds and Reptiles. In birds and reptiles, uric acid is not only the end-product of purine metabolism, but it is likewise the chief end-product of protein metabolism. It is believed that in these animal forms the catabolism of amino acids results first in the formation of urea, and that this is the precursor of uric acid. Wiener[115] has suggested that lactic acid may be oxidized in the liver to tartronic acid, which, by combining with urea, may yield uric acid. These reactions, which are essentially hypothetical, may be represented as follows:

$$
\begin{array}{ccc}
\underset{\text{Urea}}{\begin{array}{c} \text{HNH} \\ | \\ \text{O}=\text{C} \\ | \\ \text{HNH} \end{array}} +
\underset{\text{Tartronic acid}}{\begin{array}{c} \text{HOC}=\text{O} \\ | \\ \text{CHOH} \\ | \\ \text{HOC}=\text{O} \end{array}} \rightarrow
\underset{\text{Dialuric acid}}{\begin{array}{c} \text{HN}-\text{C}=\text{O} \\ |\quad\ | \\ \text{O}=\text{C}\ \ \text{CHOH} \\ |\quad\ | \\ \text{HN}-\text{C}=\text{O} \end{array}} + 2\text{H}_2\text{O}
\end{array}
$$

$$
\begin{array}{ccc}
\underset{\text{Dialuric acid}}{\begin{array}{c} \text{HN}-\text{C}=\text{O} \\ |\quad\ | \\ \text{O}=\text{C}\ \ \text{CHOH} \\ |\quad\ | \\ \text{HN}-\text{C}=\text{O} \end{array}} +
\underset{\text{Urea}}{\begin{array}{c} \text{H}_2\text{N} \\ \diagdown \\ \quad\text{C}=\text{O} \\ \diagup \\ \text{H}_2\text{N} \end{array}} \rightarrow
\underset{\text{Uric acid}}{\begin{array}{c} \text{HN}-\text{C}=\text{O} \\ |\quad\ | \\ \text{O}=\text{C}\ \ \text{C}-\text{NH} \\ |\quad\ \| \quad\diagdown\text{C}=\text{O} \\ \text{HN}-\text{C}-\text{NH}\diagup \end{array}} + 2\text{H}_2\text{O}
\end{array}
$$

Excretion of Uric Acid. Uric acid is excreted in combination with sodium, potassium, and ammonium in the form of urates. In addition to uric acid, there are probably smaller amounts of other purines in the urine, such as adenine, xanthine, hypoxanthine, and methyl-purine derivatives. The daily excretion of uric acid is subject to considerable variation, being influenced by diet and other factors.[116] On a purine-free diet, the normal daily excretion is between 0.2 and 0.4 gram. The content of uric acid in the blood usually varies between 1 and 3 mg. per 100 cc. Marked retention of uric acid occurs in nephritis, in gout, and, as shown by Lennox,[117] during starvation. According to Lennox, uric-acid retention is in some way associated with ketosis. In conditions such as leukemia and pneumonia, which are associated with marked destruction of nuclear material, the uric-acid content of the blood and urine increases appreciably.

The effect of muscular work on purine metabolism has not been clearly defined, owing to a lack of sufficient data. Burian[118] observed

[115] *Beitr. chem. Physiol. Path.*, **2**, 42 (1902).

[116] For a detailed discussion of the uric acid problem and the factors influencing its excretion see Folin, O., Berglund, H., and Derick, C., *J. Biol. Chem.*, **60**, 361 (1924).

[117] *J. Biol. Chem.*, **66**, 521 (1925).

[118] *Z. physiol. Chem.*, **43**, 532 (1905).

an increased endogenous uric acid excretion in individuals subjected to heavy gymnastics. In agreement with this is Rakestraw's finding[119] of a rise in blood uric acid following severe exertion. Labor is likewise associated with an increased concentration of uric acid in the blood and urine. In this connection it is interesting to note that Kerr,[120] working in Embden's laboratory, demonstrated a marked increase in the purine fraction of isolated frog muscle stimulated to the point of exhaustion.

Certain organisms of the alimentary tract are said to be capable of synthesizing purines and even uric acid. Accordingly, it has been suggested by McDonald and Levine[121] that in addition to the exogenous and endogenous sources of urinary uric acid a portion may owe its origin to bacterial synthesis in the bowel.

Opposed to this is the evidence of Lucke[122] that in man a certain amount of uric acid (30–50 mg.) is excreted daily into the gastric juice and bile and that the greater part of this is destroyed by bacteria in the alimentary canal.

SULFUR

The main features of sulfur metabolism were discussed in the preceding chapter in connection with the fate of cystine in the body. Cystine and methionine represent the most important sources of sulfur in metabolism and one or the other is apparently essential for maintenance. A small amount of sulfur is probably derived from the sulfur-containing lipids or sulfatides of the diet. Inorganic sulfates are apparently of no importance from the standpoint of nutrition.

Among the more familiar physiological constituents, other than protein, that contain sulfur, may be mentioned glutathione, taurine, insulin, and the sulfolipids contained in the tissues of the central nervous system and in the secretions of the skin. Sulfur is removed from the body in several ways. In the growth of hair, considerable quantities are lost in the form of cystine, which is especially abundant in the albuminoid, keratin. The bile contains sulfur compounds which, if not reabsorbed, are excreted in the stools. The saliva, urine, and bile contain thiocyanates, probably formed in the detoxication of small amounts of CN arising in metabolism. The urine is the most important channel of excretion of the end-products of protein metabolism, including those

[119] *J. Biol. Chem.*, **56**, 121 (1923).
[120] *Z. physiol. Chem.*, **210**, 181 (1932).
[121] *Am. J. Physiol.*, **78**, 437 (1926).
[122] *Z. ges. exp. Med.*, **70**, 468; **72**, 953; **74**, 329 (1930); **76**, 180, 188 (1931).

containing sulfur. These have been referred to previously and will receive further attention in the next chapter.

The Ratio of Nitrogen to Sulfur. A considerable amount of work has been done in studying the ratio of the excretion of sulfur to the excretion of nitrogen with a view to elucidating certain problems in protein metabolism. The results obtained by one group of workers (von Wendt,[123] etc.) have led them to believe that after the ingestion of protein, the sulfur is excreted earlier than the nitrogen. If this were true, it would mean that the protein which the body retains is poorer in sulfur than the original protein of the diet.

In contrast to this, others (Gruber,[124] etc.) have found that the N : S ratio is identical with that of the protein fed. Then there are the observations of Lewis[125] and of Fay and Mendel,[126] who have shown a frequent and apparently specific retention of sulfur after periods of starvation. This is highly suggestive, for it indicates that the organism may be capable of storing protein of varying composition in response to specific needs, a concept which has considerable additional evidence in its favor (Wilson).[127] For a summary of the recent literature, the student is referred to Lewis' excellent reviews[128] on sulfur metabolism.

As to the numerical value of the starvation N : S ratio, von Wendt determined it to be about 9.3, but nearly all other investigators have obtained values ranging between 13 and 16 with an average of about 14. This means that for every gram of sulfur normally excreted in the urine, the nitrogen excretion is about 14 grams. These values correspond rather well to the proportions of sulfur and nitrogen in muscle proteins.

Summary. Some of the main features of protein and nucleic-acid metabolism are summarized in the diagram given on p. 445.

[123] *Skand. Arch. Physiol.*, **17**, 211 (1905).

[124] *Z. Biol.*, **42**, 407 (1901); compare with S. Morgulis, *J. Biol. Chem.*, **77**, 627 (1928).

[125] *J. Biol. Chem.*, **26**, 61 (1916).

[126] *Am. J. Physiol.*, **75**, 308 (1926).

[127] *Biochem. J.*, **19**, 322 (1925); **20**, 76 (1926); *J. Physiol.*, **72**, 327 (1931); **77**, 240 (1933). See also E. P. Cathcart, "The Physiology of Protein Metabolism," 1921 edition, pp. 105, 123.

[128] *Physiol. Rev.*, **4**, 394 (1924); *Ann. Rev. Biochem.*, **1**, 171 (1932); **2**, 95 (1933).

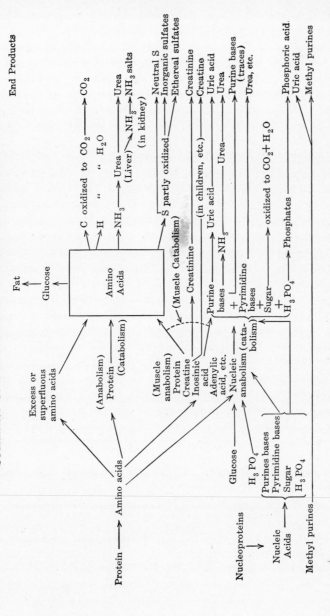

SUMMARY OF PROTEIN AND NUCLEIC-ACID METABOLISM

CHAPTER XIV

EXCRETION: THE URINE

Channels of Excretion. The removal of waste products from the body is accomplished largely, but not solely, by the lungs and kidneys. The former are concerned mainly with the excretion of gaseous waste products, the latter with the elimination of solids in solution. Among the other organs which may be regarded as at least in part excretory are the liver and the gall-bladder. These are concerned with the removal of cholesterol, bile pigments, and other substances. The intestinal epithelium excretes inorganic constituents, especially those foreign to the body. The saliva contains small quantities of nitrogenous and other waste products. Not only water, but also compounds such as urea, uric acid, lactic acid, and sodium chloride are excreted by way of the skin. The daily output of perspiration contains about 0.2–0.3 gram of nitrogen.[1] An additional 0.1 gram of nitrogen is lost to the body daily in the growth of hair and nails. In careful studies of nitrogen balance, it is desirable to take into account all the channels of excretion, so as to allow for all losses. Due allowance must also be made for the excretion of nitrogenous material by the intestinal epithelium, as this usually amounts, even in starvation, to about 0.5 gram per day. Thus the extra-renal excretion of nitrogen may be estimated at about 1.0 gram.

Formation of Urine. Textbooks of physiology and histology contain descriptions of the kidney. For a proper understanding of what is to follow, the student should be familiar with the microscopic anatomy of this organ.

Various theories have been proposed to explain kidney secretion. According to the theory advanced by Ludwig in 1844, the glomeruli filter from the blood its non-colloidal constituents. Large amounts of fluid thus pass into the tubules. During its passage through the tubules, the fluid becomes concentrated by the reabsorption of water.

---

[1] G. A. Talbert and his associates have published a series of papers on the composition of sweat: *Am. J. Physiol.*, **81**, 74 (1927); **82**, 153, 639 (1927); **84**, 577 (1928); **97**, 426 (1931); **100**, 328 (1932); see also H. H. Mosher, *J. Biol. Chem.*, **99**, 781 (1932–33); E. H. Fishberg and W. Bierman, *ibid.*, **97**, 433 (1932).

According to the theory postulated by Bowman and Heidenhain, water and salts are secreted by the glomerulus, whereas the organic constituents are added to the urine as a result of the secretory activity of the renal tubular epithelium.

Cushny[2] in his monograph, " The Secretion of the Urine," reviews the evidence for and against these theories, and advances what he terms the " modern theory," according to which water and the non-colloidal constituents of the plasma are filtered through the glomerulus. He states that as the glomerular filtrate proceeds through the tubules, only those substances are reabsorbed that are necessary to the plasma and tissues. Such substances are water, glucose, salts, amino acids, sodium bicarbonate, etc., and are termed " threshold " substances. There is no absorption of unnecessary constituents, such as urea and creatine. These are termed " non-threshold " substances.

Starling and Verney[3] have attempted to reconcile the conflicting views of Ludwig and Bowman. They consider that the glomeruli filter from the blood plasma its non-protein constituents, but that certain constituents such as urea and sulfate are also secreted by the tubule cells, and pass into the glomerular fluid. Phenolsulfonphthalein, when injected into the dog, is likewise eliminated by the tubules. In turn, the tubule cells are said to reabsorb water, chloride, bicarbonate, and glucose. According to Starling, the cells that reabsorb water occupy a lower position in the tubules than the cells concerned in the reabsorption of chloride.

Experiments conducted in Richards' laboratory[4] have materially strengthened the view that the glomerular urine is an ultrafiltrate of the plasma. With the aid of ingenious technical procedures and adaptations of available micro-analytical methods, it has been shown that the glomerular fluid has the same molecular and electrolyte concentrations as the plasma. Extending the investigation to single constituents (urea, chloride, uric acid, phosphate, creatinine, glucose), it was further shown that the content of each of these is the same in both fluids. Inasmuch as water is reabsorbed by the tubules, the concentration of most of these constituents was found to be greater in the bladder urine than in the glomerular urine. Of the compounds studied there were, however, two

---

[2] A. R. Cushny, "The Secretion of the Urine," Longmans, Green & Co., New York, 1917.

[3] *Proc. Royal Soc. (London)*, B, **97**, 321 (1925).

[4] *Am. J. Physiol.*, **71**, 209 (1924); *J. Biol. Chem.*, **66**, 247 (1925); **87**, 467, 479, 499, 523 (1930); **91**, 593 (1931); **101**, 179, 193, 223, 239, 255 (1933). Co-authors: A. N. Richards, J. T. Wearn, A. E. Livingston, A. M. Walker, L. E. Bayliss, J. Bordley, J. A. Reisinger, and J. P. Hendrix.

exceptions, sugar, which is nearly completely, and chloride which is partly, reabsorbed by the tubules.

Blood pressure and the volume of blood flow through the kidney influence the amount of urine formation. Richards and Plant[5] perfused the rabbit's kidney with hirudinized blood in a manner which permitted of variations in the pressure within the renal circulation without alterations in the rate of blood flow. It was found that changes in renal blood pressure produced parallel changes in the rate of urine flow.

The rate with which certain substances, such as urea and phosphates, are excreted by the kidneys seems to be regulated not only by their concentration in the blood but by a variety of other factors. For details the student is referred to the review of Marshall, the papers of Addis and his associates,[6] and to the discussion of urea clearance (p. 463).

It is instructive to compare the concentration of various constituents in the blood and urine. The values given here, though in no sense fixed, are nevertheless fairly representative. Urine contains 25 times as much uric acid, 40 times as much ammonia, 60 times as much urea, 100 times as much creatinine, 30 times as much PO_4, and 60 times as much SO_4, as is contained in an equivalent volume of blood plasma. On the other hand, there is little difference in the concentration of chloride, sodium, calcium, and magnesium; and, in the case of glucose, much less is present in the urine than in the blood. On the basis of Cushny's theory, this would mean the filtration of large quantities of plasma per day. Basing his computations on the difference in the concentrations of urea, Cushny has calculated that in the formation of 1 liter of urine, 67 liters of plasma would have to filter through the glomeruli.

This obviously must entail a considerable amount of work, the evaluation of which has been attempted by various investigators, notably by Borsook and Winegarden,[7] who have approached the problem from the standpoint of thermodynamics. Their study indicates that the excretion of a urine isotonic with the plasma would entail no work on the part of the kidney. Ordinarily, the work *performed* by the kidney in man is of the order of magnitude of 0.7 gm. calorie per cc. of urine, or 70 gm. calories per gram of nitrogen excreted. However, this is a very small fraction of the energy *consumed* by the kidneys. This has been estimated to be 6–11 kg. calories per gram of nitrogen,

[5] *Am. J. Physiol.*, **59**, 144 (1922)

[6] E. K. Marshall, *Physiol. Rev.*, **6**, 440 (1926); Addis, Barnett, and Shevky, *Am. J. Physiol.*, **46**, 1, 39, 52 (1918); Addis and Drury, *J. Biol. Chem.*, **55**, 105, 629, 639 (1923); Addis, Meyers, and Bayer, *Am. J. Physiol.*, **72**, 125 (1925).

[7] *Proc. Nat. Acad. Sci.*, **17**, 3, 13 (1931).

showing that although the normal kidney has a great capacity for work, the " efficiency " with which it is performed is probably not greater than 1–2 per cent. In disease of the kidney, its capacity for work is markedly reduced.

Physical Properties; *Volume.* The volume of urine secreted per day (twenty-four hours) may vary within wide limits. A normal adult usually excretes 1200–2000 cc. The most important factor determining the output of urine is obviously the water intake, in the form of water, milk, soup, or beverages. Temperature is another important modifying factor. During the summer months or in warm climate, less urine is formed, because of the loss of water in perspiration. Urination is, as a rule, more frequent in winter than in summer. A high-protein diet, by giving rise to nitrogenous end-products having a diuretic effect, causes an increased elimination of urine. Muscular exercise, on the contrary, results in a diminished volume of urine, Nervousness and excitement may cause abnormally frequent and abundant micturition. It is generally believed that mentally deranged people excrete more urine than normal individuals. The diuretic effect of coffee, tea, and chocolate is due largely to the presence of caffeine and other purine derivatives.

Normally, the amount of urine secreted varies with the time of day. For an hour or two after a meal, there is usually an increase in urine formation. During the night much less urine is formed than during the day. If the total urine for twenty-four hours is 1500 cc., that formed during the night is usually about 400 or 500 cc. Simpson has observed that these relations hold even when a definite amount of water is given at hourly intervals during the day and night. Apparently there is a retention of water during the night, whereas during part of the day there is a negative water balance. These variations seem to be dependent, at least in part, on body temperature. Coincident with the rise in body temperature which occurs at about 6 A.M., there is an increased secretion of urine. Both the temperature and the urine volume continue to increase until late in the afternoon or evening, after which both begin to fall until the following morning when the cycle begins again.

The chloride and phosphate elimination and pH of the urine are likewise decreased during sleep, but it is interesting to note that these changes may occur irrespective of significant changes in the urine volume (Simpson).[8]

In nephritis, the urine collected during short intervals of the day and night shows less than the normal variation in volume and composi-

[8] *J. Biol. Chem.*, **59**, 107 (1924); **67**, 505 (1926); **84**, 393 (1929); compare N. Kleitman, *Am. J. Physiol.*, **74**, 225 (1925).

tion. As a rule, the night urine of nephritics is more abundant than that of normal individuals. The condition in which an excessive amount of urine is secreted at night is called nocturia.

The determination of urine volume may be of value in diagnosing kidney disease. In acute nephritis due to mercuric chloride, there may be complete suppression of urine, or anuria. Oliguria is the condition of low urine output and is observed in eclampsia, cardiac derangements, fever, and diarrhea. Polyuria, or excessive secretion of urine, occurs especially in diabetes insipidus and after injury to the pituitary gland. In diabetes insipidus, the daily elimination of urine may exceed 20 liters, and there is at least one case on record in which 50 liters were excreted during a period of twenty-four hours.

Color. Normal urine is pale yellow in color, but may vary from a slight yellow tinge to deep amber-yellow, depending on its concentration. In fever, the urine is usually dark yellow or brown-red in color. In jaundice, the presence of bile pigments gives the urine a greenish yellow or greenish brown color. The presence of blood or hemoglobin would obviously cause a reddish tinge. Brown and black urine may be due to the presence of methemoglobin, melanin, and phenol derivatives such as are excreted in carbolic-acid poisoning. Drugs excreted in the urine may likewise give rise to peculiar colors.

Drabkin[9] has made the important observation that normally the output of urinary pigment is constant from day to day and is independent of the diet. It is accordingly a product of endogenous metabolism, being eliminated in quantities which are proportional to its intensity. Experimentally the output of pigment was increased by fasting, the administration of acids, or the administration of calorigenic agents such as epinephrin or thyroxin. A diminished urinary pigment output was observed after the administration of alkali, or following the surgical removal of the thyroid gland. In exophthalmic goiter, the quantity of pigment is abnormally high. In one case which was followed daily, the amount of urinary pigment paralleled the patient's metabolic rate.

Transparency. Freshly voided urine is usually clear and transparent, except after a hearty meal, when the precipitation of calcium phosphate, due to the alkalinity of the urine (alkaline tide), may render it turbid. Strict vegetarians, as well as herbivorous animals, normally excrete an alkaline and turbid urine. Clear urine may become turbid on standing, owing to the precipitation of mucin derived from the urinary tract. The conversion of urea into ammonia by bacteria may cause an acid transparent urine to change into an alkaline turbid urine, the turbidity here being due, likewise, to the precipitation of calcium phosphate.

[9] *J. Biol. Chem.*, **75**, 443, 481 (1927); **88**, 433, 443 (1930).

In the abnormal condition known as chyluria, the urine has a milky appearance, which is due to the presence of fat globules. In inflammations of the urinary tract, large amounts of pus may be excreted with the urine, causing it to acquire a turbid appearance.

Odor and Taste. Urine has a faint aromatic odor which has been attributed to a substance of unknown chemical composition, called urinod. The odor of urine may be influenced by the ingestion of drugs and vegetables. Asparagus causes a peculiar odor, due to methyl mercapatan. Abnormal constituents, such as acetone bodies, may modify the odor of urine. Putrefactive changes cause urine to acquire an ammoniacal odor. Normal urine is salty to the taste; diabetic urine has a sweetish taste.

Specific Gravity. The specific gravity of urine depends on its concentration. The greater the volume, the lower is the concentration, and hence the specific gravity. Accordingly, the specific gravity of normal urine is not fixed but may vary within a wide range of values. The normal range is usually given as 1.008–1.030. A rough estimate of the total solids of the urine, in grams per liter, may be obtained by multiplying the last two figures of the specific gravity (i.e., the second and third decimal places) by the factor 2.66 (Long's coefficient).

Reaction. Whereas the blood is faintly alkaline in reaction (pH 7.35–7.43), the urine is normally acid. Indeed, on an ordinary diet, about 250–350 cc. of $N/10$ acid is excreted daily. Henderson and Palmer[10] have calculated that the kidneys may normally remove from the body 600–700 cc. of $N/10$ acid, and in diabetes the excretion of acid may be ten times as great. It is because of this that the kidneys enable the blood to maintain its reaction within certain narrow limits. When the kidneys fail to function properly, retention of urinary constituents occurs in the blood and is followed by the well-known symptoms of intoxication, which have been incorrectly classed under the term of uremia or uremic poisoning. The coma that characterizes the terminal stages of nephritis is not due so much to the retention of urea and other nitrogenous constituents as to the accumulation of acid. Cushny[11] makes the statement that acid is probably the most poisonous of all the waste products of metabolism known at present.

The kidney exerts its regulatory effect by eliminating acid and at the same time retaining, for the use of the organism, as much alkali as possible. In the blood the ratio $Na_2HPO_4 : NaH_2PO_4$ is in favor of the basic phosphate, whereas in the urine there is a preponderance of the acid phosphate. The change which brings about this altered rela-

---

[10] *J. Biol. Chem.*, **13**, 393 (1913).

[11] A. R. Cushny, "The Secretion of the Urine," p. 165.

tion, and which is believed to take place in the tubule, may be represented as follows:

$$Na_2HPO_4 + H_2O \rightarrow NaH_2PO_4 + Na^+ + OH^-$$

The sodium is retained in combination as the bicarbonate. The important point to be emphasized here is this: The glomerular filtrate resembles in composition the blood plasma. Both, therefore, contain Na_2HPO_4 and NaH_2PO_4 in approximately the same proportion. It may be supposed that the acid phosphate is excreted unchanged, although we should not disregard the possibility of a certain amount of conversion into $NH_4H_2PO_4$. The Na_2HPO_4, on the other hand, as it proceeds through the tubule, gives up a part of its Na, which is reabsorbed by the tubular epithelium.

The shift from basic to acid phosphate and the replacement of fixed base by ammonia in the kidney have been demonstrated by a number of workers. Hendrix and Sanders,[12] for example, observed that the injection of dibasic phosphate caused a marked rise in the titratable acidity and ammonia in the urine. A similar effect was produced when sodium hippurate was injected. In fact, the rise in total acidity plus ammonia was very nearly equivalent to the total phosphate and hippurate injected. From these observations it may be surmised that when the rate of flow of glomerular fluid through the tubules is markedly increased, as in diuresis, there is an incomplete absorption of non-threshold substances. In later experiments, Hendrix and Calvin[13] have shown that, in diuresis produced by the injection of certain neutral salts (sodium chloride, sodium nitrate, and sodium sulfate) and urea, there is a loss of base through the kidney over and above that lost normally. The excretion of base is reflected in a marked fall in the alkali reserve of the blood, which occurs simultaneously and which is obviously due to the removal of fixed base from the body. These changes are apparently due to a failure in reabsorption from the tubules, since these are flooded and overtaxed in diuresis, and cannot be supposed to function with their normal efficiency in the retention of basic ions.

Titratable Acidity. A measure of urinary acidity may be obtained by titration. The method in general use is that of Folin, according to which a certain amount of urine (25 cc.), to which 15–20 grams of finely pulverized potassium oxalate has been added, is titrated with standard sodium or potassium hydroxide ($N/10$), phenolphthalein being used as the indicator. The end-point is not sharp, because of the presence of ammonium salts. The oxalate is added to precipitate the calcium

---

[12] *J. Biol. Chem.*, **58**, 503 (1923–24).   [13] *Ibid.*, **65**, 197 (1925).

as oxalate, for otherwise it would interfere with the end-point by prematurely forming insoluble calcium phosphate as the point of neutrality was approached. The acidity is usually expressed in terms of cubic centimeters of $N/10$ alkali required to neutralize the twenty-four-hour output of urine.

The reaction of urine is dependent upon the character of the diet. Accordingly, the titratable acidity may fall normally within a wide range of values (150–500 cc.). The average is probably about 300–350 cc. Even an alkaline urine ($pH > 7$) has a titratable acidity, for the color change of phenolphthalein is well over on the alkaline side ($pH = 8.5$). On diets rich in acid-forming foods (meat, fish, oatmeal, rice, wheat, egg yolk, prunes, etc.), a very acid urine is produced. Values of 600–900 for titratable acidity may be obtained easily if sufficient quantities of such food are eaten. Most vegetables and fruits (oranges, potatoes, beans, raisins, apples, bananas, carrots, beets, etc.) are base-forming and yield an alkaline urine. This accounts for the fact that the urine of herbivorous animals is normally alkaline, whereas carnivorous animals ordinarily secrete an acid urine.

Urinary acidity bears a relationship to the excretion of ammonia, low acidity being associated with low values for ammonia, whereas urines having high acidities contain much larger quantities of ammonia. An exception to this is often observed in nephritis, where high acidity values are not always associated with correspondingly high values for ammonia.

Van Slyke and Palmer[14] have shown that men normally excrete the equivalent of about 6.0 cc. of $N/10$ organic acid per kilo of body weight in twenty-four hours. In starvation and in diabetes, the organic acid elimination is markedly increased. A similar alteration, commensurate with the changes in titratable acidity, is observed in the ammonia output in the urine. Increase in ammonia elimination may be produced experimentally by feeding acid (Fiske and Sokhey[15]). In a recent experiment, Fiske[16] observed that when exceedingly large doses of acid were given there was relatively more loss of fixed base, and less of ammonia production, than when the dose was smaller; but for several days after the acid administration, the output of fixed base was lower than normal, whereas the ammonia elimination continued to be high, showing that there was a retention of fixed base at the expense of ammonia.

Blatherwick and Long[17] have observed that drinking large amounts of orange juice resulted in the production of alkaline urines, an

[14] *J. Biol. Chem.*, **41**, 567 (1920).   [16] *Ibid.*, **67**, 385 (1926).
[15] *Ibid.*, **63**, 309 (1925).   [17] *Ibid.*, **53**, 103 (1922); **57**, 815 (1923).

increased organic acid excretion, and a decreased output of ammonia. The explanation of the increased organic acidity is that a certain amount of the citric acid escapes oxidation and is eliminated in the urine as citrate and thus increases the titration value for organic acids. However, this affects only a small part of the citric acid even when large amounts are taken; in fact the authors state: " It was impossible to overreach the organism's ability to oxidize the contained citric acid even though the amounts (of orange juice) drunk in one day were the equivalent of 48 grams of acid." Accordingly, the excess of base in the orange juice in Blatherwick's experiments was sufficient to balance the organic acidity which escaped oxidation and to cause an alkaline urine, as well as a marked depression in the ammonia excretion.

The increased urinary acidity produced by eating prunes and cranberries is due to hippuric acid.

Hydrogen-ion Concentration. The pH may be taken as a truer index of urinary acidity than is afforded by titration. Determinations of pH of urine are usually made by means of indicators. The extreme range is usually given as pH 4.80–7.50, the average normal value being about 6.0. Deviations from this mean value are dependent on the character of the diet, a high-acid diet yielding urine of low pH, whereas on a low-acid diet the urine obtained has a high pH. Low pH values are found in pathological conditions, especially in diabetes and cardiorenal disorders.

Perhaps the most striking change in the reaction of the urine is that which occurs after meals, when the urine becomes less acid and may even acquire a neutral or alkaline reaction. This is referred to as the " alkaline tide," and has been attributed to the withdrawal of hydrogen ions, attending the formation of the hydrochloric acid of the gastric juice. Inasmuch as in conditions of anacidity (lack of HCl formation) Hubbard, Munford, and Allen[18] did not observe an alkaline tide, it may be inferred that the secretion of gastric juice is an important factor in causing it. Possibly the moderate diuresis which occurs after meals is another factor. The increased acidity of the urine secreted during sleep has been referred to in another connection. A large number of persons show on awakening a marked urinary alkalinity which persists through the morning period (Hubbard, *et al.*). This " morning tide," is, however, unrelated to the secretion of acid by the stomach, nor is it connected with the taking of a meal.[19]

---

[18] *Am. J. Physiol.*, **68**, 207 (1924). *J. Biol. Chem.*, **101**, 781 (1933); *ibid.*, **84**, 191, 199 (1929); *Proc. Soc. Exp. Biol. Med.*, **27**, 212, 327 (1929–30).

[19] For a recent review of the subject of "alkaline tide" the student is referred to C. E. Brunton, *Physiol. Rev.*, **13**, 372 (1933).

Composition of Urine. In view of all that has been written in the preceding chapters, it would be superfluous to explain why the composition of urine is so variable. It will therefore be sufficient, at this point, to review briefly the better-known constituents of normal urine. These may be grouped under three heads:

1. Nitrogen-containing waste products: urea, uric acid, creatinine, creatine (in children), hippuric acid, indican (indoxyl-potassium sulfate), skatoxyl-sulfuric acid (as salt in traces), allantoin (absent or in traces), traces of purine bases other than uric acid (adenine, guanine, xanthine, epiguanine, para-xanthine, heteroxanthine, *l*-methylxanthine), amino acids.
2. Nitrogen-free organic constituents: glucose, glucuronic acid or similar reducing substances in traces, aromatic oxyacids, oxalates, traces of acetone bodies, volatile fatty acids (acetic, formic and butyric in traces).
3. Inorganic constituents: chlorides, sulfates, phosphates, carbonates, of calcium, sodium, and potassium, traces of nitrates, silicates, fluorides, iron, copper, and zinc.

In addition to these there are the pigments, chief of which is urochrome, a number of neutral sulfur compounds, some of which contain nitrogen as well (cystine, chondroitin-sulfuric acid, thiocyanates, taurine derivatives, oxyproteic acid), ethereal sulfates other than those mentioned (phenol and para-cresol-sulfuric acids and pyro-catechol-sulfuric acid), traces of oxaluric acid, benzoic acid, peptides, phenaceturic acid, certain organic phosphates (glycerophosphoric acid, phosphocarnic acid), etc.[20]

An idea of the quantitative relations of the chief urinary constituents may be obtained from the data in Table L, taken from Mitchell.[21] The values given are not supposed to show the average composition of human urine. They are based upon a limited number of analyses but are nevertheless fairly representative results.

Composition of Urine in Relation to Diet. At this stage of the discussion, it may be profitable to consider how the composition of the diet influences that of the urine. By this time, the student has no doubt become aware that the study of certain phases of metabolism requires a knowledge of the end-products appearing in the urine. The

[20] Based on table given in P. B. Hawk's "Practical Physiological Chemistry," 9th edition, 1926, p. 592.

[21] P. H. Mitchell, "General Physiology," McGraw-Hill Book Co., New York, 1923, p. 635.

type of information which may be obtained from the quantitative analysis of urine will be illustrated by a few simple examples.

TABLE L

REPRESENTATIVE COMPOSITION OF NORMAL HUMAN URINE

Volume for 24 hours, 1250 cc.

Specific gravity, 1.019

	Weight, Grams	Approximate Per Cent
Water	1212.0	95.1
Solids	61.7	4.9
Nitrogen-containing constituents:		
Urea	28.5	2.28
Creatinine	1.7	0.13
Ammonia, computed as NH_3	0.7	0.05
Uric acid	0.65	0.05
Hippuric acid	0.6	0.04
Indican, indoxyl potassium sulfate	0.01	0.0008
Allantoin (not always present)	0.005	0.0004
Creatine (not usually present in the urine of healthy adults but may occur in traces).		
Nitrogen-free organic constituents:		
Glucose or similar carbohydrate	0.7	0.05
Aromatic oxyacids	0.05	0.004
Oxalates, as oxalic acid	0.015	0.001
Acetone, acetoacetic acid	0.01	0.0008
Inorganic constituents:		
Chlorides, as NaCl	11.0	0.90
Phosphates, as P_2O_5	2.2	0.18
Sulfates, as SO_3	1.7	0.14
Potassium	1.6	0.12
Calcium	0.2	0.01
Magnesium	0.2	0.01
Iron	0.005	0.0004

Let us suppose that the student wishes to study the effect of changing the amount of protein of the diet on the composition of the urine. He may proceed to do so by first examining the urine on a diet containing the amount of protein to which he is normally accustomed. The composition of the food should be known. This information may be obtained by analyzing the food, or it may be calculated from known data, since the composition of the common foodstuffs has been determined. On a given day the urine should be collected over a period of exactly twenty-four hours. This urine is then analyzed for the constituents to be given presently, as well as for any others which the student may wish to determine.

Having performed this preliminary experiment, the student may now vary his protein intake. It is desirable that he be on the experimental diet (high-protein intake, low-protein intake, etc.) not only on the day when the urine is collected, but for two or three days preceding this. The reason for beginning the experimental diet several days before collecting the urine is that an alteration in the diet does not produce an immediate effect on the composition of the urine. There is usually a lag in the elimination of the nitrogenous end-products of metabolism. This is referred to as the " nitrogen lag."

In table LI are recorded the results of representative analyses of twenty-four-hour specimens of urine collected:

(a) On a diet containing an ordinary amount of protein (equivalent to about 15 grams of nitrogen per day).

(b) On a diet containing more than the usual amount of protein (equivalent to about 25 grams of nitrogen, given in the form of meat and eggs, etc.).

(c) On a diet containing very little protein (cream, starch, butter, potatoes) but adequate as regards caloric requirements.

TABLE LI

INFLUENCE OF PROTEIN INTAKE ON THE COMPOSITION OF URINE

(Daily output)

	Usual Protein Intake	Protein-rich Diet	Protein-poor Diet
Total nitrogen (g.)	13.20	23.28	4.20
Urea nitrogen (g.)	11.36	20.45	2.90
Ammonia nitrogen (g.)	0.40	0.82	0.17
Creatinine nitrogen (g.)	0.61	0.64	0.60
Uric acid nitrogen (g.)	0.21	0.30	0.11
Undetermined nitrogen (g.)	0.62	1.07	0.52
Titratable acidity (cc. 0.1 N)	284.0	655.0	160.0
Total sulfur as SO_3 (g.)	2.65	3.55	0.86
Inorganic sulfate as SO_3 (g.)	2.16	2.82	0.64
Ethereal sulfate as SO_3 (g.)	0.18	0.36	0.11
Neutral sulfur as SO_3 (g.)	0.31	0.37	0.11
Total phosphates as P_2O_5 (g.)	2.59	4.07	1.06
Chlorides as NaCl (g.)	12.10	15.10	9.80
Volume (cc.)	1260	1550	960

The subject was male and weighed 67 kg.[22]

Urea nitrogen is usually 80–90 per cent of the total nitrogen, but when the total nitrogen is very low the urea nitrogen may be only 60–70 per cent of the total. On a high-protein diet, particularly on one containing meat, the output of total sulfur and phosphorus is increased as well as the titratable acidity. The change in acidity influences the ammonia output, as indicated above. The increase in uric acid on the protein-rich diet and the decrease on the protein-poor diet are to be attributed to the presence of nucleic acid in the protein fed (part of it was meat). The undetermined nitrogen represents the nitrogenous constituents, other than those given, which are present in urine. The most important of these are probably hippuric acid and purine bases. Like ammonia, hippuric acid is believed to be synthesized in the kidney. Upon this fact is based a method for testing renal function, which consists in determining the rate of excretion of hippuric acid after the administration of sodium benzoate (Kingsbury and Swanson).[23] On a high-protein diet, there is usually a greater amount of intestinal putrefaction than otherwise occurs. This may account for the increase in ethereal sulfates on the protein-rich diet. No special significance need be attached to the changes in the elimination of chlorides and water. When large quantities of food are consumed, an increased intake of chlorides and water is usually incidental.

The influence of purine-free and purine-rich diets is indicated in the following table. In the experiments represented by the data contained therein, an attempt was made to maintain the total nitrogen intake at approximately the same level as on the day of the normal protein diet described above. The purine-rich diet consisted largely of glandular tissues (thymus, pancreas, and liver). On the low-purine diet, the most important changes were those involving the titratable acidity and the output of uric acid and phosphates. All three were increased on the purine-rich diet and diminished on the low-purine diet. These changes were due to the relative abundance, in the first case, of uric acid and phosphate precursors, and the relative lack of these in the second case. With the increased acidity on the high-purine diet, there was a corresponding rise in ammonia excretion. The high value for undetermined nitrogen on this diet was due, no doubt, to an increased elimination of purine bases other than uric acid.

[22] Total nitrogen is determined by the Kjeldahl method. For purposes of comparison, the concentrations of the nitrogenous constituents are expressed usually in terms of nitrogen. The analytical procedures are described in laboratory manuals of biochemistry.

[23] *J. Biol. Chem.*, **46**, iv (1921).

It will be observed that there was very little, if any, change in the creatinine values in this and in the preceding series of experiments, as migl t be expected from the fact that creatinine is derived from endogenous and not exogenous sources.

TABLE LII

INFLUENCE OF HIGH- AND LOW-PURINE DIETS ON THE COMPOSITION OF URINE

(Daily Output)

	High-Purine Diet	Low-Purine Diet
Total nitrogen (g.)	15.75	13.54
Urea nitrogen (g.)	12.97	11.88
Ammonia nitrogen (g.)	0.90	0.51
Creatinine nitrogen (g.)	0.61	0.60
Uric acid nitrogen (g.)	0.43	0.11
Undetermined nitrogen (g.)	0.84	0.44
Titratable acidity (cc. 0.1 N)	638	182
Total sulfur as SO_3 (g.)	3.64	2.00
Inorganic sulfate as SO_3 (g.)	2.81	1.53
Ethereal sulfate as SO_3 (g.)	0.46	0.22
Neutral sulfur as SO_3 (g.)	0.39	0.25
Total phosphates as P_2O_5 (g.)	3.94	1.40
Chlorides as NaCl (g.)	13.20	12.80
Volume (cc.)	1620	1410

Equally illuminating are the changes that occur during starvation. The results on p. 460 are based upon analyses of urine collected during the first and fourth days of a fasting period.

It is obvious that, during the first day of the fasting period, sufficient glycogen was available to supply most of the energy requirements. Consequently, relatively little protein was broken down for this purpose, as shown by the data. Since glucose metabolism was taking place, there was complete conversion of creatine to creatinine. There was, likewise, complete oxidation of fatty acids, as evidenced by the fact that the urine did not contain abnormal quantities of acetone bodies. The excretion of ammonia, uric acid, sulfate, and phosphate, and the titratable acidity, were less than on the normal diet, owing to the diminished metabolism of amino acids and purines.

By the fourth day, the glycogen stores had been fairly well depleted, for there was on that day an increase in tissue breakdown (rise in total N), as well as incomplete conversion of creatine into creatinine

TABLE LIII

INFLUENCE OF FASTING ON THE COMPOSITION OF URINE

(Daily Output)

	First Day of Fast	Fourth Day of Fast
Total nitrogen (g.)	7.08	14.40
Urea nitrogen (g.)	5.80	11.82
Ammonia nitrogen (g.)	0.21	1.32
Creatinine nitrogen (g.)	0.59	0.44
Creatine nitrogen (g.)	....	0.16
Uric acid nitrogen (g.)	0.15	0.08
Undetermined nitrogen (g.)	0.33	0.58
Titratable acidity (cc. 0.1 N)	176	720
Total sulfur as SO_3 (g.)	1.22	2.01
Total phosphates as P_2O_5 (g.)	1.71	1.14
Chlorides as NaCl (g.)	5.20	1.26
Acetone bodies (g.)	(trace)	3.86
Volume (cc.)	860	880

and failure in fat combustion (appearance of large amounts of acetone bodies). The continued decrease in uric-acid elimination may be explained on the ground that there was diminished nuclear metabolism and probably a retention of uric acid in the blood, in accordance with the suggestion of Lennox.[24] Commensurate with this change, there was a marked decrease in the excretion of phosphates. Nevertheless, the titratable acidity was higher than normal, owing to the acetone bodies. Accordingly, there was a corresponding increase in the formation and excretion of ammonia. Creatine appeared in the urine at the expense of creatinine. Chloride elimination decreased to a low level.

Pathological Constituents of Urine. Except in cases of alimentary glycosuria, the presence of more than traces of glucose in the urine is of pathological significance. As a result of exercise, particularly when it involves emotional stress, as on the football field, considerable amounts of sugar may be excreted. The so-called " afternoon glycosuria "

[24] *J. Biol. Chem.*, **66**, 521 (1925).

For a discussion of the sugars of urine compare V. J. Harding, and D. L. Selby, *Biochem. J.*, **25**, 1815 (1931) and E. S. West, *et al.*, *ibid.*, **26**, 1720, 1728, 1742 (1932). H. T. Edwards, T. K. Richards, and D. B. Dill, *Am. J. Physiol.*, **98**, 352 (1931). F. A. Hellebrandt, *Ibid.*, **101**, 357 (1932).

has been mentioned elsewhere (p. 342). Fructose occurs frequently, together with glucose, in diabetic urine, but has been likewise observed in non-diabetic individuals. This is a rare anomaly, called fructosuria. Pentosuria is another rare anomaly. Failure to remove milk from the mammary glands of lactating animals may lead to the appearance of lactose in the urine. This condition, called lactosuria, is occasionally observed during pregnancy and lactation and is somewhat more frequent during the weaning period.

Albuminuria, or the presence of albumin or globulin in the urine, is usually indicative of renal injury, or nephritis, but it also occurs in a small proportion of normal individuals, and especially after exercise. In this condition the kidneys become abnormally permeable to protein, with the result that a certain amount of it is excreted. However, protein may enter the urine below the kidneys, in which case the condition is usually called post-renal or " false " albuminuria in contradistinction to " true " albuminuria. Certain individuals, on standing for a variable length of time, develop albuminuria. This condition may be the result of stasis of the blood in the kidney, due to low blood pressure. It is called orthostatic or postural albuminuria.

In pneumonia, diphtheria, osteomalacia, atrophy of the kidneys, carcinoma, and other conditions, proteoses and peptones are frequently found in the urine. Perhaps the most important of the proteoses is " Bence-Jones protein," which has the property of precipitating at low temperatures and of redissolving as the temperature is raised. The presence of this substance in the urine is of diagnostic value in multiple myeloma.

Among the other proteins that are occasionally found in the urine are oxyhemoglobin and nucleoprotein. The former usually appears as a result of hemolysis, whereas the presence of the latter may be due to nephritis, pyelitis, or inflammation of the bladder.

The formation of a communicating channel between the lymph vessels and the urinary tract, due to a lesion, may result in the appearance of fat in the urine. This condition is called chyluria. The appearance of blood in urine (hematuria) may be due to a lesion in the kidney or in the urinary passages. Inflammation of the genito-urinary tract leads to the presence of pus in urine (pyuria). In icterus or jaundice, bile pigments and bile salts appear in the urine.

The urine of persons with melanotic tumors, on exposure to air, gradually turns dark brown or black, owing to the presence of an oxidizable substance (melanogen) which on oxidation yields a black pigment (melanin). Another pigment found in certain pathological conditions (pulmonary tuberculosis, typhoid fever, nephritis, etc.) is urorosein, present as a chromogen which Herter[25] found to be indole-acetic acid. Homogentisic acid is present in the urine of alcaptonurics, and cystine in that of cystinurics.

Creatine and the acetone bodies have been discussed elsewhere.

Sediment. Urine sediments may be collected readily by centrifuging the urine. Among the constituents that settle out are calcium phosphate, uric acid, and urates. Calcium carbonate occurs in the urine of herbivorous animals, but very rarely in human urine. Calcium oxalate crystals are frequently observed, especially after apples or sweet potatoes have been eaten. Crystals of leucine, tyrosine, and cystine are present occasionally, even in normal urine.

Among the cellular elements are epithelial cells and cell débris derived from the lining epithelium of the urinary tract. An occasional pus cell may be found, even in normal urine, on examining the sediment. These constituents are markedly increased in inflammatory conditions of the pelvis, kidney, ureters, bladder, or urethra. Spermatozoa may also be present in urine.

Microscopic examination of urinary sediment is often made with the object of determining the presence or absence of casts. These are derived from the renal-tubular epithelium and are usually cylindrical in shape, having parallel sides and rounded ends. Casts are classified according to their morphological characteristics. There are the so-called hyaline, granular, epithelial, and fatty casts. These are described in detail in textbooks devoted to clinical pathology. The presence of casts in the urine, together with a positive test for albumin, is diagnostic of renal disorder.

Renal Function. Of the numerous clinical procedures that have been introduced for the estimation of the functional capacity of the kidneys, perhaps the most widely used is the phenolsulphonphthalein test. When a small amount of this dye (6 mg.) is injected, from 60 to 85 per cent is normally recovered in the urine within the succeeding two hours. A markedly diminished elimination is an indication of severe renal insufficiency. This test, though of considerable clinical value, has many limitations.[26]

Impairment in renal function is usually associated with a marked inability of the kidneys to concentrate the urine. The kidneys are also rendered less sensitive to the influences and stimuli which produce the normally wide variations in specific gravity. In consequence the urine

[25] *J. Biol. Chem.*, 4, 253 (1908).

[26] For a description of various renal function tests the reader is referred to A. M. Fishberg, "Hypertension and Nephritis," Lea & Febiger, Philadelphia, 3d edition, 1934, Chap. 2.

formed has a specific gravity which varies within a narrow range of values. This relative fixation in specific gravity has also been utilized clinically in various forms for the estimation of renal efficiency. Three new procedures have been introduced in recent years. These are of sufficient interest to justify a brief description in this connection.

Creatinine Excretion. Creatinine has been considered as a non-threshold substance, or relatively so. On the assumption that this constituent is neither absorbed nor secreted by the tubules, its content in the urine may be taken as a measure of glomerular filtration. This is entirely in harmony with the results obtained recently in Richards' laboratory, referred to elsewhere (p. 447). On this basis, Rehberg[27] introduced a test which depends on the rate of excretion of creatinine after a definite amount is ingested. By comparing the creatinine concentration of the plasma and urine at different intervals, a measure is obtained, not only of the kidney's capacity to excrete this constituent, but presumably also of the rate of glomerular filtration. In the majority of his experiments, Rehberg found the excretion per minute to be equal to the amount of creatinine contained in 110–150 cc. of plasma. Hence this value may be considered to represent the volume of glomerular filtrate. Inasmuch as the volume of urine per minute is relatively small, usually 1–2 cc., the difference may be taken to represent the volume of fluid reabsorbed by the tubules.

In a recent study by Hayman,[28] the "creatinine clearance" in 59 normal subjects (130 observations) was found to average 148 cc. per minute. As compared with this were the conspicuously low values (as low as 0.6 cc.) obtained in cases of renal insufficiency.

Urea Clearance. Studies of the rate of urea excretion by numerous workers have established a certain correlation between the concentrations of urea in the blood and urine. On the basis of such relationships as have been obtained, various formulas have been proposed for the calculation of renal efficiency from observed data.

The procedure developed in Van Slyke's laboratory[29] depends essentially on this principle. To obtain the necessary data, two one-hour specimens of urine and one specimen of blood are required. The best time for conducting the test is between the hours of breakfast and lunch (10 to 12 A.M.), when the excretion is least liable to fluctuation. The bladder may be emptied at 10 o'clock and a glass of water taken.

[27] *Biochem. J.*, **20**, 447 (1926).

[28] J. M. Hayman, J. A. Halsted, and L. E. Seyler, *J. Clin. Investigation*, **12**, 861 (1933); see also R. Dominguez and E. Pomerene, *J. Biol. Chem.*, **104**, 449 (1934).

[29] E. Möller, J. F. McIntosh, and D. D. Van Slyke, *J. Clin. Investigation*, **6**, 427, 485 (1928); E. M. MacKay, *ibid.*, 505 (1928).

The subject then remains quiet and urine is collected in two succeeding periods of one hour each. If the interval is somewhat shorter or longer, no error is introduced, provided the calculations for the excretion per minute are based on the actual time. The blood is taken within a few minutes after the first urine specimen is collected.

The urea content is determined in each specimen of urine and the values averaged. The blood is likewise analyzed for this constituent.

If the urine volume exceeds 2 cc. per minute, the " maximum clearance," C_m, is calculated.

$$C_m = \frac{UV}{B},$$

where U = concentration of urea in the urine (per unit volume, such as 100 cc.), B = concentration of urea in the blood, and V = the urine volume in cubic centimeters per minute.[30]

If the urine volume (corrected volume for children) is less than 2 cc. per minute, the " standard clearance," C_s, is determined.

$$C_s = \frac{U\sqrt{V}}{B}$$

where $\sqrt{V}$ is the square root of the volume.

The maximum clearance varies within relatively wide limits (64–99 cc.) even in normal individuals, the accepted average being 75 cc.

The standard clearance likewise varies within a wide range of values (41–65 cc.), the accepted average being 54 cc.

However, in kidney disease, departures from the normal are usually very conspicuous.

The results may be expressed in terms of the normal renal function, by applying either of the following formulas, depending on whether the maximum or standard urea clearance has been determined.

$$\text{Percentage of normal function} = \frac{C_m \times 100}{75}$$

$$\text{Percentage of normal function} = \frac{C_s \times 100}{54}$$

Xylose Excretion. The excretion of xylose as an indication of impaired renal function has been likewise the subject of intensive

---

[30] In children a correction for body size is required. The volume is multiplied by the factor 1.73/body area in square meters. This correction is also applied to adults of unusually low stature. Consult J. F. McIntosh, E. Möller, and D. D. Van Slyke, *J. Clin. Investigation*, **6**, 467 (1928). See also J. P. Peters and D. D. Van Slyke, "Quantitative Clinical Chemistry," Vol. 1, p. 345, and Vol. II, p. 564.

investigation. The fact that it is not metabolized and the constancy of its excretion in the normal individual have particularly recommended the " xylose clearance " test as a delicate indicator of damage to the kidney. Moreover, H. W. Smith and associates[31] consider the tubules capable of secreting creatinine, which, if true, would obviously invalidate its use especially from the standpoint of the estimation of the volume of glomerular filtrate. Then it has also been contended that there is a certain amount of tubular reabsorption of urea. Whatever the merits of these contentions may be as applied to the estimation of renal efficiency, the use of xylose has been found practicable. The problem has been studied experimentally by Smith and associates. In human subjects, Fishberg and Friedfeld[32] found that, after the administration of 50 grams of xylose, the kidneys of normal individuals were able to concentrate it to 2.5 per cent within two hours and to excrete 25 per cent within twenty-four hours. In cases of renal insufficiency, a concentration in the urine of only 0.1 per cent was observed in one case. The curve of non-fermentable reducing substance in the blood was found to approach its normal value within five hours, with intact kidney function, whereas in patients with impaired renal function the curve continued upward so that values of 100 mg. per 100 cc. and more were encountered.

[31] N. Jollife and H. W. Smith, *Am. J. Physiol.*, **98**, 572 (1931); **99**, 101 (1931–32); **100**, 301 (1932); J. A. Shannon, Jollife, and Smith, *ibid.*, **101**, 639 (1932); Jollife and Chasis, *ibid.*, **104**, 677 (1933); Clarke and Smith, *J. Cell. and Comp., Physiol.*, **1**, 131 (1932); *J. Clin. Investigation*, **12**, 1083 (1933).

[32] *J. Clin. Investigation*, **11**, 501 (1932).

CHAPTER XV

INTERNAL SECRETIONS OR HORMONES

The glands of internal secretion, or *endocrine organs*, will be considered in this chapter mainly from the standpoint of the chemistry of their physiologically active substances and of their effect in chemically correlating the various activities of the animal organism. Certain glandular secretions, not those with which we are concerned here, are transported by means of ducts. The gastric and pancreatic juices and the saliva are familiar examples of such secretions. In contrast to these it has been discovered that certain glands pour their products directly into the blood stream. These *ductless* glands and their secretions are the subject of the present chapter. The internal secretions are of the utmost importance to the animal body because of their action in controlling and integrating its manifold activities; in fact, certain secretions are indispensable to life.

Although the subject of endocrinology may be said to have an earlier history, nevertheless, the work done by Bayliss and Starling[1] on *secretin*, in 1902, is usually regarded as marking the beginning of the modern development of this important branch of physiology and biochemistry. Bayliss and Starling recognized that substances of the type of secretin were probably chemical in nature, and, since such substances appeared to stimulate or arouse organs and tissues to activity, they suggested the term *hormone*, from the Greek, meaning " I rouse to activity."

Since a hormone has been conventionally defined as a substance formed in one organ and carried to another organ where it sets up definite physiological activity, even such compounds as urea and carbon dioxide might possibly be regarded as hormones. Urea has its origin in the liver and stimulates the kidney; carbon dioxide exerts an effect on the respiratory center. While it is difficult at present to make an absolute rule as to what to include and what to exclude under the definition, nevertheless, the substances mentioned are not classed with the hormones. If all the by-products of metabolism that incidentally have

[1] *J. Physiol.*, **28**, 325 (1902).

a regulatory effect on bodily functions were included under the definition of hormone, then, as Taylor[2] has stated the case, the number of hormones would be illimitable. The internal secretions with which we are principally concerned are those of the pancreas, thyroid, parathyroids, adrenals, sex glands, placenta, and hypophysis. Of these, the pancreas and the generative glands have both internal (ductless) and external (duct) secretions. Whether the liver should also be included, in view of the discovery in this organ of a substance which is a specific curative agent for pernicious anemia, is uncertain. As yet, it has not been determined that the active constituent is in the nature of a hormone. Moreover, a similar principle is normally present in the gastric mucosa. Finally, we should consider the internal secretions of the gastric and intestinal mucosa which are concerned with the function of digestion.

Hormones of the Gastro-intestinal Tract. These have been discussed in the chapter on digestion and will therefore be reviewed only very briefly at this point.

As has been stated elsewhere (p. 166), extracts of the pyloric mucous membrane, when injected into the circulation, cause an increased secretion of gastric juice, an effect that has long been attributed to a specific secretagogue, in the nature of a hormone, called *gastric secretin* or *gastrin*. According to the work of Ivy and associates this hormone is identical with histamine.[3]

Secretin is of special interest because its discovery by Starling in extracts of the duodenal mucosa in no small measure stimulated research in this important field of physiological chemistry. Its relation to pancreatic secretion is well established. In all probability, secretin is a relatively simple substance. It is diffusible through a parchment membrane and soluble in acids and in 95 per cent alcohol (which indicates that it is not a protein). It is not destroyed by heat, but is sensitive to the action of alkali, in which it is also soluble. The chemical nature of secretin remains to be determined.[4]

Associated with secretin in the intestinal mucosa is another hormone, *cholecystokinin*, which is apparently concerned with the contractility and evacuation of the gall-bladder. Extracts of the intestinal mucous membrane have been prepared which seem to be free from secretin and which when injected intravenously into dogs exert this specific effect

[2] N. B. Taylor in Macleod's "Physiology and Biochemistry in Modern Medicine," 1920 edition, p. 766.

[3] J. Sacks, A. C. Ivy, J. P. Burgess, and J. E. Vandolah, *Am. J. Physiol.*, **101**, 331 (1932).

[4] E. U. Still, "Secretin," *Physiol. Rev.*, **11**, 328 (1931).

on the gall-bladder. According to Ivy,[5] its discoverer, *cholecystokinin* is closely related to, but probably not identical with, secretin. It is formed in the upper intestinal mucosa when in contact with acids, and probably fatty acids and other substances that cause secretin formation.

Insulin; Hormone of the Pancreas. One of the most fascinating and inspiring chapters in the history of medicine began in the year 1889 when von Mering and Minkowski[6] in some experiments involving the removal of the pancreas from dogs discovered that this produced a condition similar to the diabetes observed in man. It had previously been suspected that the pancreas might be related in some way to this condition as lesions in this organ were occasionally found in severe cases. As in human diabetes, the most prominent symptoms observed in the experimental form of pancreatic diabetes were the appearance of sugar in the urine, thirst, voraciousness, emaciation, and death in coma.

Some years later, Minkowski[7] grafted a piece of pancreas under the skin of a dog and subsequently removed the pancreas of the animal, leaving the grafted piece which by this time had established circulation with the blood. It was found that in this way diabetes could be prevented or delayed for several months. Similar experiments were performed by Hédon.[8]

Among the numerous experiments which ultimately led to the adoption of the idea that the action of the pancreas in regulating carbohydrate metabolism was due to a hormone, may be mentioned that of Forschbach,[9] who made an anastomosis of the blood supply of two dogs and then removed the pancreas of one of the animals. Neither dog developed diabetes. Interpreted in the light of our present knowledge, the pancreas of the unoperated dog obviously supplied sufficient hormone to take care of the metabolism of both animals.

An equally ingenious experiment is that of Carlson,[10] who depancreatized a number of pregnant bitches and observed no glycosuria in these animals, presumably because of the functional activity of the pancreases of the fetuses. Lusk,[11] however, cites some experiments of Murlin, who found that such dogs have diabetic respiratory quotients (0.69). Murlin suggests that the absence of glucose from the

[5] A. C. Ivy, "Factors Concerned in the Evacuation of the Gall-Bladder," *Medicine*, **11**, 345 (1932).

[6] *Arch. exp. Path. Pharm.*, **26**, 371 (1890).

[7] *Ibid.*, Supplementary volume, 1908, p. 399.

[8] Arch. physiol., 65e série, 269 (1894).

[9] *Arch. exp. Path. Pharm.*, **60**, 131 (1909).

[10] *J. Biol. Chem.*, **17**, 19 (1914).

[11] Lusk, "The Science of Nutrition," 1917 edition, p. 453.

urine may have been due to the retention of carbohydrate by the fetuses. According to more recent observations of Schlossmann[12] the placenta is impermeable to insulin.

The observations of Knowlton and Starling[13] were likewise suggestive of a hormone mechanism. These workers demonstrated an increase in the consumption of glucose by a heart taken from a depancreatized animal and perfused with blood from the same animal, when there was added to the blood an extract prepared from the pancreas.

The Islands of Langerhans. Pancreatic tissue contains certain structures consisting of clumps of cells which differ in appearance and staining reactions from the remaining acinous or secreting epithelium. Because of their *insular* appearance, these structures have been named the *islands of Langerhans.*[14] Even before there was any certainty that the pancreatic hormone was formed in these islands, the belief grew up that this was the case. In fact, the hormone was named *insulin* by Sir Edward A. Schäfer in 1916 when its existence was still hypothetical. However, there was available some evidence to show that the lesions of the pancreas in severe diabetes were limited to the islets of Langerhans, but the value of these observations was more or less neutralized by contradictory observations. The degeneration of the acinous tissue of the pancreas, with relatively little injury to the insular cells, may be brought about by ligating the ducts from the pancreas. This was accomplished by several workers as early as 1900 and is of historical interest in connection with the important experiments of Banting to be described shortly.

Twenty years ago the outstanding problem of diabetes was clearly defined. It was a question of isolating and of determining the chemical nature of the pancreatic hormone. The first part of the problem was solved in 1922 by a group of active students in Macleod's laboratory at the University of Toronto. Before speaking of the achievements of these men, it is fitting to make some mention of the efforts of other workers who attempted to isolate the pancreatic hormone. In this country, Scott,[15] Clark,[16] Kleiner,[17] and Murlin and Kramer,[18] and others both in America and elsewhere, performed experiments which suggested the probable usefulness of pancreatic extract in relieving the

[12] *Arch. exp. Path. Pharm.*, **159**, 213 (1931).

[13] *J. Physiol.*, **45**, 146 (1912).

[14] The first to describe these structures was Langerhans (Inaugural Diss., Berlin, 1869).

[15] *Am. J. Physiol.*, **29**, 306 (1911).

[16] *Johns Hopkins Hosp. Rept.*, **18**, 229 (1919).

[17] *J. Biol. Chem.*, **40**, 153 (1919).

[18] *Ibid.*, **15**, 365 (1913); **27**, 481, 517 (1916).

symptoms of diabetes. One of the main obstacles in the way of obtaining active preparations appeared to be the destructive action of trypsin. The toxicity of the extracts was another disturbing factor which discouraged therapeutic experimentation.

Guided by the work of Zuelzer,[19] W. G. MacCallum,[20] Bensley,[21] and others, Banting and Best[22] proceeded to prepare more active preparations in which the effect of trypsin would be eliminated. By ligating the pancreatic ducts in dogs they succeeded in producing considerably more degeneration of the acinuous cells than of the insular tissue. After a few weeks the dogs were depancreatized. Extracts prepared from these pancreases, when injected subcutaneously or intravenously into normal and diabetic animals, proved to be very effective in causing a reduction of the blood sugar and in otherwise relieving the symptoms of diabetes. At about this time Collip joined Banting and Best in their work and in a very short time developed methods for the preparation of extracts, first from fetal calf pancreases and subsequently from ordinary beef glands, that were suitable for use in human diabetes. Thus was inaugurated a new era in the treatment of diabetes.

It would be beyond the scope of this book to review the enormous amount of work that has been done on insulin since its discovery by Banting and his associates; nor is it possible to enter here into a discussion of the clinical aspects of the problem. A review of the earlier phases of the subject has been prepared by J. J. R. Macleod,[23] and further information may be found in the current medical and biochemical literature. Nevertheless, some of the more important features of the problem will be considered briefly.

Source and Preparation. Insulin is widely distributed in both vertebrates and invertebrates. The main source at present is the pancreas of cattle. Fetal pancreases, lacking in functional acinous tissue, yield active preparations of insulin. Collip's [24] method for the preparation of insulin consists in fractional precipitation with alcohol. Various modifications have been proposed, among which may be mentioned that of Doisy, Somogyi, and Shaffer,[25] which consists in the further purification of insulin by precipitation at the isoelectric point (pH 5.0–6.0). Another

[19] *Z. exp. Path. Therap.*, **5**, 307 (1908–09).

[20] *Bull. Johns Hopkins Hosp.*, **20**, 265 (1909).

[21] *Am. J. Anat.*, **12**, 297 (1911); Harvey Lectures, 1914–15, p. 250.

[22] *Am. J. Physiol.*, **59**, 479 (1922); *J. Lab. Clin. Med.*, **7**, 251, 464 (1922). (Numerous other papers.)

[23] *Physiol. Rev.*, **4**, 21 (1924); "Carbohydrate Metabolism and Insulin," Longmans, Green & Co., 1926.

[24] *Trans. Roy. Soc. Canada*, **16**, 28 (1922).

[25] *J. Biol. Chem.*, **55**, Proc. xxxi (1923).

method is that devised by Dudley.[26]   It consists in precipitating the
insulin from solution with picric acid as the picrate. It is subsequently
converted to the hydrochloride and washed free from fat and certain
other impurities with acetone and ether, in which insulin hydrochloride is
insoluble. Dodds and Dickens[27] have modified Dudley's procedure.
According to their method the finely minced pancreas is mixed with
picric acid. This combines with the insulin to form the picrate, which is
extracted with acetone. The extract is evaporated and the residue
again extracted with ether to remove the fat and picric acid. The
picrate is then converted to the hydrochloride and further purified as
in Dudley's method.

The occurrence of insulin in animal tissues other than the pancreas,
and of insulin-like substances in plants, has been reported by many
workers, but this has been recently questioned by Best and associates.[28]

Chemical Properties of Insulin. The first work on insulin indicated
that it might be a protein-like substance. Banting and Best[29] determined that insulin is readily destroyed by trypsin, an observation soon
confirmed by Dudley,[30] who showed, moreover, that pepsin produces
the same effect. This behavior explains, no doubt, the ineffectiveness of
insulin when given by mouth.

Important advances in our knowledge of the chemistry of insulin
have emanated from the laboratory of J. J. Abel[31] at the Johns Hopkins
University, where methods for preparing highly purified, optically active,
crystalline insulin were first developed. Crystallization was obtained
at a pH of 5.55 to 5.65, which is approximately the isoelectric point of
insulin. Repeated recrystallization of crude preparations of beef
insulin and later of fish insulin, using widely different methods, yielded
a uniform product, both as to crystalline structure, chemical composition, and physiological potency.[32] The identity of insulin from various

[26] *Biochem. J.*, **17**, 376 (1923).

[27] *Brit. J. Exp. Path.*, **5**, 115 (1924).

[28] C. H. Best, C. M. Jephcott, and D. A. Scott, *Am. J. Physiol.*, **100**, 285 (1932).
This paper contains a comprehensive bibliography of the subject in question.

[29] *J. Lab. Clin. Med.*, **7**, 251 (1922).

[30] *Biochem. J.*, **17**, 376 (1923).

[31] J. J. Abel, *Proc. Nat. Acad. Sci.*, **12**, 132 (1926); Abel, E. M. K. Geiling, C. A.
Rouiller, F. K. Bell, and O. Wintersteiner, *J. Pharmacol.*, **31**, 65 (1927); V. du
Vigneaud, H. Jensen, and Wintersteiner, *ibid.*, **32**, 367, 387 (1927–28); du Vigneaud,
Geiling, and C. A. Eddy, *ibid.*, **33**, 497 (1928); H. Jensen, Wintersteiner, and Geiling,
ibid., **36**, 115 (1929).

[32] See also C. R. Harington and D. A. Scott, *Biochem. J.*, **23**, 384 (1929). These
investigators found certain commercial preparations of amorphous insulin with a
potency almost as high as that of crystalline insulin. This would indicate that the
preparation of the crystalline product is not a matter of isolating a highly active

sources (beef, hog, sheep, and fish pancreases) was further demonstrated by the work of Scott.[33] All of these preparations were of similar crystalline structure, possessed the same physiological activity (approximately 24 international units per milligram; see p. 473), and contained the same amount of sulfur (about 3.2 per cent) that was found by Abel and associates on analyzing their preparations. Tenfold recrystallization of insulin did not alter its potency or other properties.

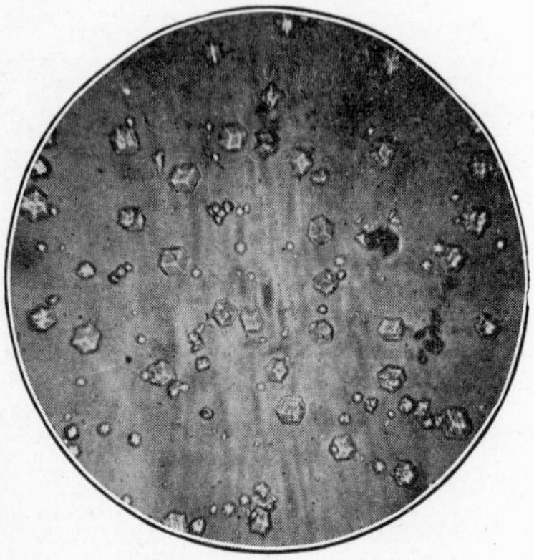

FIG. 31.—Crystalline Insulin.

(Reproduced from a photomicrograph kindly furnished by Professor John J. Abel.)

The isoelectric point of *crystalline* insulin is at pH 5.3–5.35, as determined by Wintersteiner and Abramson,[34] employing electrophoretic methods. Howitt and Prideaux,[35] investigating *amorphous* insulin of approximately the same activity as the crystalline product, found the isoelectric point at pH 5.4. Their observations are of particular significance in that they found no evidence that fractionation of physiological activity had occurred during electrophoresis. This points to the fundamental chemical identity of the amorphous preparation, when it is sufficiently purified, and the crystalline insulin. These measurements are also of interest in that they reflect the essential accuracy of the determinations of the isoelectric point of insulin (pH 5–6) by Doisy, Somogyi, and Shaffer,[25] made early in the history of the insulin problem.

Analysis of crystalline insulin (Jensen and Wintersteiner)[36] has revealed the following distribution of amino acids (in per cent): tyrosine 12, cystine 12, glutamic acid 21, leucine 30, arginine 3, lysine 2. Crystalline insulin appears to contain no tryptophane.[37] The amounts of other amino acids that may be present remain to be determined.

The weight of evidence at present favors the view that insulin is a

---

substance from a crude mixture, but rather a process analogous to the crystallization of a protein.

[33] *J. Biol. Chem.*, **92**, 281 (1931).

[34] *J. Biol. Chem.*, **99**, 741 (1932–33).

[35] *Proc. Roy. Soc.* (*London*), *B*, **112**, 13 (1932).

[36] *J. Biol. Chem.*, **98**, 281 (1932).

[37] T. D. Gerlough and R. W. Bates, *J. Pharmacol.*, **45**, 19 (1932).

protein and that the crystalline product described represents the hormone in its purest and most active form. The molecular weight, according to Sjögren and Svedberg,[38] is 35,100.[39]

Insulin treated with dilute hydrochloric acid ($N/10$) in a boiling water bath forms a coagulum which is physiologically inactive. However, the inactivation is reversible, for neutralization with alkali yields a product which it has not been possible to crystallize, but which nevertheless has approximately the same activity as the original insulin. When insulin is similarly treated with alkali, both sulfur and ammonia are split off and it is irreversibly inactivated. Irreversible inactivation of insulin apparently results from the loss of sulfur.[40]

Aldehydes, acetic anhydride, and reducing agents inactivate insulin.[41] Indeed even so mild a reducing agent as cysteine exerts this effect,[42] presumably through the reduction of the disulfide (—S—S—) bond, upon which according to one school of investigators the physiological activity of the hormone depends.

Standardization. To insure uniform potency of commercial preparations and to avoid the grave dangers of overdosage, great care is exercised in the standardization of insulin. It was recognized early that the rabbit is a suitable animal (mice are now also used) for purposes of insulin assay, and, therefore, at the first meeting of the Standardization Committee of the League of Nations, it was decided provisionally to define a unit of insulin as one-third of the amount required to lower the blood sugar of a normal rabbit, weighing 2 kg. and

[38] *J. Am. Chem. Soc.*, **53**, 2657 (1931).

[39] According to analysis and on the basis that the insulin molecule contained one atom of sulfur, the formula $C_{45}H_{69}O_{14}N_{11}S$ was assigned by Abel. But, inasmuch as it was shown by du Vigneaud (*J. Biol. Chem.*, **75**, 393 [1927]) that insulin contains a disulfide linkage, the empirical formula was revised to $C_{90}H_{138}O_{28}N_{22}S_2$ (mol. wt. about 2040), it being understood that the actual molecule was probably larger, being a multiple of this value. Freudenberg and co-workers have estimated the molecular weight to be about 20,000, while Gerlough and Bates consider it to be approximately two or two and a half times as much.

For a comprehensive summary of the chemical study of insulin, the reader is referred to an article by H. Jensen, *Science*, **75**, 614 (1932).

[40] Compare K. Freudenberg, W. Dirscherl, and H. Eyer, *Z. physiol. Chem.*, **187**, 100 (1930). Freudenberg has been an intensive student of the chemistry of insulin. The following are references to some of the more recent contributions from his laboratory: *Z. physiol. Chem.*, **202**, 97, 116, 159, 192 (1931); *ibid.*, **213**, 226, 248 (1932–33).

[41] Jensen states that as yet reactivation of the products formed by these agents has not been successful. However, according to reports from Freudenberg's laboratory,[40] partial restoration of activity has been accomplished in certain instances.

[42] V. du Vigneaud, A. Fitch, E. Pekarek, and W. W. Lockwood, *J. Biol. Chem.*, **94**, 233 (1931–32); O. Wintersteiner, *ibid.*, **102**, 473 (1933).

previously fasted for twenty-four hours, to the convulsive level (0.045 per cent) within three hours. At the present time the Health Committee of the League keeps under its auspices a preparation of insulin hydrochloride which serves as an international standard. One milligram of this standard is equivalent to 8 units. Accordingly, the definition of the international unit is the quantity (of a given preparation) which produces an effect on carbohydrate metabolism equal to that of one-eighth of a milligram of the standard preparation of insulin hydrochloride. By this definition, the mode of assay is not prescribed. It may be mentioned here that 1 mg. of crystalline insulin (as prepared by Abel and his associates) is equivalent to approximately 24 international units.[43]

Action. The administration of insulin by mouth is without influence. Insulin is effective when given subcutaneously, but produces its maximum and most rapid effect when injected intravenously. The introduction of insulin into the duodenum, when the stomach is not digesting, is said to diminish hyperglycemia and glycosuria in diabetic animals. Insulin increases the storage of glycogen in the liver and promotes its utilization in the tissues, the latter being evidenced by an elevation in the respiratory quotient (p. 505). Accordingly, the injection of this hormone is followed by a rapid fall in blood sugar, and if a sufficient quantity is given, marked hypoglycemia develops. When the blood-sugar level is reduced to about 0.04 per cent, characteristic convulsions develop, particularly in the rabbit. If these symptoms are not relieved at once the animal dies. The amount of reserve glycogen is a factor, and where this is present in abundance, convulsions do not develop quite as readily as in poorly nourished animals. Insulin convulsions may be relieved by injecting glucose, and to a less extent by mannose, galactose, levulose, and maltose, but not by the pentoses xylose and arabinose nor by the disaccharides sucrose and lactose. In sheep, it may be noted, even very large doses of insulin do not cause any convulsions or other distress. The blood sugar may be depressed to about 30 mg. per 100 cc. and remain at that level for hours.

In the case of the diabetic individual, insulin relieves at once the symptoms of hyperglycemia, glycosuria, acetonuria, and acidosis. There is a marked improvement in the utilization of carbohydrates, as determined by an elevation of the respiratory quotient, and in the deposition of glycogen in the liver. With these changes there is also an improvement in fat metabolism and in the conservation of the tissue

---

[43] It is essential not to neglect the factor of animal variability in bio-assay. This question has been particularly well analyzed by J. W. Trevan, *Proc. Roy. Soc.* (*London*), *B*, **101**, 483 (1927). See, also, Bur. Standards Research Paper No. 263.

proteins. Through the continued and regulated use of insulin, patients
with diabetes may be maintained indefinitely in a more or less normal
metabolic and nutritional state.[44]

Hyperinsulinism. The more familiar manifestation of abnormal
pancreatic function is deficient secretion of insulin (*hypoinsulinism*), this
being the underlying factor of the symptoms of diabetes, such as hyperglycemia, impaired utilization of carbohydrate, etc. Since the discovery
of insulin, the results of experimental and therapeutic overdosage with
this hormone have also received considerable attention. The outstanding effect of the presence of an excessive amount of insulin is
hypoglycemia, which is accompanied by a train of symptoms, showing
in man considerable variation. At first there is usually a feeling of
nervousness or tremulousness; sometimes there is a feeling of hunger.
This is followed by weakness and a sense of depression, and later a cold
perspiration breaks out; frequently there is an increase in the pulse

---

[44] For a number of years before the advent of insulin, the method of treatment of
diabetes which seemed to give the best results was the Allen method of controlling the
diet. This was based upon the obvious fact that, at best, there was no point in
giving the diabetic carbohydrate and other food which he was unable to utilize and
was therefore forced to excrete. Periods of starvation and strict regulation of the
diet therefore constituted, until several years ago, the most effective method of com-
bating the disease. The method of treatment employed by Allen involved wherever
necessary a preliminary period of starvation lasting sufficiently long to render the
urine of the diabetic free from sugar and acetone bodies. From this point on, by
carefully controlling the diet, it was often possible to keep the patient free from these
symptoms for long periods.

However, such a procedure was practically futile in the case of children. A few
capable clinicians were in a measure able to cope with the situation and even succeeded in prolonging for a few years the lives of some of their young patients; but,
as the method of treatment consisted in the strict limitation of the food intake, the
growth of the children was limited. The situation is now improved; normal growth
and development have been reported in many diabetic children treated with insulin.

F. N. Allan and R. M. Wilder have recently compared the mortality of diabetic
children before and after the discovery of insulin (*J. Am. Med. Assoc.*, **94**, 147 [1930]).
Of a group of 30 children observed at the Mayo clinic during the period Oct. 1, 1919,
to Oct. 1, 1922, the deaths numbered 22, or 73.3 per cent. During the period Oct. 1,
1922, to Oct. 1, 1928, 167 patients were studied, including the 8 who survived the
pre-insulin period. Of these patients, 164 have been traced and a total of 17 deaths
recorded. The per cent mortality was therefore only 10.4. For the years 1925–
1928, the mortality rate averaged only about 4 per cent. Of the few deaths that
occurred, several might have been avoided if the patients had continued their dietary
restrictions and insulin injections after returning to their homes.

Tuberculosis is a frequent complication in diabetes. The difficulties formerly
encountered in treating tuberculous diabetics may be readily imagined. To control
the diabetes, periods of starvation and subsequent limitation of the diet were thought
imperative, whereas to control the effects of tuberculosis, an ample diet was called for.

rate. Extreme anxiety, sometimes excitement and emotional instability, confusion and delirium become evident, followed ultimately by collapse. Convulsions do not occur in man, according to the description given by Fletcher and Campbell.[45] A blood-sugar concentration of 0.035 per cent is usually accompanied by coma.

Through a better understanding of the action of insulin clinical cases of *hyperinsulinism* have been more readily recognized[46] and more effectively studied. Most important of the conditions associated with spontaneous hypoglycemia, due apparently to an increased production of insulin, is malignancy of the pancreas with proliferation of the islet tissue. The first case of this type to be thoroughly studied was one of carcinoma of the islands of Langerhans with metastases in the liver and lymph nodes, described by Wilder, Allan, Power, and Robertson.[47] Their patient experienced frequent attacks of extreme weakness, faintness and paresthesia, accompanied by *hypoglycemia*. These symptoms could be relieved by eating between meals or taking sweet drinks. When food was withheld for 3 hours and 20 minutes after the noon meal, the blood sugar concentration fell to 0.055 per cent. At this time the patient appeared apprehensive and depressed. Fifteen minutes later perspiration and tremor were noted; at 4 hours the blood sugar had fallen to 0.036 per cent and 15 minutes later to 0.027 per cent, at which time the patient was stuporous and no longer able to speak and was jerking about convulsively. At this point 15 gm. of glucose were given by mouth; the blood sugar rose to 0.065 per cent and the patient became rational and able to converse. Hourly doses of glucose were required to prevent the patient from developing too severe an hypoglycemia.[48]

The Thyroid Gland. In man, the thyroid gland is a bi-lobed, reddish yellow, highly vascular organ, surrounded by a capsule of connective tissue; it weighs on the average about 20 or 25 grams and is situated at the sides of the larynx and trachea. Histologically, the organ appears to be composed of numerous closed alveoli or vesicles containing a single layer of cuboidal epithelium and filled with translucent material known as *colloid*.

Baumann,[49] in 1895, made the important discovery that the thyroid

[45] The first complete study of the climical effects of an overdose of insulin was made by A. A. Fletcher, and W. R. Campbell, *J. Metab. Research*, **2**, 637 (1922).

[46] S. Harris, *J. Am. Med. Assoc.*, **83**, 729 (1924); *Endocrinology*, **16**, 29 (1932); *J. Am. Med. Assoc.*, **101**, 1958 (1933).

[47] *J. Am. Med. Assoc.*, **89**, 348 (1927).

[48] The various conditions in which hypoglycemia may develop have been reviewed by G. D. Gammon and W. C. Tenery, *Arch. Internal Med.*, **47**, 829 (1931).

[49] *Z. physiol. Chem.*, **21**, 319, 481 (1896).

gland of mammals contains iodine in firm organic combination. On acid hydrolysis of the thyroid, he obtained an iodine compound which was named *iodothyrine*. Oswald[50] studied the colloid material of the thyroid gland and found it to be mainly globulin. He found, moreover, that in general the amount of iodine varied with the amount of visible colloid, although hyperplastic thyroids could be rich in globulin and yet be iodine-free. It was Oswald who introduced the term *iodothyreoglobuline* for the globulin-iodothyrine complex. This is now more commonly designated as *thyroglobulin*.

Thyroxin. The isolation of the active principle of the thyroid gland was reported by Kendall[51] in 1916. From 3 tons of the fresh organ he obtained 33 grams of a substance which had the same pharmacological properties as whole thyroid gland. About 10 years later, Harington[52] improved the method of isolation and obtained yields as high as 0.027 per cent from fresh gland and 0.12 per cent from dried thyroid gland.

The relation of thyroxin to tyrosine and its chemical constitution was determined by Harington (and independently by Dakin[53]). Later Harington and Barger[54] accomplished its synthesis.

$$HO-\underset{I}{\overset{I}{\bigcirc}}-O-\underset{I}{\overset{I}{\bigcirc}}-CH_2CHNH_2\cdot COOH$$

Thyroxin
($C_{15}H_{11}O_4NI_4$)

β-[3 : 5-Diiodo-4-(3′ : 5′-diiodo-4′-hydroxyphenoxy) phenyl]-α-aminopropionic acid

Harington[55] has resolved the racemic form, *dl*-thyroxin, into its two optically active isomers. It has been found that *l*-thyroxin is physiologically much more active than *d*-thyroxin.

More recently *l*-thyroxin has been isolated from thyroid substance by the action of proteolytic enzymes.[56] The digestion of thyroglobulin by trypsin has also been investigated.[57]

[50] *Ibid.*, **23**, 265 (1897); **32**, 121 (1901).
[51] Collected papers of the Mayo Clinic, **8**, 513 (1916); *J. Biol. Chem.*, **40**, 265 (1919); see also *Ann. Clin. Med.*, **1**, 256 (1923).
[52] *Biochem. J.*, **20**, 293, 300 (1926).
[53] See footnote in paper by Harington and Barger.
[54] *Ibid.*, **21**, 169 (1927).
[55] *Ibid.*, **22**, 1429 (1928); J. H. Gaddum, *ibid.*, **22**, 1434 (1928).
[56] C. R. Harington and W. T. Salter, *Biochem. J.*, **24**, 456 (1930).
[57] B. O. Barnes, A. J. Carlson, and A. M. Riskin, *Am. J. Physiol.*, **98**, 86 (1931); Barnes, *ibid.*, **101**, 583 (1932).

It is now generally conceded that in the thyroid gland, thyroxin does not occur as such, but in combination as thyroglobulin. Indeed, while it has been possible to demonstrate the presence of the latter in the blood and lymph leaving the gland, thyroxin itself has not been detected so far, from which it has been inferred that thyroglobulin and not free thyroxin is secreted by the thyroid.[58] Harington and Salter[56] have suggested, however, that the thyroid probably secretes a simple peptide, containing thyroxin. It should be noted that when thyroid substance is fed, it is converted in the course of digestion into similar products.

Only about one-fourth of the organic iodine contained in the thyroid is in the form of thyroxin.[59] Another iodine derivative of tyrosine is present, namely 3, 5-diiodotyrosine, discovered independently by Harington and Randall[60] and by Foster.[61] From a sample of 100 grams of partially purified thyroglobulin, containing 760 mg. of iodine, Foster isolated 0.44 gram of diiodotyrosine, containing 248 mg. of iodine. This accounted for 33 per cent of the total iodine. The thyroxin which was isolated accounted for an additional 16 per cent of iodine. These observations indicate that thyroglobulin may contain still other iodine compounds and also that 3, 5-diiodotyrosine may be the precursor of thyroxin. It is to be noted, however, that this derivative of tyrosine is without the physiological properties possessed by thyroxin.[62]

Diiodotyrosine is not readily utilized by the organism, as shown in an experiment by Foster and Gutman,[63] who fed it to rabbits. Of the total iodine recovered in the urine, 10 per cent was present as inorganic iodide, 60 per cent as unchanged diiodotyrosine, 18 per cent as 3, 5-diiodo-4-hydroxyphenyl-lactic acid, and the remaining 12 per cent in undetermined forms of combination.

3, 5-Diiodotyrosine is widely distributed in certain marine organisms. It was first discovered by Drechsel[64] among the hydrolytic products of the axial skeleton of the Gorgonian coral. Mörner[65] found

---

[58] L. Hektoen, A. J. Carlson, and K. Schulhof, *ibid.*, **81**, 661 (1927); Schulhof, *ibid.*, **93**, 170 (1930).

[59] J. P. Leland and G. L. Foster, *J. Biol. Chem.*, **95**, 165 (1931); see also N. F. Blau, *ibid.*, **102**, 269 (1933).

[60] *Biochem. J.*, **23**, 373 (1929).

[61] *J. Biol. Chem.*, **83**, 345 (1929).

[62] Compare with the observations of Abderhalden on tadpoles, *Arch. ges. Physiol.* **206**, 467 (1924).

[63] *J. Biol. Chem.*, **87**, 289 (1930).

[64] *Z. Biol.*, **33**, 85 (1896).

[65] *Z. physiol. Chem.*, **51**, 33 (1907); **55**, 77, 223 (1908).

it in the skeleton of certain Anthozoa and Wheeler and Mendel[66] in sponges.

The oxidative processes of the organism are under the control of thyroxin. Excessive secretion of the thyroid hormone stimulates cellular oxidation and hence elevates the rate of metabolism. On the contrary, cellular oxidation and the metabolic rate are depressed when there is an insufficiency of the thyroid hormone. This is true not only for the intact organism, but likewise for the metabolism of isolated tissues from thyroidectomized and thyroid-treated animals.[67]

Diseases of the Thyroid Gland. There are many classifications of thyroid disease in medical literature, largely because clinicians have been forced to base their distinctions on symptomatology alone. The manifestations of deranged thyroid function are exceedingly variable; nevertheless, most symptoms can be regarded as the result either of diminished function (hypofunction) or increased function (hyperfunction) of the thyroid gland.

Myxedema is a manifestation of hypothyroidism. This condition results from atrophy of the thyroid gland and the consequent reduction in the secretion of the hormone thyroxin. It may be produced also by partial or complete extirpation of the thyroid. Inasmuch as the hormone regulates cellular oxidation, its deficiency results in a marked reduction of the basal metabolic rate (see next chapter). The temperature of the body and the pulse rate tend to be subnormal. Chilliness, even when it is warm, and sensitiveness to cold are characteristic features. The face and hands become puffed and swollen. This is not due to edema, but to thickening of the subcutaneous connective tissue. The skin is thick and has an unhealthy appearance, and the hair tends to fall out. Myxedematous individuals are sluggish both mentally and physically, are often anemic, and tend to be obese, although this is not always the case.

These symptoms, which profoundly affect the personality of the afflicted individual, are frequently relieved on feeding thyroid gland or extracts of it, or upon the administration of thyroxin. The effects of the administered thyroid hormone may last for several weeks. However, when treatment is discontinued for longer periods there is a relapse, showing that the active principle of the thyroid gland is not stored indefinitely.

---

[66] *J. Biol. Chem.*, **7**, 1 (1909).

[67] J. E. Davis and A. B. Hastings, *Proc. Soc. Exp. Biol. Med.*, **28**, 747 (1931); D. McEachern, *Bull. Johns Hopkins Hosp.*, **50**, 287 (1932); R. W. Gerard and M. McIntyre, *Am. J. Physiol.*, **103**, 225 (1933). J. A. Dye and G. H. Maughn, *Proc. Soc. Exp. Biol. Med.*, **26**, 439, 441 (1929); Dye, *Am. J. Physiol.*, **105**, 518 (1933).

Cretinism. Failure in the embryonic development of the thyroid or its atrophy during fetal life or childhood results in the condition commonly called cretinism, but which would be more accurately designated by the term *infantile* or *childhood myxedema.* There are two forms of this disease. The endemic form is due presumably to goitrous degeneration of the gland and is found in districts where goiter is endemic. The failure in thyroid development in this form may be due to a lack of iodine in the organism of the mother. The sporadic form of cretinism may occur anywhere. As to its etiology, nothing is known except that it may have the same underlying causes as myxedema.

The most noticeable symptom is the practically complete cessation of physical and mental development, resulting in drawfism and idiocy. Cretins are typically pot-bellied, ugly, and somewhat obese. The hair is thick and coarse, and the skin dry and pale. As in myxedema of adults, the basal metabolic rate is low.

Concerning the deficiency of the thyroid hormone in this condition, there can be little question. Cretins fed on whole thyroid gland or treated with thyroxin tend to develop normally. There is almost immediate improvement both mentally and physically; an ugly, idiotic child may be converted into an almost normal one. The cures which have been accomplished in this way are most remarkable. However, in the case of cretinism of long standing, treatment is not as successful.

Endemic or Colloid Goiter. Hyperplasia or enlargement of the thyroid does not necessarily indicate hyperfunction and may be due fundamentally, as in this case, to a deficiency in the hormone mechanism. Being easily recognized by the marked swelling which develops in the region of the neck, this disease was known to the ancients. The enlargement is due to an increase in the colloid material of the gland, hence the name " colloid goiter."

Goiter is endemic in many parts of the world, but is especially prevalent in certain sections of Switzerland and in the region of the Great Lakes in the United States. That it is due to a lack of iodine was shown by Marine and Kimball.[68]

McClendon[69] has reported the results of analyses of drinking water obtained from regions where goiter is endemic and from other regions. These show higher values for iodine in the water from non-goitrous regions than in that from regions where goiter is prevalent. Not only

[68] *J. Am. Med. Assoc.*, **77**, 1068 (1921); D. Marine, "The Functions of the Thyroid Gland," *Physiol. Rev.*, **2**, 521 (1922).

[69] *J. Am. Med. Assoc.*, **82**, 1669 (1924); see also the review "The Distribution of Iodine with Special Reference to Goiter," *Physiol. Rev.*, **7**, 189 (1927).

the water but also the soil and hence the vegetation in such areas are low in iodine. Because of this deficiency, the normal formation of thyroxin and thyroglobulin is impaired, and it has therefore been surmised that in an attempt to compensate for the poorness in the quality of the secretion, the gland is stimulated to hyperactivity and the production of excessive amounts of colloid. That not infrequently the metabolism of patients with endemic goiter is approximately normal is evidence that the hyperplasia of the gland may compensate more or less for the deficiency. Just as often, however, the basal metabolic rate tends to be low indicating that, despite overactivity, which is sometimes very pronounced, sufficient thyroxin for the needs of the organism is not being produced.

Recognition by Marine and associates of the etiological relationship of iodine deficiency to endemic goiter led them to suggest as the method of treatment the administration of small doses of iodides. Prophylactic measures are now taken in many goiter regions by adding simple inorganic iodides to the drinking water supply, and to the table salt, and by periodically administering therapeutic doses of iodide to school children. This procedure is to be especially recommended in the case of adolescent girls and during pregnancy.

Simple goiter is so prevalent in the Great Lakes basin that a large proportion of the dogs and other animals of the region are afflicted with it. The practice of administering small amounts of iodide to stock animals for the purpose of preventing goiter has yielded remarkably beneficial results.

The possibility that iodine deficiency is not the only factor in endemic goiter is suggested by the work of Hellwig,[70] who considers that hyperplasia of the thyroid results from the combined effects of an excess of calcium in the diet and a deficiency of iodine.

Goiter may be produced in rabbits by prolonged feeding of cabbage from certain localities.[71] A search for the goitrogenic factor involved, by Marine and associates,[72] has revealed it to be cyanide. Further experiments have shown that substances which depress oxygen consumption may increase thyroid activity and that cyanides are among the most potent of these goitrogenic agents. Accordingly, the view has been expressed that a deficiency of iodine, though certainly the immediate cause of thyroid hyperplasia, is in most cases only relative,

[70] *Arch. Pathol.*, **11**, 709 (1931).

[71] A. M. Chesney, T. A. Clawson, and B. Webster, *Bull. Johns Hopkins Hosp.*, **43**, 261 (1928); Webster, *Endocrinology*, **16**, 617 (1932).

[72] D. Marine, E. J. Baumann, A. W. Spence, and A. Cipra, *Proc. Soc. Exp. Biol. Med.*, **29**, 772, 822 (1931–32).

and is due to the increased demands for iodine caused by a goitrogenic agent.

Van Dyke[73] has determined the relative absorption of iodine and various iodine compounds, potassium iodide, potassium iodate, and thyroxin, when injected intravenously, by the hyperplastic thyroid gland of the dog. He found that iodide iodine was most readily absorbed and that iodate iodine was also taken up in considerable amount. Free iodine was absorbed in small amount, probably because a considerable proportion must have combined with the unsaturated lipids of the blood. The least effect in increasing the iodine content of the thyroid was obtained on administering thyroxin, which was apparently taken up by the gland very slowly and in only minute amounts.

Exophthalmic goiter (also known as *Graves'* and as *Basedow's disease*) is the most important example of hyperthyroidism. An increased basal metabolic rate is the most prominent finding in this condition. The temperature of the body is usually above normal; the heart rate is faster than normal and is irregular. There is usually an enlargement of the thyroid gland. Among other symptoms are a marked tendency to emaciation, restlessness, hyperexcitability, and gastro-intestinal disturbances. Usually, though not always, there is protrusion of the eyeball (" exophthalmos ").

Most physiologists believe exophthalmic goiter to be due to hypersecretion of the thyroid hormone, in view of the fact that some of the symptoms of this disease may be produced by the administration of sufficient doses of thyroxin. Another point in support of this general idea is that many of the symptoms of exophthalmic goiter are exactly the reverse of those noted in myxedema. Since the disease is presumably due to excessive secretion, the methods of treatment consist in diminishing the amount of active thyroid by partial extirpation of the gland, by ligation of the thyroid arteries, or by exposure to Roentgen rays or radium. Most cases usually yield to these methods of treatment, although it is not always possible to clear up the exophthalmos and the cardiac symptoms.

Certain clinicians believe that simple goiter, which is essentially a condition of hypothyroidism, may pass over into Graves' disease. In the opinion of Marine, expressed in an early paper, there is no adequate evidence for the view that exophthalmic goiter is due to hypersecretion. Marine has in fact expressed the view more recently[74] that the primary etiological factor in Graves' disease may be a deficiency of the internal secretion of the suprarenal cortex.

[73] *Arch. Internal Med.*, **41**, 615 (1928).
[74] *Proc. Soc. Exp. Biol. Med.*, **28**, 327 (1930–31).

A study of the iodine partition in the thyroid in clinical hyperthyroidism has disclosed that in untreated cases the gland is relatively low with respect to its thyroxin content, this doubtless representing a depleted or exhausted state of the gland.[75] However, the administration of iodine (this being an accepted method of temporarily treating cases of exophthalmic goiter and thyroid adenoma) results in a marked increase of both the inorganic- and thyroglobulin-iodine fractions. A definite change in the chemical nature of the thyroglobulin is indicated by the relative and absolute increases in the thyroxin fraction and a consequent relative, though not absolute, decrease in the percentage of thyroglobulin iodine present as diiodotyrosine.

In a recent report, the functional and structural changes of the muscular system in Graves' disease have been related to an impairment of the creatine-phosphate mechanism (p. 424). As has been stated elsewhere (p. 428), a disturbance in muscle metabolism occurs in hyperthyroidism, as evidenced by a marked creatinuria.

Biological Significance of the Thyroid. A few additional words may be said concerning the thyroid in relation to development. The metamorphosis of tadpoles into frogs is dependent on thyroid secretion; if the gland is removed, this change does not take place, although the tadpole may continue to grow, as such. If at any time thyroid is given, prompt metamorphosis occurs. Gudernatsch[76] discovered that the feeding of thyroid to young tadpoles results in premature metamorphosis with the formation of exceedingly small frogs, often no larger than a fly. Abderhalden[62] reported similar results with 3, 5-diiodotyrosine. Traces of iodine may exert a similar effect, according to Swingle.[77] There is a species of salamander, found in Mexico, which never undergoes metamorphosis, apparently because of the absence of the thyroid. Metamorphosis can be induced artificially, however, by thyroid feeding.

It may be pointed out here that thyroid function is apparently closely related to the activity of other organs of internal secretion (adrenals, pituitary, thymus, pancreas, etc.). For example, sexual development is depressed in conditions of hypothyroidism. That a relationship exists between the thyroid and the generative glands of the female is also indicated by the fact that enlargement of the thyroid occurs at puberty, during menstruation, and during pregnancy. Other relationships will be mentioned as we proceed in our discussion of the endocrine organs.

[75] A. B. Gutman, E. M. Benedict, B. Baxter, and W. W. Palmer, *J. Biol. Chem.*, **97**, 303 (1932).

[76] *Zentr. Physiol.*, **26**, 323 (1912).

[77] *J. Gen. Physiol.*, **1**, 593 (1919).

It has been estimated that in man approximately 1 mg. of thyroxin is secreted per day. The administration to a normal individual of an additional milligram is sufficient to produce a definite calorigenic effect, and 2 mg. will raise the basal metabolic rate by about 20 per cent.[78]

The Parathyroid Glands. The earlier physiologists and surgeons had observed that thyroidectomy frequently led to the development of tetany, followed by death. That this outcome was actually due to the accidental removal of an independent set of glands was not generally appreciated until the beginning of the present century, despite the fact that the parathyroid glands had been discovered twenty years previously (1880) by the Danish anatomist Sandstrom.[79] There are usually two pairs of parathyroid glands, one pair lying on each side of the neck, close to the thyroid or embedded in it. At least in some animals (cat, rabbit, etc.) there are probably additional or accessory parathyroid structures scattered along the trachea near by. The parathyroids are small glands, yellowish brown to brown-red in color, usually bean-shaped in structure, and about the size of a hemp-seed or somewhat larger; in man they are variable in length (3–15 mm.), about 2–3 mm. in breadth and 2 mm. in thickness.

In 1925, Hanson[80] and Collip,[81] working independently, succeeded in preparing an active and relatively pure extract from the parathyroid gland. The hormone preparation, named parathormone, exhibited a marked effect in raising the calcium concentration of the blood both in normal and parathyroidectomized animals. As yet, the chemical nature of the parathyroid hormone has not been determined; Collip's purest preparations give positive tests for protein and are said to contain sulfur and iron. The work of this investigator has contributed much toward establishing the theory that the parathyroid glands secrete a hormone which is concerned with the regulation of calcium metabolism and with controlling, in some way, the concentration of calcium in the blood.

Hypoparathyroidism. The extirpation of the parathyroids in man and most animals, particularly the carnivora, results in *tetany.*[82]

[78] H. S. Plummer, *J. Am. Med. Assoc.,* **77,** 243 (1921).

[79] *Upsala läkerför. forh.,* **15,** 44 (1880).

[80] *Military Surgeon,* **52,** 434 (1923); **54,** 76, 218, 554 (1924); *Proc. Soc. Exp. Biol. Med.,* **22,** 560 (1925).

[81] *J. Biol. Chem.,* **63,** 395 (1925).

A review on the subject of the parathyroid glands has been prepared by D. L. Thomson and J. B. Collip, *Physiol. Rev.,* **12,** 309–383 (1932). Work which has appeared since the preparation of this review has been summarized by these authors in *Ann. Rev. Biochem.,* **2,** 242 (1933).

[82] The relation of parathyroid insufficiency as the cause of tetany was established by W. G. MacCallum and C. Voegtlin, *J. Exp. Med.,* **11,** 118 (1909).

The dog is especially susceptible. Usually in from one to four days after the operation, symptoms of intoxication become manifest. There is loss of appetite, the motor nerves become hyperexcitable to electrical but not to mechanical stimuli, and there is marked restlessness. Diarrhea, often bloody, is a frequent symptom. Soon fine tremors set in, and the animal gradually becomes stiff. The tremors become more and more violent, the temperature, respiration, and heart action increase. After nine or ten days the animal dies in spasm or convulsions, or from exhaustion.[83] The effects of loss of parathyroid function are especially severe where the calcium requirement is increased as in pregnant or lactating animals, or in animals with active rickets. In parathyroid tetany, the outstanding change in the composition of the blood is a marked decrease in the concentration of calcium. Normally human and dog serum contains 10 to 11 mg. of calcium per 100 cc. Following the removal of the parathyroid, the concentration may fall to 5 to 6 mg., and even lower. The symptoms may be relieved at this time by the administration of calcium salts, such as calcium lactate, the disappearance of the symptoms being associated with an increased concentration of calcium in the blood. However, the administration of parathyroid extract is much more effective, especially if administered together with calcium lactate. The use of parathyroid hormone clinically has, on the whole, yielded satisfactory results.

The parathyroid hormone is reversibly inactivated by formaldehyde or acidified methyl alcohol and irreversibly by acetic anhydride or nitrous acid (Tweedy and Torigoe).[84] Accordingly it has been suggested that the " active " group, upon which depends the physiological properties of the hormone, is either a primary amino or imino group.

Tetany may occur spontaneously, especially in infants and children, and as in parathyroidectomized animals is associated with a low serum calcium. When it cannot be ascribed to known causative factors, such as dietary deficiency with respect to calcium and vitamin D, the condition is usually designated as *idiopathic tetany*. Inasmuch as relief from symptoms has been obtained in some instances through the administration of parathyroid hormone, the presumption is that it may represent a form of depressed parathyroid function, or *hypoparathyroidism*.

Hyperparathyroidism. Collip found that the administration of parathyroid hormone to dogs resulted in a sharp rise of the serum calcium to 15 mg. per 100 cc., and higher, an effect quite the opposite from that associated with diminished or absent parathyroid function.

---

[83] For a detailed description of the symptoms of parathyroid tetany consult L. R. Dragstedt, *Physiol. Rev.*, **7**, 499 (1927).

[84] *J. Biol. Chem.*, **99**, 155 (1932–33).

Just as the intensive study of insulin ultimately focused attention on the subject of pancreatic hyperfunction, or *hyperinsulinism*, so the work of Collip was doubtless a factor which attracted attention to the problem of clinical *hyperparathyroidism*.[85]

Guniea-pigs, rabbits, and rats have been stated to be immune to parathyroid hormone. However, A. Bodansky, Blair, and Jaffe produced hypercalcemia in guinea-pigs and Jaffe, Bodansky, and Blair found in these animals characteristic bone lesions.[86]

Enlargement of the parathyroid glands in patients suffering from diseases of bone, notably *osteitis fibrosa cystica* (*Recklinghausen's* disease of bone), was noted by the pathologist Askanazy in 1904, but the significance which clinicians and others attached to this and similar observations was that the enlargement was a compensatory hypertrophy, secondary to the bone disease. However, the beneficial effects obtained by Mandl[87] twenty years later in a case of generalized osteitis fibrosa cystica by removal of a parathyroid adenoma suggested that the disease in the bone was perhaps the *result* and not the cause of the hyperactivity of the gland. Soon followed reports of other cases in which the hypercalcemia, decalcification of bone, and other changes in this disease were related to hyperfunction of the parathyroids. The concept of the etiological relationship of hyperparathyroidism to Recklinghausen's disease of bone was finally established through the demonstration by Jaffe, A. Bodansky, and Blair [86] that a similar condition may be produced experimentally in dogs and guinea-pigs by the regulated administration of parathyroid hormone.

As has been stated elsewhere, the serum calcium is usually elevated in hyperparathyroidism; in one clinical case as high a value as 23.6 mg. per 100 cc. has been recorded. The inorganic phosphate tends to be low. However, these changes are not always noted. A negative calcium balance may exist and considerable amounts of this element may be excreted, without being reflected by an increased calcium content in the serum. Such findings are more likely to occur in individuals (or experimental animals) maintained on a low calcium intake. Indeed, under these conditions even hypocalcemia may develop.

Another characteristic change in hyperparathyroidism is an increase in serum (or plasma) *phosphatase*.[88, 89] This is an enzyme, occurring

[85] The term "hyperparathyroidism" was first applied to clinical Recklinghausen disease by D. P. Barr and H. A. Bulger, *Am. J. Med. Sci.*, **179**, 449 (1930).

[86] *J. Exp. Med.*, **52**, 669 (1930); *Arch. Pathol.*, **11**, 207 (1931); *J. Biol. Chem.*, **88**, 629 (1930); *J. Exp. Med.*, **53**, 591 (1931).

[87] F. Mandl, *Arch. klin. Chir.*, **143**, 1, 245 (1926).

[88] H. D. Kay, *J. Biol. Chem.*, **89**, 249 (1930).

[89] A. Bodansky, *ibid.*, **101**, 93 (1933).

in the intestinal mucosa, kidney, leukocytes, bone, cartilage, and connective tissue, which possesses the ability to liberate inorganic phosphate from organic phosphate compounds. It is also capable of reversing the reaction, thus participating in the synthesis of organic phosphates. Its full significance and the mechanism of its action in bone metabolism remain to be clarified.[90]

The Adrenals. The *adrenal* or *suprarenal* glands are two small, highly vascular organs, situated in most animals at the upper poles of the kidneys and each weighing, in man, about 6 or 7 grams. Two parts are distinguishable, the *cortex* and the *medulla*. These differ from each other embryologically, histologically, and functionally. The medulla is stained by potassium dichromate, hence it has been described as the chromaffin tissue. It is closely related to the sympathetic nervous system, developmentally and physiologically. The importance of the adrenals is indicated by the fact that their extirpation results fatally. It is now generally held that death in adrenalectomized animals is due primarily to the absence of the cortex.

However, it was from the adrenal medulla that the first hormone was isolated. It is variously called adrenalin, epinephrin, or suprarenin.

Epinephrin was first obtained as the benzoyl derivative by Abel[91] and subsequently as the free base by Aldrich[92] and Takamine.[93] It has since been prepared in the laboratory by synthetic methods. Epinephrin is closely related to tyrosine, as shown by the formula:

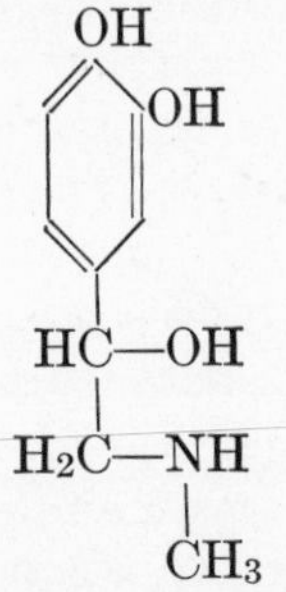

$$OH$$
$$OH$$
$$HC{-}OH$$
$$H_2C{-}NH$$
$$CH_3$$

Epinephrin or Adrenalin

Before the discovery of adrenalin, Oliver and Schäfer[94] had shown

[90] A detailed review of the clinical, experimental, and pathological aspects of hyperparathyroidism has been prepared by H. L. Jaffe, *Arch. Pathol.*, **16**, 66, 236 (1933).

[91] *Bull. Johns Hopkins Hosp.*, **9**, 215 (1898); **12**, 80 (1901).

[92] *Am. J. Physiol.*, **5**, 457 (1901).

[93] *Am. J. Pharmacy*, **73**, 523 (1901).

[94] *J. Physiol.*, **18**, 230 (1895).

that extracts of the adrenals exert a powerful effect in raising blood pressure. It has since been shown that 0.001 mg. of adrenalin, when injected into a cat, is sufficient to cause constriction of the arterioles and, hence, a rise in blood pressure. With few exceptions the effects of adrenalin on various organs and tissues are the same as those produced by stimulating the sympathetic nerve supply.[95]

From the standpoint of metabolism may be mentioned the effect of adrenalin in causing increased glycogenolysis. The immediate effect is hyperglycemia. There is also an increase in the metabolic rate as well as in the respiratory quotient, the latter change showing an increased utilization of carbohydrate. Associated with these changes is an increase in muscular power and an apparent resistance to fatigue.

[95] To explain the significance of adrenalin, W. B. Cannon ("Bodily Changes in Pain, Hunger, Fear and Rage," Appleton, New York and London, 1915) postulated the theory that this substance enables the organism to cope with emergencies. Cannon believes that fear, rage, and other emotions stimulate the adrenals to increased production of adrenalin, which, on entering the circulation, produces prompt mobilization of carbohydrate. This provides ready fuel for the muscles. Among the other manifestations of hypersecretion or injection of adrenalin are an increase in blood pressure and increased efficiency of muscular contraction, including that of the heart muscle. These changes Cannon believes to be adaptations which enable the organism to work at its maximum capacity in the face of danger. The effect of adrenalin in diminishing the clotting time of blood is regarded by Cannon as another adaptation, useful to the organism in preventing excessive hemorrhage in the case of wounds.

In a well-known experiment, Cannon compared the concentration of adrenalin in the blood of normal cats with the concentration observed in the blood when the cats were frightened by the barking of a dog. Whereas, in the normal state, no evidence of adrenalin was found, the blood of the frightened animals was found to contain demonstrable amounts of this substance. These observations and conclusions have been questioned by Stewart and Rogoff. According to Stewart (*Physiol. Rev.*, **4**, 163 [1924]), the best evidence for the view that the epinephrin output exerts no important or indispensable function is that, after its suppression, the animals do not differ notably from normal animals in their blood-sugar content, in their capacity to meet the emergencies of life, or in a variety of other ways in which Cannon observed significant differences.

The existence of an epinephrin-like hormone outside the adrenal medulla and possibly in connection with the sympathetic nervous system is indicated by work from Cannon's laboratory. This substance has been called "sympathin." *Am. J. Physiol.*, **96**, 377, 392 (1931).

From Szent-Gyorgyi's laboratory has come the report of the occurrence in the adrenal medulla of a hormone similar in action, but much more potent than adrenalin. *J. Physiol.*, **76**, 181 (1932). The substance has been called "novadrenin."

Finally, Kendall has reported the presence in the adrenal medulla of an adrenalin-lactic acid compound. Its significance is in doubt especially as it possesses very little physiological activity. *J. Biol. Chem.*, **97**, iv (1932).

Opinion is divided regarding the effect of epinephrin on muscle glycogen. In rats, G. T. Cori[96] observed a decrease accompanied by an increase in lactic acid, but no change in creatine-phosphate. Contrary results with respect to the disappearance of glycogen have been reported by Soskin[97] in experiments on dogs and by Firor and Eadie[98] in the cat.

Recent experiments by Davis and Hastings[99] seem to indicate that adrenalectomy in mice (an animal which possesses accessory adrenal tissue) produces a compensatory hypertrophy of the thyroid and that this condition continues until the accessory adrenal tissue develops sufficiently to make further compensation unnecessary.

Adrenal Cortex Insufficiency; Addison's Disease. In 1855, an English physician named Addison pointed out that the peculiar and fatal disease often associated with bronzing of the skin was in some way connected with degeneration of the adrenals. This condition, now known as Addison's disease, though usually associated with tuberculosis of the adrenal glands as in the cases studied by Addison, may, however, be due to destruction of these glands by any process.[100] The more important symptoms are pigmentation or bronzing of the skin and hair, excessive muscular weakness leading to prostration, mental depression and other nervous symptoms, gastro-intestinal disturbance including vomiting, atrophy of the sex organs, and hypoglycemia. Addison's disease appears to be due to *hypofunction* of the adrenals, and it now seems to be definitely established that the more severe symptoms are the result of cortical involvement.[101]

Several years ago the results of investigations conducted in several laboratories made it seem very probable that the adrenal cortex possessed a hormone indispensable to life.[102] It was even shown that totally adrenalectomized animals treated with extracts of the cortex survived longer than untreated animals. Intensive effort was then concentrated in the attempt to isolate the hormone, or at least to obtain a more potent preparation. This effort was soon rewarded. Almost simultaneously two groups of investigators working independ-

---

[96] *Am. J. Physiol.* **94**, 557 (1930).

[97] *Ibid.*, **81**, 383 (1927).

[98] *Ibid.*, **94**, 615 (1930).

[99] *Ibid.*, 105, 110 (1933).

[100] O. Brenner, "Addison's Disease with Atrophy of the Cortex of the Suprarenals," *Quart. J. Med.*, **22**, 121 (1928); H. G. Wells, "Addison's Disease with Selective Destruction of the Suprarenal Cortex," *Arch. Path.*, **10**, 499 (1930).

[101] For a review of the literature on adrenal insufficiency up to 1930, consult S. W. Britton, *Physiol. Rev.*, **10**, 617 (1930).

[102] F. A. Hartman, K. A. Brownell, and W. E. Hartman, *Am. J. Physiol.*, **95**, 670 (1930).

ently announced the partial solution of this intricate problem.   The adrenal cortical hormone was isolated by Hartman and associates[102] on the one hand, and by Swingle and Pfiffner[103] on the other, in a form sufficiently pure for clinical use. With this preparation adrenalectomized animals have been maintained indefinitely in good health. Equally remarkable have been the results obtained by clinicians in the treatment of Addison's disease.[104]

The chemical nature of the adrenal cortical hormone has not yet been determined; its properties indicate, however, that it is not a protein. Its physiological functions are both varied and remarkable. These include the influence which it exerts on general metabolism,[105] the maintenance of body temperature,[106] carbohydrate metabolism,[107] and in the regulation of blood volume as well as the concentration of sodium and other ions in the blood.[108]   Either directly or indirectly the adrenal cortical hormone also appears to affect the body's resistance to infection.[109]

Thus Webster, Pfiffner, and Swingle[105] found that after bilateral adrenalectomy in cats there was a maximum fall of approximately 50 per cent in metabolism.   Return to normal resulted from the administration of the adrenal cortical hormone to these animals.

Similar observations had been previously reported on adrenalectomized rats by Hartman, Brownell, and Crosby.[106]   In these animals the metabolism was usually lowered only 10 to 20 per cent.   However, in addition these investigators confirmed an earlier observation that adrenalectomized mammals when exposed to cold show a marked fall in body temperature due to decreased heat production and an inability to increase it as does the normal animal in response to the change of the environmental temperature.   The administration of *cortin* (the name by which Hartman has designated the hormone of the adrenal cortex) enabled such animals to produce heat almost normally.   The possibility that the absence of adrenalin secretion may have been an important factor in the experiment was controverted by the observation that injected adrenalin did not increase the resistance of adrenal-

[103] *Anat. Rec.*, **44**, 225 (1929); *Science*, **71**, 321 (1930); for a review of the work of Swingle and Pfiffner, see *Medicine*, **11**, 371 (1932).

[104] L. G. Rowntree, C. H. Greene, et al., *J. Am. Med. Assoc.*, **97**, 1446 (1931).

[105] *Am. J. Physiol.*, **99**, 710 (1932).

[106] *Ibid.*, **98**, 674 (1931).

[107] *Ibid.*, **99**, 15 (1932); **100**, 693, 701 (1932).

[108] R. F. Loeb, et al., *J. Exp. Med.*, **57**, 775 (1933); *Proc. Soc. Exp. Biol. Med.*, **31**, 130 (1933); G. A. Harrop, et al., *J. Exp. Med.*, **58**, 17 (1933); see also Swingle, et al., *Science*, **77**, 58 (1933).

[109] D. Perla and J. Marmoston, *Arch. Pathol.*, **16**, 399 (1933).

ectomized rats to cold. It was also found that in normal rats, exposure to cold for 20 hours, or longer, was accompanied by an increase in the weight of the adrenals.

The relation of the adrenal cortex to carbohydrate metabolism has been investigated in considerable detail by Britton and Silvette.[107] Among the conspicuous effects of adrenalectomy, according to these investigators, is the reduction in blood sugar and liver glycogen and an associated decrease in muscle glycogen. Inasmuch as these changes are not brought about when the adrenal medulla alone is extirpated and are relieved by the administration of cortico-adrenal extracts, Britton has concluded that the cortical hormone participates in the regulation of carbohydrate metabolism.

A considerable body of evidence has recently accumulated to show that sodium and water metabolism are regulated by the adrenal cortical hormone. Both in experimental animals and in clinical cases of cortico-adrenal insufficiency a definite reduction in total base concentration of the blood, with a relatively more marked diminution in the content of sodium, have been demonstrated. Associated with the increased excretion of sodium chloride which occurs is an increase in the output of water. The loss of fluid from the body is partly sustained by the plasma (hence the marked concentration of the blood), but to a far greater extent by the tissues. In Addison's disease (as well as in adrenalectomized animals), the administration of sodium chloride has been shown to produce beneficial results. Contrarily, the withdrawal of salt from the diet of patients with this disease promptly induces symptoms of severe adrenal insufficiency.

Hyperfunction of the Adrenals. Hyperactivity, though usually associated with the existence of a tumor (hypernephroma), may also result from simple hypertrophy of the adrenal cortex. The outstanding manifestations of such hyperfunction are mainly related to sexual development. According to Hoskins,[110] the situation may be epitomized by the statement that the masculine characteristics are strongly accentuated. " In the male, the result is a paragon of virility. The female becomes a masculinized caricature of her former self."

When over-activity of the cortex arises in childhood, sexual precocity is the result. A boy of six or seven will rapidly acquire the sexual development of a much older individual. There will be enlargement of the testes, together with the appearance of hair in the pubic region. There may also be the beginning of the growth of a beard or mustache. Girls similarly afflicted show evidence of hypertrophy of the breasts

[110] R. G. Hoskins, "The Tides of Life," W. W. Norton & Co., New York. This is a readable summary of Endocrinology by an authority on the subject.

and enlargement of the uterus; in some cases menstruation may occur. In a general way, these children may be said to resemble small men and women. In the girls thus afflicted there is usually a superimposition of masculine characteristics.

It should be added, however, that there is no evidence as yet that the substance formed by a hypernephroma is chemically the same as the normal cortical hormone. Moreover, direct experimental proof of an interrelationship of the adrenal cortical hormone and the gonads is also lacking.[111]

The Internal Secretions of the Reproductive Organs.[112] *Testicular or Male Hormone.* The interstitial cells (cells of Leydig) of the testes are believed to be concerned with the production of a hormone, the influence of which on the development of the sexual characteristics of the male is very profound. The view that the interstitial cells are solely concerned in the formation of the hormone is not conceded universally. Other cells may be involved, in conjunction with the interstitial cells, or by themselves, in the production of the testicular hormone. The extreme condition of deficient testicular function is represented by the complete removal of the glands (castration). This has been practiced since ancient times, particularly in oriental countries, where there has always been a considerable demand for eunuchs as household servants. Both in man and animals, if the operation is performed at an early age, the secondary sex characteristics fail to develop (growth of beard and development of larynx in man, growth of antlers in stags, and of comb, spurs, wattles, etc., in the cock). On the other hand, female characteristics may become more or less prominent. Thus a eunuch will develop large breasts and hips, and his general contour, partly because of excessive fat deposition, will resemble that of a female. Profound changes are likewise observed in related organs of internal secretion, including atrophy of the thyroid and hypophysis and hypertrophy of the thymus and suprarenal cortex. The testicular hormone apparently stimulates metabolism, perhaps indirectly owing to its influence on the thyroid gland. The excessive deposition of fat may represent a derangement in metabolism. There is also evidence of low carbohydrate tolerance and of creatinuria in eunuchs.

[111] R. Gaunt and W. M. Parkins, *Am. J. Physiol.*, **103**, 511 (1933).

Grollman and Firor have reported the extraction of the cortical hormone from normal urine. *Proc. Soc. Exp. Biol. Med.*, **30**, 669 (1933).

The important fact has also been determined that the adrenal cortex, as well as the medulla, are rich sources of ascorbic acid, believed to be vitamin C (p. 585).

[112] A detailed discussion of the older literature of the subject will be found in Marshall's "Physiology of Reproduction," London, 1922, as well as in a review by the same author in *Physiol. Rev.*, **3**, 335 (1923).

Extracts of the lipid fraction of bull testicles, prepared in F. C. Koch's laboratory,[113] have been shown to produce a striking effect on the secondary sex characters of the capon. The potency of these preparations may also be demonstrated in castrated mice and rats because of the stimulating response produced on the atrophic seminal vesicles. The male sex hormone has also been extracted from the urine of young men (Funk, Harrow, and Lejwa).[114]   Womack and Koch[115] did not detect this hormone in the urine of boys under ten years of age.   In adolescent boys it was present in about the same amount as in mature men.   Quite startling was their observation that the male sex hormone likewise occurs in the urine of both normal and pregnant women.

The chemistry of the male sex hormone requires further elucidation. According to Dodds and associates[116] it is inactivated by pepsin, trypsin, and oxidation, but is resistant to boiling with acids and alkalies. These properties are discordant with other evidence.   Butenandt[117] has reported the isolation of the hormone in crystalline form.   The yield was 15 mg. from 25,000 liters of male urine.   According to this investigator, the male hormone is a saturated keto-hydroxy compound with four rings, probably $C_{19}H_{30}O_2$, and is closely related chemically to oestrin, the ovarian hormone.   The following structural formula has been tentatively suggested:

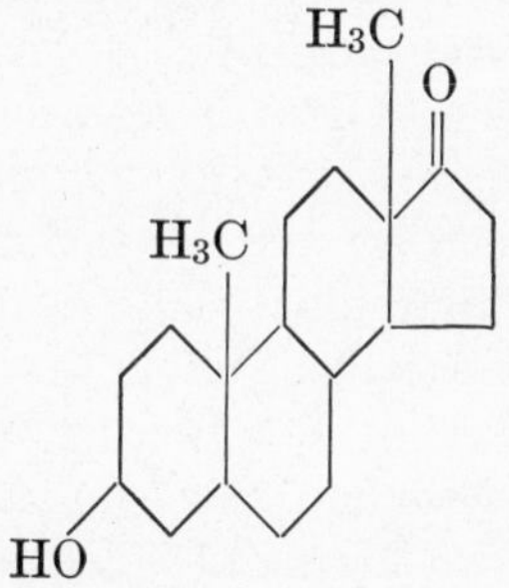

Testicular hyperfunction may occur as a result of a testicular tumor in boys.   The condition manifests itself in the premature development of secondary sex characteristics, such the growth of hair on the face

[113] L. C. McGee, M. Juhn, and L. V. Domm, *Am. J. Physiol.*, **87**, 406 (1928); C. R. Moore and McGee, *ibid.*, **87**, 436 (1928); T. F. Gallagher and F. C. Koch, *J. Biol. Chem.*, **84**, 495 (1929); Koch, *J. Am. Med. Assoc.*, **96**, 937 (1931).

[114] *Am. J. Physiol.*, **92**, 440 (1930).

[115] *Endocrinology*, **16**, 273 (1932).

[116] *Biochem. J.*, **24**, 1031 (1930).

[117] *Nature*, **130**, 280 (1932); *Z. Angew. Chem.*, **45**, 655 (1932); cited in *Ann. Rev. Biochem.*, **2**, 232 (1933).

and deepening of the voice. A case of this type has been described in which a boy less than ten years old had actually grown a black beard. A marked tendency to return to normal occurs after removal of the tumor.

Female Sex Hormones. *The ovary.* In 1923, Allen and Doisy[118] ·demonstrated the existence in follicular fluid of an agent capable of inducing oestrus in immature female rats. Soon it became known through the work of these and other investigators that a similar substance was present in amniotic fluid, placenta, and the urine of pregnant women. From the latter, Doisy, Veler, and Thayer,[119] and Butenandt,[120] working independently, finally succeeded in isolating the hormone in crystalline form. *Theelin* was the name assigned to it by Doisy and associates. It has also been named ketohydroxy-oestrin.

Many other workers were engaged on this problem, which accounts for the various names that have been introduced: *oestrin, folliculin, menformon,* and *amniotin.*

Butenandt[121] and Doisy[122] and their associates are now agreed regarding the chemical constitution of theelin. It may be represented by the formula $C_{18}H_{22}O_2$. It contains one hydroxyl or alcohol group and one keto group. The following structural formula has been tentatively proposed:

Theelin

The urine of pregnant women and the amniotic fluid of animals slaughtered for food are at present the main commercial sources for this hormone.

Closely related to theelin is a second oestrogenic substance, first

[118] *J. Am. Med. Assoc.,* **81**, 819 (1923).

[119] *Am. J. Physiol.,* **90**, 329 (1929); *J. Biol. Chem.,* **86**, 499 (1930).

[120] *Naturwissenschaften,* **17**, 879 (1929).

[121] *Abhandl. ges. Wiss.* (Göttingen), **3**, 1 (1931); cited by Thomson and Collip, *Ann. Rev. Biochem.,* **1**, 413 (1932).

[122] S. A. Thayer, L. Levin, and E. A. Doisy, *J. Biol. Chem.,* **91**, 791 (1931).

isolated by Marrian[123] and later by Butenandt[124] and Doisy[125] and associates. Doisy has named it *theelol*, inasmuch as it has been shown to be a triatomic alcohol. It may be represented by the empirical formula $C_{18}H_{24}O_3$. When distilled from acid-potassium-sulfate it yields through the loss of a molecule of water two isomers of the formula $C_{18}H_{22}O_2$. One of these, the α-form, is *theelin*. The β-form is contained in the urine of pregnant mares, which contains in addition at least two other closely related oestrogenic substances (*equiline, epuline*).

Although theelin appears to be widely distributed in nature (it has been found, for example, in palm-nut oil),[126] its physiological action is specific. Stated briefly, theelin stimulates the female genital tract, promoting the growth of the uterus, mammary glands, and the development of secondary sex characteristics. Its oestrogenic effect has been stated. It also may exert an effect on the sympathetic nervous system. The action of theelol is similar, but less pronounced. Another related substance, *pregnandiol*, found by Marrian in pregnancy urine, seems to be physiologically inert.

Corpus Luteum. Another hormone originating in the ovary is that of the corpus luteum, for which Corner's provisional designation " progestin " may be accepted. It differs from theelin in suppressing the oestral rhythm. However, it stimulates the uterus in the early stages of pregnancy and seems to be concerned with the formation of the placenta. Thus it acts partly as an antagonist of theelin and partly in conjunction with it.

Placenta. The hormones of the placenta are obviously of significance only in the pregnant mammal. Theelin and theelol have been isolated from the placenta. A second fraction contains an oestrogenic principle which is assumed to be different from other oestrogenic substances, being active when given by mouth, and exerting its maximum effects in the presence of the ovaries. This hormone was originally named *emmenin* by Collip,[127] who considered its main physiological rôle to be the stimulation of the ovaries and the control thereby of theelin production. The work of Browne,[128] a pupil of Collip, has, however, brought emmenin into closer relation with theelin and theelol, both chemically and physiologically. A third placental fraction was found by Collip to contain a hormone which is similar to, if

[123] *Biochem. J.*, **24**, 435, 1021 (1930).
[124] A. Butenandt and F. Hildebrandt, *Z. physiol. Chem.*, **199**, 243 (1931).
[125] *J. Biol. Chem.*, **91**, 641, 647, 655 (1931).
[126] A. Butenandt and H. Jacobi, *Z. physiol. Chem.*, **218**, 104 (1933).
[127] *International Clin.*, Series *42*, **4**, 51 (1932).
[128] *Canad. J. Research*, **8**, 180 (1933).

not identical with, the sex-stimulating hormone of the anterior pituitary.

Mammary Glands. The growth of the mammary glands in adolescent girls is believed to be due principally to the action of theelin from the ovary. Further development occurring during pregnancy is again probably due to theelin, from the ovary as well as the placenta. Progestin has been considered as a secondary factor in this regard. The onset of lactation, however, depends on an hormonal influence from the anterior pituitary. Riddle[129] has postulated the existence of a specific hormone, *prolactin*, in the pituitary.

The interruption of menstruation which occurs, not invariably, however, during lactation has led to the suggestion that this control may be due to a hormone formed by the active mammary gland. There is no concrete evidence, however, for this supposition.

The Hypophysis or Pituitary Gland. The hormones of the pituitary gland constitute an extraordinarily complex problem. The multiplicity and divergence of the functions exhibited by the posterior and anterior lobes suggest the existence of a number of active principles, some of which have been isolated. With the progress of knowledge it has become increasingly evident that the hypophysis commands a dominant position because of the existing interrelationships between it and the other organs of internal secretion. Lack of space makes it impossible to do more than briefly summarize the essential functions of this gland and the hormones that are believed to be involved.

The Posterior Lobe. Extracts of the posterior lobe stimulate the contraction of smooth muscle (bladder, intestine, mammary gland, uterus, etc.). Particularly striking are the contractions of the uterus (*oxytocic* effect), a property that has found important clinical applications. The oxytocic principle has been isolated by Kamm and associates[130] and designated by them as *α-hypophamine*. It is also referred to as *oxytocin*. The effect of this purified substance on smooth muscle in general requires further study.

Another important effect of posterior pituitary extracts (*pituitrin*) is the elevation of blood pressure. It is not altogether clear to what extent this " pressor " effect is due to stimulation of the heart muscle and particularly of the smooth muscle of the walls of the blood vessels. However, Kamm and co-workers have isolated from the posterior pituitary a hormone which is devoid of the oxytocic effect and which specifically raises the blood pressure. This hormone has been designated *β-hypophamine*. *Vasopressin* is another term commonly used in

---

[129] *Proc. Soc. Exp. Biol. Med.*, **29**, 1211 (1931–32).
[130] *J. Am. Chem. Soc.*, **50**, 573 (1928).

describing it. At present, our chemical knowledge of these substances is incomplete.

The disease *diabetes insipidus* was formerly associated with injury to the posterior lobe. In this condition large quantities of urine are excreted; indeed a daily elimination exceeding 50 liters has been occasionally reported. The same effect on water metabolism seems to result, however, from injury to the hypothalamic region of the brain. The important consideration here is that extracts of the posterior pituitary markedly decrease the urine volume, both in these individuals and normally. An opposite effect is produced in the anesthetized animal. According to Kamm this action of the posterior pituitary may be attributed to the " pressor substance." Others consider the control of the water metabolism to be dependent on a specific hormone.

It also appears that the pigmentation of amphibia, reptiles, and other organisms is in some way dependent on the pituitary through a controlling effect on the expansion and contraction of the melanophores, or pigment cells.

Recent work has brought to light a possible interrelationship to carbohydrate metabolism. Injections of pituitrin have been shown to lessen the effect of administered insulin. This antagonistic action has been brought out even more clearly by the administration of insulin to animals deprived of the posterior lobe. Such animals exhibit a marked sensitivity to the action of insulin. There is also a definite indication of a relation of the posterior lobe to fat metabolism. Deficiency of pituitary secretion is associated with a high fat content in the blood and the deposition of fat in the tissues, leading to obesity. On the contrary the injection of posterior lobe extracts results in a diminution in the blood fat and although there is a corresponding increase of fat in the liver, the resultant effect is a greater utilization of this substance in the body.

In short, although only two hormones have been isolated from the posterior lobe thus far, the physiological properties suggest the possible existence of others. The question has been raised, however, whether these hormones ever escape into the circulation and play their physiological rôle in the normal mammalian organism. The proper answer to this, as well as to other baffling questions, will be determined by the results of future research.

The Anterior Lobe. The extirpation of the anterior lobe or of the entire gland, in young animals, has a marked inhibitory effect upon growth. In a celebrated experiment, Aschner[131] selected two puppies

[131] *Arch. d. ges. Physiol.*, **146**, 1 (1912).

from the same litter, removed the hypophysis of one and used the other as a control. The dog without the hypophysis remained stunted, whereas the control animal grew to normal size.

Similar retardation of growth, as well as atrophy of the sex organs, occurs in rats following hypophysectomy, as shown by P. E. Smith.[132] If such dwarfed rats are given injections of anterior lobe substance, growth and the development of the sex organs are resumed. Almost normal growth was obtained by Smith in a group of hypophysectomized rats in which a daily homeotransplant of anterior lobe tissue was made. The rôle of the anterior lobe is believed to be due mainly to the presence of at least two hormones, one of which promotes sexual development and the other growth, particularly the growth of bone and connective tissue.[133] The possible existence of a third hormone, *prolactin*, has been mentioned elsewhere.

In man, as in animals, the most conspicuous effects of hypopituitarism are inhibition in growth, which if severe enough may result in dwarfism, and sexual immaturity.

It has also been observed that following the removal of the anterior lobe marked atrophy occurs of the thyroid, parathyroid, and adrenal cortex.

The association of hypopituitarism with *dystrophia adiposo-genitalis* (Fröhlich's disease) is not clearly defined and is incompatible with what is known at present of the functions of the anterior lobe of the hypophysis. The view that it is rather the result of a disturbance in the adjacent hypothalamic region has a considerable element of probability.

Hyperactivity of the anterior lobe of the hypophysis usually results from the development of a tumor (eosinophile adenoma) in this region of the gland. The clinical manifestations of such hyperfunction are well defined. If the condition develops before union of the epiphyses has taken place, that is in very young individuals, there is in consequence growth of the long bones to gigantic proportions, and *gigantism* is the result. The giants of the circus are as a rule victims of this disease. While the subjects ordinarily attain a height of 6.5 to 8 feet, there are records of even taller individuals (9 and 9.2 feet).

[132] *Anat. Rec.*, **33**, 289 (1926); *Am. J. Physiol.*, **80**, 114; **81**, 20 (1927); *J. Am. Med. Assoc.*, **88**, 158 (1927). See also G. L. Foster and P. E. Smith, *J. Am. Med. Assoc.*, **87**, 2151 (1926); Smith and E. T. Engle, *Am. J. Anat.*, **40**, 159 (1927–28); H. M. Evans, Harvey Lecture, 1923–24, p. 212.

[133] For the growth-promoting hormone, van Dyke and Wallen-Lawrence have proposed the name *phyone* (φύω, I cause to grow). For the gonad-stimulating substance they have suggested the name *hebin* (ἥβη, puberty): *J. Pharm. Exp. Therap.*, **40**, 413 (1930); **43**, 93 (1931).

After epiphyseal union has taken place, symmetrical growth is no longer possible. In consequence the skeletal changes consist in an overgrowth of certain parts only. The jaw enlarges and protrudes, the spine is bowed, and the hands and feet increase in size. Because of the associated connective tissue hyperplasia, the nose is widened, the lips, tongue, scalp, and skin generally become greatly thickened. The altered appearance has been likened to a " reversion to the gorilla type." Such in part is the picture of *acromegaly*. It generally begins in early middle life. In an individual of 20 years of age, or older, hyperpituitarism of the severity described would give the typical picture of acromegaly. If the condition should develop in early adolescence, acromegalic characteristics are superimposed upon those of gigantism.

Inasmuch as the anterior part of the gland contains the gonad-stimulating hormone, hyperfunction as in gigantism and acromegaly should be associated with increased sexual virility, and in fact this occurs at first. But as the disease runs its course, sexual activity diminishes or disappears, for not infrequently the condition of hyperfunction gives way to hypofunction. However, the changes in the skeleton being fixed, it is obvious that they cannot be undone.

Gigantism has been produced experimentally in rats by the continued administration of an extract of the anterior pituitary. Similarly typical acromegaly has been experimentally produced in a dog.

In addition to the changes mentioned, there is in gigantism and acromegaly a marked increase in the size of the internal organs (splanchnomegaly).

As soon as pregnancy is initiated, the anterior lobe is stimulated to secrete large amounts of the gonad-stimulating hormone, indicating a reciprocal relation between the ovary and the anterior pituitary. A considerable proportion of this hormone is excreted in the urine. Inasmuch as little, if any, gonad-stimulating hormone is normally present in the urine, its occurrence there in large amounts during pregnancy has been utilized as a test for pregnancy. Such urine injected into immature mice produces evidence of stimulation of the ovaries and of the genital tract. This is the basis of the well-known Ascheim-Zondek test. Similar changes are produced in the ovaries of the rabbit; indeed, pregnancy urine stimulates the male gonads of rats and other animals. These findings have been utilized in various modifications of the original pregnancy test.

Internal Secretions of Other Organs. The thymus, pineal body, spleen, and kidneys have also been studied from the standpoint of endocrinology. On the basis of available information, their status as organs of internal secretion is, at best, uncertain.

CHAPTER XVI

ANIMAL CALORIMETRY

The unit of measurement of heat in animal calorimetry is the large or kilogram Calorie. It is the amount of heat required to raise the temperature of 1 kg. of water from 15° to 16° C. When 41,860,000 ergs (work units) are changed or dissipated into heat, 1 Calorie is formed.

The calorific value of organic compounds is usually determined by means of the bomb calorimeter. The essential part of this apparatus is a combustion bomb in which is supported a platinum capsule. The latter is used as the container for the material to be analyzed. A wire having electrical connections with the outside dips into it. Before an analysis, the bomb is closed tightly, filled with oxygen under a pressure of 20 to 25 atmospheres, and placed in a vessel containing water. Passing an electric current through the wire causes it to glow, thereby igniting the material in the platinum capsule. The heat evolved is calculated from the observed change in the temperature of the water.

Calorific Value of Foodstuffs. The combustion calorimeter has been used extensively in determining the heat values of foodstuffs. Somewhat more elaborate methods are required for the determination of the calorific value of foods when burned in the body. These will be discussed presently. The combustion of 1 gram of a monosaccharide yields about 3.75 calories.[1] One gram of a disaccharide yields 3.95 calories; and a gram of starch, 4.23 calories. Hence, 4.0 or 4.1 is usually taken as the average calorific value of 1 gram of carbohydrate. This amount of heat is evolved whether the combustion occurs in the air or inside the body. The heat value of fats is considerably higher. Approximately 9.3 calories are obtained on combustion of 1 gram of fat. Here also, the amount of heat produced is the same whether the fat is burned in a bomb calorimeter or in the body. The situation is somewhat different in the case of the proteins. When burned in the bomb calorimeter, 1 gram of protein yields on an average about 5.7 calories, but in the body, the heat of combustion is found to be only about 4.1 calories. Proteins may differ somewhat in calorific value.

[1] In this chapter, unless specified otherwise, the term "calorie" will be used in referring to the large or kilogram calorie.

500

Thus, casein produces 4.4 calories, whereas the vegetable proteins yield about 4.0 calories. The divergence in the calorific values of protein when burned outside and inside the body is due to the fact that protein combustion in the tissues is never complete. The end-products of protein metabolism (urea, etc.), though of no value as energy producers in the body, are capable of undergoing further combustion in the bomb calorimeter. One gram of urea, for example, on oxidation, yields 2.52 calories. It has been determined that on a mixed diet the ratio of carbon to nitrogen in the urine is about 0.75, and that a gram of urinary nitrogen is equivalent to 8.09 calories. This value is not constant, being influenced by a variety of factors. Following the ingestion of large amounts of carbohydrate, the urine, though practically free from sugar, may contain sufficient amounts of intermediary products of glucose metabolism to increase the calorific equivalent of a gram of urinary nitrogen to as much as 13 calories. After meat has been eaten, the calorific value of 1 gram of urinary nitrogen is 7.46 (Rubner, cited by Lusk[2]); during starvation, it is 8.49 calories.

Heat Production and Respiratory Exchange. Total metabolism in the body may be determined by direct or indirect methods of calorimetry. The direct method consists in placing the individual in a suitably constructed chamber and measuring the amount of heat evolved. In principle, animal and bomb calorimeters are similar. By the indirect method, the heat given off is computed from the respiratory exchange. By determining the consumption of oxygen, the elimination of carbon dioxide, and the excretion of nitrogen in the urine, the necessary data are obtained for calculating, not only total heat production, but the nature and amount of each of the substances metabolized, as well.

Various forms of apparatus have been designed for the measurement of heat production in man and animals either by the direct or indirect method. For use in experiments on human beings, an exceedingly accurate calorimeter was invented by Atwater and Rosa[3] and improved by Benedict.[4] This apparatus measures heat production and respiratory exchange simultaneously.

Principle of the Atwater-Rosa-Benedict Respiration Calorimeter. The respiration calorimeter is shown in Fig. 32, and is diagrammatically represented in Fig. 33. There are three walls, an inner and an outer copper wall and an insulating wall. The two copper walls are separated from each other by a dead-air space. A similar space separates the

[2] G. Lusk, "Science of Nutrition," 1928 edition, p. 39.

[3] Atwater and Rosa, Report of the Storrs Agr. Exp. Sta., p. 212 (1897).

[4] Atwater and Benedict, Carnegie Inst. of Washington Pub., No. 42 (1905); Benedict and Carpenter, *ibid.*, No. 123 (1910).

outer copper wall from the insulating wall. The latter is constructed
of two layers of compo-board separated by a layer of cork. Between
the insulating wall and the outer copper wall are water pipes, along
which run resistance wires, carrying an electric current. Thus the
temperature of the interspace, as well as that of the outer copper wall,
may be kept under control, either by the passage of cold water through
the pipes or by warming. It is essential that the temperature of the two
copper walls be maintained the same, for otherwise there would be an

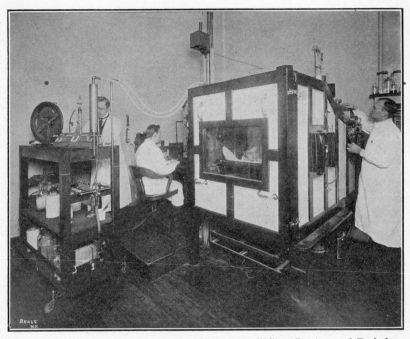

FIG. 32.—The respiration calorimeter of the Russell Sage Institute of Pathology
(After a photograph loaned by Dr. Eugene F. Du Bois)

exchange of heat between them and, hence, either a gain or loss of
heat by the inner wall. Thermocouples are arranged between the two
walls to determine their temperature. During the course of an experiment, this is done at intervals of about four minutes.

Inside the calorimeter, the temperature is maintained practically
constant by passing a current of cool water through a series of pipes.
The heat lost by an individual in the calorimeter through radiation and
conduction is thus removed by the water. The total volume of water
passing through the calorimeter is measured. Likewise, the temperature of the ingoing and outgoing stream of water is recorded at short

intervals during the experiment. A considerable amount of heat is used in the evaporation of water. The water evaporated from the skin

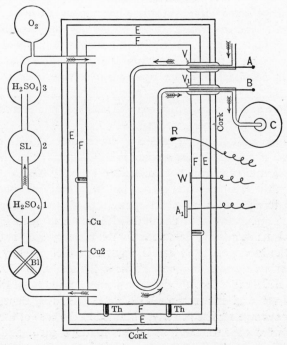

FIG. 33.—Schematic diagram of the Atwater-Rosa-Benedict respiration calorimeter. (After Graham Lusk, "Elements of the Science of Nutrition," Saunders & Co., 1928 edition, p. 70.)

Ventilating System:
  O_2, Oxygen introduced as consumed by subject.
  3, H_2SO_4 to catch moisture given off by soda lime.
  2, Soda lime to remove CO_2.
  1, H_2SO_4 to remove moisture given off by patient.
  Bl, Blower to keep air in circulation.

Indirect Calorimetry:
  Increase in weight of H_2SO_4 (1) = water elimination of subject.
  Increase in weight of soda lime (2) + increase in weight of H_2SO_4 (3) = CO_2 elimination.
  Decrease in weight of oxygen tank = oxygen consumption of subject.

Heat-absorbing System:
  A, Thermometer to record temperature of ingoing water.
  B, Thermometer to record temperature of outgoing water.

V, Vacuum jacket.
C, Tank for weighing water which has passed through calorimeter each hour.
W, Thermometer for measuring temperature of wall.
A_1, Thermometer for measuring temperature of the air.
R, Rectal thermometer for measuring temperature of subject.

Direct Calorimetry:
  Average difference of A and B × liters of water + (g. water eliminated × 0.586) ± (change in temperature of wall × hydrothermal equivalent of box) ± (change of temperature of body × hydrothermal equivalent of body) = total calories produced.

Th, thermocouple; Cu, inner copper wall; Cu_2, outer copper wall; E. F. dead airspaces.

and the water vapor in the expired air are taken up by sulfuric acid absorbers outside the chamber. From the amount of water thus collected, the latent heat is calculated. It is estimated that about one-quarter of the total heat produced by the human body is present as latent heat in the water vapor which is given off. Although the temperature of the air entering the calorimeter is always heated to exactly the same temperature as the air leaving it, nevertheless, the temperature of the calorimeter is determined at the beginning and end of an experiment and a correction introduced, if necessary. Another correction may be necessary, should a change in the body temperature occur. The chamber has a port-hole with inner and outer airtight doors. By opening these, one at a time, food may be passed in and excreta removed, without loss or gain of heat.

So well have the technical details of the calorimeter been worked out that when a given amount of alcohol is burned in it, and the heat production measured, the value obtained is practically identical with that found when the combustion is carried out in a bomb calorimeter. This is referred to as the alcohol check. Another way of testing the accuracy of the apparatus is to generate within it a measured amount of heat by means of an electric current. When everything is functioning properly the heat produced in this way may be completely accounted for by calorimetric measurement. This is the electric check.

Moreover, there is exceedingly close agreement in the results obtained by the direct and indirect methods. Atwater and Benedict[5] compared the average results per day, obtained in the case of three individuals who were experimented upon for 40 days each, and found an average difference of only 0.2 per cent.

	Average Calories per Day
Indirect calorimetry	2717
Direct calorimetry	2723
Difference	0.2 per cent

Murlin and Lusk[6] performed a series of twenty-two experiments on a dog and found the average difference in the results obtained by direct and indirect calorimetry to be only 0.6 per cent.

For the determination of respiratory exchange alone, less elaborate equipment is required than for the measurement of heat output by direct calorimetry. The fact that the indirect method yields results which are both reliable and valuable in the study of metabolic disorders

[5] Cited by Lusk, "Science of Nutrition," 4th edition, p. 62. The student is referred to this book for a detailed description of the Atwater-Rosa-Benedict calorimeter.

[6] J. Biol. Chem., 22, 15 (1915).

has been the stimulus for the invention of a large variety of appliances to be used in the determination of respiratory exchange.[7]

Respiratory Quotient, Influence of Metabolism. The ratio between the carbon-dioxide output and the oxygen intake is termed the " respiratory quotient (R. Q.)" Early in the history of the science of nutrition, it was realized that this ratio was profoundly affected by the character of the material metabolized and that, therefore, the determination of the respiratory quotient would yield information concerning the nature of the substances which were being utilized. In the combustion of carbohydrate, the volume of carbon dioxide produced is equal to the volume of oxygen used. The respiratory quotient, $\dfrac{CO_2}{O_2}$, is therefore 1.

$$C_6H_{12}O_6 + 6O_2 = 6CO_2 + 6H_2O$$

The combustion of a fat (triolein) may be represented by the equation:

$$C_{57}H_{104}O_6 + 80O_2 = 57CO_2 + 52H_2O$$

Hence, the respiratory quotient of triolein is

$$R. Q. = \frac{57}{80} = 0.71$$

There are slight variations in the respiratory quotients of different fats, owing to the differences in molecular weight. For tripalmitin, the quotient is 0.703; for human fat, 0.713, etc.

It is somewhat more difficult to represent the oxidation of protein. The respiratory quotient may be computed as follows (Loewy[8]):

100 grams of meat protein contain:

$$52.38 \text{ g. C}$$
$$7.27 \text{ g. H}$$
$$22.68 \text{ g. O}$$
$$16.65 \text{ g. N}$$
$$1.02 \text{ g. S}$$

[7] Some of the methods employed in the measurement of respiratory exchange in man and animals are to be found in the monograph by A. Krogh, "The Respiratory Exchange of Animals and Man," Chap. II, London and New York, 1916. See also Du Bois, "Basal Metabolism in Health and Disease," Lea & Febiger, Philadelphia, 1924, and W. M. Boothby and I. Sandiford, "Laboratory Manual of the Technique of Basal Metabolism Determinations," Philadelphia, 1920. The student is also referred to H. B. Richardson's review, "The Respiratory Quotient," in *Physiol. Rev.*, **9**, 61 (1929).

[8] Oppenheimer's "Handbuch der Biochemie," **4**, 1, 279 (1911); cited by Lusk, 4th edition, p. 64.

Of these amounts, the following portions are excreted in the urine and feces:

Urine	Feces
9.406 g. C	1.471 g. C
2.663 g. H	0.212 g. H
14.099 g. O	0.889 g. O
16.28 g. N	0.37 g. N
1.02 g. S	

This leaves a residuum for the respiratory process of:

$$41.50 \text{ g. C}$$
$$4.40 \text{ g. H}$$
$$7.69 \text{ g. O}$$

The amount of oxygen here is sufficient to oxidize 0.961 g. of hydrogen, leaving for further oxidation

$$41.50 \text{ g. C}$$
$$3.439 \text{ g. H}$$

To oxidize these would require 138.18 grams of oxygen. The carbon-dioxide production would be 152.17 grams. These values may be converted into their volume equivalents, since 1 gram of oxygen occupies 0.699 liter and 1 gram of carbon dioxide 0.5087 liter. Computing for the value of the respiratory quotient:

$$\frac{77.39 \text{ l. } CO_2}{96.63 \text{ l. } O_2} = 0.801$$

If the combustion of carbohydrate alone were possible, the respiratory quotient would be 1; if only protein were being burned, it would be about 0.80–0.82; if fat, about 0.71. Under certain conditions, values outside the range 0.7 to 1.0 have been observed. Indeed, a quotient as high as 1.38 was obtained by Bleibtreu[9] on geese which were being stuffed and which were presumably converting carbohydrate (an oxygen-rich substance) into fat (an oxygen-poor substance). This process obviously involves the liberation of oxygen. Before hibernating, animals also show high respiratory quotients. Values lower than 0.70 have been observed in hibernating animals, the calorific requirements of which are obviously met by the stored fat. The glycerol arising in fat metabolism in these animals is probably converted, at least in part, into sugar. In diabetes, the respiratory quotient is low, since carbohydrate metabolism is deficient; and when the condition is especially severe, it may fall some-

[9] *Arch. ges. Physiol.*, **85**, 345 (1901).

what below 0.7 as a result of the conversion of amino acids and glycerol into glucose. In phlorhizin diabetes, Chambers and Deuel[10] recently observed a reduction in the respiratory quotient after the administration of glycerol, for, in the conversion of the latter into glucose, oxygen was required. Under ordinary conditions, the respiratory quotient is about 0.85, but it may vary within rather wide limits. The Hindoos and Chinese, who live largely on rice, are said to have a high respiratory quotient (above 0.9).

The amount of protein represented by 1 gram of urinary nitrogen requires for oxidation 5.923 liters (8.471 grams) of oxygen and produces 4.754 liters (9.347 grams) of carbon dioxide (Zuntz and Schumberg[11]). The calorific equivalent of 1 gram of urinary nitrogen (about 6.25 grams protein) is 26.51 calories (Lusk[12]).

Given the total oxygen consumption, carbon-dioxide production, and urinary-nitrogen elimination for a certain period, it is possible to calculate the amounts of protein, fat, and carbohydrate metabolized during that period. This may be illustrated by a simple example.

Suppose that Mr. A during a period of 24 hours consumed 400 liters of oxygen and eliminated 340 liters of carbon dioxide and 12 grams of nitrogen. For the combustion of the protein represented by the urinary nitrogen,

$$12 \times 5.923 = 71.076 \text{ liters of oxygen were used, and}$$

$$12 \times 4.754 = 57.048 \text{ liters of carbon dioxide produced.}$$

Subtracting these values from the total volumes:

Total O_2 used	400 liters
O_2 used for protein	71 liters
O_2 used by carbohydrate and fat	329 liters
Total CO_2 produced	340 liters
CO_2 produced by protein	57 liters
CO_2 produced by carbohydrate and fat	283 liters

The ratio $\frac{283}{329} = 0.86$ is the non-protein respiratory quotient. From this figure may be computed the relative amounts of carbohydrate and fat used, or these may be determined more simply from the table

[10] J. Biol. Chem., **65**, 21 (1925).

[11] "Studien zu einer Physiologie des Marsches," Berlin (1901).

[12] For further details and other methods of calculation, consult the books by Lusk and Du Bois, previously cited.

of Zuntz and Schumberg, modified by Lusk[13] and by McClendon[14] (p. 509). It is to be noted that when the non-protein R. Q. is 0.86, 1 liter of oxygen is equivalent to 0.622 gram of carbohydrate and 0.249 gram of fat. Hence, 329 liters of oxygen are equivalent to 329 × 0.622 = 204.6 grams of carbohydrate and 329 × 0.249 = 81.92 grams of fat. Accordingly, during the period of experimentation, the following amounts were utilized:

Protein (12 × 6.25)..................... 75   grams
Fat .... 81.92 grams
Carbohydrate.......................... 204.6 grams

From these figures may be calculated the total calorific output:

$$[75 \times 4.1] + [81.92 \times 9.3] + [204.6 \times 4.1] = 1908.3 \text{ calories}$$

According to Loewy:

1 liter of O_2 from protein corresponds to.......... 4.485 calories
1 liter of O_2 from fat corresponds to.............. 4.686 calories
1 liter of O_2 from carbohydrate corresponds to..... 5.047 calories

Referring to Table LIV, it will be seen that when the non-protein respiratory quotient is 0.86, 1 liter of oxygen corresponds to 4.875 calories. From this value and the figure given by Loewy for protein, the calorific output may be computed readily as follows:

$$[71 \times 4.485] + [329 \times 4.875] = 1922.3 \text{ calories}^{15}$$

These calculations illustrate the method for computing heat production by indirect calorimetry.

Basal Metabolism. The respiratory exchange and, hence, the heat production of an individual may vary within wide limits, being influenced by such factors as muscular activity, emotional stress, food intake, and external temperature. The influence of these factors is reduced to a minimum when the individual is lying perfectly still, sufficiently long after the last meal, so that no digestion is going on, and at a temperature ranging between 30° and 35° C. This condition of minimum metabolism and heat production is called basal metabolism (*Grundumsatz*—Magnus Levy). It is also referred to as maintenance metabolism (*Erhaltungsumsatz*—Loewy), post-absorptive metabolism (F. G. Benedict), basal

---

[13] Lusk, "Science of Nutrition," 1928 edition, p. 65.

[14] McClendon and Medes, "Physical Chemistry in Biology and Medicine," p. 158.

[15] The slight discrepancy between this value and 1908.3 calories (less than 1 per cent) is due to the somewhat divergent factors introduced by different authorities and to dropping, in the calculations, of the last decimal places by the present author.

metabolic rate (Plummer and Boothby), and standard metabolism (Krogh).[16]

TABLE LIV

THE SIGNIFICANCE OF THE NON-PROTEIN RESPIRATORY QUOTIENT AS REGARDS THE HEAT VALUE OF 1 LITER OF OXYGEN, AND THE RELATIVE QUANTITY IN CALORIES OF CARBOHYDRATE AND FAT CONSUMED (ZUNTZ AND SCHUMBERG, MODIFIED BY LUSK, MODIFIED BY MCCLENDON)

One Liter of Oxygen is Equivalent to

Non-Protein Respiratory Quotient	Grams		Calories
	Carbohydrate	Fat	
0.707	0.000	0.502	4.686
0.71	0.016	0.497	4.690
0.72	0.055	0.482	4.702
0.73	0.094	0.465	4.714
0.74	0.134	0.450	4.727
0.75	0.173	0.433	4.739
0.76	0.213	0.417	4.751
0.77	0.254	0.400	4.764
0.78	0.294	0.384	4.776
0.79	0.334	0.368	4.788
0.80	0.375	0.350	4.801
0.81	0.415	0.334	4.813
0.82	0.456	0.317	4.825
0.83	0.498	0.301	4.838
0.84	0.539	0.284	4.850
0.85	0.580	0.267	4.862
0.86	0.622	0.249	4.875
0.87	0.666	0.232	4.887
0.88	0.708	0.215	4.899
0.89	0.741	0.197	4.911
0.90	0.793	0.180	4.924
0.91	0.836	0.162	4.936
0.92	0.878	0.145	4.948
0.93	0.922	0.127	4.961
0.94	0.966	0.109	4.973
0.95	1.010	0.091	4.985
0.96	1.053	0.073	4.998
0.97	1.098	0.055	5.010
0.98	1.142	0.036	5.022
0.99	1.185	0.018	5.035
1.00	1.232	0.000	5.047

[16] For a summary of recent advances in the study of basal metabolism the reader is referred to a review by E. F. Du Bois, *J. Nutrition*, **3**, 217, 331 (1930–31).

Relation to Surface Area. It was pointed out by Voit[17] that the heat production, during rest, of such animals as the mouse, rabbit, fowl, dog, and horse, was dependent on the surface area. Calculated on this basis, the heat output of these animals, as well as of man, would amount to about 1000 calories per square meter per day. In proportion to its weight, the mouse has a greater surface and a greater heat output than the horse. Rubner[18] postulated the law that the metabolism is proportional to the superficial area of an animal. In the normal male, between the ages of 20 and 40 years, the heat output per square meter per hour is, on an average, 39.5 calories; in females between these ages, it is somewhat lower, namely, 36.5–37 calories.

The surface area of human subjects may be calculated by means of the following formula, proposed by D. Du Bois and E. F. Du Bois:[19]

$$A = W^{0.425} \times H^{0.725} \times 71.84$$

where A = area in square meters, W = weight in kilograms, and H = height in centimeters.

Influence of Age and Sex. New-born infants have a low basal metabolism, as was clearly demonstrated by Hasselbach,[20] who found that the heat production per kilogram of body weight was about the same during the first 24 hours of life as in the adult, despite the relatively larger surface of the infant. These findings were confirmed by Benedict and Talbot,[21] who observed a caloric output per square meter per 24 hours of 612 calories or about 25 calories per square meter per hour; and by Murlin, Conklin, and Marsh,[22] who obtained a value of 700 calories in the new-born. It is interesting to note that during the first hours of life the respiratory quotient is high, often approximating 1, which means that the infant is burning carbohydrate, for the

---

[17] Z. Biol., **41**, 120 (1901).

[18] Rubner, "Energiegesetze," 1902, p. 282.

[19] The surface area of human subjects may be determined more directly from a chart prepared by D. and E. F. Du Bois. For the methods employed in deriving the equation, consult the original papers by Du Bois (Arch. Internal Med., **15**, 868 [1915]; ibid., **17**, 863, 887 [1916]), and the book previously cited.

The surface area of fetuses and children has been investigated by R. E. Scammon and associates, Proc. Soc. Exp. Biol. Med., **27**, 445, 449, 456, 461, 463 (1929–30). A. G. Hogan and C. I. Skouby (J. Agr. Research, **25**, 419 [1923]) have developed formulas for the surface areas of swine and cattle. G. R. Cowgill and D. L. Drabkin have derived a formula for the surface area of dogs (Am. J. Physiol., **81**, 36 [1927]).

[20] Trans. Pub. No. 233, Carnegie Inst., Wash., 1915.

[21] Carnegie Inst., Wash., 1921 Pub. No. 302; see also, Talbot, "Basal Metabolism of Children," Physiol. Rev., **5**, 477 (1925).

[22] Am. J. Diseases Children, **29**, 1 (1925).

most part. The quotient falls rapidly, so that at the end of the first day it may approximate 0.7 to 0.72. It then increases gradually until the fifth or sixth day, when it reaches 0.81, or the respiratory quotient of the adult. Carpenter and Murlin[23] made the interesting observation that the energy metabolism of the pregnant mother, immediately before delivery, is equal to the sum of the metabolism of the mother and infant taken 3–10 days after childbirth.

This has been confirmed by Rowe and Boyd,[24] who determined the changes in metabolism in a series of 77 pregnant women. During the third and fourth months of gestation a rapid decline in basal metabolism was observed. This was followed during the last 6 lunar months by a steady rise amounting to 13 per cent, or more, in excess of that conditioned by the gross increase in body weight. Taking into consideration the constancy of heat output in terms of surface area when the fetal area was added to that of the mother, the conclusion was reached that the excess in metabolism was contributed primarily by the fetus.

The basal metabolism of premature infants is lower than that of full-term infants, both at birth and for several months thereafter. The basal metabolism of the child increases very rapidly during the first year of life and continues to be high for three or four years thereafter (15–20 per cent per square meter of surface above adult). A second rise has been reported by Du Bois preceding puberty (twelfth to thirteenth year). This is said to reach a maximum when the menses are established in girls and sexual maturity in boys.[25] It is followed by a gradual decline after puberty is reached. These points require further substantiation, however. According to Boothby and Sandiford,[26] there is a decrease in the basal metabolism of male children between the ages of 5 and 21 and a more rapid decrease in female children between the ages of 5 and 17, followed in both sexes by a gradual and nearly parallel decline to old age. The influence on metabolism of age and sex is shown in table LV.

The greater variability in the metabolism of women is to be related, at least partly, to the effects of the menstrual cycle. Usually the highest metabolism is attained in the premenstrual period and the lowest during the menstrual days.[27]

[23] *Arch. Internal Med.*, **7**, 184 (1911).

[24] *J. Nutrition*, **5**, 551 (1932).

[25] A. Topper and H. Mulier, *Am. J. Diseases Children*, **43**, 327 (1932).

[26] *Am. J. Physiol.*, **90**, 290 (1929).

[27] F. G. Benedict and M. D. Finn, *Am. J. Physiol.*, **86**, 59 (1928); F. A. Hitchcock and F. R. Wardwell, *J. Nutrition*, **2**, 203 (1929); F. R. Griffith and co-workers, *Am. J. Physiol.*, **87**, 602 (1929); C. J. Conklin and J. F. McClendon, *Arch. Internal Med.*, **45**, 125 (1930).

TABLE LV

The Du Bois Normal Standards as Modified by Boothby and Sandiford

Calories per square meter per hour

Age	Males	Females	Age	Males	Females
5..............	(53.0)	(51.6)	20–24.........	41.0	36.9
6..............	52.7	50.7	25–29.........	40.3	36.6
7..............	52.0	49.3			
8..............	51.2	48.1	30–34.........	39.8	36.2
9..............	50.4	46.9	35–39.........	39.2	35.8
10.............	49.5	45.8	40–44.........	38.3	35.3
11.............	48.6	44.6	45–49.........	37.8	35.0
12.............	47.8	43.4	50–54.........	37.2	34.5
13.............	47.1	42.0	55–59.........	36.6	34.1
14.............	46.2	41.0			
15.............	45.3	39.6	60–64.........	36.0	33.8
16.............	44.7	38.5	65–69.........	35.3	33.4
17.............	43.7	37.4			
18.............	42.9	37.3	70–74.........	(34.8)	(32.8)
19.............	42.1	37.2	75–79.........	(34.2)	(32.3)

Seasonal, Climatic, Racial, and Other Variations. According to Gustafson and Benedict[28] metabolism tends to be at a low level in winter and to rise to a higher level during the spring and summer.

The factor of climate, apart from the racial factor, has not been sufficiently defined. That climate probably exerts some effect is indicated by the results of various comparisons that have been made in different regions of the United States. For example, Tilt[29] found the basal metabolism of young college women in Tallahassee, Florida (Lat. 30°), to be about 10 per cent below that of a similar group in Chicago, Illinois (Lat. 42°).[30] Essentially the same result was obtained by Coons[31] in her study of a group of college girls in Stillwater, Oklahoma (Lat. 36°). However, a survey of the habitual food intake of her subjects has convinced her that it is less than that of women in other sections of the United States and that this probably has an important bearing on their low basal metabolic rates.

Low values for white inhabitants of the Tropics have been reported

[28] *Am. J. Physiol.*, **86**, 43 (1928).

[29] *J. Biol. Chem.*, **86**, 635 (1930).

[30] K. Blunt, J. Tilt, L. McLaughlin, and K. B. Gunn, *ibid.*, **67**, 491 (1926).

[31] *Am. J. Physiol.*, **98**, 692, 698 (1931); C. M. Coons and A. T. Schiefelbusch, *J. Nutrition*, **5**, 459 (1932).

by de Almeida[32] (Brazil), Sundstroem[33] (North Queensland, Australia), and others.

In the study of regional variation of basal metabolism, the racial factor has received most of the attention. Unfortunately many of the data that have been reported have been either unsubstantiated, or the subject of controversy. Nevertheless certain significant facts have been determined. Thus MacLeod, Crofts, and Benedict[34] found the metabolism of Oriental female students (7 Chinese and 2 Japanese) attending American colleges to be on the average 10 per cent below the standard for American women of the same age, despite the fact that all were living essentially under the same conditions. Necheles[35] found the basal metabolism of adult Chinese (20 to 30 years) to be equal to, or below, the lower limit of Westerners. In younger individuals (below 20 years) the metabolism was relatively higher than that of adult Chinese, perhaps even higher than that of Western youths. The lower metabolic rate generally observed in Orientals, Necheles has attributed to a greater degree of constant muscular relaxation. He also found that, unlike Caucasians, the Chinese do not show as marked a drop in basal metabolism during sleep, from which he has assumed that the average Chinese is nearly as relaxed when awake as when asleep.

Low metabolic rates have also been observed in Filipinos.[36] Contrary to the observations of others, studies on Japanese by Japanese investigators have yielded results which are approximately within the range of variation for Europeans and Americans.[37]

A series of investigations conducted by Benedict and associates[38] has shown that the male Mayas of Yucatan have a high basal metabolic rate, average about 6.5 per cent above the normal standard for whites.

Perhaps the highest values (average of 33 per cent above normal) have been reported for Eskimos living in the Baffin Bay region (Heinbecker).[39] The lowest appear to be those obtained by Wardlaw and Horsley[40] on full-blooded Australian aborigines (average of −30.7

[32] J. physiol. path. gén., **32**, 12 (1924).
[33] Physiol. Rev., **7**, 320 (1927).
[34] Am. J. Physiol., **73**, 449 (1925); Proc. Nat. Acad. Sci., **11**, 342 (1926).
[35] Chinese J. Physiol., **6**, 153, 201 (1932); Am. J. Physiol., **91**, 661 (1930).
[36] M. Ocampo, N. Cordero, and I. Concepcion, J. Nutrition, **3**, 237 (1930–31).
[37] S. Okada and associates, Arch. Internal Med., **38**, 590 (1926); also Takahira, cited by Du Bois.[16]
[38] G. D. Williams and F. G. Benedict, Am. J. Physiol., **85**, 634 (1928); G. C. Shattuck and F. G. Benedict, **96**, 518 (1931); M. Steggerda and Benedict, **100**, 274 (1932).
[39] J. Biol. Chem., **80**, 461 (1928).
[40] Australian J. Exp. Biol. Med. Sci., **5**, 263 (1928).

below the Aub-Dubois standard). That the factor of climate is only partly responsible is indicated by the fact that the white Australian in the same region has a basal metabolism which is only about 10 per cent below the normal standard.

Of interest too are the observations of Turner[41] on the basal metabolism of women in the Near East. In certain racial groups, such as the Armenians, the metabolism was found to be within the normal range of variation for Westerners. Typical Syrian women, however, were found to have a low metabolism (-12.1 per cent as compared with an average value of -7.1 per cent obtained in a small group of European and American women living in Syria who served as controls). The native well-to-do Syrian women habitually lead an inactive physical life. Four of the women were apparently not pure Syrian Arabs, being light-haired and blue-eyed, traits which are presumably an inheritance from the days of the Crusaders. These women manifested a basal metabolism which deviated little from the normal. A somewhat similar illustration of the possible effect of racial admixture on basal metabolism is given by Wardlaw and Horsley, who state that the offspring of Australian aborigines, crossed with the white stock, have approximately the same metabolism which characterizes the white inhabitants of the district.

Very low values have also been reported for female Tamils and Malayalis, natives of South India.[42]

It is therefore evident that race is probably a specific factor, but that other influences are superimposed on this is also apparent. Thus, the high metabolism of Eskimos is not only a racial characteristic, but may be related to climatic conditions and the mode of life—strenuous physical activity, a high meat diet, good physical development, etc. On the contrary, the low metabolism of the Australian aborigines may be associated with the warm climate, their lethargic habit of life, poor physical development, accompanying a chronic state of undernutrition.

The factor of diet is probably significant, although on this point also unequivocal data are lacking. Prolonged vegetarianism (five years, or longer) has been associated with a low basal metabolic rate by Wakeham and Hansen.[43] McClellan and associates[44] have studied the effect of an exclusive meat diet in two individuals. During the first few weeks a definite increase in metabolism was noted, but at the

[41] *J. Am. Med. Assoc.*, **87**, 2052 (1926); E. L. Turner and E. Aboushadid, *Am. J. Physiol.*, **92**, 189 (1930).

[42] E. D. Mason and F. G. Benedict, *Indian J. Med. Research*, **19**, 75 (1931).

[43] *J. Biol. Chem.*, **97**, 155 (1932).

[44] *Ibid.*, **93**, 419 (1931).

end of a year on this diet the metabolism was practically the same
as at the beginning of the experiment.

Mental State. Apprehension, the anticipation of physical pain,
tenseness, or an over-active, talkative, elated mental state tend to accelerated metabolism; neuroses, associated with a depressed mental state,
are often accompanied by a somewhat reduced basal metabolism.

Starvation. Turning to the abnormal variations of the basal metabolic rate, we may consider first the effect of undernutrition and starvation. In a celebrated experiment, Benedict[45] studied the changes in
basal metabolism of a man subjected to a fast of 31 days. At the
beginning of the experiment the subject weighed 60.64 kg.; on the
thirty-first day the weight was 47.39 kg. On the first day of the fast
the heat output was 904 calories per square meter of body surface. By
the twenty-first day this had diminished to 664 calories. Then followed
an increase to 737 calories on the last day of the experiment.

Horst, Mendel, and Benedict[46] have made a study of the metabolism
of albino rats during prolonged fasting at two different environmental
temperatures, namely 16° and 26° C. At the beginning of the fast, the
average weight was 222 grams. The total metabolism of the individual
rats kept at 16° was distinctly higher (about 80 per cent) than that of
the animals kept at 26°, and while in the former group there was little
change in metabolism (per square meter per 24 hours), in the latter
group an average decline of 36 per cent was recorded on the seventh
day. As this fact would suggest, the loss in weight was therefore more
rapid in the group kept at the lower temperature. The animals fasting
at 26° survived on an average 16.5 days and lost 49 per cent of their
initial body weight, while the animals kept at 16° lost nearly as much
weight (44 per cent) within a period of 11 days, this being the average
survival time in this group. The respiratory quotient, within a few
hours after feeding, varied from 0.8 to 0.89. Determinations made
after a fasting interval of 20 hours yielded values that were in no instance
above 0.75 and usually below this point, indicating that the glycogen
reserves were almost completely withdrawn at this time, an observation agreeing with one previously reported by Cori and Cori.[47]

The effect of undernutrition has been studied in individuals who,
voluntarily or otherwise, were victims of chronic inanition.[48] During

[45] Carnegie Inst. Pub., No. 203, 1915; *Am. J. Physiol.*, **41**, 292 (1916).

[46] *J. Nutrition*, **3**, 177 (1930–31); see also Benedict, Horst, and Mendel, *ibid.*, **5**, 581 (1932).

[47] *J. Biol. Chem.*, **70**, 557 (1926).

[48] The subject of fasting and undernutrition is discussed in a book of that name by S. Morgulis, Dutton & Co., New York, 1923.

the period of the Great War, Zuntz and Loewy[49] followed their own basal metabolism and observed reductions of 15 and 12 per cent, respectively. Benedict[50] placed a squad of athletic men, who had been accustomed to a daily caloric intake of 3200–3600 calories, on a diet containing 1400 calories for a period of three weeks. As a result, the men lost, on an average, 12 per cent of their weight. The basal metabolism was reduced 18 per cent. After this the men were able to maintain themselves, without further loss of weight, on 1950 calories, although on this reduced intake they were not as active or energetic as previously, nor were they able to withstand the cold as well. Clearly, undernourishment and starvation are effective in lowering basal metabolism.

Influence of Disease. An increase of 1 degree Centigrade in the body temperature causes a rise in metabolism of about 13 per cent. Thus, in typhoid fever there may be an increased heat production of as much as 40 or 50 per cent above the normal level. Similar changes are observed in pneumonia and malaria, but not in tuberculosis, where alterations in metabolism with changes in body temperature are not so marked. It is believed that the toxic destruction of protein, which is characteristic of certain febrile conditions, is responsible for the increased metabolism. It is not definitely known whether the rise in temperature in fever is the cause or the result of increased catabolism.

The determination of basal metabolism has found wide application in the study of pathological conditions, particularly those associated with the thyroid gland. Boothby and Sandiford[51] have summarized their observations on 1689 patients with thyroid disorders, and find that 92 per cent of their cases of exophthalmic goiter show a basal metabolism which is 20 per cent or more above normal. Fifty-two per cent of their 452 cases of exophthalmic goiter show a basal metabolism of 50 per cent and more above normal. On the other hand, the basal metabolic rate of 83 per cent of their myxedema cases are subnormal by 20 per cent or more, the remaining 17 per cent being 11 to 15 per cent below normal.[52] Following operative treatment in cases of hyperthyroidism, the basal metabolic rate tends to approach normal levels. In myxedema, the administration of thyroxin is followed by an increase in metabolism.

[49] *Biochem. Z.*, **90**, 244 (1918).

[50] Benedict, Miles, Roth, and Smith, Carnegie Inst. Pub., No. 280 (1919).

[51] *Physiol. Rev.*, **4**, 69 (1924).

[52] These calculations are based on the Du Bois normal standards. Thus, if the normal basal metabolism of a woman for a given age is 37 calories per square meter per hour, and the actual metabolism is 44.4 calories, the metabolism is 44.4 − 37 = 7.4; 7.4/37 × 100 = + 20 per cent.

Boothby and Sandiford have likewise summarized their results on 1642 individuals with different diseases other than those of the thyroid gland. These show that 89 per cent are within 15 per cent of the Du Bois normal standards. Of the pathological conditions listed in this group, leukemia shows the only marked variations from the normal. Of 15 cases of lymphatic and myelogenous leukemia cited, 10 have a basal metabolism which is 20 per cent or more above normal.

Subnormal metabolism is indicated in many of the cases diagnosed as hypopituitarism. On the experimental side, Benedict and Homans[53] have shown a decrease in the basal metabolism of dogs following hypophysectomy. Low metabolic rates are also frequent in obesity, whether due to castration, to hypopituitarism, or to some other cause.[54] A large proportion of obese individuals, however, maintain a normal energy exchange on the basis of their surface area and hence an increased heat production, when computed on the basis of what should be their proper weight.[55]

Returning to derangements of the thyroid, Talbot[56] observed a minus 20 per cent metabolism in a $3\frac{2}{3}$-year-old cretin. In a 36-year-old cretin, Du Bois[57] found the basal metabolism to be low by 18 to 25 per cent. A metabolism of minus 48 per cent was observed in a case of cretinism studied by Janet,[58] and similar values are occasionally encountered in cases of severe myxedema. The administration of thyroid extract or thyroxin in these conditions causes a rise in metabolism, whereas discontinuance of the treatment is followed by a marked fall of the basal metabolic rate.

Regulation of Body Temperature. Animals may be divided into two groups according to their ability to maintain a constant body temperature. The temperature of cold-blooded animals varies with the environment, and they are therefore called heterothermic or poikilothermic. Reptiles, batrachians, fish, molluscs, and insects belong to this group. At low temperatures (1–20° C.), these animals are usually warmer than their environment by about 1° C. (Burns[59]). When the temperature of the environment of a frog is increased to about 40° C., its own temperature remains somewhat lower.

[53] J. Med. Research, **25**, 409 (1912).
[54] Consult Lusk, "Science of Nutrition."
[55] J. M. Strang and F. A. Evans, J. Clin. Investigation, **6**, 277 (1928–29); see also D. M. Lyon, D. M. Dunlop, and C. P. Stewart, Biochem. J., **26**, 1107 (1932).
[56] Am. J. Diseases Children, **12**, 145 (1916).
[57] J. Am. Med. Assoc., **63**, 827 (1914).
[58] J. méd. français, **12**, 1, No. 6 (1923); cited by Talbot.
[59] D. Burns, "An Introduction to Biophysics," London, 1921, Chap. XXXI.

Birds and mammals belong to the group of homoiothermic animals, which are able to resist environmental temperature changes. It is not to be supposed, however, that the mechanism for the maintenance of body temperature in these animals is never broken down. Reference has already been made to the body-temperature changes which occur during fever. During hibernation, the homoiothermic animal is essentially heterothermic. Curare produces a similar effect. This drug inhibits the transmission of motor impulses to voluntary muscles and causes, in addition, the breakdown of the temperature-regulating mechanism (Roehrig and Zuntz[60]). Its administration is also followed, at ordinary temperatures, by a marked diminution in metabolism. It is a matter of general knowledge that the regulation of body temperature is deficient in infants as well as in other new-born warm-blooded animals. These are usually unable to withstand long exposure to temperatures below 20° C.

The temperature of birds varies with the size and is usually between 40° and 43° C. Small mammals have a higher body temperature (39°–40° C.) than larger mammals. In man, the temperature is normally about 37.5° C., but may fall somewhat below 37° during sleep.

Loss of Heat from the Body. Heat is lost from the body through the following channels:

1. Conduction and convection.
2. In warming the inspired air (conduction).
3. In warming the ingested food.
4. In excreta (CO_2, urine and feces are warm).
5. Radiation.
6. Evaporation of water from lungs and skin.

Among the factors that influence the dissipation of heat from the body are the area and moistness of the surface, time of exposure, temperature gradient between the surface and outside atmosphere, humidity of the atmosphere, and the force of the wind, if any. The loss of heat by radiation is affected by the color of the surface. A black surface has a higher absorptive and emissive power than a white surface. Accordingly, there should be a greater amount of heat lost by radiation from the body of a negro than from that of a white person. On the whole, however, the loss of heat by radiation is comparatively small. In the following table (taken from Burns[61]) is given a rough estimate

[60] *Arch. ges. Physiol.*, **4**, 57 (1871).

[61] For further discussion of the factors, consult Burns' "An Introduction to Biophysics," Churchill, London, 1921 edition, p. 348; see also Lusk's "Science of Nutrition," Chap. IV.

of the amount of heat lost per day through the more important channels:

TABLE LVI
Loss of Heat from the Body

	Per Cent	Calories per Day
1. Radiation and conduction...................	73.0	1792
2. Evaporation:		
(a) Lungs, etc............................	7.2	182
(b) Skin.................................	14.5	364
3. Excreta:		
(a) CO_2................................	3.5	84
(b) Urine and feces......................	1.8	48
Total heat loss per day.....................	....	2470

Having considered the way in which the accumulation of heat is prevented, we may now turn our attention to the factors which prevent the excessive loss of heat from the body when the temperature of the environment is reduced. These are usually discussed under two heads, namely:

1. Physical regulation.
2. Chemical regulation.

Regulation of the temperature by physical forces is believed to predominate above 20° C. Below this temperature, chemical regulation enters into play to a greater degree than physical regulation.

Physical Regulation. Man adjusts the temperature of his environment by living in houses, by heating his dwelling during the winter, and by wearing clothes. Animals, likewise, provide themselves with shelter and have fur and feathers to enable them to diminish the loss of heat by conduction. The thickness of the skin and the amount of subcutaneous fat are additional factors which reduce loss of heat from the body. It is well known that lean people suffer more from cold and less from heat than obese individuals.

Heat and cold exert an important effect on the cutaneous nerve endings, causing a reflex vasomotor stimulation. When the temperature is high, the blood vessels of the skin and respiratory passages become dilated; there is an increased flow of blood to these areas, and hence a greater effective cooling surface, together with increased evaporation of water from sweat glands and mucous surfaces. On the other hand, cold, by causing vaso-constriction, decreases the flow of blood to the skin and respiratory surfaces and therefore diminishes the cooling area as well as the amount of perspiration.

In sleeping, an animal will curl up when it is cold and stretch out when hot, thereby diminishing or increasing the area of the exposed surface.

Chemical Regulation. The increased heat production incident to exposure to cold is referred to as the heat of chemical regulation. Opinion is divided as to its cause. Voit[62] suggested the view that exposure of the skin to cold brought about a reflex stimulation of metabolism in muscle cells without necessarily causing muscular activity such as shivering. From the work of Loewy,[63] Johansson,[64] Lusk,[65] Swift,[66] and others, however, it appears that the increased heat output is to be attributed to involuntary muscular activity. Shivering in man begins when the skin attains a temperature of approximately 19° C. (Swift). During the period of shivering which follows immersion in a cold bath, the heat production may increase to 180 per cent above the normal (Lusk). In the series of observations by Swift on human subjects in a basal condition, exposed to an environmental temperature of about 2° C., the metabolism was found to increase as much as 400 per cent during the period of intense shivering. The energy required for involuntary muscular activity is derived from the metabolism in the tissues. It is well known that exposure to cold is an effective method of depleting the glycogen supply of the body, but that this is not necessarily due to the preferential oxidation of carbohydrate has been suggested by Swift. The probable importance of fat, as well as carbohydrate, is indicated by two results: (1) there is no change in the protein metabolism corresponding to the increase in energy metabolism; (2) the reaction to cold in a general way varies inversely as the amount of subcutaneous fat.

Shivering may be avoided, however, by voluntary muscular exercise, for in either case the effect on combustion in the tissues is the same. When the difference in temperature between the body and the surrounding medium becomes so great that the dissipation of heat from the former is markedly increased, the " fires of metabolism " are caused to burn more briskly in order to make up for this loss. The chemical regulation of body temperature is thus essentially the result of increased metabolism.

[62] *Z. Biol.*, **14**, 80 (1878).
[63] *Arch. ges. Physiol.*, **46**, 189 (1890).
[64] *Skand. Arch. Physiol.*, **7**, 123 (1896); cited by Krogh.
[65] *Am. J. Physiol.*, **27**, 427 (1910).
[66] *J. Nutrition*, **5**, 213, 227 (1932).

Influence of Food on Metabolism; Specific Dynamic Action. For a variable period (usually 12 to 18 hours) after the ingestion of food, the calorific output is greater than that determined under basal conditions. To illustrate what is meant, let us suppose that the basal metabolism of a given individual is found to be 1800 calories per day. If exactly 1800 calories were now supplied to this individual in the form of a mixed diet, over a period of 24 hours, his heat production for that period would be, not 1800 calories, but more nearly 2000 calories. The problem we have to consider is the cause of this increased heat production.

It is conceivable that the processes of digestion and absorption may constitute a factor; but when this supposition is subjected to experimental study, it is found that the energy requirement due to increased activity of the muscles and glands of the alimentary tract accounts for but a fraction of the increased heat production. Meat extract, though stimulating the digestive glands to secretion, nevertheless produces no appreciable effect on metabolism; nor does the presence of agar in the alimentary canal influence the rate of metabolism, although it probably increases the muscular activity of the intestinal wall. Moreover, it has been shown that the intravenous injection of glucose and amino acids leads to an increase in metabolism which is almost comparable to that observed following the administration of these substances by mouth (Benedict and Carpenter.[67])

The effect of foods in stimulating metabolism is called the *specific dynamic action*. In the study of this phenomenon, Rubner[68] was the pioneer. Among other discoveries, he made the important observation that the heat due to specific dynamic action can be used by the animal organism in the regulation of body temperature. Our knowledge of the effect of foodstuffs in stimulating metabolism has been greatly extended by the work of Lusk and his students in this country. The effect is not the same for all foods. Williams, Riche, and Lusk[69] showed an increase of 30 calories in heat production for every 100 calories contained in the protein of 1220 grams of meat given to a dog. Numerous similar observations place the value for the specific dynamic action of protein at about 30 per cent, and this is approximately the same whether food protein or body protein is being metabolized. In the case of fat, Rubner thought it to be about 12 per cent; and of carbo-

[67] Carnegie Inst. Wash., Pub. No. 261, 1918.

[68] M. Rubner, "Die Gesetze des Energieverbrauchs bei der Ernährung," Leipzig, 1902.

[69] *J. Biol. Chem.*, **12**, 371 (1912); cited by Lusk, "Science of Nutrition," 1928 edition, p. 283.

hydrate, 5 to 6 per cent. The value for fat has been revised, however, to approximately 4 per cent by Murlin and Lusk.[70]

From the standpoint of nutrition, the significance of specific dynamic action is of considerable importance. Let us imagine a hypothetical organism which has a basal metabolism of 100 calories. Suppose that this animal were given exactly 100 calories in the form of protein. As a result, the actual heat production would be about 130 calories. The 30 additional calories must obviously come from the combustion of the organism's own tissues. If this process were continued, the organism would eventually diminish in size until its basal metabolism, plus the specific dynamic action, would be 100 calories. From that point on, it would remain in caloric equilibrium. But, if we persisted in giving the animal its basal requirements from day to day, it would ultimately die. The same would be true if carbohydrate were given, except that the initial 100 calories given in the form of carbohydrate would result in the production of 106 calories, the extra 6 calories representing the specific dynamic effect of the carbohydrate. If 100 calories were given in the form of fat, it would stimulate sufficient additional metabolism to yield 4 more calories. In arranging a dietary, about 15 per cent should therefore be added to the basal caloric requirement to allow for the specific dynamic action (or S. D. A.) of the foodstuffs.

As to the fundamental cause of this phenomenon, there is much uncertainty. In attempting to elucidate the significance of the specific dynamic action of foodstuffs, attention has been directed particularly toward the behavior of the amino acids. Long ago Lusk[71] showed that both glycine and alanine exert a very marked effect, whereas some other amino acids do not. Phenylalanine has a greater specific dynamic action than any other amino acid (Rapport and Beard[72]). The products of the intermediary metabolism of amino acids do not exhibit this effect, nor is there, according to many observers, an obvious relationship between the specific dynamic action and the rate or extent of deamination.

Seth and Luck[73] studied the effect of administering various amino acids on the amino-nitrogen concentration of the blood, and reached the conclusion that the specific dynamic action of an amino acid is proportional to its power of increasing the amino nitrogen content of the

[70] *Ibid.*, **22**, 15 (1915).

[71] Lusk, *J. Biol. Chem.* **12**, 349 (1912); **20**, viii (1915); Atkinson and Lusk, **36**, 415 (1918); Lusk, **49**, 453 (1921); also Lusk "Science of Nutrition," 4th edition, Chap. XII.

[72] *J. Biol. Chem.*, **73**, 299 (1927).

[73] *Biochem. J.*, **19**, 366 (1925).

blood. This may be accepted as evidence in support of the idea that the velocity of oxidative reactions in the tissues is modified by the concentration of the metabolites, as would be expected from the law of mass action.

Rapport and Katz[74] have shown that when glycine is added to perfused muscle, the oxygen absorption is 40 per cent higher than otherwise, indicating that the presence of the amino acid stimulates the combustion of other tissue constituents. According to Rapport and Beard, the specific dynamic action of meat and gelatin may be accounted for by the summated effect of five of their amino acids, namely glycine, alanine, leucine, phenylalanine, and tyrosine.

Wilhelmj and Bollman[75] observed that the injection of alanine, glycine, or phenylalanine causes an immediate rise in heat production, which usually reaches its height during the injection, and with glycine and alanine the return to the basal value may take from $4\frac{1}{2}$ to 9 hours. Accompanying the increased heat production there is a definite elevation of the respiratory quotient, indicating the probable utilization of carbohydrate in the process. Of particular significance is the observation of Wilhelmj, Bollman, and Mann[76] that, in hepatectomized dogs, injected amino acids do not exert any specific dynamic action, indicating that this phenomenon may be associated with the metabolism of the amino acids in the liver and not, as suggested by Rapport and Katz, with a general stimulation of the cells of the body.

In brief, the Lusk school, as well as other workers, such as Aubel,[77] have attempted to relate the specific dynamic action of proteins and amino acids to the conversion of the deaminized residues of the amino acids into glucose or glycogen. Thus, in the case of alanine, the probable pathway of its transformation has been represented as follows:

$$2C_3H_5NH_2O_2 + O_2 = 2C_3H_4O_2 + 2NH_3$$

$$2 \times 388 \text{ cal.} = 2 \times 274.5 \text{ cal.} + 2 \times 91.6 \text{ cal.} + 44 \text{ cal.}$$
$$\text{Alanine} \qquad\qquad \text{Pyruvic acid} \qquad\qquad \text{Ammonia}$$

$$2C_3H_4O_2 + 2H_2 \qquad C_6H_{12}O_6$$

$$2 \times 274.5 \text{ cal.} + 132 \text{ cal.} = 681 \text{ cal.}$$
$$\text{Pyruvic acid} \qquad \text{Ammonia} \qquad \text{Glycogen hydrate}$$

From this it is seen that the conversion of 2 gram-molecules of alanine to pyruvic acid requires 44 calories, and to convert the latter to glycogen an additional 132 calories; in all, therefore, 176 calories. Inasmuch as the physiological heat value of the alanine deprived of the

[74] Am. J. Physiol., **80**, 185 (1927).   [76] Am. J. Physiol., **87**, 497 (1928).
[75] J. Biol. Chem., **77**, 127, (1928).   [77] Biochem Z., **225**, 81 (1930).

ammonia is $776 - 183 = 593$ calories and it requires 176 calories to transform it to glycogen, it follows that the extra energy expenditure involved is about 30 per cent. Actually, the administration of alanine to a dog results in a specific dynamic effect of about 50 per cent.

A brief consideration of the problem on thermodynamic grounds by Adams[78] has led him to conclusions that are essentially not at variance with Lusk's conception.[79]

However, Borsook and Winegarden[80] have examined the data of a representative series of investigations of the subject, including the contributions of Lusk and his pupils, and have pointed out that the course of the specific dynamic action of protein and amino acids parallels the course of nitrogen excretion. On the basis of their study of the energy cost of urine excretion (p. 448) they maintain that 25 to 60 per cent of the values of the specific dynamic action is due to the work imposed upon the kidney, the remainder being due to other causes, presumably the extra metabolism, other than excretion, of the nitrogen and carbon.

Influence of Work on Metabolism. Work is accomplished by the body at the expense of increased metabolism, whether food is eaten or not. In a series of experiments, Rubner[81] was able to show that heat production incident to mechanical work is independent of the heat produced because of specific dynamic action, especially in the case of protein food. This is indicated by the data in Table LVII.

TABLE LVII

INFLUENCE OF DIET AND MECHANICAL WORK ON METABOLISM

Diet and Conditions	Calories Produced		
	24 Hours, Calories	Increase, Per Cent	Increase Due to Work, Calories
No food, rest..........................	1976		
Cane sugar 600 g. + rest..............	2023	2.4	
Same + work (100,000 kg-meters)......	2868	45.2	845
Protein (meat) + rest.................	2515	27.2	
Protein + work (100,000 kg-meters)....	3370	70.5	855

[78] *J. Biol. Chem.*, **67**, Proc. xxi (1926).

[79] Lusk has summarized his point of view in the following reviews: *J. Nutrition*, **3**, 519 (1930–31); *Ergebnisse Physiol.*, **33**, 103 (1931).

[80] *Proc. Nat. Acad. Sci.*, **17**, 75 (1931); **17**, 13 (1931).

[81] *Sitzber. preuss. Akad. Wiss.*, **16**, 316 (1910); cited by Lusk, p. 409.

However, Rapport[82] has presented evidence that the specific dynamic action of fat, as well as of glucose, is abolished during muscular exercise; in short, that the extra energy which at rest appears as waste heat is utilized as free energy in muscular work. In experiments with protein, the specific dynamic effect was not abolished. Nevertheless these observations, if confirmed, constitute a distinct departure from Rubner's fundamental concept.

Although, fundamentally, there is little similarity between the animal body and the steam or gasoline engine, it is nevertheless of interest to compare the efficiency of external muscular work with the thermal efficiencies of mechanical devices. The efficiency of the steam engine is 8–10 per cent. The usual type of gasoline motors have an efficiency of about 20 per cent; i.e., of every 100 gallons of gasoline which are burned to completion, about 20 are converted into mechanical energy. It has been estimated that the efficiency of the human body is between 25 and 33 per cent. In this regard, it is excelled only by special types of engines, such as the Still-Diesel combination which is said to have an efficiency of about 44 per cent.[83]

Training is apparently a factor determining the amount of energy required in the performance of a given task. An individual unaccustomed to a certain type of muscular exertion, such as mountain climbing, uses proportionately more energy than one who has been trained for this work. It has also been determined that the speed with which muscular work is done influences the degree of energy expenditure. Less energy is used in covering a given distance by slow walking than in covering it by fast walking or running.

Provided an adequate amount of fat and carbohydrate is available, muscular exercise does not influence materially the amount of protein metabolism. In fact, in the well-nourished individual, violent exertion is associated with a high respiratory quotient without marked alteration in nitrogen excretion, showing that carbohydrate is the chief fuel under these circumstances.[84, 85]

Heat produced in doing mechanical work can take the place of heat of chemical regulation. In other words, there is not a summation of these factors when an individual performing muscular exercise is exposed to cold.

[82] *Am. J. Physiol.*, **91**, 238 (1929–30).
[83] In this connection the reader is referred to an article by W. O. Fenn, *ibid.*, **92**, 583 (1930).
[84] Compare with D. Rapport and A. Canzanelli, *ibid.*, **101**, 85 (1932).
[85] In this connection the student is referred to a review "The Fuel of Muscular Activity of Man," by T. M. Carpenter, *J. Nutrition*, **4**, 281 (1931).

Caloric Requirements. Rubner developed the conception that, under certain conditions, the foodstuffs may replace one another in accordance with their heat-producing value. This is known as the *isodynamic law.* According to this view, 100 grams of fat, 232 grams of starch, and 243 grams of protein (as dried meat, etc.) are equally effective in providing the animal body with the energy required for muscular work as well as with heat. Rubner's hypothesis has been questioned by Cathcart,[86] who believes that glucose and fat are not interchangeable in providing energy demands, since carbohydrate is a more effective protein-sparer than fat. Evidence has been presented, likewise, by Krogh,[87] which shows that carbohydrate is superior to other foodstuffs in supplying energy for muscular contraction.[88] Accordingly, the isodynamic law is not to be interpreted too strictly. As pointed out by Cathcart, the calorific value is simply a very convenient physical standard for the assessment of diets; but the mere fact that such a standard has proved of great utilitarian value is not a real justification for adopting this standard as the foundation stone of hypotheses framed to offer an explanation for cellular activity. The calorific value of a given amount of food is therefore not necessarily a criterion of its nutritional or tissue-sparing effect. With this in mind, we may continue our discussion of the caloric requirements of the animal body.

The caloric needs of man and animals are determined by the total heat production due to the various factors which have been discussed in the preceding paragraphs. When the caloric intake is equivalent to the output, the condition of calorific balance or equilibrium is said to exist. This is the normal state in the adult individual; but in the growing animal the intake should exceed the outgo. The energy of maintenance, including that of the vital functions (circulation, respiration, secretion, excretion, maintenance of muscle tone, etc.), is represented by the basal heat production. The basal metabolism of an adult, weighing 70 kg., is approximately 1750 calories for 24 hours. The heat production is increased above the basal level even by slight activity, such as sitting or standing. Depending on the character of the diet, allowance should be made for the specific dynamic action of the food ingested. An allowance of 10–12 per cent above the basal metabolic requirement is ordinarily sufficient when the individual is maintained on a mixed diet.

[86] *Biochem. J.*, **16**, 747 (1922).

[87] *J. Physiol.*, **52**, p. lxxiv (1919).

[88] The energy transformations which occur in muscle have been discussed elsewhere (pp. 430, 471). A good summary of the subject is to be found in D. M. Needham's monograph "The Biochemistry of Muscle," Methuen, London, 1932.

The most variable factor to be reckoned with is the food required for the performance of physical work. The relation of occupation to energy requirement has been the subject of numerous investigations both in this country and abroad. Individuals engaged in sedentary occupations have a total daily metabolism of 2500–2800 calories. These figures allow 550–900 calories for the performance of mechanical work (walking to and from work, etc.).

In Finland, Becker and Hämäläinen[89] made a study of the energy requirements of men and women engaged in various occupations. A portion of their results is summarized in Table LVIII.

The food consumption of the average American farmer is about 3500–4000 calories. Lusk states that a bicyclist riding for 16 hours may have a metabolism amounting to 9000 calories daily. The food ration of a Maine lumberman may rise to 7000 and even 8000 calories per day.[90]

TABLE LVIII

Sex	Occupation	Calorific Requirement for 24 Hours
Men	Tailors (2)...................................	2400 to 2500
	Bookbinder.................................	2700
	Shoemaker.................................	2800
	Metal workers (2)...........................	3100 and 3200
	Painters (2)................................	3200 and 3300
	Carpenters (2)..............................	3200 and 3300
	Stonemasons (2)............................	4300 and 4700
	Men sawing wood (2).......................	5000 and 5400
Women	Seamstress (needle).........................	1800
	Seamstress (machine).......................	1900 and 2100
	Household servants.........................	2300 to 2900
	Washerwomen (2)...........................	2600 and 3400

Thus far, we have not considered the allowance to be made for " chemical regulation." This factor would become operative only when an individual doing little or no work is exposed to extreme

[89] *Skand. Arch. Physiol.*, **31**, 198 (1914).

[90] For a review of the food requirements of soldiers, see Lusk, "Science of Nutrition," 4th edition, pp. 469–473.

A critical discussion entitled "Some of the Difficulties in the Quantitative Assessment of Human Diets," by E. P. Cathcart, *Nutr. Abst. Rev.*, **1**, 6 (1931–32), will be found instructive.

cold, a combination of circumstances not ordinarily met with. In considering the quantitative relation between work and total metabolism, it is important to bear in mind the interplay of all the factors. The heat due to mechanical work can replace the heat of chemical regulation. Demands for chemical regulation of body temperature may be met, likewise, by the specific dynamic action of foodstuffs. Accordingly, protein would be more effective in this regard than carbohydrate. On the other hand, it is problematical whether the energy of specific dynamic action of foodstuffs can be converted into muscular work.

It is a mistaken idea that a child is a fraction of an adult as far as its food requirements are concerned. There are three points to be considered in this connection, namely, the relatively high basal metabolic rate during childhood, the unusual physical activity of boys and girls, and the necessity of maintaining the caloric intake well above the expenditure in order to allow for growth. Between the ages of 1 and 2 years, infants require approximately 1000–1200 calories per day. It has been estimated that between the ages of 10 and 13 years, the requirements of a boy are 2300–3000 calories, and even more in the case of a very active child. This explains the apparent voraciousness of boys and girls, particularly the former. That there is actually a physiological need for large quantities of food is shown in the work of several authorities,[91] all of whom recommend a most liberal food allowance for the growing child.

[91] The problem of energy requirements of children is discussed in the contribution of F. G. Benedict and Talbot (Carnegie Inst. of Washington, Publication No. 302 (1921), as well as in the monograph of Mendel, "Nutrition—The Chemistry of Life," Yale University Press, 1923). A valuable summary is also to be found in the "Report of the Committee on Growth and Development, White House Conference on Child Health and Protection," Part III, Nutrition, Century Co., New York, 1932, pages 334–424.

CHAPTER XVII

NUTRITION

Sir Michael Foster likened the growth of knowledge to the ascent of a spiral stair from which the observer periodically surveys the same landscape, but each time from a higher level than the last.—JOSEPH BARCROFT.

The chemistry of nutrition is conventionally treated from the standpoints of (*a*) caloric, (*b*) mineral, (*c*) protein, and (*d*) vitamin requirements. These are generally regarded as the most important factors to be considered. There is, however, some evidence that although the body is capable of synthesizing fat from carbohydrate and indirectly from protein, nevertheless, a certain amount of it, present in the food as such, is indispensable to proper nutrition. The water balance of the organism, as has been pointed out in other connections, is another factor to be considered, being of special importance in the young. When deprived of sufficient water, animals develop complete anorexia.[1]

It is only in recent years that scientific research has revealed the intricacies of the problems of nutrition and the relation of certain diseases to specific dietary deficiencies. We have also just come to the realization that human experience and tradition cannot be relied upon invariably as a guide to proper nourishment. In the words of an eminent authority, Sir Frederick Gowland Hopkins:[2]

It is often felt that concerning matters so urgent as its own nutrition, humanity, with all the experience of the ages behind it, can have little to learn from modern science, yet, as in the case of so many other established traditions, an assumption of this kind is wholly unjustified. Tradition accumulates prejudices quite as often as truths, and the former are apt to be more potent in their influence. With sufficient space it would be easy to show that faulty nutrition has played a large part in inhibiting human progress, and even to show that few races have at any time been ideally nourished.

To be adequate, a diet must provide for all the needs of the organism, particularly for maintenance, growth, and reproduction. The

---

[1] F. C. Bing and L. B. Mendel, *Am. J. Physiol.*, **98**, 169 (1931).

[2] *Nutr. Abst. Rev.*, **1**, 3 (1931–32).

minimum requirements for proper nutrition are fulfilled only (a) when the organism is maintained in caloric equilibrium; (b) when it is maintained in nitrogen equilibrium; (c) when there is an adequate supply of inorganic elements; and (d) when there is an adequate supply of vitamins. As can be readily appreciated, the needs of the young and growing animal are far in excess of the minimal requirements.

In addition to these factors, consideration may also be given to certain others which are presumably of secondary importance. There is some reason for believing that variety in the selection of food is beneficial. The Eskimo is limited by his environment to a few staples and subsists in certain localities largely on fish and meat. The everyday food of the Oriental of the poorer classes is rice with variable additions of fish. Europeans and Americans seek a more varied diet. The benefits of this may be purely psychological; but it is reasonable to suppose that the larger the variety of foods, the less would be the likelihood of missing some essential ingredient.[3]

There is also the question of cooking, seasoning, and flavoring. Aside from the effect of cooking in increasing the digestibility of many substances, the beneficial effect of these treatments is due largely to the increased palatability, and, hence, to increased consumption of food. Moreover, seasoning and flavoring materials are not without influence in stimulating the secretion of digestive juices (both chemical and psychic stimulation). Although these substances can hardly be regarded as essential to nutrition, they may nevertheless be included here as constituting a factor of secondary importance. It may also be pointed out, in this connection, that diet is too often a matter of habit. Certain individuals and peoples relish foods that others find distasteful.

Caloric Requirements. A large portion of the preceding chapter was devoted to the energy factor in nutrition. The subject may therefore be dismissed here with a few words. The normal adult requires just sufficient calories to balance the total loss from his body. It is obvious that the manual laborer needs more calories than the individual who is engaged in light work. The caloric demands are also influenced by external temperature and, hence, by climate. When more calories are given off by an individual than are taken in the form of food, he is no longer in a state of caloric equilibrium. Calories are produced, under these circumstances, at the expense of the tissues, and there is a loss of weight. It is important to bear in mind that the growing child should be provided with more food than is sufficient for the mainte-

---

[3] The dietary habits of man in different parts of the world are described by E. V. McCollum and N. Simmonds in "The Newer Knowledge of Nutrition," Macmillan & Co., New York, 4th edition (1929), Chap. XXVII.

nance of the energy balance. The normal state for the growing animal is a condition of positive caloric balance.

Mineral Requirements. The extraordinary influence of the mineral elements of nutrition, though appreciated to some degree for many years, was not clearly understood or quantitatively studied until quite recently. In a long series of experiments which began a little over twenty years ago, originally planned by Babcock and carried out by Hart, McCollum, and Steenbock,[4] the growth and reproduction of cattle upon restricted diets of various grains were studied. These investigators divided their experimental animals into four groups. All the animals received approximately the same amount of sodium chloride. The ration which was fed to one group was derived solely from the wheat plant and consisted of wheat straw, wheat gluten, and the entire wheat grain. The second group received a ration derived from the corn plant. The third group was fed on the products of the oat plant. The fourth group of animals received a ration consisting of a mixture of wheat, corn, and oats in about equal proportions. It was discovered that the nutritive condition of the corn-fed animals was much better than that of any of the remaining groups. The wheat-fed cattle fared worst. The corn-fed animals gave birth to normal young and reared them. The offspring of the wheat-fed cows were not carried to full term, and those that were not born dead usually died several days after birth. The behavior of the animals in the remaining two groups was intermediate between the two extremes observed in the corn-rationed and wheat-rationed groups. The untoward manifestations noted in the wheat-fed animals, as well as in those maintained exclusively on oats, were shown to be due largely to a deficiency in inorganic constituents, chiefly calcium.

Much of the progress attained in the field of nutrition has been made possible by using small animals, particularly albino rats. These reach maturity and begin to breed at about ninety days of age and rarely live to be more than three years old. Thus it is possible to study, in a comparatively short time, the complete life cycle of the animal. The use of synthetic or artificial diets in feeding experiments may likewise be mentioned in this connection. It is possible to maintain rats and other animals in excellent nutritive condition upon a diet consisting of purified protein, fat, carbohydrate, and salts, provided the necessary vitamins are added to the food. These may be derived from yeast, butter, cod-liver oil, and other sources. The value of

---

[4] For details of these studies the student is referred to McCollum and Simmonds, "Newer Knowledge of Nutrition," as well as to Mendel's monograph on nutrition, Chap. II.

employing suitable artificial mixtures in nutrition studies is obvious, for it becomes possible by this method to exclude, at will, more or less completely, one or more ingredients. It then remains only to compare the progress of the experimental animals in respect to growth, reproduction, etc., with control animals maintained on an adequate diet. Osborne and Mendel and their followers have done much to establish the concept, attributed to Liebig, that a deficiency of any factor essential for growth is followed by a failure in growth of the body as a whole, and not by the production of abnormal tissues due to the lack of some element. When the minimum requirements are not met, even with regard to a single constituent, such as a growth-promoting vitamin, an essential amino acid, or an inorganic element like calcium, failure in growth results.

Before considering the specific rôle of individual elements in nutrition, brief reference may be made to the effects resulting from a general mineral-salts impoverishment. It has been shown by Winter, Smith, and Mendel[5] that on diets low with respect to the inorganic constituents, rats cease to grow in weight, but continue to grow in length because of a persistent increment in the length of the long bones. An abnormal increase in the size of the kidney is another conspicuous finding. The increase in the weight of the long bones is largely accounted for by the higher content of organic residue (Smith and Schultz).[6] The spleen tends to diminish in size. The development of polycythemia is very striking and is especially marked when practically all the inorganic constituents are excluded from the diet. The erythrocytes become progressively smaller in size, but contain the normal percentage of hemoglobin; however, the absolute amount in each cell is diminished (Swanson and Smith).[7]

Sodium, Potassium, and Chloride. Osborne and Mendel[8] in an experimental study found the sodium and chloride requirements to be very low. Normal growth occurred in rats on rations containing only 0.04 per cent (per cent of total food), or even less of each of these elements. The growth of the animals was fairly satisfactory on a potassium intake of about 0.03 per cent, provided that the sodium intake was adequate. When both sodium and potassium were reduced in amount, growth ceased. Under these circumstances, the addition of sodium alone, at an early stage of growth, did not result in gain; but when potassium was added, normal growth was resumed. At a later stage in development, Osborne and Mendel found it possible to replace sodium for potassium.

[5] *Am. J. Physiol.*, **80**, 576 (1927).
[6] *Ibid.*, **94**, 107 (1930).
[7] *J. Biol. Chem.*, **98**, 479, 499 (1932).
[8] *Ibid.*, **34**, 131 (1918).

With regard to the potassium requirement, the observations of Miller[9] differ somewhat from the findings of Osborne and Mendel. Miller noted that the growth of rats could be greatly retarded by reducing the potassium content of the ration below a certain level, approximately 0.1 per cent. The minimal requirement, according to this author, is therefore at least three times as much as that given by Osborne and Mendel. Moreover, Miller observed that potassium deficiency during the early development of the organism may not only prevent the growth of the body but also cause abnormal physiological disturbances which make themselves apparent later. In fact, rats deprived of potassium early in life usually die despite an adequate supply of potassium at a later stage (fourth to eleventh week) of development. Miller did not obtain normal growth by substituting sodium for potassium. Nor is it possible to substitute potassium for sodium in a sodium-deficient diet (St. John).[10]

According to Mitchell and Carman[11] the lack of sodium and chlorine limits the food value of rations composed largely of corn. Miller,[12] on the other hand, found corn rations to contain sufficient chlorine for growth and maintenance.

An oft-repeated observation, first made by Bunge,[13] is that the administration of potassium increases the excretion of sodium and chlorine in the urine. According to Whelan,[14] the increased elimination of these elements may be due to the diuretic effect of potassium. It has been supposed that the tissues retain potassium at the expense of sodium and other elements because of its relatively greater physiological importance (regulatory effect upon the heart, muscular contraction, presence in red corpuscles, etc.). However, in view of observations of Miller,[15] it is probably incorrect to assume that a high level of potassium intake continues indefinitely to modify the excretion of other elements which may be needed for normal physiological development. In Miller's experiments, the introduction of potassium salts into the diet caused an immediate increase in the total output of sodium and chlorine, after which the loss of these elements in the urine was only slightly greater than on a basal ration. As to calcium and phosphorus, the levels of excretion on a high-potassium intake were but slightly increased over the low-potassium period.

[9] J. Biol. Chem., **55**, 61 (1923); **62**, 259 (1924); **70**, 587 (1926).
[10] J. Agr. Res., **37**, 55 (1928).
[11] J. Biol. Chem., **68**, 165 (1926).
[12] Ibid., **70**, 759 (1926).
[13] Z. Biol., **9**, 104 (1873).
[14] J. Biol. Chem., **63**, 585 (1925).
[15] Ibid., **55**, 45 (1923); **67**, 71 (1926); **70**, 593 (1926).

From the standpoint of adequacy in nutrition, no difficulties present themselves in the selection of diets containing sufficient amounts of sodium, chlorine, and potassium. The last is especially abundant in both plant and animal tissues, and the quantities derived from these sources are far in excess of the normal requirements for proper nutrition. Sodium and chlorine are likewise widely distributed in nature. An adequate supply of these elements, particularly in the nutrition of man, is not difficult to secure, since the quantities of common salt used in seasoning are greater than the natural requirements. In herbivorous animals, however, particularly during lactation, there is occasional evidence of salt deficiency. It is well known that buffalo and deer frequently travel long distances and brave many dangers in search of rock-salt deposits, or salt licks. Observations reported by Babcock[16] have proved that the milk of cows deprived of salt may become very low with respect to the sodium chloride content and that continued deprivation may result even in the death of these animals. The practice of supplying common salt to cattle therefore has a scientific basis.

Calcium Requirement. In a study of a large number of American dietaries, Sherman[17] was led to the conclusion that the intake of calcium in this country is frequently below the level of requirement and that the adequate supply of this element in a "mixed diet" constitutes a real problem in human as well as in animal nutrition. From a study of calcium excretion in adults, Sherman has determined that the minimum requirement of calcium is, on an average, about 0.45 g. per day (equivalent to 0.63 g. when expressed in terms of CaO). If a margin of safety of 50 per cent is allowed—a practice which has been found valuable in computing the needs for protein and other essential components of the diet—the so-called "standard requirement" of a normal adult of about 70-kg. weight would be 0.68 g. per day. The data given by Sherman show that 52 per cent of the dietaries studied were below this level, and that as many as 16 per cent were below even the minimal requirement of 0.45 g.

The effects of calcium deficiency are especially serious in children. In a study of calcium and phosphorus metabolism, Sherman and Hawley[18] have shown that children from 3 to 13 years old require an intake of 1 g. of calcium per day, an amount which is necessary to induce optimum storage of this element and to insure the proper development

---

[16] Wisconsin Agr. Exp. Sta. Ann. Report, 129 (1905); cited by McCollum and Simmonds, "The Newer Knowledge of Nutrition," 4th edition, 1929, p. 411.

[17] *J. Biol. Chem.*, **44**, 21 (1920); see also "The Harvey Lectures," 1917–1919, p. 114.

[18] *J. Biol. Chem.*, **53**, 375 (1922).

of bones and teeth. Milk is the best and most available source of calcium, particularly for children, who do not seem to utilize the calcium of vegetables very efficiently. McClugage and Mendel[19] have reported that the calcium supply of the organism is normally derived from milk in greater abundance than from any other dietary source and that the calcium in spinach and carrots is poorly assimilated. Accordingly it has been concluded that vegetables should not be used extensively as a substitute for milk with the idea of providing the requisite amount of calcium. However, it is not impossible, in the case of adults, to meet the maintenance needs of calcium, as well as phosphorus, from exclusively vegetable sources, such as carrots, as has been shown by M. S. Rose,[20] Blatherwick and Long,[21] and others.

Sherman and Hawley[18] have recommended 750 to 1000 cc. of milk per day for the growing child. The calcium derived from this amount of milk, together with that obtained from other dietary sources, would provide about 1 g. of the element.

That growth is not necessarily a criterion of the adequacy of the calcium supply has been stressed by Sherman and Booher.[22] In experiments on rats they found that increase of body weight may be practically the same on rations containing from 0.16 to 0.5 per cent calcium. More calcium is stored on the higher levels of intake. Accordingly, Sherman and Booher have suggested that a calcium-poor condition of the body may co-exist throughout much or all of the period of growth with normal increases of height and weight. It is considered, moreover, that the maximal rate of calcium retention is the optimal, until the body has attained the normal percentage of calcium for its age.

The calcium factor is even more of a problem during pregnancy and lactation. The demands of the fetus on the maternal organism are considerable. It has been estimated that the fetus at 40 weeks contains approximately 30 g. of calcium.[23] Under normal conditions of nutrition the maternal organism is in *positive* calcium balance and stores an amount of this element far in excess of the fetal requirement. So constant is this tendency in the human individual,[24] as well as in experimental animals,[25] particularly toward the end of lactation, that it may be inferred that the storage of calcium is physiological, anticipat-

[19] *Ibid.*, **35**, 353 (1918).

[20] *Ibid.*, **41**, 349 (1920).

[21] *Ibid.*, **52**, 125 (1922).

[22] *Ibid.*, **93**, 93 (1931); H. C. Sherman, *J. Am. Med. Assoc.*, **97**, 1425 (1931).

[23] C. F. Shukers, I. G. Macy, and co-workers, *J. Nutrition*, **5**, 127 (1932).

[24] C. M. Coons and K. Blunt, *J. Biol. Chem.*, **86**, 1 (1930); I. G. Macy and co-workers, *ibid.*, **86**, 17 (1930).

[25] H. Goss and C. L. A. Schmidt, *ibid.*, 86, 417 (1930).

ing later emergencies and requirements. Retention of phosphorus accompanies that of calcium.

With the onset of lactation it is not uncommon to find *negative* calcium and phosphorus balances in spite of large intakes of these elements (Hunscher).[26] In time the balance is restored in the well-nourished individual, and later, when less milk is secreted, both calcium and phosphorus may be stored in the maternal body.[27] Better utilization of calcium and phosphorus in the nursing mother may be obtained through the daily administration of cod-liver oil and yeast (Macy and associates).[28]

In view of these circumstances, the effects of a low calcium intake during pregnancy and lactation when the needs of both the mother and child are involved may be readily imagined. Calcium and phosphorus deficiency under these conditions results in decalcification of the bones[29] and the loss of teeth. If the depletion of mineral from the bones is sufficient, they tend to become soft, a condition described as *osteomalacia*. The victims become badly deformed, owing to the flexibility of the bones. Osteomalacia is said to be very prevalent among women in certain parts of India and China.

Calcium deficiency is an important factor in the development of rickets, as will be seen shortly in another connection (p. 590). Other phases of calcium metabolism are reserved for the discussion on bone (p. 601).

The following foods are among the better sources of calcium: cheese, milk, egg yolk, beans, lentils, wheat bran, cottonseed meal, linseed meal, nuts, dried figs, leafy vegetables such as cabbage, especially the outermost leaves, turnip tops, cauliflower, asparagus. The animal organism is also capable of utilizing inorganic and organic salts of calcium, such as the carbonate, phosphate, and lactate.[30]

The Phosphorus Requirement. The intimate relation between calcium and phosphorus metabolism has been referred to in the preceding paragraphs. Both enter into the structure of bone and either may in consequence be the limiting factor in growth. Moreover, large amounts of phosphorus are utilized for other purposes. Birds require this element, as well as calcium, in the production of eggs. In the lactating mammal, phosphorus is needed in the formation of casein and other milk

---

[26] *Ibid.*, **86**, 37 (1930).

[27] For studies of the calcium balance of cows during lactation, see E. B. Forbes, *et al.*, *ibid.*, **52**, 281 (1922); E. B. Hart, *ibid.*, **54**, 75 (1922).

[28] *Ibid.*, **86**, 59 (1930).

[29] See for example K. U. Toverud and G. Toverud, *Biochem. J.*, **26**, 1424 (1932).

[30] T. B. Osborne and L. B. Mendel, *J. Biol. Chem.*, **34**, 131 (1918); see also H. Steenbock and co-workers, *ibid.*, **56**, 375 (1923).

constituents. Meigs, Blatherwick, and Cary[31] have reported that phospholipids and inorganic phosphates are probably the only phosphorus compounds present in normal blood plasma. In the lactating cow, the phospholipid content of the plasma is much higher than normal, and this constituent is probably the precursor of nearly all the fat and phosphorus contained in the milk.

Phosphates are utilized in maintaining the acid-base balance of the blood and in the synthesis of such important cell constituents as the phospholipids and nucleoproteins. The presence in muscle and other tissues of phosphoric acid in combination as creatine phosphate, adenylic acid, adenylic acid pyrophosphate (or triphosphate), hexose-phosphate, etc., suggests the manifold physiological importance of phosphorus in nutrition.

The requirement of the growing animal for phosphorus is relatively high. This is also true for the pregnant or lactating individual. In the adult, where phosphorus is required merely to replace the loss from the body, the minimum requirement averages about 0.88 g. per day. In his statistical studies, Sherman found that only 4 per cent of the American dietaries examined fell below this level. As a rule, there is therefore in the case of the adult less danger of phosphorus deficiency than of calcium deficiency. Phosphorus deficiency is also an important factor in the nutrition of cattle, particularly in regions where the soil and vegetation are poor in this element. Cattle may develop an intense craving for phosphorus, which manifests itself in bone-eating. This condition is known as osteophagia. An outbreak of this abnormality in South Africa has been described by Green,[32] who states that the craving may be produced experimentally upon phosphorus-low rations and removed by administration of phosphorus compounds and by phosphatic manuring of the soil.

The condition of *aphosphorosis* (phosphorus deficiency) in ruminants and the condition of *acalcerosis* (calcium deficiency) which may accompany it are evidently much more prevalent and widely distributed than was formerly appreciated. An admirable survey of the subject has recently been prepared by Sir Arnold Theiler and Green.[33]

Among the richer sources of phosphorus are the following foods: cheese, milk, egg yolk, beans, peas, lentils, bread, especially rye and whole wheat, fish, meat, cottonseed meal, linseed meal, oatmeal, barley. The phosphorus requirement may be supplied, even in the growing animal, exclusively from inorganic sources (Osborne and Mendel).[30]

[31] *J. Biol. Chem.*, **37**, 1 (1919); **40**, 469 (1919).
[32] *Ibid.*, **46**, Proc. xix (1921); *Physiol. Rev.*, **5**, 336 (1925).
[33] *Nutr. Abst. Rev.*, **1**, 359 (1931–32).

As will be seen presently, phosphorus deficiency is an important factor in rickets. It is now also recognized that a proper balance must exist between the intake of calcium and phosphorus. The most favorable Ca : P ratio for growth and bone formation is evidently between 1 and 2. Even if the absolute amount of phosphorus is unchanged a rise in the Ca : P ratio to 5 is associated with a pronounced decrease in growth, bone ash content, and the percentage of inorganic phosphorus in the blood serum (Bethke, Kick, and Wilder).[34]

Experience in the rearing of lions and other carnivorous animals in several zoological gardens has brought out very strikingly the importance of calcium and phosphorus in nutrition. It is now evident that the difficulty formerly encountered in bringing up lions in captivity was due largely to the fact that the diet, after weaning, was inadequate, consisting as it did almost entirely of raw meat. Even lions, when they are young, find it difficult to chew large bones, and this was formerly the chief source of calcium and phosphorus provided to them. As a result, the young animals kept on this diet frequently developed a severe form of rickets and succumbed. However, when the diet was supplemented by the addition of calcium- and phosphorus-rich food, such as milk and crushed bones, and by the addition of cod-liver oil (the latter contains the antirachitic vitamin), the animals grew normally and the condition of those which had previously developed rickets was frequently improved.

Other aspects of phosphorus metabolism will be considered in the section on bone (p. 601).

Magnesium. The magnesium requirement is low as shown by the experiments of Osborne and Mendel in which diets containing 0.01 per cent of magnesium were found adequate for growth. Because of the abundance of this element in both plant and animal tissues, the supply is doubtless in excess of the needs of the body and hence the condition of magnesium deficiency presents no problem in nutrition.

That it is nevertheless an essential element for certain bodily activities, growth, and life has been recently brought out in a series of contributions from McCollum's laboratory.[35] A diet containing only 1.8 parts per million of magnesium was fed to young rats. Within 3 to 5 days the exposed skin areas of these animals became vividly red from vasodilation and hyperemia. Soon hyperirritability of the nervous system developed, followed by cardiac arrhythmia, spasticity, and tonic-clonic convulsions. On the same diet in dogs the symptoms of

[34] *J. Biol. Chem.*, **98**, 389 (1932); see also Brown, Shohl, *et al.*, *ibid.*, **98**, 207 (1932).

[35] H. D. Kruse, E. R. Orent, and E. V. McCollum, *J. Biol. Chem.*, **96**, 519 (1932); **100**. 603 (1933): Orent, Kruse, and McCollum, *Am. J. Physiol.*, **101**, 454 (1932).

vasodilation, hyperexcitability, and tetany were less intense, but the trophic and nutritive changes were more conspicuous than in the rat. The tetany is described as distinct from other forms, being characterized by vasomotor spasm and the absence of both carpopedal spasm and laryngospasm.

Magnesium deficiency results in a progressive decrease of the serum magnesium content, a rise in cholesterol, chiefly in the form of esters, and a commensurate decrease in total fatty acids. Kruse and associates have related the low serum magnesium to the development of tetany, while the changes in the blood lipids have been interpreted as a reflection of failing fat metabolism.

Of interest are the earlier observations of Mendel and Benedict,[36] who noted that, in dogs, cats, and rabbits, an increased excretion of magnesium could be induced by the administration of calcium, and that an increased elimination of calcium could be brought about by the administration of magnesium. Similar relations have been shown to hold for man by Bogert and McKittrick.[37]

Approximately two-thirds of the magnesium in the body is present in bone. The analyses of Hammett[38] show that the ash of the femur and humerus of rats contains slightly less than 1 per cent of magnesium and that this value decreases somewhat with age. More magnesium than calcium is present in muscle tissue. Katz[39] analyzed fresh human muscle and found it to contain 0.212 parts per thousand of magnesium as compared with 0.075 parts per thousand of calcium.

Medes[40] found little variation in the concentration of magnesium in rats. Analyses of a series of whole animals, at 29, 60, and 90 days of age, revealed the interesting fact that the magnesium content remained constant during growth, the amount determined in all cases being 0.045 per cent. These observations are similar to those of Buckner and Peter,[41] who had shown previously that, whereas the percentages of phosphorus and calcium increased with age, the magnesium content remained about the same percentage of the body weight. It is of interest to note, at this point, that the contents of calcium, potassium, and magnesium are higher in female than in male rats. Another interesting conclusion reached by Medes is that the composition of the rat with respect to magnesium is more constant under varying conditions (as influenced by diet, etc.) than with respect to calcium.

[36] *Am. J. Physiol.*, **25**, 1, 23 (1909-10).
[37] *J. Biol. Chem.*, **54**, 363 (1922).
[38] *Ibid.*, **64**, 693 (1925).
[39] *Arch. ges. Physiol.*, **63**, 1 (1896).
[40] *J. Biol. Chem.*, **68**, 295 (1926).
[41] *Ibid.*, **54**, 5 (1922).

Iron. Sherman[42] has placed the iron requirement of the adult at approximately 10 mg. per day. He has expressed the opinion that there is comparatively little danger of iron deficiency in freely chosen diets. A similar amount of iron is sufficient to meet the maintenance and growth requirements of children, according to recent investigations.[43] In a study of the iron balance in women during pregnancy, Coons[44] found that with intakes varying from 9.69 to 19.45 mg. per day, the retention varied from +0.88 to +6.97 mg. The iron was in negative balance only once in twenty-three determinations (−2.2 mg.). It is thus seen that the maternal organism assimilates during the period of pregnancy enough iron to supply the new-born infant the needed reserves.

Most animals are born with an extra supply of iron (the guinea-pig is an exception) which is utilized during the early period of life when milk is the chief, if not the sole, article of diet. Milk is very low in iron. Human milk contains from 1 to 2 mg. per liter. Even lower values have been recorded for cow's milk. If an animal's diet is restricted to milk for much longer than its normal lactation period, anemia may result, as has been shown by Bunge,[45] Abderhalden,[46] and numerous other workers.

Considerable interest has been aroused in recent years in the problem of nutritional or milk anemia, partly as a result of the discovery by Hart that copper is an effective agent in stimulating the utilization of iron and the production of hemoglobin and of red blood corpuscles. If sufficiently purified, iron fails to correct this form of anemia in rats and rabbits, according to Hart[47] and other observers.

One of the richest sources of iron is to be found in organ meats, or " extra carcass parts " (liver, heart, kidney, spleen). In addition to meat, other good sources among foods are: egg yolk, whole wheat, fish, oysters, clams, nuts, dates, figs, beans, lentils, asparagus, spinach, molasses, oatmeal.

Iron salts, such as ferric chloride or pyrophosphate, can function as the sole source of iron for hemoglobin synthesis.[48] Rose and Vahl-

---

[42] Harvey Lectures (1917–19), p. 117.

[43] M. S. Rose, et al., J. Nutrition, **3**, 229 (1930–31); J. M. Leichsenring and I. H. Flor, ibid., **5**, 141 (1932).

[44] J. Biol. Chem., **97**, 215 (1932).

[45] Z. physiol. Chem., **13**, 399 (1889).

[46] Z. Biol., **39**, 193 (1900).

[47] Hart, Steenbock, Elvehjem, and Waddell, J. Biol. Chem., **77**, 797 (1928); **83**, 243, 251 (1929); **84**, 115 (1929).

[48] C. A. Elvehjem, E. B. Hart, and W. C. Sherman, J. Biol. Chem., **103**, 61 (1933).

teich[49] have recently shown that hemoglobin regeneration in anemic rats occurs more readily on a diet of whole wheat than on white flour supplemented with copper and iron.[50]

Iodine. The indispensability of iodine in nutrition is unquestioned. It is utilized partly in the production of thyroxin, the hormone of the thyroid gland. In regions where the water, soil, and in consequence the vegetables, are iodine-poor, goiter is prevalent.[51] On the other hand, where iodine is abundant goiter is rare. Among the Japanese, for example, goiter is practically non-existent, there being about one goiter per million of population. It is instructive to note that the iodine intake of the Japanese is probably greater than that of any other people, owing to the fact that seaweed is a common ingredient of the diet. Seaweed contains about 1000 times as much iodine as any other food (McClendon).[52]

Lunde and Closs[53] have estimated that the amount of iodine necessary to meet all the requirements of metabolism is about 0.05 mg. per day. According to Fellenberg,[54] a third of this amount is sufficient for the maintenance of iodine balance in an adult. The prevention of endemic goiter could probably be accomplished in many instances with about 50 mg. of iodine a year administered at proper intervals. Larger amounts (400 mg. of potassium iodide a year) are, however, recommended. During pregnancy and lactation, at puberty and the menopause, as well as during infections, the iodine requirement is believed to be somewhat above normal.

Sea foods constitute a rich source of iodine. Fish contain about 1 mg. per kg. The quantity is variable, however, depending on the locality and the food supply. Oysters have been found to contain an even larger amount, 16 mg. per kg. South Carolina spinach has been found to contain 800 to 1200 parts of iodine per billion, on a dry basis, whereas, according to the analyses of McClendon and Remington,[55] California spinach contained only 32 parts per billion. Similar differ-

---

[49] M. S. Rose and E. McC. Vahlteich, *ibid.*, **96**, 593 (1932).

[50] A comprehensive review on iron metabolism is that of W. Lintzel, *Ergebnisse Physiol.*, **31**, 844–919 (1931).

[51] For the geographical distribution of goiter, as well as for the historical aspects of the subject, the reader is referred to C. R. Harington, "The Thyroid Gland," London, 1933, Chap. III.

[52] *J. Biol. Chem.*, **102**, 91 (1933).

[53] *Nord. med. Tidskrift.*, **1**, 475 (1929); cited by W. Weston, *Am. J. Pub. Health*, **21**, 715 (1931).

[54] *Biochem. Z.*, **142**, 246 (1923).

[55] *J. Am. Chem. Soc.*, **51**, 394 (1929).

ences, though not of the same magnitude, have been noted for other vegetables—beans, asparagus, potatoes, lettuce, carrots, etc.

Other Mineral Constituents. When evidence first began to accumulate that certain elements, such as copper, zinc, manganese, nickel, and cobalt, were present in traces in a large variety of plant and animal tissues, no particular importance was attached to the findings. It seemed logical to suppose that their occurrence was essentially adventitious. Gradually, however, the point of view has changed and increasing effort has been directed in the attempt to evaluate the nutritional and physiological significance of the so-called " trace " elements.[56]

Copper. Of the physiologically rare elements, copper has received most of the attention. That it may accumulate in tissues due to its presence in foodstuffs is not to be denied. Yet it is a curious fact that fetal and infant organs (brain,[57] liver[58]) contain a greater amount of copper than is present in adult tissues, which argues against the purely adventitious origin of copper in the organism.

Outside of its special rôle as a component of the hemocyanin molecule, copper seems to play, in conjunction with iron, an important function in the production of hemoglobin. This was first demonstrated by Hart and co-workers[47] in the type of nutritional anemia produced in rats restricted to a milk diet. Purified iron alone is ineffective. Certain investigators have contended, however, that iron alone is an effective hematopoietic agent; others have reported that nickel, germanium, manganese, etc., produce the same effect as copper.[59] However, the weight of evidence at present is that the effect of copper in hemoglobin formation is specific and that other elements do not have this stimulating effect.

Elvehjem and Sherman[60] have attempted to determine more precisely the function of copper in hematopoiesis. They found that the addition of pure iron to the milk fed to anemic rats increased the total

[56] For a general review of the nutritional significance of the mineral elements occurring in traces in the animal body, the student is referred to M. S. Rose, *Yale J. Biol. Med.*, **4**, 499 (1932); see also "Report of the Committee on Growth and Development, White House Conference on Child Health and Protection," Part III, pp. 282–306, Century Co., 1932.

[57] M. Bodansky, *J. Biol. Chem.*, **48**, 361 (1921).

[58] D. B. Morrison and T. P. Nash, *ibid.*, **88**, 479 (1930).

[59] H. H. Beard, V. C. Myers, *et al.*, *ibid.*, **94**, 71, *et seq.* (1931–32); D. L. Drabkin and C. S. Waggoner, *ibid.*, **89**, 51 (1930). Compare with F. A. Underhill, J. M. Orten, and R. C. Lewis, *ibid.*, **91**, 13 (1931); Orten, Underhill, and Lewis, *ibid.*, **96**, 1 (1932); H. S. Mitchell and L. Miller, *ibid.*, **92**, 421 (1931); H. L. Keil and V. E. Nelson, *ibid.*, **93**, 49 (1931); I. J. Cunningham, *Biochem. J.*, **25**, 1267 (1931).

[60] *J. Biol. Chem.*, **98**, 309 (1932); see also H. W. Josephs, *ibid.*, **96**, 559 (1932).

iron content of the liver and spleen. However, no increase in hemoglobin was observed. When copper was substituted, the stored iron in the liver was used directly in the building of hemoglobin. As compared with the decreased iron content in the liver, the change in the spleen was slight.

According to Elvehjem and Hart,[61] nutritional anemia in the pig also may be corrected by supplementing the diet with copper. The efficacy of this element in the nutritional anemia of childhood, or in other forms of anemia in man, remains to be established.

The copper content of plant and animal foods has been determined by various investigators, notably Lindow, Elvehjem, and Peterson.[62] Among the more abundant sources of copper are the following: liver (calf liver more than beef liver), oysters, cocoa, molasses, nuts, currants, split peas.

Oysters from certain localities have been found to exert a marked beneficial effect in milk anemia, presumably because of their high copper content.[63] Robscheit-Robbins, Elden, Sperry, and Whipple[64] have observed that apricots, which are high in copper, are likewise effective in stimulating blood regeneration.

That copper may exert an erythropoietic action, independent of any influence on hemoglobin formation, is indicated by the recent experiments of Stein and Lewis.[65]

Manganese. Disturbance of the oestrus cycle has been observed by Kemmerer, Elvehjem, and Hart[66] in mice kept on a manganese-deficient diet. Although this effect was not evident in rats in the experiments of Orent and McCollum,[67] there was, however, failure in the development of the mammary tissue in the females with the result that the mothers were incapable of suckling their young. In male rats complete degeneration of the germinal epithelium occurred. These effects were avoided when the manganese-free rations were supplemented by the addition of small amounts of manganese (0.005 to 0.05 per cent).

The analyses of Richards,[68] Peterson and Skinner,[69] and others have established the widespread occurrence of manganese in plant and

[61] *Ibid.*, **95**, 363 (1932).
[62] *Ibid.*, **82**, 465 (1929).
[63] H. Levine, R. E. Remington, and F. B. Culp, *J. Nutrition*, **4**, 469 (1931).
[64] *J. Biol. Chem.*, **79**, 563, 577 (1928).
[65] *J. Nutrition*, **6**, 465 (1933).
[66] *J. Biol. Chem.*, **92**, 623 (1931).
[67] *Ibid.*, **92**, 651 (1931).
[68] *Biochem. J.*, **24**, 1572 (1930).
[69] *J. Nutrition*, **4**, 419 (1931).

animal tissues. This element is especially abundant in blueberries and lettuce and seems to be a constant constituent of the reproductive organs of plants and animals. Even though the evidence is not yet complete, there is much to suggest that it may be essential for growth and more specifically for normal reproduction both in plants and animals.

Zinc. Hubbell and Mendel[70] observed a slight retardation in the growth of mice fed a highly purified diet that was practically free from zinc (0.005 mg. was the estimated daily intake on this diet). When the total zinc intake was increased to 0.02 mg., growth was more nearly normal; larger amounts retarded growth. The question has been further investigated by Newell and McCollum,[71] who prepared a diet containing less than 1 part of zinc per 10 million. Rats kept on this ration developed essentially as well as did the control animals which received a small supplement of zinc. The conclusion has therefore been drawn that zinc is probably not an essential nutritive factor in the growth of the rat. Nor is there any evidence that the ingestion of this metal in moderate excess of the quantities ordinarily present in foods produces any deleterious effects on the organism.

Aluminum. The question of the nutritional requirements of aluminum has received very little attention and consequently its significance from this standpoint is undetermined. Observations in McCollum's laboratory[72] indicate that it is probably non-essential. Aluminum is the most abundant metallic element in the earth's crust and has been found in a large variety of plant and animal tissues.[73] Partly because of the widespread use of aluminum cooking utensils, the question of its toxicity has been intensively studied. Although the problem can in no sense be considered closed, there is at present no evidence that aluminum, in amounts even considerably larger than those ordinarily encountered, is toxic for man.

Nickel, Cobalt, and Silicon. There is at present no evidence that these elements are essential in nutrition. The interesting observation has been made in R. C. Lewis' laboratory[74] that cobalt produces a characteristic polycythemia in young rats.

Fluorine. The recent report by Sharpless and McCollum[75] shows that rats grow normally on a diet low in fluorine and that the content

[70] *J. Biol. Chem.*, **75**, 567 (1927).

[71] *J. Nutrition*, **6**, 289 (1933).

[72] E. V. McCollum, O. S. Rask, and J. E. Becker, *J. Biol. Chem.*, **77**, 753 (1928).

[73] V. C. Myers and J. W. Mull, *J. Biol. Chem.*, **78**, 625 (1928); Myers and D. B. Morrison, *ibid.*, **78**, 615 (1928); F. P. Underhill, F. I. Peterman, *et al. Am. J. Physiol.*, **90**, 1–82 (1929).

[74] *J. Biol. Chem.*, **96**, 11 (1932).

[75] *J. Nutrition*, **6**, 163 (1933).

of this element in bones and teeth can be reduced to a negligible amount (6–25 parts per million in bone; practically 0 in teeth) without any gross evidence of deleterious effect. This disposes of earlier assumptions of the essential nature of fluorine in bone formation. Certain it is that if it is in any sense required by the organism, the amount necessary is extremely small. On the other hand, it has now been established that fluorides are toxic, interfering particularly with the retention and deposition of calcium in teeth and bones. Mottled teeth, a condition in which the enamel deteriorates, owing to the absence of intercementing material, is very prevalent in certain sections of the United States and other parts of the world. This abnormality has been recently associated with the presence in the drinking water of excessive amounts of fluoride.[76]   In one community in which mottled enamel is endemic, the drinking waters were found to contain 3.8 to 7.15 mg. of fluorine, as compared with 0 to 0.3 mg. in waters of other localities where this condition is not endemic (Smith, Lantz, and Smith).[77]   It was found that every child exposed to the environmental conditions of this community during the years of growth of the enamel of the permanent teeth was certain to have mottled enamel.[78]

THE PROTEIN REQUIREMENT IN NUTRITION

Amount of Protein Needed. The statistical studies of Voit in Germany showed, for adults, an average daily consumption of 118 grams of protein. Atwater in this country, and other workers both in America and in Europe, have made similar estimates of the average protein intake. This quantity, therefore, was formerly accepted by many students of nutrition as representing an adequate supply. As this amount of protein provides less than 500 calories, the energy needs of the body must obviously be met largely from carbohydrate and fat. From this standpoint, a well-balanced diet for an individual engaged in moderate physical work may include 50–60 grams of fat (465 to 560 calories, and about 500 grams of carbohydrate (approximately 2000 calories).

Chittenden[79] studied the protein requirement in human nutrition very exhaustively and reached the conclusion that the Voit standard

---

[76] F. S. McKay, *J. Dental Research.*, **10**, 561 (1930).

[77] *Arizona Agri. Exp. Sta. Tech. Bull.* 32, June, 1931.

[78] The increasing interest in the problem of the physiological effects of fluorine is evidenced by the recent appearance of two comprehensive reviews on the subject: F. J. McClure, *Physiol. Rev.* **13**, 277 (1933); F. DeEds, *Medicine*, **12**, 1 (1933).

[79] R. H. Chittenden, "Physiological Economy in Nutrition," F. A. Stokes, New York, 1904.

of 118 grams was far in excess of the actual needs of the body. In his investigations were included individuals engaged in various occupations (soldiers, professors, students, athletes, etc.). Chittenden determined that the nitrogen requirement per day per kilogram of body weight was fairly uniform for different individuals and amounted to 0.10 to 0.12 gram. A man weighing 70 kg. would therefore require 7–8.4 grams daily, or 44–53 grams of protein. Accordingly, an allowance of 60 grams of protein per day should be entirely adequate. This calls for two assumptions, namely, that there is adequate provision, through other food elements, to meet the energy requirements, and that the protein ingested provides a complete and adequate assortment of all the amino acids essential to the formation of tissue protein. These assumptions cannot always be made, for not all proteins are of equivalent nutritive value. It is evident that fixed standards are of limited value. What the optimum proportions of the various foodstuffs will be in any particular case will depend on many circumstances. Thus, in cold climates a high level of protein intake is dictated by sound physiological reasoning. In warm climates a lower protein level would seem more suitable.[80] Fortunately, in some particulars, the dietary habits of people frequently tend in the proper direction.[81]

Hindhede[82] has also been among those advocating low-protein dietaries and has reported that it is possible for the body to remain in nitrogen equilibrium indefinitely on diets consisting of bread, potatoes, fruit, and small amounts of milk. The chief protein of the potato, tuberin, a globulin, is according to Kon[83] apparently a good, complete protein, i.e., it contains all the essential amino acids. Kon and Klein have described an experiment in which two adults, a man and a woman,

---

[80] Denis and Borgstrom (*J. Biol. Chem.*, **61**, 109 [1924]) in a large group of students in a Southern medical school found an average daily urinary excretion of 10.63 grams of nitrogen. This figure, plus 10 per cent added to account for the nitrogen lost through the feces, indicates an average consumption of 73.8 grams of protein, an amount not much higher than Chittenden's standard and distinctly below the average protein intake (121 grams) recorded for inhabitants of the United States. During the winter months the same group of students showed higher values for nitrogen excretion than in April or July. Youngburg and Finch (*Ibid.*, **68**, 335 [1926]) observed essentially the same level of protein intake in a group of medical students in the North and were unable to demonstrate seasonal variations in nitrogen excretion. Similar results reported by others show that the protein intake of students in the North and South, per 70 kg. body weight, is approximately the same (Brooks, *Am. J. Physiol.*, **89**, 403 [1929]; Beard, *ibid.*, **82**, 577 [1927]).

[81] See for example the entertaining article by L. B. Mendel, "The Changing Diet of the American People," *J. Am. Med. Assoc.*, **99**, 117 (1932).

[82] *Skand. Arch. Physiol.*, **30**, 97 (1913); "Protein and Nutrition," London, 1913.

[83] *Biochem. J.*, **22**, 258, 261 (1928).

lived over a period of 167 days in nitrogen equilibrium and in good health on a diet in which the nitrogen was almost entirely derived from the potato, the nitrogen intake averaging 5.7 grams daily.

The absolute minimum evidently falls considerably below the standard set by Chittenden. Numerous investigators have attempted to determine the minimum protein intake sufficient to maintain nitrogen balance. Folin[84] obtained a minimum excretion of 2.6 grams of nitrogen on the twelfth day of an experiment on a low-protein diet. The subject of this experiment weighed 64.0 kg. In a similar experiment Thomas[85] (body weight 76.2 kg.) obtained a minimum excretion of 2.98 grams on the nineteenth day. Deuel[86] was able to reduce his nitrogen elimination to a minimum of 2.1 grams. The injection of thyroxin was followed after an interval of 7 days by an increased output of nitrogen, due obviously to an increased "wear and tear" of the tissues. Smith,[87] by insuring for himself an abundant caloric supply in the form of carbohydrate and fat, was able to reduce his endogenous protein metabolism to an extremely low level, the lowest recorded in the literature. During the course of the last 24 days of a 28-day experiment, he excreted but 80.08 grams of nitrogen, or an average of 3.34 grams per day. The lowest point was reached on the twenty-fourth day of the experiment when the total nitrogen excreted in the urine was only 1.58 grams. These figures represent an amount of protein metabolism of 20 grams or less. From this discussion, the inference is not to be drawn, however, that a low protein intake is at all desirable. It is true that if the protein fed were one containing all the essential amino acids in suitable proportions for tissue synthesis, a daily allowance of 50 or 60 grams would be adequate. Proteins of animal origin are usually complete or adequate in this sense, but an adequate supply of the required amino acids can hardly be expected from 50 or 60 grams of many of the vegetable proteins, such as zein of corn, gliadin of wheat, hordein of barley, and phaseolin of kidney beans. It is therefore of the utmost importance to allow a liberal margin of safety, particularly when part of the protein is derived from plant sources.

Relation of Protein Intake to Kidney Disease. Few problems in nutrition have aroused more speculation than the question whether kidney damage and vascular disease may be related to a high protein dietary. Inasmuch as the kidneys carry nearly all the burden of excreting the end-products of protein metabolism, it has been inferred that deleterious

[84] *Am. J. Physiol.*, **13**, 66 (1905).
[85] *Arch. Anat. Physiol.*, Physiol. Abt., 219 (1909); cited by Smith.
[86] Deuel, Sandiford, Sandiford, and Boothby, *J. Biol. Chem.*, **76**, 391 (1928).
[87] *Ibid.*, **68**, 15 (1926).

effects might result from the habitual intake of excessive amounts of protein, and indeed definite lesions in the kidney have been reported in rabbits fed a high meat diet over a period of months. But observations on the rat, which is a more appropriate experimental animal for this purpose, have not disclosed any consistent deleterious action on the kidney even when protein was fed to the extent of 70 to 90 per cent of the total food.

Hypertrophy of the kidney does occur, however, as a result of increased activity incidental to the excretion of excessive amounts of the end-products of protein metabolism. This effect may be exaggerated by removal of one kidney, thereby throwing the entire burden of excretion on the remaining organ. Thus, Moise and A. H. Smith[88] working with unilaterally nephrectomized rats were able to demonstrate marked hypertrophy of the remaining kidney, but no pathological changes in the young. In the maturer animals, tubular changes were noted.

When the protein intake is raised to the level of 70 per cent in unilaterally nephrectomized animals, in addition to hypertrophy of the remaining kidney, the only function really affected adversely is lactation (Parsons, Smith, Moise, and Mendel).[89]

Those[90] who have studied the dietary habits of Eskimos, whose daily consumption of protein may exceed 500 grams, have not observed any unusual prevalence of cardiac or renal disease among them. Nor has a detailed metabolic study of two distinguished Arctic explorers, maintained on an exclusive meat diet for one year, given any evidence suggesting that renal damage had occurred.[91] This evidence, however, is not conclusive proof that protein intake is entirely unrelated to kidney disease. It is possible that tolerance to protein may be a matter of adaptation, particularly in the case of the Eskimo.

In short, such positive changes as have been obtained have resulted from the imposition upon the kidney of a burden of excretion far outside the range of physiological limits. This point has been emphasized by Bischoff,[92] who in a recent review of the literature has reached the conclusion that " the survey of animal experiments, of diet habits of various peoples, and of clinical diet procedures, leaves one with the impression that diet may have little to do with the spontaneous kidney and blood

[88] J. Exp. Med., 46, 27 (1927).
[89] Arch. Pathol., 10, 1 (1930).
[90] W. A. Thomas, J. Am. Med. Assoc., 88, 1559 (1927).
[91] E. Tolstoi, J. Biol. Chem., 83, 753 (1929).
[92] J. Nutrition, 5, 431 (1932).

vessel changes observed in lower animals and with the cardiovascular-renal diseases found in man."[93]

Qualitative Differences in the Nutritional Value of Proteins. That the value of a protein in nutrition depends largely on the nature and amounts of the amino acids which it yields on hydrolysis seems to be definitely established. Not only are there differences in the proportions in which the amino acids are present in different proteins, but one or more amino acids are totally lacking in some of them. The question therefore arises as to whether a protein that does not have a complete assortment of amino acids can be adequate in nutrition when it is the sole protein provided in the diet. Much depends on the nature of the deficiency. Many proteins lack glycine, but this is not a limiting factor in nutrition because the animal organism is capable of synthesizing this amino acid from other substances that are available. On the contrary, a deficiency of tryptophane, cystine, histidine, or lysine, and possibly other amino acids, materially reduces the biological value of a protein. Maintenance and growth do not occur in the absence of any one of these, for their synthesis in the animal body does not take place. This statement may be qualified to some extent. Mendel[94] states that sheep have been observed to gain many pounds over considerable periods of time on a diet of starch, denitrogenized straw, inorganic salts, and urea, an exceedingly simple nitrogenous mixture that readily disintegrates to form ammonia and carbon dioxide. In the rumen, or paunch, of the sheep, as well as in that of other ruminants, there is ample opportunity for the synthesis of amino acids by bacteria. These amino acids may even be synthesized into protein, which is incorporated into the protoplasm of the bacteria. When the bacteria pass into the acid-secreting stomach and die, this protein is presumably digested and utilized in the usual manner. However, amino-acid synthesis by bacteria is not a factor in the nutrition of man and most of the higher animals. These depend on an exogenous supply of the essential amino acids.

One method of studying the nutritive value of different proteins has been to provide rats with basal diets adequate in all other respects but containing no protein or amino acids. By this method, the protein element in the diet may be made the only limiting factor. As knowledge of the remaining factors in nutrition has increased, the composi-

---

[93] Slonaker has studied the influence of different levels of protein intake (10, 14, 18, 22, and 26 per cent) in the rat on growth, activity, fertility, lactation, mortality of young, duration of life, and other factors. *Am. J. Physiol.*, **96**, 547, 557; **97**, 15, 322, 573, 626; **98**, 266 (1931).

[94] L. B. Mendel, "Nutrition," p. 124. See also *J. Franklin Inst.*, July, 1921.

tion of the basal non-protein rations has been subjected to numerous modifications, but the principle has remained the same. By adding to such rations suitable amounts of a single protein, it has been possible to determine which are and which are not adequate for maintenance and growth.

Although several investigators had previously attempted to compare the nutritive value of different proteins, the first important contributions to the subject were the classical studies of Osborne and Mendel.[95] Osborne and Mendel have done much to establish the value of feeding isolated food substances in nutritional studies. As milk was believed to be an adequate diet for young rats, these workers thought it desirable to include in their experimental rations a protein-free milk preparation for the purpose of supplying the necessary mineral constituents and other possibly essential ingredients. The dried " protein-free milk " constituted 28.2 per cent of the ration. The other constituents were starch 20.8, agar-agar 5.0, and fat 28.0 per cent. The proteins used in the experiments were highly purified and were supplied in liberal amount (18 per cent of the total food).

The observations of Osborne and Mendel showed that growth in rats could be secured with certain proteins but not with others. The proteins which, when fed singly in suitable concentration, proved adequate for growth included:

PROTEINS OF ANIMAL ORIGIN	PROTEINS OF VEGETABLE ORIGIN
Casein (milk)	Edestin (hemp-seed)
Lactalbumin (milk)	Globulin (squash-seed)
Ovalbumin (hen's egg)	Excelsin (Brazil-nut)
Ovovitellin (hen's egg)	Glutelin (maize)
	Globulin (cottonseed)
	Glutenin (wheat)
	Glycinin (soybean)
	Cannabin (hemp-seed)

The following proteins, when fed alone, failed to induce growth:

Legumelin (soybean)	Hordein (barley)
Vignin (vetch)	Conglutin (blue or yellow lupin)
Gliadin (wheat or rye)	Gelatin (horn)
Legumin (pea)	Zein (maize)
Legumin (vetch)	Phaseolin (white kidney bean)

[95] T. B. Osborne and L. B. Mendel, "Feeding Experiments with Isolated Food Substances," Carnegie Inst. Pub., 156, Parts I and II, 1911. Osborne and Mendel, *J. Biol. Chem.*, **12**, 81 (1912); **15**, 311 (1913); **16**, 423 (1913); **17**, 325 (1914); L. B. Mendel, Harvey Lectures, 1914–1915. 101.

The inadequacy of certain proteins to promote growth cannot be attributed to any toxic effect which they may possess; nor is the effect referable to a diminished utilization due to incomplete digestion. The evidence all points in one direction, namely, that it is fundamentally a question of amino-acid deficiency. A comparison may be made of the results obtained with foods containing either casein or gliadin as the sole

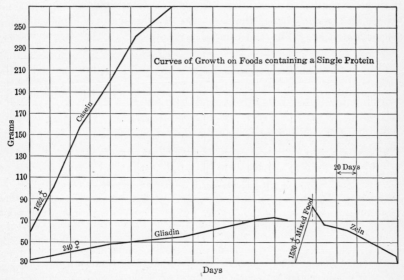

Fig. 34.—Showing typical curves of growth of rats maintained on diets containing a single protein. On the casein food (deficient in glycine) satisfactory growth is obtained; on the gliadin food (deficient in lysine) little more than maintenance of body weight is possible; on the zein food (devoid of glycine, lysine, and tryptophane) even maintenance of body weight is impossible. (After L. B. Mendel, *J. Amer. Med. Assoc.*, **64**, 1539 [1915]; "Nutrition: The Chemistry of Life," Yale Univ. Press, 1923, p. 117.)

protein. Osborne and Mendel have shown that when the former protein is fed to rats, normal growth occurs, but when gliadin is the sole protein of the diet, growth occurs very slowly or not at all. Their results are represented in Fig. 34. When a comparison is made of the amino acids present in the two proteins, it is seen that casein contains all the amino acids, although the content of cystine is low. On the contrary, gliadin lacks glycine, and, as compared with casein, is poor in lysine. The absence of glycine does not constitute an actual deficiency, for this amino acid is readily synthesized in the body. The content of lysine in gliadin is apparently sufficient for maintenance and apparently also for a slight amount of growth, but insufficient to permit normal growth. That lysine is the factor limiting the nutritional value of gliadin may be shown by supplementing such diets with this amino acid.

An even more striking illustration is to be found in the experiments (Osborne and Mendel) in which zein was fed as the sole protein. One of the curves included in Fig. 34 shows that Rat No. 1530 gained weight on a mixed diet, but that with the restriction of the protein element to zein there resulted at once a loss of weight. Zein is deficient in glycine, lysine, and tryptophane, the last two of which are indispensable to proper nutrition. The addition of tryptophane to the deficient diet

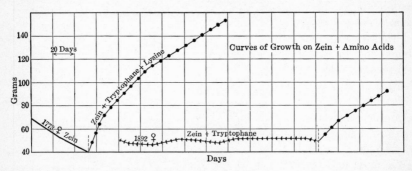

Fig. 35.—Showing the effect of the addition of the amino acids tryptophane and lysine to zein which fails to yield them. With zein alone (rat 1773) there is nutritive decline. The addition of tryptophane (rat 1892) permits maintenance without growth on foods containing zein as the sole protein. The addition of tryptophane and lysine to zein enables the animals to make considerable growth. It is interesting to note, in relation to rat 1892, that the growth of this animal was inhibited for six months without material change in its body weight. That the capacity to grow is not lost by prolonged dwarfing on imperfect food is shown by the subsequent growth of the animal when lysine was added to the food containing zein and tryptophane. (After L. B. Mendel, *J. Am. Med. Assoc.*, **64**, 1539 (1915); "Nutrition: The Chemistry of Life," p. 118.)

prevented further loss of weight but did not induce any growth, whereas the addition of both tryptophane and lysine caused prompt gain in weight (Fig. 35). The dietary deficiency caused by zein may be removed in still another way, as by the addition of small amounts of lactalbumin, a protein rich in both tryptophane and lysine. Concerning the nutritional value of lactalbumin, there has been a difference of opinion.[96] According to Osborne and Mendel,[97] lactalbumin is a "complete" pro-

[96] McCollum and Simmonds, "The Newer Knowledge of Nutrition," 1929 edition, p. 54.

[97] *J. Biol. Chem.*, **59**, 339 (1924).

tein, but others have shown that on a 9 per cent level of intake it is deficient in cystine. It is possible to select suitable combinations of two or more incomplete proteins that contain jointly a complete assortment of amino acids and are, hence, adequate for nutrition.

There is another aspect to the problem. The nutritive efficiency of a protein is determined by the content of the least abundant essential amino acid. For example, when casein is the sole protein of the diet, normal growth may be obtained in rats on an intake of 18 per cent, but when this is reduced to a lower level (9 per cent of total food intake), growth is greatly retarded. The retarding effect is not due to a lack of sufficient protein *per se*, but rather to a deficiency of cystine. The addition of cystine raises the nutritive efficiency of the ration as shown strikingly by Osborne and Mendel. Their observations are represented in Fig. 36.

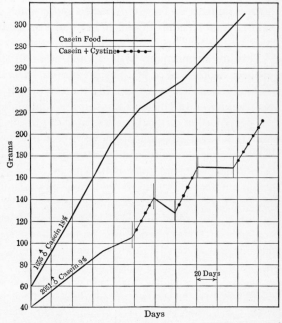

Fig. 36.—The curve for rat 1655 shows the satisfactory growth obtained when 18 per cent of casein was present in the diet as the sole protein. With a smaller amount of casein (rat 2051)—9 per cent—much less rapid growth ensued. That the insufficiency of the smaller amount of casein is essentially due to its relative deficiency in cystine-yielding groups is shown by the marked accelerating influence upon growth brought about by the addition of the amino acid, cystine, to the food containing 9 per cent of casein, and the prompt contrary effect when the cystine was withdrawn from the diet. (After L. B. Mendel, *J. Am. Med. Assoc.*, **64**, 1539 [1915].)

Similar results have been obtained with edestin, which supports growth when fed in liberal amounts (18 per cent), but which cannot support normal growth when fed in moderate amounts (9 per cent). A large number of proteins have been investigated with the object of determining their biological value. Johns and Finks[98] and others have shown that beans of the genus *Phaseolus* are deficient in cystine. The mixed proteins of corn, according to Hogan,[99] have tryptophane as the first limiting factor and lysine as the second. Lack of space does not permit even a résumé of these and similar investigations. In his recent review, Mitchell[100] has dealt with the literature pertaining to the subject.

Feeding Experiments with Amino-acid Mixtures. A more direct approach to the study of the part played by amino acids in nutrition would obviously be one involving the complete replacement of the protein fraction of the diet by mixtures of amino acids. The first important contribution of this type was made by Abderhalden,[101] who fed to dogs amino-acid mixtures prepared from meat by digestion with appropriate enzymes. With such mixtures as the sole source of nitrogen, the animals were not only maintained in nitrogen equilibrium, but a certain number of them showed remarkable gains in weight. A dog that was fed in this way for a period of 100 days showed at the end of that time an increase in weight of 9.35 kg. Abderhalden removed both tyrosine and tryptophane from protein digests. The resulting amino-acid mixture was inadequate for maintenance or growth unless supplemented by both of these amino acids.

These observations, together with the development of suitable methods for the separation of amino acids from protein digests, stimulated many similar studies, but owing to factors which were often beyond control at the time some of the earlier results were subsequently proved to be inaccurate. In the later development of the subject the contributions from W. C. Rose's laboratory have been particularly noteworthy.

Tryptophane. The isolation of this amino acid from tryptic digests by Hopkins and Cole [102] is considered by some students of the subject as having paved the way to the newer knowledge of nutrition, including the earlier research on vitamins. The significance of tryptophane deficiency in a diet in which the protein factor was limited to zein was first recognized by Willcock and Hopkins,[103] and, as we have seen, more fully defined by the work of Osborne and Mendel.[95]

[98] *Am. J. Physiol.*, **57**, 61 (1921); *J. Biol. Chem.*, **41**, 379 (1920).

[99] *J. Biol. Chem.*, **29**, 485 (1917).

[100] H. H. Mitchell, "The Nutritive Value of Proteins," *Physiol. Rev.*, **4**, 424 (1924); see also Mitchell and Hamilton, "The Biochemistry of Amino Acids," New York, 1929, Chap. X; see also Bull. Nat. Res. Council, **11**, Part 1 (1926); Mitchell and D. B. Smuts, *J. Biol. Chem.*, **95**, 263 (1932).

[101] *Z. physiol. Chem.*, **77**, 22 (1912); Abderhalden and P. Hirsch, *ibid.*, **81**, 323 (1912); *ibid.*, **83**, 444 (1913).

[102] *J. Physiol.*, **27**, 418 (1901).

[103] *Ibid.*, **35**, 88 (1906).

Employing a tryptophane-free casein digest, Berg and Rose[104] demonstrated that when the missing amino acid was supplied at long intervals (24 or 48 hours), the effect on growth was not as beneficial as that obtained by more frequent supplementation (intervals of 6 or 12 hours). Tryptophane may be replaced by synthetic, 3-indole-pyruvic acid, but not by a 3-indole-propionic acid, or other closely related derivatives (Jackson,[105] Berg, Rose, and Marvel[106]). d-Tryptophane is utilized for growth as well as the naturally occurring levo form.[107, 108] It is therefore interesting to note that the acetyl derivatives behave differently, acetyl-l-tryptophane being readily utilized while acetyl-d-tryptophane is not utilized at all.

This peculiarity has not been adequately explained, though du Vigneaud[108] has suggested that the difference may be due to the inability of the organism to hydrolyze the acetyl group when it is linked to the unnatural isomer.

Lysine. The demonstration by Osborne and Mendel of the indispensability of lysine (p. 552) seems to have left no doubts on the subject. Evidently it has not been considered necessary to supplement their evidence with the conventional type of experiment in which the effect on growth would be determined of a lysine-free casein digest, with and without the addition of the missing amino acid.

Histidine and Arginine. Ackroyd and Hopkins[109] hydrolyzed casein with acid and removed histidine and arginine from the digest. The remaining material, added to non-protein synthetic rations, was inadequate for the growth and maintenance of rats, but when either arginine or histidine was added, further loss of weight was avoided and growth was often resumed. The interpretation given to these observations was that histidine and arginine were interchangeable in metabolism, but that one or the other must be present in the diet.

The question of the transmutability of histidine and arginine into each other has been subjected to critical study by Rose and Cox.[110] These investigators compared the growth of rats upon diets in which the nitrogen was supplied (*a*) by casein, (*b*) by completely hydrolyzed casein, and (*c*) by hydrolyzed casein from which arginine and histidine had been removed. Rose and Cox were able to show that the rats fed

[104] *J. Biol. Chem.*, **82**, 479 (1929).
[105] *Ibid.*, **84**, 1 (1929).
[106] *Ibid.*, **85**, 207, 219 (1929).
[107] C. P. Berg and M. Potgieter, *ibid.*, **94**, 661 (1931–32).
[108] V. du Vigneaud, R. R. Sealock, and C. Van Etten, *ibid.*, **98**, 565 (1932).
[109] *Biochem. J.*, **10**, 551 (1916).
[110] *J. Biol. Chem.*, **61**, 747 (1924).

upon completely hydrolyzed casein grew to maturity, though at a somewhat slower rate than animals of the same age fed upon whole casein. On the contrary, the rats that were given the arginine-histidine-free rations were neither able to grow nor to maintain body weight. Instead, there was a prompt and continuous loss of weight which could be remedied or avoided only by the addition of histidine. This part of the work, therefore, showed that *histidine is an essential component of the diet.*

As to arginine, it was found that its addition to the deficient diet exerted no perceptible influence upon growth. The animals continued to lose weight as rapidly as before the addition of this amino acid. More-

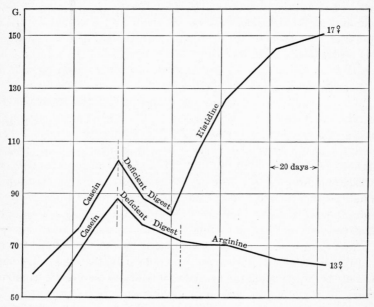

Fig. 37.—The upper curve shows the growth-stimulating effect of histidine when added to a diet deficient in histidine and arginine. The lower curve demonstrates the ineffectiveness of arginine. (After Rose.)

over, rations containing the minimum maintenance requirement of histidine and supplemented by large amounts of arginine were shown to be inadequate for growth. The work of Rose and Cox therefore furnished conclusive evidence that *arginine and histidine are not mutually interchangeable in metabolism.*

The influence of histidine and the non-effectiveness of arginine are illustrated in Fig. 37.

Additional evidence that arginine is not essential to nutrition was later supplied by Bunney and Rose.[111] By precipitation with flavianic

[111] *Ibid.*, **76**, 521 (1928).

acid, arginine was almost quantitatively removed from hydrolyzed casein. The remaining mixture when fed in sufficient amount (12 per cent of the diet) proved adequate for normal growth. Inasmuch as the possibility remained that sufficient arginine might have been left in the digest to meet the growth requirements of the animal, Scull and Rose[112] approached the problem from yet another angle. Rats were fed a diet of hydrolyzed casein practically devoid of arginine. At the outset of the experiment some of the control animals were sacrificed and their total arginine content determined. After 64 days on the arginine-deficient diet, during which time the animals gained considerable weight, their tissues were analyzed. Without exception the gain in tissue arginine was 2 to 3 times as large as could be accounted for by the total arginine content of the food eaten during the experimental period. This observation therefore warranted the conclusion that *arginine may be synthesized in the organism of the rat and that in this species at least it is not an indispensable component of the diet.*

Mention made be made in this connection of the observation of Crowdle and Sherwin[113] that birds are capable of synthesizing ornithine for the detoxication of benzoic acid, the conjugation product being ornithuric acid. Because of their close chemical relation (p. 389) the synthesis of arginine from ornithine does not seem improbable.

Cox and Rose[114] were the first to demonstrate the replacement of an indispensable amino acid by a non-amino compound. These investigators showed that the addition of *dl-β*-4-imidazole lactic acid to a histidine-deficient diet caused an immedate resumption of growth (in rats) at a rate slightly slower than that induced by the equivalent quantity of histidine. Cox and Rose state, "It is evident that under the conditions of the experiments the synthetic product in question is capable of serving in place of histidine, probably through being transformed by the cells into the amino acid." Results similar to those of Cox and Rose were obtained independently by Harrow and Sherwin.[115] The close relationship between the two compounds is brought out by the following formulas:

$$
\begin{array}{cc}
\mathrm{HC-NH} & \mathrm{HC-NH} \\
\| \quad\rangle\mathrm{CH} & \| \quad\rangle\mathrm{CH} \\
\mathrm{C-N} & \mathrm{C-N} \\
| & | \\
\mathrm{CH_2CHOHCOOH} & \mathrm{CH_2CHNH_2COOH}
\end{array}
$$

β-4-Imidazole   Histidine
lactic acid

[112] *Ibid.*, **89**, 109 (1930).   [114] *Ibid.*, **68**, 781 (1926).
[113] *Ibid.*, **55**, 365 (1923).   [115] *Ibid.*, **70**, 683 (1926).

Cystine and Methionine. The demonstration by Mendel and Osborne of growth failure in rats kept on diets in which the protein component was deficient with respect to cystine and of the corrective effect of small supplements of this amino acid provided tangible evidence of the essential nature of cystine in nutrition and paved the way to the study of the biological value of other proteins, as well as the availability of various compounds related to cystine in supplementing cystine-deficient diets. Inasmuch as casein (or even whole milk protein) on a 9 to 12 per cent level of intake, as the sole source of protein, does not contain enough cystine to provide for growth, the problem of selection of a basal diet for experimental purposes has been relatively simple and has not necessitated the use of hydrolyzed protein mixtures.

Cysteine is as effective as cystine in contributing the growth-promoting value to a cystine-deficient diet.[116,117] Certain dipeptides of cystine (diglycyl-cystine, dialanyl-cystine) are likewise available.[117] Other related compounds (taurine,[116,118] cysteinic acid,[117] dithio-diglycollic acid, β-dithio-dipropionic acid, α-dihydroxy-β-dithio-dipropionic acid)[117] have been shown to be useless in this respect.

Du Vigneaud[119] has disclosed that *d*-cystine cannot be utilized for growth purposes in lieu of the naturally occurring levo enantiomorph. In view of this remarkable specificity the discovery by Jackson and Block[120] that methionine is capable of stimulating growth in rats subsisting on a basal diet poor in cystine conveys unusual significance. But to this may now be added the striking observation of du Vigneaud and co-workers[121] that homocystine, a homologue of cystine, prepared from methionine, may be used likewise as a substitute for cystine in a cystine-deficient diet (Fig. 38). Loring and du Vigneaud[122] have succeeded, moreover, in isolating mesocystine. Like the racemic mixture, *dl*-cystine, it is optically inactive, but this is due in the case of mesocystine to internal compensation.[123] It has now been shown

[116] H. H. Mitchell, *J. Nutrition*, **4**, 95 (1931).

[117] G. T. and H. B. Lewis, *J. Biol. Chem.*, **69**, 589 (1926); **73**, 535 (1927).

[118] W. C. Rose and B. T. Huddlestun, *ibid.*, **69**, 599 (1926); B. D. Westerman and Rose, *ibid.*, **75**, 533 (1927); *ibid.*, **79**, 413 (1928).

[119] V. du Vigneaud, R. Dorfmann, and H. S. Loring, *ibid.*, **98**, 577 (1932).

[120] *Ibid.*, **98**, 465 (1932).

[121] Du Vigneaud, H. M. Dyer, and J. Harmon, *ibid.*, **101**, 719 (1933).

[122] *Ibid.*, **102**, 287 (1933).

[123] Mesocystine may be represented by the following structural formula:

$$CH_2\text{——}S\text{—}S\text{——}CH_2$$
$$CHNH_2 \qquad H_2NCH$$
$$COOH \qquad\qquad COOH$$

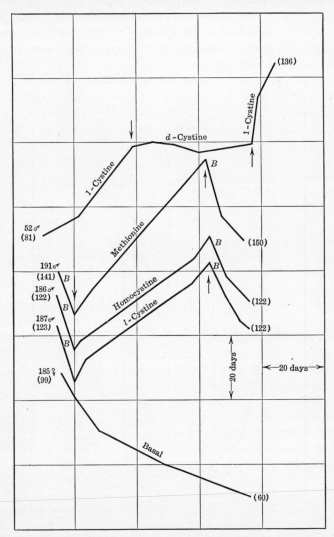

Fig. 38.—Showing curves of growth of rats maintained on a basal diet deficient in cystine. Except in control rat No. 185, the diet was supplemented for a certain interval by *l*-cystine (rats 52 and 187), *d*-cystine (rat 52), methionine (rat 191), and homocystine (rat 186). Arrow indicates point of change in diet. The numbers in the parentheses denote the initial and final weights of the rats. Note the effectiveness of all supplements, except *d*-cystine. (After du Vigneaud and associates.)

(Loring, Dofrmann, and du Vigneaud)[124] that this compound exerts the same growth-promoting effect as *dl*-cystine (Fig. 39).

In short, it appears that the presence of either of the two sulfur-containing amino acids, cystine or methionine, in sufficient amount, is essential to proper nutrition.

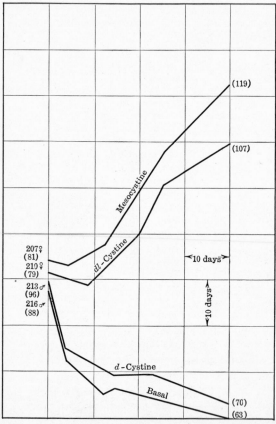

Fig. 39.—Showing curves of growth of rats maintained on a basal diet deficient in cystine, supplemented in rat No. 213 by *d*-cystine, in rat No. 210 by racemic cystine and in rat No. 207 by mesocystine. The numbers in the parentheses denote the initial and final weights. (After du Vigneaud and associates.)

Tyrosine and Phenylalanine. In a recent report Rose[125] refers to experiments in progress in his laboratory which tend to confirm the view of Abderhalden[126] that either tyrosine or phenylalanine must be

[124] *Ibid.*, 103, 399 (1933).
[125] *Ohio J. Sci.*, **33**, 372 (1933).
[126] *Z. physiol. Chem.*, **96**, 1 (1915); *Arch. ges. Physiol.*, **195**, 199 (1922).

included in the food. Hitherto there has been conflicting evidence[127] concerning the essential nature of one or the other of these amino acids and of their intermutation in metabolism.

Other Amino Acids. Aspartic acid, glutamic acid, hydroxyglutamic acid, proline, and probably hydroxyproline are apparently not essential (St. Julian and Rose).[128] In a recent summary of the problem, Rose[125] has classified the amino acids according to our present knowledge of their nutritive importance. The classification is reproduced in Table LIX.

TABLE LIX

Tentative Classification of Amino Acids with Respect to Their Nutritive Importance

Indispensable Amino Acids	Amino Acids which have not been definitely placed, but which appear to be dispensable	Amino Acids of Unknown Nutritive Importance
Lysine	Glycine	Alanine
Tryptophane	Arginine	Serine
Cystine (or methionine?)	Proline	Valine
Histidine	Hydroxyproline	Leucine
Tyrosine (or	Aspartic acid	Isoleucine
phenylalanine?)	Glutamic acid	Norleucine
	Hydroxyglutamic acid	

Complete nutritional success is evidently impossible on diets in which the protein component is entirely replaced by mixtures of highly purified amino acids. Rose[129] supplied nineteen amino acids, including adequate amounts of the known essential ones; yet the animals lost weight. When 5 per cent protein (casein, gliadin, or gelatin) was substituted for an equivalent amount of amino acids, the effect was largely averted. After an initial decline during the first four days, the animals began to gain weight. These results made it seem very probable that protein contains an hitherto unknown substance which is essential for growth. Of the three proteins, casein proved most effective. Accordingly, hydrolyzed casein was separated into various fractions of amino acids (insoluble amino acids, dicarboxylic acids, diamino acids, monoamino acids, proline, aqueous residue). The unknown essential was carried down principally in the monoamino acid

[127] H. D. Lightbody and M. B. Kenyon, *J. Biol. Chem.*, **80**, 149 (1928).
[128] *Ibid.*, **98**, 439, 445, 457 (1932).
[129] *Ibid.*, **94**, 155 (1931–32); [R. H. Ellis and W. C. Rose, *ibid.*, **94**, 167 (1931–32); W. Windus, F. L. Catherwood, and Rose, *ibid.*, **94**, 173 (1931–32).

fraction (butyl-alcohol soluble portion). Its composition seems to be unlike that of any of the known amino acids (including aminobutyric, norvaline, etc.). Its isolation and identification is a problem of the future.

THE INDISPENSABILITY OF FAT

The independent observations of McAmis, Anderson, and Mendel[130] and of Burr and Burr[131] suggested that a certain amount of fat is essential to proper nutrition. In a carefully executed series of experiments, Burr and Burr fed rats a diet containing all the ingredients known to be necessary for the rearing of healthy animals (rats). Practically all the fat, however, had been removed from these substances, including the yeast provided as a source of the vitamin B complex, by repeated extraction with fat solvents. Vitamins A and D were furnished by the unsaponifiable matter derived from a high grade of cod-liver oil. On the fat-free diet the animals grew for a time, but soon developed symptoms indicative of a dietary deficiency disease; the skin became scaly, the tip of the tail appeared inflamed and swollen, later becoming heavily scaled, ridged and necrotic. The hair on the back of the body became filled with dandruff and the hair about the face and neck tended to fall out. Hemorrhagic spots and sores appeared on the skin. Ovulation became irregular in the females; the males usually failed to mate; hematuria, albuminuria, and kidney lesions were prominent symptoms. Growth stopped about the time some of these symptoms became conspicuous, and death soon followed.

The disease could be readily prevented or cured by the addition of linoleic or linolenic acids, either in the free form, as esters (methyl linolate), or as components of certain fats (linseed oil, corn oil, cod-liver oil, tung oil, etc.). Saturated fatty acids were without effect. Oleic acid and α-eleostearic acid, an isomer of linolenic acid, were found ineffective.

Confirmatory evidence of this specific deficiency was obtained by Evans and Lepkovsky.[132] These investigators found that corn starch and rice starch were curative agents, owing to their slight but important content of unsaturated fatty acids, presumably linoleic. Other carbohydrate foods, potato starch, hog-liver glycogen, were ineffective.

According to Wesson and Burr,[131] body fat synthesized from carbohydrate provided no relief for the symptoms of the fat-deficiency dis-

---

[130] *Ibid.*, **82**, 247 (1929).

[131] *Ibid.*, **82**, 345 (1929); **86**, 587 (1930); L. G. Wesson and G. O. Burr, **91**, 525 (1931); G. O. and M. M. Burr and E. S. Miller, *ibid.*, **97**, 1 (1932).

[132] *Ibid.*, **96**, 143 (1932); **99**, 231 (1932–33).

ease. Evans and Lepkovsky have likewise shown that when rats are reared on fat-free diets, the essential substance[133] is either lacking or greatly reduced in the carcass fat and that this seems to be quite independent of the fact that the rats on such a restricted diet deposit a body fat containing unsaturated fatty acids.

The question of possible vitamin deficiency naturally looms large, inasmuch as the preparation of the fat-free ration entailed exhaustive purification by extraction with fat solvents. Burr and Burr, and Evans and Lepkovsky, were evidently satisfied that the known vitamins had been ruled out as limiting factors.[134] However, a contrary opinion has been advanced by Hume and Smith.[135] As Sinclair[136] had previously observed, the scaly tail condition described by Burr and Burr develops when rats are kept on coarse wire grids, or in cages with false bottoms. The tendency is not so marked in rats housed on fine grids or in stock cages. In short, animals that have access to their feces, which they presumably consume under the circumstances, are much less likely to develop the characteristic scaliness. Sinclair does not believe that the difference is due to the consumption of the small amount of fatty acid contained in the feces, while Hume and Smith imply that coprophagy enables these animals to overcome some deficiency of the vitamin B complex (presumably other than vitamin B_2). The condition when developed in a mild degree may be cured, according to these investigators, by the addition of whole dried yeast.

[133] Evans and Lepkovsky refer to the essential unsaturated fatty acids as "vitamin F" (*J. Biol. Chem.*, **99**, 231 (1932–33).

[134] This does not imply that the question is unrelated to the vitamin requirements, for indeed Evans and Lepkovsky have reported that fat exerts a sparing action on vitamin B. The liberal inclusion of fat in the diet enables an animal to withstand for many weeks the withdrawal, or omission of the antineuritic vitamin, and, in the presence of fat, more growth will occur at any definite level of vitamin B than is the case with a fat-free diet. The effect evidently does not depend on the degree of unsaturation, but does depend on the melting-point. Provided this is near body temperature, the sparing action can be elicited (fats melting at 38° C., exert the same sparing action as fats which are liquid at room temperature). Fats melting at about 60° are inactive. Myristin and caprylin are among the glycerides of single fatty acids which are effective vitamin B sparers, though not to the same degree as natural fats; olein is likewise effective, while stearin exerts no sparing action. *J. Biol. Chem.*, **83**, 269 (1929); **96**, 157, 165 (1932); **99**, 235, 241 (1932–33).

Contrary to Evans and Lepkovsky, Sure does not believe that fats have any sparing action on vitamin B requirements (*Proc. Soc. Exp. Biol. Med.*, **30**, 622 [1932–33]).

[135] *Biochem. J.*, **25**, 300 (1931).

[136] *Proc. Soc. Exp. Biol. Med.*; **27**, 1059 (1929–30); refer also to C. E. Graham and W. H. Griffith, *ibid.*, **28**, 756 (1930–31).

THE RÔLE OF VITAMINS IN NUTRITION

To Sir Frederick Gowland Hopkins is usually attributed the first clear statement that no animal can live upon a mixture of pure protein, fat, and carbohydrate, and that, " even when the necessary inorganic material is carefully supplied in order to supplement this diet, the animal cannot flourish." He recognized that, in diseases such as rickets and scurvy, dietary factors were involved that were as yet obscure, and he predicted in 1906 that the later development of the science of dietetics would deal with these complex unknown factors. This was indeed a remarkable prophecy.[137] The history of the vitamin problem is of extraordinary interest, but it is possible here only to outline a few of the steps which have led to its remarkable development. More adequate discussions are to be found in a number of works that are more specifically concerned with the subject.

The Discovery of Beriberi as a Deficiency Disease. The disease beriberi is known to have existed since ancient times in India, Japan, the Malay Peninsula, Southern China, the Philippine Islands, the Dutch East Indies, and, less prominently, in other portions of the globe. The symptoms of the disease vary somewhat, the early stages being generally characterized, however, by fatigue, mental depression, loss of appetite, and gastro-intestinal disturbances. As the condition progresses there is rapid atrophy of the muscles, hypertrophy of the heart, paralysis of the lower extremities, and other evidence of multiple neuritis. In so-called " wet " beriberi, as distinguished from the " dry " form just described, there is an associated edema which is evidently related to the low plasma protein, a result of protein deficiency in the diet. In particular, the development of polyneuritis and the resulting helplessness of the victim have long attracted attention.

In 1897, Eijkman,[138] a Dutch physician and chemist working in Java, reached the conclusion that beriberi was caused by long-continued consumption of polished rice. He obtained evidence that the deficiency could be removed by the addition of the rice polishings to the diet. Moreover, he succeeded in producing experimentally a similar condition in birds by feeding polished rice, having previously observed (1896)

---

[137] Hopkins was not alone in envisaging in a general way the existence and significance of unknown nutritional factors. The views of Pekelharing, published in 1905, were essentially the same as those reached independently by Hopkins the following year. Other students of nutrition were similarly impressed by the difficulty of maintaining animals on purified diets. Indeed, Lunin, a pupil of Bunge, is said to have recognized, as early as 1881, that substances other than protein, fat, carbohydrate, and salts were indispensable for proper nutrition.

[138] C. Eijkman, *Virchow's Arch.*, **148**, 523 (1897); **149**, 187 (1897); *Arch. Hyg.*, **58**, 150 (1906).

that chickens fed largely upon the remains of the food used in the hospital developed a form of polyneuritis (polyneuritis gallinarum). Eijkman originally held the view that polyneuritis was caused by a toxin contained in the polished rice and that the curative effect of the polishings was due to the presence of an antitoxin. Later, it was shown by Fraser and Stanton[139] that alcohol extracts of rice polishings exerted a curative effect on a beriberi patient. The problem was studied experimentally by Casimir Funk,[140] who fractionated extracts of rice polishings and obtained a crystalline product which was very active in curing and preventing polyneuritis in pigeons, and which he believed to be the physiologically active principle in preventing beriberi in man. Soon after, Funk reported the isolation of the same substance from brewer's yeast. His analyses showed it to contain nitrogen in basic combination, and he therefore considered that it might be in the nature of an amine. As this principle seemed to be essential to life, he suggested the term *vitamine* for substances of this character.

It was shown later that the crystalline substance which Funk had isolated was in reality the active principle contaminated by other substances. Moreover, it turned out not to be an amine. Therefore, in the original sense, the term " vitamine " was now regarded by some as a misnomer. Hopkins[141] suggested the term " accessory food factors " for the substances which Funk called " vitamines," but this designation likewise met with criticism since the word " accessory " did not imply that these components were indispensable. Ultimately it was agreed to accept the term *vitamin*.

The discovery of the importance of the water- and alcohol-soluble constituent of rice polishings as the etiological factor in beriberi stimulated many investigations of other diseases which appeared to be due to dietary deficiencies, such as scurvy, rickets, and pellagra. Since 1911, additional vitamins have been discovered. These were designated by the letters A, B, C, D, and E, this nomenclature being an outgrowth of a suggestion originally made by McCollum.

Vitamin A. In 1912, Hopkins[142] drew attention to certain observations that normal growth does not occur on rations consisting of purified foodstuffs, but that it does take place upon the addition to such rations of small amounts of milk. In the following year, Osborne and Mendel[143]

---

[139] *Lancet*, i, 733 (1910); ii, 1755 (1910).

[140] *J. Physiol.*, **43**, 395 (1911); *ibid.*, **45**, 75, 489 (1912–13); *ibid.*, **46**, 173 (1913); *Z. physiol. Chem.*, **88**, 352 (1913).

[141] *Ibid.*, **44**, 425 (1912).

[142] *Ibid.*, **44**, 425 (1912).

[143] *J. Biol. Chem.*, **15**, 311 (1913); **16**, 423 (1913); **17**, 401 (1914).

reported similar observations; they showed, moreover, that rats restricted to synthetic diets with lard as the source of fat frequently developed a peculiar infection of the eyes (ophthalmia or xerophthalmia), and that this condition could be remedied by the introduction of butterfat into the food. Evidently the butterfat contained something that was essential to nutrition. Somewhat later, Osborne and Mendel found that cod-liver oil likewise exerted an anti-xerophthalmic effect. McCollum and Davis[144] were independently engaged in the study of the problem at this time, and in 1915 attributed the growth-promoting effect induced by feeding butter, egg yolk, cod-liver oil, etc., to the presence of an essential factor differing from the water-soluble vitamin obtained by Funk from yeast and rice polishings. Thus, by the work of Osborne and Mendel, McCollum, and Davis, the second vitamin was discovered. Because of its solubility in fats, it became known as fat-soluble A, in contradistinction to Funk's vitamin, which received the designation water-soluble B. In 1917, McCollum and Simmonds[145] were able to show that xerophthalmia was due specifically to a lack of the fat-soluble A vitamin. Hence the term " anti-xerophthalmic vitamin " also came to be used in designating this vitamin. At this point, it should be emphasized that as early as 1913 Osborne and Mendel fully appreciated the nature of xerophthalmia as a deficiency disease, for they referred to it as a nutritive deficiency prevalent in animals inappropriately fed, and speedily alleviated by the introduction of butterfat into the diet.

Occurrence of Vitamin A. Milk, cream, butter, cheese, egg yolk, and the green leaves of plants are among the most abundant sources of vitamin A. Cod-liver oil is an excellent source, but it has been disclosed recently that halibut-liver oil contains even more vitamin A (this is also true for vitamin D). The following plants and vegetables have been described as excellent sources: alfalfa, broccoli, carrot, lettuce, pimento pepper, spinach, tomato, watercress. The artichoke, asparagus, cabbage, celery, chard, clover, corn (yellow), escarol, kale, pea (green), pepper (green), pumpkin, squash, string-bean, sweet-potato (yellow) are considered good sources, as are the following fruits: apricot, avocado, banana, orange, peach, pineapple. Liver, kidney, oysters, and clams are likewise listed as good sources. Vitamin A is present in beef fat, but in inappreciable amount in lard. It does not occur in vegetable oils (cottonseed, olive, almond, etc.). Mendel[146] has listed the follow-

---

[144] *Ibid.*, **15**, 167 (1913); **19**, 245 (1914); **20**, 641 (1915); **23**, 231 (1915).

[145] *Ibid.*, **32**, 181 (1917).

[146] *J. Am. Med. Assoc.*, **98**, 1981 (1932); see also R. W. Jackson, *Yale J. Biol. Med.*, **5**, 253 (1933).

ing as containing minimal or insignificant amounts of vitamin A: beets, celery, egg white, flour (white), honey, hydrogenated fats, lard, onions, radishes, rice, starch, sugar.

Chemical Properties of Vitamin A. Our present understanding of the chemistry of vitamin A may be partly traced back to the observation by Steenbock[147] of the apparent relation between the vitamin A potency of various plant and animal substances and the presence of the yellow pigment *carotene* (also spelled carotin). Thus it was found that white corn differed from yellow corn, the former being deficient, whereas the latter was relatively rich in vitamin A. Similarly, yellow butter appeared to contain more vitamin than white butter.

At the time, several circumstances stood in the way of further rapid progress, the principal one being that the requirements for growth were imperfectly understood (vitamin D had not yet been discovered). Inasmuch as the method of vitamin A assay employed growth as a criterion, the results obtained in different laboratories showed many inconsistencies and were frequently at variance.

These handicaps, however, were overcome in time. With the introduction of improved biological methods of assay and with the development of certain chemical and physical tests the way was opened to the further pursuit of the problem. With arsenic trichloride vitamin A gives a characteristic ultramarine blue color which changes to purple and then gradually fades (Rosenheim and Drummond).[148] A more lasting color is obtained with antimony trichloride ($SbCl_3$), as shown by Carr and Price.[149] Originally it was thought that these reactions were specific for vitamin A, but it has been found recently that various plant pigments react with these reagents.[150] Nevertheless, the antimony trichloride test has proven very useful, not only for the detection and estimation of vitamin A in various substances, but also in the study of the relation between it and carotene.

With vitamin A, antimony trichloride yields an intense blue color, exhibiting an absorption band at 610–630 mμ (millimicrons). Carotene, on the other hand, reacts to give a greenish blue color, exhibiting a characteristic absorption band at 590 mμ. Another striking property is that discovered by Takahashi.[151] He found that oils rich in vitamin

[147] *Science*, **50**, 353 (1919); H. Steenbock and P. W. Boutwell, *J. Biol. Chem.*, **41**, 81 (1920); Steenbock and E. G. Gross, *ibid.*, **41**, 149 (1920); Steenbock and M. T. Sell, *ibid.*, **51**, 63 (1922).

[148] *Biochem. J.*, **19**, 753 (1925).

[149] *Ibid.*, **20**, 497 (1926).

[150] H. von Euler, P. Karrer, and Rydbom, *Ber.*, **62**, 2445 (1929).

[151] *Tokio Inst. Phys. Chem. Research*, **3**, 81 (1925).

A give an absorption band in the ultraviolet, at 328 mμ. This band is not exhibited by carotene. Still another difference is that carotene is intensely yellow in color, while relatively pure preparations of vitamin A frequently have little or no color. In short, on the basis of these properties there was no reason to suppose that any relation existed between carotene and vitamin A.

In 1928, Euler[152] prepared pure carotene from carrots. It proved very effective in supplementing vitamin A deficient diets. The daily administration of only 0.005 mg. was sufficient to promptly restore the growth of rats suffering from vitamin A deficiency. The efficacy of carotene as a substitute for vitamin A both in promoting growth and in curing ophthalmia in rats was soon confirmed by others, notably by Moore.[153] This investigator found, moreover, that the liver oil of a rat depleted of vitamin A did not give a reaction with antimony trichloride. When highly purified carotene, or carrots, were fed, not only did the symptoms of vitamin A deficiency clear up, but most remarkable was the fact that the liver oil now exhibited an absorption band at 328 mμ and reacted with antimony trichloride to give the characteristic color reaction for vitamin A, as well as the absorption band at 610–630 mμ. No other conclusion seemed possible than that carotene, or some part of it, had been transformed in the body into vitamin A.

Evidence rapidly began to accumulate in other laboratories substantiating these results. It was found that a large variety of food substances containing carotene, when consumed, were sources of vitamin A. The transformation is believed to occur in the liver, which is also the main site of vitamin A storage, although accumulation of the vitamin may occur in other organs (lung, kidney). Olcott and McCann[154] have reported the conversion of carotene to vitamin A *in vitro* by incubation with fresh liver or liver extract. They have suggested that the reaction is brought about by a specific enzyme, which they have provisionally designated *carotenase*. These results have not been confirmed, as yet.

Not all the carotene administered is necessarily absorbed, or converted into vitamin A. Thus, when carotene is fed to a cow, it is partly converted into vitamin A, a portion of unchanged carotene being found in the liver (Moore). Likewise, in butter, carotene and vitamin A co-exist in varying proportions (Baumann and Steenbock).[155]

[152] *Biochem. Z.*, **203**, 370 (1928).
[153] *Biochem. J.*, **23**, 803 (1929); **24**, 692 (1930); **25**, 275 (1931).
[154] *J. Biol. Chem.*, **94**, 185 (1931).
[155] *Ibid.*, **101**, 547 (1933).

Carotene exists in at least two isomeric forms, as disclosed by Karrer and associates[156] and independently by Kuhn and Lederer.[157] α-Carotene is optically active; β-carotene is optically inactive. According to the investigations of Euler, Karrer, and associates,[158] both isomers possess about the same physiological activity. Karrer has proposed the following formula for carotene:

$$
\begin{array}{llllll}
CH_3 \quad CH_3 & & & & & CH_3 \quad CH_3 \\
\diagdown / & & & & & \diagdown / \\
C & CH_3 & CH_3 & CH_3 & CH_3 & C \\
\diagup\diagdown \; H\,H \; | \; H\,H\,H \; | \; H\,H\,H\,H \; | \; H\,H\,H \; | \; H\,H \; \diagup\diagdown \\
H_2C \quad C{\cdot}C{:}C{\cdot}C{:}C{\cdot}C{:}C{\cdot}C{:}C{\cdot}C{\cdot}C{:}C{\cdot}C{\cdot}C{:}C{\cdot}C{\cdot}C{:}C{\cdot}C{:}C{\cdot}C{\cdot}C \quad CH_2 \\
| \quad\; \| & & & & & \| \quad | \\
H_2C \quad C{\cdot}CH_3 & & & & H_3C{\cdot}C \quad CH_2 \\
\diagdown / & & & & \diagdown / \\
C & & & & C \\
H_2 & & & & H_2 \\
\end{array}
$$

CAROTENE (β isomer)

These developments have stimulated unprecedented research activity in this field of investigation, embracing not only the relation of carotene to vitamin A, the isolation of the pure vitamin, but also the chemistry of the carotinoid pigments, their derivatives and related compounds.[159]

Brief reference may now be given to the reported isolation of vitamin A. This has evidently been accomplished independently in several laboratories. Karrer, Morf, and Schöpp[160] obtained a very potent preparation from halibut-liver oil. Moore[161] obtained vitamin A from the liver oil of rats and pigs that had been fed rich sources of carotene, such as red palm oil. Heilbron, Drummond, and co-workers[162] obtained their concentrate from cod-liver oil. Inasmuch as the various preparations obtained by these investigators were found to have about the same biological activity and chemical properties, it is considered probable by authorities on the subject that they represent the vitamin in a state approaching purity.

[156] Helv. Chim. Acta, **14**, 614 (1931).

[157] Ber., **64**, 1349 (1931).

[158] Helv. Chim. Acta., **14**, 839 (1931).

[159] The student is referred to the reviews by P. Karrer and A. Helfenstein, Ann. Rev. Biochem., **1**, 551 (1932); **2**, 397 (1933).

[160] Helv. Chim. Acta, **14**, 1036, 1431 (1931).

[161] Biochem. J., **25**, 2131 (1931).

[162] Ibid., **26**, 1178 (1932).

Karrer considers the following to be the probable formula for vitamin A:

$$
\begin{array}{c}
\text{CH}_3 \quad \text{CH}_3 \\
\diagdown \diagup \\
\text{C} \qquad\qquad \text{CH}_3 \qquad\quad \text{CH}_3 \\
\diagup\diagdown \quad \text{H H} \mid \text{H H H} \mid \text{H} \\
\text{H}_2\text{C} \quad \text{C} \cdot \text{C} : \text{C} \cdot \text{C} : \text{C} \cdot \text{C} : \text{C} \cdot \text{C} : \text{C} \cdot \text{CH}_2\text{OH} \\
\mid \qquad \parallel \\
\text{H}_2\text{C} \quad \text{C} \cdot \text{CH}_3 \\
\diagdown \diagup \\
\text{C} \\
\text{H}_2
\end{array}
$$

VITAMIN A

The vitamin is a viscous, somewhat yellowish oil. It distils in vacuo with partial decomposition. Vitamin A is an alcohol and forms esters. It evidently contains 5 double bonds, but not all of these react with iodine, inasmuch as the iodine number is only about 310. Crude vitamin A resists catalytic hydrogenation; the pure product is more readily reduced. This difference in behavior is also true for oxidation. As it exists in natural foods and other products, vitamin A resists destruction much more than the isolated vitamin. With ozone, vitamin A is oxidized to geronic acid; oxidized with potassium permanganate it yields acetic acid. In certain solvents (ethyl alcohol, ethyl acetate, alcoholic KOH), vitamin A is relatively stable to oxidation in air. Its stability in natural products has been attributed to the presence of antioxidants.

Nutritional Significance of Vitamin A.[163] The *growth-promoting* properties of vitamin A were the first to be recognized and studied. Soon, however, it was disclosed that deficiency with respect to this vitamin may result in a well-defined infection of the eyes, which begins in the lids and later involves the cornea. Apparently because of the impairment of the tear glands the cornea becomes dry and subsequently opaque owing to the formation of a horny layer, a process called *keratinization* or *cornification*. The disease is usually termed *xerophthalmia.*[164]

Equally characteristic are the changes in the cutaneous system,

[163] The clinical features of vitamin A deficiency have been reviewed by G. B. Eusterman and D. L. Wilbur, *J. Am. Med. Assoc.*, **98**, 2054 (1932).

[164] Yudkin (*J. Am. Med. Assoc.*, **79**, 2206 [1922]) and Yudkin and Lambert (*Proc. Soc. Exp. Biol. and Med.*, **19**, 375 [1922]) have made a study of the pathology of xerophthalmia. Of considerable importance, too, are Pillat's observations, *Nat. Med. J. China*, **15**, 614 (1929); *Arch. Ophth.*, **2**, 256, 399 (1929).

generally. The skin becomes shriveled and scaly because of keratinization.

Medical literature contains many references to the prevalence of eye disease in communities in which malnutrition may be supposed to exist. Among Japanese children, Mori[165] found the incidence of xerophthalmia to be very high, especially in times of famine. It is interesting to note in this connection how even empirical methods often prove to be a lasting value, for Mori's treatment consisted in feeding his patients cod-liver oil and chicken livers. A similar condition prevailed in Denmark several years ago. Owing to the demands of the butter industry, the use of skim milk in infant and child feeding was so general among the poor that xerophthalmia became very prevalent. Bloch[166] studied the condition exhaustively and ascribed it to fat deficiency. Butter and cod-liver oil proved effective in treating the disease. In the light of our present knowledge, the conclusion is justified that, both in Mori's and Bloch's clinical studies, the conditions were largely due to a deficiency of vitamin A. To remedy the situation in Denmark, the government found it necessary to limit the exportation of butter, thereby increasing its consumption within the country. This measure is said to have decreased, to a very marked extent, the incidence of xerophthalmia among the poorer classes.

In the United States xerophthalmia is rare. It is frequent in China, India, and Java. It is said that in Yucatan, where poverty is widespread, one child in every five of the poorer classes suffers from xerophthalmia.

Night blindness (hemeralopia) is the condition in which there is difficulty or inability to see in dim light. One form of this condition has been definitely associated with vitamin A deficiency and more specifically with the disturbance in the visual purple metabolism of the retinal rods. In animals deprived of vitamin A, Fridericia and Holm[167] have demonstrated a delay or failure in regeneration of the visual purple. It has also been shown that the retina (hog) is a remarkably abundant source of vitamin A.[168] Night blindness may occur in association with other ocular lesions accompanying vitamin A deficiency. The condition is or has been very common among the inhabitants of Newfoundland, Labrador, Russia, Japan, certain parts of India, and other places. It was evidently known to the ancients, for Hippocrates is said to have recommended, among other things, liver as a therapeutic measure.

[165] *Jahrb. Kinderheilk.*, **59**, 175 (1904); *J. Am. Med. Assoc.*, **79**, 197 (1922).

[166] *J. Hyg. (Cambridge)*, **19**, 283 (1921).

[167] *Am. J. Physiol.*, **73**, 63 (1925).

[168] A. M. Yudkin, M. Kriss, and A. H. Smith, *ibid.*, **97**, 611 (1931).

Lowered resistance to infection in vitamin A deficiency is not limited to the eyes alone. There is good reason to believe that an increased susceptibility to upper respiratory tract infections, including those of the throat, nose, ears, and sinuses, may be a manifestation of an inadequate supply of this essential vitamin in the diet. Indeed, the observations of Sherman and Burtis[169] even suggest the possibility that vitamin A deficiency early in life may render the organism more susceptible to infectious diseases at a later age. This is in line with the experience of Bloch[170] that there is an abnormally high premature death-rate among individuals who as children suffered from eye disease of dietary origin.

Keratinization of epithelial tissues in vitamin A deficiency is more generalized than was formerly supposed. It occurs extensively in the respiratory tract, including the lungs (Mori),[171] the alimentary tract, the urino-genital tract, salivary glands and ductless glands (Wolbach and Howe[172]). Evans and Bishop[173] made the interesting observation that in experimental animals deprived of vitamin A, there is a constant appearance of cornified cells in the vaginal smears. Evans states that this is an even more constant finding than xerophthalmia and occurs earlier. The injury to the female reproductive tract thus produced may be sufficient to prevent the fertilization and implantation of the ovum. Vitamin A deficiency in the male (rat, mouse) leads to degeneration of the germinal epithelium and to complete sterility. According to recent observations[174] this effect is produced more rapidly than in vitamin E deficiency.

Another manifestation of vitamin A deficiency is the tendency to form calcium phosphate concretions in the urinary tract. This was first described by Osborne and Mendel[175] and has since been confirmed by van Leersum and others.[176] This condition of urolithiasis occurs extensively in the tropics and the Far East, which suggests the possibility of its being associated with a dietary low in fat and fat-soluble vitamins (Mendel).

It is not improbable, though the evidence is as yet incomplete, that

---

[169] *Proc. Soc. Exp. Biol. Med.*, **25**, 649 (1928); H. C. Sherman and S. L. Smith, "The Vitamins," Chemical Catalog Co., New York, 2d edition, 1931, p. 285.

[170] *Am. J. Diseases Children*, **42**, 263 (1931).

[171] *Bull. Johns Hopkins Hosp.*, **33**, 357 (1922).

[172] *J. Exp. Med.*, **42**, 753 (1925); **57**, 511 (1933).

[173] *Anat. Rec.*, **23**, 17 (1922); Evans, *J. Biol. Chem.*, **77**, 651 (1928).

[174] J. M. Wolfe and H. P. Salter, *J. Nutrition*, **4**, 185 (1931); K. E. Mason, *J. Exp. Zool.*, **55**, 101 (1930): H. M. Evans, *Am. J. Physiol.*, **99**, 477, (1932).

[175] *J. Am. Med. Assoc.*, **69**, 32 (1917).

[176] *J. Biol. Chem.*, **76**, 137 (1928).

lesions to the central nervous system may result from prolonged vitamin A deficiency.[176a]

The new-born mammal, including the human infant, has a low vitamin A reserve. It cannot be materially improved by feeding an abundance of vitamin A or its precursor, carotene, to the mother during the period of gestation. Although it is possible to impoverish the milk by depriving the lactating animal of vitamin A, it is impossible to enrich it greatly by providing an abundance of the vitamin. During the suckling period, the young animal does, however, accumulate a small reserve. It has been suggested by Dann[177] that in human beings direct feeding of vitamin A to the infant must be employed to build up its reserves. In young animals in which a considerable store had been laid down by feeding cod-liver oil, subsequent deprivation does not result at once in the cessation of growth or in the development of other signs of vitamin A deficiency. Indeed growth may continue for a considerable period.

In short, our present knowledge of the subject leads to the conclusion that vitamin A is essential for growth and that it is concerned with maintaining the integrity of epithelial structures. It may thus increase the resistance of the organism to infection and possibly to other degenerative changes. In man, vitamin A deprivation has been associated with night blindness and with changes in the epithelium of the eyeball and para-ocular glands, which ultimately lead to xerophthalmia. Mucous membranes are particularly affected, and this may be a factor in the development of upper respiratory infections. In animals there is likewise involvement of the genito-urinary tract, but to what extent this occurs in A-avitaminosis in man has not been established.

The Vitamin B Complex. What was formerly taken to be the water-soluble, growth-promoting, antineuritic (anti-beriberi) vitamin is not an entity, but is composed of at least two different factors. Of these the antineuritic vitamin (which evidently also exerts specific effects on appetite, growth, metabolism, etc.) is destroyed by heat, whereas the growth-promoting and, as shown by Goldberger and associates,[178] the pellagra-preventing vitamin is relatively stable.

British biochemists have designated the heat-labile factor by " B_1 " and the heat-stable factor by " B_2," reserving " B " to identify the complex of these two and possibly other related vitamins. In America, " B " is commonly used to designate the more heat-stable (antineuritic)

[176a] H. M. Zimmerman, *J. Exp. Med.*, **57**, 215 (1933).

[177] *Biochem. J.*, **26**, 1072 (1932).

[178] U. S. P. H. Reports, **40**, 927 (1925); **41**, 297, 1025 (1926); **42**, 2383 (1927); **43**, 172 (1928).

factor, the term " G " being employed to denote the more heat-stable, water-soluble dietary factor, which was called the P—P (pellagra-preventive) factor by Goldberger, and which also has to do with maintenance and growth.

The first experimental evidence which directed attention to the possible dual nature of vitamin B was presented by Emmett and Luros.[179] They found that the antineuritic factor in unmilled rice was destroyed by autoclaving at 120° C. and 15 pounds pressure for 2 to 6 hours. There remained, however, a water-soluble growth-promoting principle. Other facts contributed to the changing point of view. Mitchell[180] was perhaps the first to call attention to the discrepancy in the distribution of the antineuritic and growth-promoting principles. Cabbage, spinach, and other green vegetables, as well as the carrot, were evidently good sources of the water-soluble B, as regards the growth-promoting effect (*Note:* vitamin A is the fat-soluble, growth-promoting factor), but, as compared with whole cereal grains, were low in the concentration of the antineuritic principle.

Various samples of baker's and brewer's yeast studied by Levene and Muhlfeld[181] showed no correlation between their antineuritic and growth-promoting effects. Smith and Hendrick[182] found that auto-claved yeast exhibited no antineuritic principle, but contained a water-soluble, growth-promoting factor. At the same time, Goldberger and associates demonstrated that (1) autoclaved yeast as the source of " vitamin B " did not alleviate polyneuritis in rats, nor was it adequate in providing for growth, or even for the maintenance of weight; (2) an alcoholic extract of corn meal cured polyneuritis, but as a source of the water-soluble vitamin it too did not provide for growth or maintenance; (3) the combination of the two cured polyneuritis and promoted growth. This was strong evidence for the existence of two separate factors. Moreover, it was found that autoclaved baker's yeast as well as untreated yeast was effective in preventing and, in many cases, curing pellagra in man and the pellagra-like disease, " black-tongue," experimentally produced in dogs. A supposedly analogous condition, produced in rats, was likewise amenable to treatment with yeast.

It is to be appreciated that while the earlier studies on " vitamin B " taught us important lessons in nutrition, the newer developments necessitated not only a reinterpretation of all previous work, but a repetition of a considerable part of it, including a reassessment of the

[179] *J. Biol. Chem.*, **43**, 265 (1920).
[180] *Ibid.*, **40**, 399 (1919).
[181] *Ibid.*, **57**, 341 (1923).
[182] U. S. P. H. Reports, **41**, 201 (1926).

foodstuffs as sources of the two water-soluble vitamins. Not so long ago the supposition was that the principal sources of vitamin B were: yeast, eggs, plant seeds, milk, fruits, and vegetables.

Occurrence of Vitamin B (B_1). Brewer's yeast is the richest known source of vitamin B. Taking it as the standard and assigning the value 100 as the measure of its potency, Roscoe[183] has compared the vitamin B (B_1) content of various foodstuffs, with the following results, on a dry-weight basis: wheat germ 50; liver (ox), watercress, lettuce, orange, cabbage (etiolated), carrot, spinach, 10–20; green cabbage, turnip, tomato, egg yolk, onion, 5–10; meat (beef), banana, potato, apple, 2.5–5. Owing to differences in water content, the order for these foodstuffs in the fresh form is different. On this basis, wheat embryo is an even richer source than yeast; liver and yolk are excellent, but none of the other substances contain more than one-tenth the vitamin present in yeast and in most the concentration is less. This emphasizes the important point that although vegetables and such fruits as the orange may contribute somewhat to the vitamin B requirement, they cannot be depended upon to furnish very much and hence richer sources must be provided. Not included in the preceding list are nuts, rich in vitamin B. Whole grain cereals are excellent sources. Oysters contain a fair amount of this vitamin; clams do not. Milk, it is now realized, is deficient,[184] as is white bread. Vegetable oils and fats are apparently devoid of vitamin B. With the exception of cream, this seems to be true also of animal fats. Beer as a source of vitamin B is insignificant.

Occurrence of Vitamin G (B_2). Brewer's yeast and ox liver (and liver extract) are the best known sources of vitamin G. Compared on a dry basis, yeast is somewhat better; on a fresh basis, liver is the richer source. Kidney is likewise an excellent source. Egg white, watercress, green cabbage, and spinach are very good sources, having been assayed (Roscoe) at 20–40 on the basis of 100 for yeast (dry weights). Milk (cow's), meat, lettuce, carrot, turnip, egg yolk have been graded 10–20; wheat germ, onion, orange, banana, and tomato, 5–10; peas, wheat, apple, potato, whole maize (white), 2.5–5; millet,

[183] H. Chick and M. H. Roscoe, *Biochem. J.*, **23**, 498 (1929); *ibid.*, **24**, 1754 (1930); *ibid.*, **25**, 1205, 2050 (1931). See also R. H. A. Plimmer, W. A. Raymond, and J. Lowndes, *Biochem. J.*, **25**, 691, 1788 (1931). The distribution of vitamin B is well summarized by B. Sure, "The Vitamins in Health and Disease," Baltimore, 1933.

[184] T. B. Osborne and L. B. Mendel, Carnegie Inst. Wash. Yearbook, **19**, 389 (1920); I. G. Macy and associates, *J. Biol. Chem.*, **73**, 189 (1927); F. L. Gunderson and H. Steenbock, *J. Nutrition*, **5**, 199 (1932); L. T. Samuels and F. C. Koch, *ibid.*, **5**, 307 (1932).

whole maize (yellow), rice, <2.5. It is to be noted that whereas milk is low in vitamin B (B_1), it contains a fair amount of G (B_2). Liver, meat, the green leaf vegetables, and egg yolk are richer sources of vitamin B_2 than of B_1, but the reverse is true of wheat germ, whole cereals, and orange (Roscoe).

Chemical Properties of Vitamin B (B_1). Among the conspicuous properties of this vitamin are solubility in water and alcohol and its susceptibility to destruction by heat, especially in the presence of alkali. Under the influence of an electric current, the vitamin behaves as a base. It is generally conceded that ordinary cooking temperatures have little effect in destroying the vitamin. Many other properties have been described, but these may be disregarded for the present, inasmuch as it now appears that vitamin B has been isolated.

Exceedingly active concentrates have been prepared by a number of investigators, but the first to announce the isolation of the antineuritic vitamin in crystalline form (as the hydrochloride) were Jansen and Donath,[185] who considered their product to have the formula $C_6H_{10}N_2O$. Kinnersley and Peters[186] tested this preparation and found that the injection of 0.007 mg. daily was a sufficient curative antineuritic dose for pigeons, and 0.005 mg. for rats.

Jansen and Donath evidently overlooked the presence of sulfur in their crystalline product, for the crystalline vitamin isolated by Windaus and co-workers[187] has been reported to have the formula $C_{12}H_{17}N_3OS$. Kinnersley, O'Brien, and Peters[188] have repeated Windaus' work. From 2000 kg. of yeast they isolated 500 mg. of the crystalline vitamin, the potency of which is higher than that observed with Windaus' product, 1.6 ± 0.4γ (γ = .001 mg.) being the curative antineuritic dose for the pigeon. Kinnersley's crystals of the vitamin (as the dihydrochloride) have a melting-point at 250° C. (Windaus obtained 245° as the melting-point for his preparation, and Odake,[189] who has likewise reported having isolated the vitamin, found it to be 250° C.) Maximum absorption is shown in the ultraviolet at 248–9 mμ. Windaus' preparation gave an absorption band at 250–260 mμ. According to Kinnersley, Windaus' preparation is not the pure vitamin, but judgment in this matter must be reserved for the future. From all appearances, all the crystalline preparations that have been reported (Jansen and Donath,[185] Odake,[189] van Veen,[190] and Windaus[187]) have much in common; it has now

[185] *Verslag. Akad. Wetensch.*, **35**, 923 (1926).

[186] *Biochem. J.*, **24**, 1824 (1930).

[187] *Z. physiol. Chem.*, **204**, 123 (1932).

[188] *Biochem. J.*, **27**, 232 (1933).

[189] *Bull. Agr. Chem. Soc. (Japan)*, **7**, 775 (1931); **8**, 11 (1932).

[190] *Z. physiol. Chem.*, **208**, 125 (1932).

been verified that even Jansen and Donath's contains sulfur. Spectroscopic and other evidence points to a possible relationship of vitamin B_1 to the purines and pyrimidines.

Chemical Properties of Vitamin B_2 (G). Though more heat-stable than the antineuritic vitamin, vitamin G may be destroyed at high temperatures. When it was heated for 2 hours at 90 to 100° C., at pH 5, Chick and Roscoe [191] could detect no loss in activity; at 123°, however, 50 per cent loss occurred. In an alkaline solution (pH 10) considerable loss occurred even at room temperature.[191, 192] The antipellagra factor is adsorbed by fuller's earth, optimum adsorption occurring at pH 4. Vitamin B_1 is soluble in 92 per cent alcohol; B_2 is not.

Block and Farquhar [193] have reported that yeast and liver preparations show no decrease in vitamin G (B_2) potency after autolysis, digestion, treatment with alkali in the cold, or prolonged heating after having been previously dried.

It is possible that this vitamin is not an entity, but a complex of more than one substance. According to Kuhn and associates,[194] one of the factors of the vitamin G complex is *ovoflavin*, the yellow pigment which they have isolated from egg white. This has been assigned the formula $C_8H_{10}N_2O_3$. Booher [195] has announced the preparation of a concentrate from milk-whey powder. Its vitamin G potency is 2000 times that of fresh whole milk. She considers lactochrome, a water-soluble, yellow, green-fluorescent pigment, to be the major constituent of the concentrate.

Nutritional Significance of Vitamin B (B_1).[196] Beriberi is a condition of extreme vitamin B deficiency. It has been reproduced experimentally in birds, notably the pigeon, and in the rat. The conspicuous manifestation is multiple peripheral neuritis, hence the designation *polyneuritis.* Both the clinical and experimental forms of this condition are evidently the result of shortage rather than complete absence of the antineuritic vitamin.[197] Sherman and Sandels[198] in experiments on rats found that when the allowance of vitamin was too small to maintain weight, but sufficient to prolong life, the classical symptoms

[191] *Biochem. J.*, **24**, 105 (1930); H. Chick and A. M. Copping, *ibid.*, **24**, 932 (1930).

[192] N. Halliday, *J. Biol. Chem.*, **95**, 371 (1932).

[193] *Ibid.*, **103**, 643 (1933).

[194] R. Kuhn, P. György, and T. Wagner-Jauregg, *Ber.*, **66**, 317, 576 (1933).

[195] *J. Biol. Chem.*, **102**, 39 (1933).

[196] This subject has been reviewed by H. D. Kruse and E. V. McCollum, *J. Am. Med. Assoc.*, **98**, 2201 (1932) and by Geo. R. Cowgill, *ibid.*, **98**, 2282 (1932).

[197] W. H. Sebrell and E. Elvove, U. S. P. H. Reports, **46**, 917 (1931).

[198] M. R. Sandels, *J. Nutrition*, **2**, 409 (1930); H. C. Sherman and Sandels, *ibid.*, **3**, 395 (1930–31).

of polyneuritis appeared regularly.   Increasing the allowance sufficiently
to maintain weight was attended by a subacute type of polyneuritis.
When the animals were completely deprived of vitamin B_1, death
resulted early and before apparent symptoms of polyneuritis developed.

An outstanding symptom of vitamin B deficiency is the loss of appetite, or *anorexia*.   Osborne and Mendel had observed in their earlier
nutritional studies that animals deprived of what are now recognized as
the water-soluble vitamins lost the desire to eat.   This symptom was
examined more closely by Karr[199] in Mendel's laboratory, using the
dog as the experimental animal.   He found that " some relation exists
between the desire to partake of food and the amount of the so-called
water-soluble B vitamin ingested."   These findings were confirmed and
greatly extended by Cowgill and his pupils, whose detailed studies over
a period of years have definitely established the specificity of the effect
of vitamin B (B_1) on appetite, not only in experimental animals (mouse,
rat, pigeon, dog), but in man as well.   Indeed this vitamin seems to
play a dominant rôle in the maintenance of appetite, a fact which is
likely to receive increasing recognition and application in clinical
medicine.

Inasmuch as the physiological basis of the hunger sensation is
recognized to be the contractions of the empty stomach, attention has
been directed to the gastro-intestinal tract in the endeavor to explain
the effect of vitamin B_1 on appetite.   Cowgill and co-workers[200] observed no pronounced change in gastric motility in the early stages of
vitamin B deficiency, but the later stages were characterized by marked
atony, not only of the stomach, but of the intestinal tract as well.   The
injection of vitamin B concentrate was followed by a sharp improvement
in gastro-intestinal motility.

Among the reported changes in severe vitamin B deficiency is the
development of lesions in the gastro-intestinal tract,[201] and depressed
gastric and pancreatic secretion, accompanied by reduced enzymatic
activity.[202]

The lowered food consumption resulting from the loss of appetite in
vitamin B deficient animals is obviously an important factor hindering
growth.   This has rendered difficult the differentiation of the specific
effect of the vitamin on growth.   The problem has been considerably

[199] *J. Biol. Chem.*, **44**, 255 (1920).

[200] *Am. J. Physiol.*, **77**, 389 (1926); **91**, 531 (1932). Cowgill's papers on the relation
of vitamin B to anorexia have appeared in the same journal, the first being **57**, 420
(1921).

[201] R. McCarrison, *Brit. Med. J.*, **2**, 36 (1919); **1**, 822 (1920).

[202] C. J. Farmer and H. E. Redenbaugh, *Am. J. Physiol.*, **75**, 45 (1925–26).

clarified by the experiments of Sure,[203] in which he found that rats deprived of the antineuritic vitamin lost weight and died, while their litter-mates consuming similar amounts of food (considerably less than the normal intake), but provided with a liberal amount of vitamin B, survived for a long time, and even grew. Accordingly, it has been concluded that vitamin B produces growth in two ways: (a) it stimulates the appetite so that there is an increase in food consumption; (b) it produces a specific influence on growth, unrelated to the plane of nutrition, and is therefore essential for growth.

The relation of vitamin B to lactation is of considerable interest. Macy[204] found that the lactation requirement of vitamin B is about 3–5 times greater than for growth. This extraordinary need and the apparent dissipation of the vitamin have been confirmed by Sure,[205] who on further investigation of the problem reached the conclusion that vitamin B exerts a specific effect on lactation. To secure successful lactation and prevent infant mortality in rats an adequate supply of vitamin B must be assured.

As stated elsewhere, Macy's studies have shown that milk is deficient in its vitamin B content. Although this is subject to variation and tends to be even lower than usual when the maternal diet is restricted, it cannot be increased materially by supplementing the diet even with such rich sources as yeast. Certain students of the subject therefore share the opinion that at best the supply of vitamin B furnished to the nursing infant is barely adequate. In the case of mothers subsisting on a deficient diet, the situation for the infant is certainly critical. Where poverty and poor nutrition are widespread, in the Far East and elsewhere, infantile beriberi is prevalent.

Hypertrophy of the heart is a conspicuous finding in vitamin B deficiency. The cause is not fully understood, but it seems to be associated with marked retention of water in the musculature. The administration of vitamin B causes a rapid return of the heart to normal size. Drury and co-workers[206] have made the remarkable observation that deprivation of vitamin B in rats leads to severe bradycardia (slowing of the pulse). This can be readily cured by the injection of vitamin B concentrate. It is considered that the lowered heart rate may be due to the accumulation of lactic acid in the heart.

[203] J. Biol. Chem., 97, 133 (1932); compare with W. H. Griffith and C. E. Graham, ibid., 97 (Proc.) vii (1932).

[204] Ibid., 73, 189 (1927).

[205] Ibid., 76, 685 (1928); B. Sure and D. J. Walker, ibid., 91, 69 (1931); Sure and M. E. Smith, J. Nutrition, 5, 147 (1932).

[206] A. N. Drury, L. J. Harris, and C. Maudsley, Biochem., J. 24, 1632 (1930).

Evidence has accumulated to show that vitamin B probably affects carbohydrate metabolism, avitaminosis B being characterized by depressed tissue oxidation and the accumulation of lactic acid in the tissues[207] (brain, muscle, blood, etc.). It has also been reported that the vitamin B requirement is proportional to the rate of metabolism. Vitamin B also seems to be related to water balance. Its presence as an essential component of cell nuclei, the atrophy of lymphoid tissue and of the organs of internal secretion (except the adrenals) in avitaminosis B, and other phenomena suggest that numerous problems on the physiology of the antineuritic vitamin await solution.

Nutritional Significance of Vitamin B_2 (G). Pellagra is the condition in man which is associated with extreme, though not necessarily absolute, vitamin B_2 deprivation. This disease has been recognized as a clinical entity for more than two hundred years and is very prevalent in the United States, where more than 7000 deaths have been reported annually during the period 1928–1930. At present not all are agreed that pellagra is due to uncomplicated vitamin B_2 deficiency. The fact remains, however, that foodstuffs (and yeast) containing this vitamin exert a protective and curative effect on pellagra,[208] hence the designation of B_2(G) as the " antipellagra " vitamin.

Conditions analogous to pellagra have been produced experimentally in the dog and rat. Because of the characteristic changes in the skin and the specific preventive and curative effects of the B_2 factor, the latter has also been described as the " antidermatitis " vitamin. The weight of evidence indicates likewise that vitamin B_2 is essential for growth. Day[208a] has reported the development of cataract in albino rats maintained on a diet deficient in vitamin B_2.

Other Components of the Vitamin B Complex. It is not improbable that certain sources of the antineuritic and antipellagra vitamins contain other factors necessary for nutrition. The problem of differentiating these is extremely complicated; the experimental procedures have many limitations, and the criteria on which the interpretations are based have not been clearly defined. Most of the alleged additional B factors (usually designated B_3, B_4, B_5, etc.) have been related in one way or another to growth, though other specific functions, such as

---

[207] N. Gavrilescu and R. A. Peters, *Biochem. J.*, **25**, 2150 (1931).

[208] For a recent review of the subject of pellagra, the reader is referred to W. R. Aykroyd, *Nutr. Abstr. Rev.*, **3**, 337 (1933). See also F. P. Underhill, "Clinical Aspects of Vitamin G Deficiency," *J. Am. Med. Soc.*, **99**, 120 (1932); B. Sure, "The Present Status of Vitamin B_2," *ibid.*, **99**, 26 (1932).

[208a] *J. Nutrition*, **7**, 97 (1934).

lactation, have also been considered.[209] A crystalline substance has been recently isolated,[210] as the hydrochloride, from yeast, which possesses a high vitamin B_4 (growth-promoting) potency. Analyses suggest the formula $C_4H_4N_4 \cdot HCl \cdot \frac{1}{2}H_2O$.

Bios. As early as 1901, Wildiers[211] emphasized the fact that yeast contains a substance essential for its growth and without which yeast cells do not multiply in artificial media. He assigned the term " bios " to the growth-promoting factor of yeast. Interest in Wildiers' bios was revived after the discovery of the antineuritic principle in yeast, and certain investigators even adopted the view that bios and " vitamin B " were identical. This has been denied, however, though more recently it has been observed that crystalline vitamin B_1 (Jansen and Donath's preparation) is a powerful growth-stimulant for yeast. The isolation of bios in crystalline form has been reported by Eddy and associates[212] and others. Narayanan[213] has obtained a concentrate which he considers more powerful and therefore purer than the products obtained by earlier investigators. Williams and Truesdail[214] have reported the separation of bios into two components.

Vitamin C, or Ascorbic Acid, The Antiscorbutic Vitamin. Authentic accounts of scurvy may be found in the literature of the fifteenth century. Lind in 1752 wrote a treatise on scurvy which is still a source of valuable information. This is indeed remarkable, for we rarely go back so far to past generations for authoritative accounts of nutritional disorders. The history of scurvy has been traced by Hess[215] in his excellent monograph on the subject.

As to the prevalence of scurvy, it is stated that between 1556 and 1887 there are known to have occurred 143 epidemics of this disease on land. In most cases the outbreaks were among troops, prisoners, and inmates of institutions. In times of famine and war, scurvy has been very prevalent. During the siege of Paris, which lasted from September 17, 1870, to January 27, 1871, scurvy broke out among the inmates of the prisons, patients in the military hospitals, as well as among the civilian population. In the Russo-Japanese War, after the siege of Port Arthur, it was found that one-half of the garrison of

[209] A good summary is given by L. J. Harris, *Ann. Rev. Biochem.*, **1**, 350 (1932); **2**, 261 (1933).

[210] H. Barnes, J. R. P. O'Brien, and V. Reader, *Biochem. J.*, **26**, 2035 (1932).

[211] E. Wildiers, "La cellule," **18**, 314 (1901).

[212] *J. Am. Chem. Soc.*, **46**, 2846 (1924).

[213] *Biochem. J.*, **24**, 6 (1929).

[214] *J. Am. Chem. Soc.*, **53**, 4171 (1931).

[215] A. F. Hess, "Scurvy—Past and Present," Lippincott, Philadelphia, 1920; see also *J. Am. Med. Assoc.*, **98**, 1429 (1932).

17,000 men had scurvy. Scurvy was likewise prevalent during the Great War, the highest incidence having been reported from Austria. Both the civilian population and troops suffered from this deficiency disease in Russia. It is at present very common among the natives of South Africa and the aborigines of Central Australia.

Scurvy has been more frequently associated with life at sea. On long voyages, such as those made by the early explorers, serious outbreaks of the disease occurred. An early account of such an outbreak is that of Vasco da Gama, who, about 1497, reached the East Indies by way of the Cape of Good Hope. In our own day, explorers have suffered most from scurvy, particularly in Arctic and Antarctic expeditions. This does not apply, of course, to the extremely well-organized expeditions of the last few years, such as those of Rear Admiral Byrd. The relation of diet to scurvy has been known to sailors and explorers since the eighteenth century. Sprouted barley, wheat, beans, and lentils were used as a protection against the disease. The high incidence of scurvy at sea is readily comprehended when one considers that for many months the diet of the sailors lacked fresh animal and vegetable foods. The efficacy of the juice of limes, lemons, and oranges was likewise known at an early date, and, in 1795, lime and lemon juice were introduced into the rations of sailors in the British Navy, with the result that the incidence of scurvy decreased to a remarkable extent. Occasionally outbreaks occurred on what appeared to be liberal allowances of lime juice and consequently many lost faith in its value as an antiscorbutic. As we shall see presently, the antiscorbutic substance is readily destroyed, and this may have occurred in the process of preparation of the juice. Moreover, not all limes are equally efficacious; those grown in the Mediterranean region apparently contain more of the antiscorbutic factor than those grown in the West Indies.

The more prominent symptoms of scurvy in man are loss of weight, pallor (due often to anemia), weakness, breathlessness, palpitation of the heart, swelling of the gums, loosening of the teeth, hemorrhage into the skin and mucous membranes, pains in the bones and joints, edema, nervousness, and hypersensitivity to pain. Scorbutic patients frequently die in delirium, but death may also occur suddenly, suggesting the possibility of cardiac involvement. The pathology and symptomatology of scurvy, both in adults and infants, are adequately discussed by Hess.[215]

In 1895, Theobald Smith[216] reported a peculiar hemorrhagic condition in guinea-pigs restricted to a diet containing cereal but no grass,

---

[216] U. S. Dept. Agr. Bureau Animal Industry Ann. Rept., 1895–96, 172.

clover, or succulent vegetable like cabbage. The importance of this observation was not appreciated until Holst and Frölich,[217] in 1912, pointed out the similarity between this disease in guinea-pig and human scurvy. The resemblance is indeed very striking, for a diet that causes scurvy in man likewise produces it in the guinea-pig, and those substances that exert a curative effect in man are equally efficacious in experimental scurvy in the guinea-pig. However, despite the acceptance of the vitamin theory in relation to beriberi and xerophthalmia, the idea that scurvy might also be a deficiency disease, brought about by some form of avitaminosis, did not gain much headway at first. Several important papers led ultimately to the adoption of the present view.

In 1917, Chick and Hume[218] emphasized certain differences in the distribution of the antineuritic vitamin and the factor which prevented scurvy, and discussed the independent need of both factors in nutrition. In a critical study, Cohen and Mendel,[219] in 1918, produced scurvy in guinea-pigs maintained on rations adequate in all respects and containing liberal amounts of vitamins A and B.

Rats, birds, and as shown more recently, dogs seem to be immune to scurvy, as they do not develop the disease on diets that produce it in man, guinea-pigs, and monkeys. Why this should be is not clear, although there is evidence to indicate that these species are capable of synthesizing the antiscorbutic substance. Harden and Zilva[220] in 1918, expressed the view that " rats existing on a scorbutic diet, although capable of gaining in weight and reproducing themselves without any apparent manifestation of pathological symptoms for months, do not thrive as well as animals which have their diets supplemented with an anti-scorbutic." Drummond[221] reached similar conclusions, and in 1919 proposed the admission into the family of vitamins of the antiscorbutic substance, or vitamin C.

Occurrence of Vitamin C. As in the case of the other vitamins, the assay of vitamin C in foodstuffs and other materials has been based in the past on the determination of either the preventive or curative dose, in this particular instance for scurvy. However, with the advances recently made in the chemistry of vitamin C, purely physicochemical methods have been introduced for its estimation, and a limited amount

[217] *Z. Hyg. Infect-Krank.*, **72**, 1 (1912).

[218] *J. Roy. Army Med. Corps*, **29**, 121 (1917); *Proc. Roy. Soc. (London)*, B, **90**, 44 (1917).

[219] *J. Biol. Chem.*, **35**, 425 (1918).

[220] *Biochem. J.*, **12**, 408 (1918).

[221] *Ibid.*, **13**, 77 (1919).

of data is now available in which the vitamin C content is expressed in quantitative terms.[222]

Fruits, especially of the citrus variety, vegetables and berries are as a rule good or excellent sources of vitamin C. Grain products, sugars, starches, fats, oils, and yeast do not contain this vitamin. Among the common articles of diet in which vitamin C is abundant are: lemon, orange, grapefruit, mango, pineapple, certain varieties of apple (particularly in the skin), tomato, cabbage, parsley, watercress, fresh spinach, rutabaga, leaf lettuce, strawberries. Svirbely and Szent-Györgyi[223] have discovered that paprika (Hungarian red pepper) is very rich in vitamin C. According to the analyses of Bessey and King,[224] red pepper contains 2.3 mg. per g., green pepper 1.83 mg., as compared with 0.57 mg. for lemon juice, 0.53 mg. for grapefruit and 0.71 mg. for oranges. Among animal tissues, the suprarenal cortex is conspicuous for its high vitamin C content, as first shown by Szent-Györgyi. The corpus luteum is equally rich. According to the analyses of Bessey and King, these contain 1.4 to 2.3 mg. per g. The brain, liver, testes, ovaries, and other glandular tissues comprise a second group ranging considerably lower (0.1–0.4 mg. per g.).

Milk is a relatively poor source of vitamin C. It has been estimated that 500 cc. of cow's milk (16 ounces), per day, is the minimum required to protect an infant from scurvy. Hess's experience has been that 12 ounces of the best grade of raw milk, per day, is at times insufficient to effect a cure.

Chemical Properties of Vitamin C. In 1928 Szent-Györgyi[225] isolated a reducing substance from various plant sources (orange, lemon, cabbage, etc.) and from the suprarenal cortex. He recognized it to be *hexuronic acid*, $C_6H_8O_6$. As a result of a series of investigations by Tillmans and Hirsch[226] a remarkable correlation was disclosed between the reducing potential of various foods and their vitamin C content. Working independently, King and associates[227] in preparing certain vitamin C concentrates from lemon juice were impressed by the strong reducing action of the physiologically active material. Waugh and King[228] finally succeeded in isolating a crystalline sub-

[222] T. W. Birch, L. J. Harris, and S. N. Ray, *ibid.*, **27**, 590 (1933).

[223] *Ibid.*, **27**, 279 (1933).

[224] *J. Biol. Chem.*, **103**, 687 (1933).

[225] *Biochem. J.*, **22**, 1387 (1928).

[226] *Untersuch. Lebensm.*, **60**, 34 (1930); **63**, 1, 27, 241, 267, 276 (1932); *Biochem. Z.*, **250**, 312 (1932).

[227] J. L. Svirbely and C. G. King, *J. Biol. Chem.*, **94**, 483 (1931–32); F. L. Smith and King, *ibid.*, **94**, 491 (1931–32).

[228] *Ibid.*, **97**, 325 (1932).

stance which on repeated recrystallization remained constant in its antiscorbutic activity, 0.5 mg. daily being adequate to protect the guinea-pig against scurvy. This crystalline material proved to be identical with the hexuronic acid first isolated by Szent-Györgyi[225] (and later by Kendall)[229] from the adrenals and other sources.

Independently, Svirbely and Szent-Györgyi[230] likewise established the antiscorbutic property of hexuronic acid. Pursuing the problem further[231] and employing the red pepper (*Capsicum annum*) as a source they obtained 450 g. of the acid in crystalline form. To prove its identity with vitamin C they prepared the monoacetone derivative, recrystallized it, and then recovered the hexuronic acid. The final product possessed the same activity as the original material, and in agreement with the observations in King's laboratory, 0.5 mg. was found to be the protective daily antiscorbutic dose for the guinea-pig.

As these remarkable achievements were taking place, the chemical constitution of hexuronic acid, newly designated by the more specific term, *ascorbic acid*, was under intensive investigation in various laboratories. On the basis of chemical as well as X-ray and crystallographic data, Hirst and co-workers[232] have reached the conclusion that ascorbic acid may be represented by the following structural formula:

$$CH_2OH$$
$$|$$
$$CH(OH)\cdot CH \underset{\underset{OH}{|}}{C} = \underset{\underset{OH}{|}}{C} \quad CO \quad \diagdown O \diagup$$

Ascorbic acid

Natural ascorbic acid is the *l*-variety. This and the *d*-variety have been synthesized in the laboratories of Hirst[232] and of Reichstein.[232a] The latter investigator obtained the same melting point (187–189° C.) for both the natural ascorbic acid and the synthetic *l*-variety. A somewhat higher value (191–192°) is given by Hirst and

[229] *Proc. Staff Meetings Mayo Clinic*, **6**, 296 (1931).

[230] *Biochem. J.*, **26**, 865 (1932).

[231] *Ibid.*, **27**, 279 (1933).

[232] R. W. Herbert, E. L. Hirst and associates, *J. Chem. Soc.* (*London*), 1270, 1419, 1564 (1933); 62 (1934).

[232a] T. Reichstein, A. Grüssner, and R. Oppernauer, *Nature*, **132**, 280 (1933); *Helv. chim. Acta*, **16**, 1019 (1933); cited in *Nutrition Abst. and Rev.*, **3**, 710 (1934).

associates. Reichstein and co-workers have reported that the synthetic *l*-form has the same antiscorbutic potency as natural ascorbic acid. *d*-Ascorbic acid, on the contrary, was found inactive in doses four times as great as the protective dose of the *l*-form.

The ascorbic acid obtained by Svirbely and Szent-Györgyi is described as consisting of white, well-formed crystals, which melt sharply at 192°; specific rotation $[\alpha]_D^{20°} = + 24°$; molecular weight 176. It is soluble in water and certain organic solvents (methyl alcohol, ethyl alcohol, acetone); it is insoluble in fat solvents; it may be precipitated as the lead salt (see also Waugh and King), is strongly reducing and unstable toward alkali and oxidizing agents, I_2, NaIO, $KMnO_4$, etc.; it is relatively stable in an alkaline solution in the absence of oxygen. Ascorbic acid exhibits an absorption band in the ultraviolet, at 263 to 265 mμ.

Ascorbic acid reduces the indicator 2 : 6-dichlorophenolindophenol, as shown by Tillmans. This property has been utilized in the development of a titration method for the quantitative estimation of the vitamin C content of various substances.[222]

Long before the chemical nature of vitamin C was even suspected it was known to be readily destroyed by heat, especially in the presence of oxygen. For example, cabbage when boiled for one hour at a temperature of about 100° C. may lose as much as 90 per cent of its antiscorbutic property. Heating at high temperatures for short periods is less destructive than heating at lower temperatures for longer periods. The destruction of the vitamin is essentially an oxidative process. Vitamin C is likewise destroyed in the process of drying and aging of foods. Foods may also lose their antiscorbutic property during storage. Evidently the presence of copper catalyzes the oxidative destruction of vitamin C. These factors have constitued serious problems in the preserving, canning, and storage of food. Accordingly, procedures have been developed, especially in the canning industry, with the object of minimizing oxidation during the heating process.

The important observation has been made by Tillmans and confirmed by Johnson[233] that lemon juice (and other fruit and vegetable juices) oxidized with phenolindophenol, iodine, or hydrogen peroxide can regain its reducing capacity when treated with a reducing agent (hydrogen sulfide) immediately after oxidation occurs.

Nutritional Significance of Vitamin C. Scurvy is the disease associated with extreme vitamin C deficiency. Among the conspicuous pathological changes are those of the blood vessels, leading to a tendency

---

[233] *Biochem. J.*, **27**, 1287 (1933).

to hemorrhage.[234] Equally striking are the structural changes in the bones and teeth[235] and the enlargement of the adrenal glands.

In addition to manifest scurvy, which is comparatively rare, are the latent and borderline conditions which are probably much more prevalent, especially in times of economic stress.

Breast-fed infants and those given raw milk are much less likely to develop scurvy than are infants maintained exclusively on pasteurized, condensed, or evaporated milk. The greatest incidence has been observed in cases where proprietary infant foods have been permitted to replace a part of the daily milk allowance. Human milk possesses about the same antiscorbutic power as raw cow's milk and ordinarily protects the nursing infant. However, modern pediatric practice has justifiably emphasized the desirability of providing a supplement of vitamin C from such rich sources as orange or tomato juice.

From recent research there has emerged the significant fact that the adrenal cortex is perhaps the main site of storage of vitamin C. The observations of Gough and Zilva[236] suggest, however, that the anterior lobe of the pituitary may possibly be even more important in this respect. In any event this is in marked contrast with the storage, principally in the liver, of vitamins A, B(B$_1$), G(B$_2$), and D. Harris and Ray have determined that the suprarenal gland of the normal guinea-pig possesses marked antiscorbutic activity, but that this is lost when the animal is deprived of vitamin C, an observation in harmony with the simultaneous and independent finding by Svirbely and Szent-Györgyi[237] that ascorbic acid disappears from the adrenals of the scorbutic guinea-pig. In other species (cat, dog, etc.) which are capable of synthesizing their own vitamin when none is provided in the diet, the antiscorbutic activity and the ascorbic acid content of the adrenals remain unaffected.

[234] A clinical method has been introduced to test the ability of small blood vessels to withstand increased intravascular pressure. This is the so-called "capillary resistance test." G. F. Göthlin, *Skand. Arch. Physiol.*, **61**, 225 (1931); see also A. Hess, *loc. cit.*

[235] Vitamin C deficiency is regarded by Hanke (*J. Am. Dent. Assoc.*, **17**, 957 [1930]) to be the principal etiological factor in dental caries and other diseases of the gums and teeth. He has stated, "It is possible, by means of a diet containing an abundance of vitamin C, to produce solid gum tissue, to arrest caries and, with the aid of prophylactic measures, to cure pyorrhea and induce bone regeneration in the alveolar tissue."

For other aspects of the problem see S. B. Wolbach and P. R. Howe, *Arch. Path.*, **1**, 1 (1926); A. W. Meyer and L. M. McCormick, "Studies on Scurvy," Stanford Univ. Press, 1928.

[236] *Biochem. J.*, **27**, 1279 (1933).

[237] *Ibid.*, **27**, 303 (1933).

Vitamin D. In 1919, Mellanby[238] published a paper in which he
described the experimental production of rickets in puppies and set forth
the view that rickets is due probably to a lack of the fat-soluble A vitamin. In 1922, McCollum, Simmonds, Becker, and Shipley[239] subjected cod-liver oil to oxidation, thereby destroying vitamin A, as
demonstrated by the fact that the product failed to cure xerophthalmia.
It was now a question of determining whether the power to cure rickets
had likewise been destroyed in the process. A year earlier, Shipley,
Park, McCollum, Simmonds, and Parsons[240] were able to show that
the sudden introduction of cod-liver oil into the diet of a rachitic rat
is followed by a beautiful deposition of lime salts in bone, in a trans-
verse line across the cartilage, at right angles to the long axis of the shaft.
This phenomenon was employed by this group of investigators at Johns
Hopkins University in developing a delicate biological test, the so-called
"line test," by which curative effects in rickets could be determined.
Using this method, McCollum and his associates found that the oxidized
cod-liver oil, though lacking vitamin A, had nevertheless retained its
power of curing rickets. It was determined, moreover, in this investigation, that coconut oil, though deficient in fat-soluble A, possessed the
power of stimulating the deposition of calcium in a manner similar to
that of cod-liver oil. It was therefore concluded " that the power of
certain fats to initiate the healing of rickets depends on the presence
in them of a substance which is distinct from fat-soluble A." The
existence of a fourth vitamin was thus demonstrated.

Relation of the Antirachitic Factor to Radiant Energy. Park[241] has
summarized the earlier literature dealing with the influence of radiant
energy in the prevention and cure of rickets. The value of sunlight in
the treatment of this disease has been frequently emphasized by clinicians for about forty years, but clear-cut demonstrations of curative
effects were naturally lacking, as X-ray methods of diagnosis, making
possible periodic examination of the condition of the bones, had not
yet been developed sufficiently. The effect of ultraviolet radiations
in causing the deposition of calcium salts in bone and curing rickets in
children was clearly shown by Huldschinsky[242] in 1919, with the aid
of X-ray photography. Hess and Unger[243] obtained similar results
by exposure to sunlight. These studies were soon extended to experi-

[238] *Lancet*, **1**, 407 (1919).
[239] *J. Biol. Chem.*, **53**, 293 (1922).
[240] *Ibid.*, **45**, 343 (1921).
[241] *Physiol. Rev.*, **3**, 106 (1923).
[242] *Deut. med. Wochschr.*, **45**, 712 (1919).
[243] *J. Am. Med. Assoc.*, **77**, 39 (1921).

mental animals, and it was found that rachitic lesions could be prevented in rats by short exposures to direct sunlight. It is important to bear in mind that window glass filters out of sunlight the ultraviolet rays. Accordingly, light received by a child behind windows does not protect it against rickets. It has been determined that light of wavelength 300 mμ or shorter is most effective.

The problem of rickets acquired a novel aspect upon the appearance, in 1924 and 1925, of a number of papers in which was described the remarkable effect of ultraviolet irradiation in endowing foods, otherwise ineffective, with antirachitic potency. Attention was called to this phenomenon at approximately the same time by two groups of workers in this country, Hess and Weinstock, and Steenbock and his students. It was observed by Steenbock and Nelson[244] that a ration which ordinarily induced rickets in rats could be made definitely antirachitic by the simple expedient of exposing it to ultraviolet light. Hess[245] reported that, by means of irradiation, vegetable oils, green vegetables, dry milk, and other substances could be endowed with antirachitic properties.

Occurrence of Vitamin D. Halibut oil is the richest known source of the antirachitic vitamin. Cod-liver oil and the oils derived from other fish (burbot, puffer, herring, sardine, salmon, etc.) are excellent sources. Of the common foods, egg yolk and oysters contain the vitamin in relative abundance, but nearly all other foodstuffs, including milk, are comparatively poor in this respect.

Chemical Properties of Vitamin D. In 1925, it was reported[246] that cholesterol when exposed to ultraviolet light of wavelength 300 mμ acquired antirachitic properties. It soon became evident, however, that highly purified cholesterol did not behave in this way and that the actual substance involved was ergosterol ($C_{27}H_{41}OH$).[247] This is an unsaturated sterol discovered by Tanret in ergot. Yeast is its principal source, although it has a wide distribution in plant and animal tissues. Ergosterol, which is itself inactive, upon being exposed to ultraviolet light (wavelength of about 300 mμ) acquires the properties of vitamin D.

Effort directed toward the isolation of the vitamin finally met with

[244] *J. Biol. Chem.*, **62**, 209 (1924–25).

[245] *Am. J. Diseases Children*, **28**, 517 (1924); *J. Biol. Chem.*, **62**, 301 (1924–25); **64**, 181 (1925).

[246] Hess and Weinstock, *J. Biol. Chem.*, **64**, 193 (1925); Steenbock and Black, *ibid.*, **64**, 263 (1925).

[247] Rosenheim and Webster, *Biochem. J.*, **21**, 127, 389 (1927); Windaus and Hess, *Nachr. ges. Wiss., Göttingen*, **175**, 84 (1927).

success. In 1930–31, Askew and co-workers[248] separated from among the irradiation products of ergosterol a crystalline substance which they considered to be the active principle. It was designated *calciferol*. At about the same time, Windaus and associates[249] likewise reported the isolation of the vitamin, which they described as vitamin D_1, inasmuch as there were indications that a second antirachitic principle existed. Further research disclosed, however, that D_1 was in reality the vitamin in combination with an inert isomer, *lumisterol*. Askew found that his original calciferol was likewise not the pure vitamin, but that it was combined with two biologically inactive sterols, one of these being lumisterol. Further purification resulted in the isolation of the vitamin; this was accomplished independently in the laboratories of both Windaus and Askew. Askew has retained the term *calciferol* for the vitamin, while Windaus has thus far designated it D_2.

The vitamin (calciferol) consists of clusters of colorless needles of melting-point 114.5 to 117. It is optically active, $[\alpha]_D^{20°} + 102.5$ in alcohol. It is very soluble in most organic solvents. The antirachitic potency is 40,000 units per mg. (1 mg. of International standard solution of irradiated ergosterol = 1 unit).

Irradiation of ergosterol apparently results in the formation of a group of isomers. The first formed is believed to be *lumisterol*, which on further irradiation yields *tachysterol* and in turn vitamin D (*calciferol*). Tachysterol does not possess antirachitic activity and is toxic. When given in excessive doses calciferol is likewise toxic. Vitamin D, on continued irradiation, yields *suprasterol* I and II and *toxisterol*, the latter being characterized, as the name suggests, by its marked toxicity.

Nutritional Significance of Vitamin D. The disease known as rickets is very prevalent among children, and is associated with faulty bone formation. Depending upon the degree of its severity, the disease leads to various types of malformation, such as bow legs, deformed chest and skull, knock knees, etc. Concerning the etiology, it is now believed that any one or more than one of the following factors may be operative: (*a*) calcium deficiency, (*b*) phosphorus deficiency, (*c*) improper balance between calcium and phosphorus, (*d*) lack or deficiency of vitamin D, (*e*) lack of direct sunlight which includes ultraviolet radiations. These factors are closely interrelated, and it even appears that

[248] F. A. Askew and others, *Proc. Roy. Soc.* (*London*), B, **107**, 76, 91 (1930); **108**, 340 (1931); **109**, 488 (1931–32).

[249] A. Windaus and others, *Ann. Chem.*, **489**, 252 (1931); **492**, 226 (1932); **499**, 188 (1932); P. Setz, *Z. physiol. Chem.*, **215**, 183 (1933); F. Laquer and O. Linsert, *Klin. Wochschr.*, **12**, 753 (1933).

the antirachitic vitamin may be completely replaced by ultraviolet light. Rickets is essentially a condition of deranged calcium and phosphorus metabolism.

The form of rickets which is most frequently seen clinically is the so-called low-phosphorus rickets. In this condition the concentration of serum calcium may be normal, but the inorganic phosphate content is reduced. This form is associated with the skeletal abnormalities previously mentioned. In low-calcium rickets, the phospate is usually normal, or somewhat diminished, but the calcium tends to be low, this being often accompanied by tetany. Rickets is characterized by a high serum phosphatase content.

That vitamin D promotes the utilization of calcium and phosphorus and regulates their metabolism is now generally conceded. Its value in the treatment of rickets has been likewise definitely established.

Macy[250] and her associates have demonstrated the necessity of furnishing an adequate supply of vitamin D during pregnancy and lactation (in human cases) to prevent a negative calcium (or phosphate) balance. Inasmuch as milk is an inefficient source of the antirachitic vitamin, competent pediatricians now recognize the importance of administering this factor from earliest infancy. It has been determined that the vitamin content of cow's milk may be materially increased by feeding irradiated ergosterol, or better, irradiated yeast. The significance of vitamin D in tooth formation and the etiological relationship of vitamin D deficiency to such dental diseases as caries has received increasing attention in recent years.[251]

Reports have appeared showing that the administration of massive doses of irradiated ergosterol produces a condition of " hypervitaminosis " which is associated with diminished fecal excretion of calcium (and phosphorus), hypercalcemia, the widespread deposition of calcium in blood vessels and in various organs and tissues, other pathological changes, and death. Though it suggests the necessity for caution, this does not reflect against the therapeutic usefulness of irradiated ergosterol, for the quantities required to produce experimental hypervitaminosis are many thousand times as great as the amounts needed to produce the desired effect in experimental rickets.

Vitamin E; the Reproductive Factor in Nutrition. The existence of a specific reproductive factor was established through the independ-

[250] *J. Biol. Chem.*, **86**, 59 (1930); *ibid.*, **91**, 675 (1931).

[251] M. Mellanby and C. L. Pattison, *Brit. Med. J.*, **1**, 507 (1932); Mellanby, *ibid.*, **2**, 749 (1932); R. G. and M. C. Agnew, *J. Dental Research*, **11**, 478 (1931).

ent observations of Evans,[252] Mattill,[253] Sure,[254] and their associates. Rats maintained on diets adequate in other respects, but deficient in the fat-soluble vitamin E, developed sterility, the effect of the deficiency differing in the two sexes. In the male as shown by Mason,[255] as well as by Beard[256] and others, vitamin E deprivation leads to degenerative changes of the germinal epithelium. A similar effect is produced by vitamin A deficiency, but the difference lies in the fact that the testicular changes due to avitaminosis A are reparable, fertility being restored on subsequent vitamin A administration, whereas the damage produced (in the male) by vitamin E deprivation is irrevocable.

In the female, vitamin E deficiency affects neither the ovaries nor the ova; indeed, there is not even interference with the earlier stages of gestation. The embryos develop normally for about five days, or even longer, after which they succumb, fetal resorption then taking place. A single dose of vitamin E, administered as late as the fifth day, permits the continuation of the pregnancy and its ultimate successful conclusion. It thus appears that vitamin E deficiency primarily affects the embryo and not the maternal organism.

As regards the reproductive process, it is evident that not only vitamin E, but each of the other known vitamins, exerts its own special influence.

Occurrence of Vitamin E. The absence of the antisterility vitamin at least in certain brands of cod-liver oil was largely responsible for its early discovery, inasmuch as rats supplied with cod-liver oil as a source of vitamins A and D characteristically developed sterility. Wheat germ oil is the richest known source of vitamin E. The seeds of cereals and plants contain (especially in the fat of the embryo) an abundance of this vitamin (cottonseed, corn, palm oils, etc.). Certain oils are, however, relatively deficient (linseed, coconut, sesame, palm kernel, commercial corn oil). Egg yolk is an excellent source; milk is relatively poor in this respect. The green leaves of watercress, lettuce, spinach, alfalfa are among the best known sources of vitamin E. Muscle and body fats contain more than the liver, kidneys, gonads, the latter organs being surprisingly low in their vitamin E content.

Chemical Properties of Vitamin E. The oxidative changes in fats associated with the development of rancidity are destructive for both

[252] H. M. Evans and K. S. Bishop, *J. Metabolic Research*, **1**, 319 (1922). For a recent review of the subject, the reader is referred to Evans, *J. Am. Med. Assoc.*, **99**, 469 (1932).

[253] H. Mattill and N. C. Stone, *J. Biol. Chem.*, **55**, 443 (1923).

[254] *Ibid.*, **58**, 693 (1924).

[255] *J. Exp. Zool.*, **45**, 159 (1926).

[256] *Am. J. Physiol.*, **75**, 682 (1926).

vitamins A and E, especially the latter.   Wheat germ oil is conspicuous for its marked protective action against such oxidation.   This effect is apparently due to the co-existence in the unsaponifiable fraction of certain hydroxy-compounds, which have been described as *anti-oxidants*, or *anti-oxygens*.

Ferric salts destroy vitamin A.   This sensitivity to oxidative destruction is even surpassed by vitamin E.   The addition of a small amount of ferric salt to the diet causes sterility despite the original presence of vitamin E.

The association of vitamin E and the anti-oxidant effect in fats and oils has been brought out particularly by the work pursued in Mattill's laboratory.   At one time it was suspected that vitamin E itself may be in the nature of an anti-oxidant.   Olcott and Mattill[257] have, however, succeeded in fractionating the unsaponifiable lipids of the lettuce and are of the opinion that the anti-oxidant and vitamin E are two distinct entities.   The anti-oxidant has been isolated in crystalline form; it contains an hydroxy-phenyl group and is considered to have the formula $C_{13}H_{14}O_5$.   A concentrate of vitamin E which has been obtained has resisted crystallization.   Neither acetylation nor hydrogenation destroyed its activity.   It distils *in vacuo* at a temperature of 190–220° and is therefore evidently resistant to heat.   Other properties have been determined on crude preparations containing anti-oxidant and perhaps other substances.   Such preparations are soluble in ether and other fat-solvents, stable to light and to oxidation by air, cooking, drying, and steam distillation.

Nutritional Significance of Vitamin E.   The relation of vitamin E to sterility in the experimental animal is no longer questioned.   Inasmuch as this vitamin is so widely distributed in nature, it is not considered probable that its deficiency in man and animals would be encountered ordinarily.   However, Vogt-Møller[258] has reported having obtained a curative effect in spontaneously occurring sterility in cattle through the administration of vitamin E.   Later he reported favorable results in two women, who, after repeated miscarriages, each gave birth to a live child.   These reports notwithstanding, the status of vitamin E in human and animal sterility is at present unsettled.

Summary.   In this chapter the requirements of proper nutrition have been considered.   It has been pointed out that the organism should receive an adequate amount of food to supply its calorific needs. A sufficient supply of inorganic elements is likewise imperative.   Fortunately, our ordinary food contains many of these in amounts that

[257] *J. Biol. Chem.*, **93**, 59, 65 (1931); **97**, Proc., x (1932).

[258] Cited by L. J. Harris, *Ann. Rev. Biochem.*, **1**, 399 (1932); *Lancet*, **2**, 182 (1931).

are in excess of the natural requirements, but frequently the supply of such elements as calcium, phosphorus, iron, and iodine may be deficient. The protein of the diet should be adequate, both from the standpoint of quantity and from that of quality. The biological value of proteins depends upon the presence of certain essential amino acids, without which the organism is unable to restore its worn-out tissue or to maintain nitrogen equilibrium. The vitamins are equally indispensable. In the absence of vitamin A, growth ceases, the normal integrity of epithelial tissues is not maintained, and there is a lowered resistance of cells to injury and infection, resulting in such disease manifestations as xerophthalmia. Moreover, it has been suggested that vitamin A deficiency early in life may produce lasting effects on the ability of the organism to resist infection and disease later in life. Without sufficient water-soluble vitamin B (B_1), there is marked loss of appetite, growth ceases, the heart hypertrophies; in women, lactation is adversely affected, and in extreme cases beriberi (polyneuritis) develops. Vitamin G (B_2) is believed to promote growth and prevent pellagra. In the absence of vitamin C, scurvy is produced. Vitamin D, which may be derived from ergosterol by ultraviolet light irradiation, is an important factor in controlling calcium and phosphorus metabolism and exerts a beneficial effect in curing rickets and osteomalacia. Vitamin E is believed to be essential to reproduction.

Until quite recently it was conventional to define the vitamins as substances of unknown chemical nature. Indeed, had it not been for the remarkable insight of the pioneers who first opened up this important field of investigation hardly more than twenty years ago, their existence would have been unsuspected. Then followed a relatively small group of workers, whose extraordinary technical ingenuity and intensive effort were ultimately rewarded by discoveries that stagger the imagination. Nearly all of the known vitamins have now been isolated and their chemical composition determined. Moreover, the way has been opened to a more fundamental understanding of the physiological significance of these life-essentials.

There are other aspects to the problem of nutrition that have not been considered and which in fact have been observed so recently that their significance is not yet fully appreciated. Thus, a new phase has been brought out by the studies of Sherman and Campbell[259] which indicate that a diet that is more than adequate, in the accepted sense, may have a direct influence in prolonging the normal life-span of experimental animals. In addition to this possible relationship of diet

---

[259] *Proc. Nat. Acad. Sci.*, **14**, 852 (1928); *J. Nutrition*, **2**, 415 (1930).

to longevity which would affect the individual, there is perhaps another relationship of even greater biological significance. It has been the experience of those[260] who have been engaged for many years in the study of nutrition and who have had an opportunity to observe colonies of white rats through many generations that under favorable dietary and environmental conditions the individuals of successive generations grow more rapidly, are larger and more flourishing. While the elements of selection and heredity are not to be excluded, there is obviously a nutritional factor which is responsible for the improvement of the stock. Those who are interested in individual and racial physical betterment may well be guided by scientific observations such as these.

[260] T. B. Osborne and L. B. Mendel, *J. Biol. Chem.*, **69**, 661 (1926); Mendel and Cannon, *ibid.*, **75**, 779 (1927); see also A. H. Smith and F. C. Bing, *J. Nutrition*, **1**, 179 (1928); W. E. Anderson and A. H. Smith, *Am. J. Physiol.*, **100**, 511 (1932).

CHAPTER XVIII

THE COMPOSITION OF MILK AND CERTAIN TISSUES

Milk. The young mammal depends for its nourishment almost entirely upon milk, which despite certain deficiencies is nevertheless probably the most complete single food found in nature. It contains protein, fat, the sugar lactose, inorganic salts, organic acids, certain non-protein nitrogenous constituents, and vitamins, of which A and G (B_2) are present in abundance, and B_1, C, and D, in smaller amounts, as has been stated in other connections.

Milk is normally slightly acid in reaction, having a pH of approximately 6.6 to 6.9.

Of the proteins in cow's milk, all but about 15 per cent is casein. The remainder is lactalbumin together with a small amount of lactoglobulin and traces of other proteins. In human milk, in which the protein content is considerably less than in cow's milk, being ordinarily about 1 per cent, there is, according to Macy's data,[1] approximately equal distribution between casein and the remaining proteins. The protein of milk is derived from the amino acids of the blood, the synthesis occurring in the mammary glands.[2,3]

About 90 per cent of milk fat is composed of the glycerides of the higher fatty acids, including myristic, palmitic, stearic, and oleic. The remainder consists of the glycerides of the lower fatty acids, butyric, caproic, caprylic, capric, and lauric. Very small amounts of other lipids are present, including lecithin, kephalin, cholesterol, and free fatty acids. Milk fat is believed to have its origin in the phospholipids of the blood.[4]

The lactose of the milk (milk sugar) is derived from the glucose of the blood.[3,5]

The inorganic salts and other constituents are likewise derived

[1] I. G. Macy and others, *Am. J. Diseases Children*, **39**, 1186 (1930); **42**, 569 (1931); **43**, 40, 828, 1062 (1932). For a review of the nutritive aspects of milk, the reader is referred to Macy, *Yale J. Biol. Med.*, **4**, 451 (1932).

[2] C. A. Cary, *J. Biol. Chem.*, **43**, 477 (1920).

[3] J. H. Blackwood and J. D. Stirling, *Biochem. J.*, **26**, 357, 362, 772, 778, 1127 (1932).

[4] E. B. Meigs, N. R. Blatherwick, and C. A. Cary, *J. Biol. Chem.*, **37**, 1 (1919).

[5] M. Kaufman and H. Magne, *Compt. rend. Acad. Sci.*, **143**, 779 (1906).

from the blood, some by a process of simple filtration. The ash content of milk varies in different mammals, being, for example, much higher in cow's than in human milk. The elements contained in the ash are: Ca, P, K, Na, Mg, S, Cl, and traces of Fe, I, Cu, Zn, etc.[6] The amounts in which the more important of these are present are indicated by the following data:[7]

TABLE LX

	Cow's Milk, Per Cent	Human Milk, Per Cent
Phosphorus (inorganic)........	0.087	0.0148
Calcium....................	0.144	0.0354
Magnesium.................	0.013	0.0030
Potassium..................	0.120	0.0711
Sodium....................	0.055	0.0147
Chlorine...................	0.076	0.0711
Total ash..................	0.725	....

The factors which influence the yield and composition of cow's milk are: breed, age, stage of lactation, frequency of milkings, diet, pain, anxiety, fatigue, etc.[8] The data in Table LXI show the limits of variation, as well as the average values, for the composition of cow's and goat's milk.[9]

Human milk is likewise influenced by various factors. These have been studied exhaustively in a limited number of individuals by Macy and associates (Hunscher, Donelson, Nims, etc.).[1] They observed marked individual variation; one subject secreted over 2000 cc. daily, and not infrequently more than 3000 cc., whereas another subject rarely exceeded 1500 cc. The composition was approximately the same in both cases. Significant variations in the volume output of individual

[6] In addition to these elements Wright and Papish (*Science*, **69**, 78 [1929]) have reported the detection, spectroscopically, of traces of the following elements: Al, Mn, Si, B, Ti, Vd, Rb, Li, and Sr.

[7] According to Bosworth (*J. Biol. Chem.*, **20**, 707 [1915]), the probable condition of these constituents in human milk is as follows: Calcium, in combination with protein, 0.014 per cent; calcium chloride, 0.059 per cent; mono-potassium phosphate, 0.069 per cent; sodium citrate, 0.055 per cent; potassium citrate, 0.0103 per cent; mono-magnesium phosphate, 0.027 per cent.

[8] Consult, E. B. Meigs, "Milk Secretion as Related to Diet," *Physiol. Rev.*, **2**, 204 (1922).

[9] A. E. Leach, "Food Inspection and Analysis," revised by A. L. Winton, 4th ed., John Wiley & Sons, Inc., 1920, p. 113.

women were also observed from day to day and from hour to hour. As emphasized by Macy, such fluctuations may have an appreciable influence on the nurturing of the average breast-fed infant. It was found that frequent and complete emptying of the breasts encouraged the flow of milk, as did a liberal protein intake, provided, of course, that the food was otherwise adequate and well-balanced. The flow of milk was reduced by excessive exercise and heavy work, and even moderate exercise had a depressing effect. Milk flow is also suppressed by emotional disturbance, such as excitement, fear, anxiety.

TABLE LXI

	No. of Analyses	Specific Gravity	Water	Fat	Lactose	Total Protein	Casein	Albumin	Ash	Fuel Value per Lb., Calories
Cow's milk....	800									
Maximum...		1.0370	90.32	6.47	6.12	6.40	6.29	1.44	1.21	
Minimum...		1.0264	80.32	1.67	2.11	2.07	1.79	0.25	0.35	
Average.....		1.0315	87.27	3.64	4.88	3.55	3.02	0.53	0.71	310
Goat's milk....	200									
Maximum...		1.0360	90.16	7.55	5.77	.....	3.94	2.01	1.06	
Minimum...		1.0298	74.47	2.81	2.76	.....	3.59	0.83	0.13	
Average.....		1.0305	85.71	4.78	4.46	4.29	3.20	1.09	0.76	364

During the progress of a single nursing, the fat, protein, and total solids tend to increase. Macy found the two breasts functioned differently in the total production of milk and milk nutrients, but the concentrations of the various constituents were the same in the two secretions. Fluctuations in composition were noted from day to day, but a more definite trend occurred as the period of lactation progressed, especially as regards the decrease of the protein and ash content.

Human milk differs from cow's milk in having less casein and ash, more lactose, and a greater proportion of albumin.[10]

The secretion produced by the mammary glands for two to four days after the birth of the young is termed *colostrum*. It is a yellowish, alkaline fluid of greater viscosity and specific gravity than milk and has a

[10] Leach[9] gives the following data for 94 analyses of human milk: Specific gravity, max. 1.0426, min. 1.024, av. 1.0313; water, av. 88.2 per cent; fat 9.05–0.47, av. 3.3 per cent; lactose, 8.89–4.42, av. 6.8 per cent; total protein, 5.56–0.85, av. 1.50 per cent; ash, 0.5–0.09, av. 0.20 per cent; average fuel value in calories per pound, 295.

much higher content of total solids, which in cow's colostrum may exceed 25 per cent.   Albumin is the chief constituent, frequently forming more than 15 per cent of the colostrum.   Colostrum exerts a purging effect on the new-born mammal.

Human colostrum contains 8 to 10 per cent protein and more inorganic constituents and less lactose and fat than milk.   From the fifth day *post partum* until the end of the first month the milk shows a gradual change in composition, the protein and ash contents diminishing, whereas the amounts of lactose and fat tend to increase (Bell[11]).   The milk secreted during this period is often termed "transition" milk. "Mature" milk is secreted after the first few weeks.   The limits of variation as well as the average composition of human milk at different periods are shown by the data in the following table (after Bell):

TABLE LXII

AVERAGE COMPOSITION OF HUMAN MILK AT DIFFERENT PERIODS

Time	No. of Cases	Protein			Sugar			Fat		
		Minimum	Maximum	Average	Minimum	Maximum	Average	Minimum	Maximum	Average
		Per Cent	Per Cent	Per Cent	Per Cent	Per Cent	Per Cent	Per Cent	Per Cent	Per Cent
5 days	88	1.45	2.83	2.00	4.62	7.37	6.42	0.9	8.2	3.2
9 "	88	1.12	2.65	1.73	4.76	7.65	6.73	1.6	7.1	3.7
3–4 wks.	35	1.03	1.79	1.37	6.17	7.89	7.11	1.4	6.1	3.6
5–6 "	32	0.98	1.57	1.30	5.97	8.33	7.11	1.3	7.6	4.0
7–8 "	14	1.04	1.40	1.21	6.25	7.83	7.11	1.1	7.0	4.0

Connective Tissue and Cartilage.   Connective tissue contains approximately 60 per cent water and 40 per cent solids.   Of the latter, about 0.5 per cent consists of inorganic matter.   The principal organic constituent of white fibrous connective tissue is the albuminoid collagen, which composes about 32 per cent of the tissue, the remaining 6–7 per cent being made up of elastin, mucoid, ether-soluble lipids, coagulable protein, and non-protein nitrogenous constituents, or extractives.

[11] M. Bell, *J. Biol. Chem.*, **80**, 239 (1928); see also I. S. Kleiner, J. E. Tritsch, and L. G. Graves, *Am. J. Obstet. Gynecol.*, **15**, 172 (1928).

The composition of connective tissue varies somewhat with age, the tissue of younger animals containing more water and mucoid and less collagen than that of older animals. On hydrolysis, collagen is changed to gelatin.

The principal constituent of yellow elastic tissue is the albuminoid elastin, which forms about 30–32 per cent of the tissue. About 7 per cent of collagen is also present. The remaining constituents are the same as those found in white fibrous tissue.

Collagen is likewise a constituent of cartilage, which contains in addition chondromucoid, chondroitin-sulfuric acid, and another albuminoid. The following data are typical of the composition of cartilage:

	Per Cent
Water	68–74
Solids	26–32
Organic matter	25–30
Inorganic matter	1.5–2

Considerable variation in composition may be shown by cartilage from different parts of the body.

Bone. Bone which is free from marrow contains 20 to 25 per cent of water. The organic matrix resembles the matrix of cartilage.[12] It consists principally of *ossein* which is probably identical with collagen, a mucoid, *osseomucoid*, and an albuminoid. These constitute about 40 per cent of normal, dried, marrowless bone, the remaining 60 per cent consisting almost entirely of calcium in combination with phosphate and carbonate.[13]

In chemical composition the *cement* and *dentine* of the teeth resemble bone, though the dentine contains less water. The *enamel*, which is a derivative of epithelium, contains still less water, only about 5 per cent, and is the hardest structure in the body. It differs from bone in having a higher phosphorus content and a somewhat different organic matrix, for on boiling with water, enamel does not yield gelatin as does bone.

---

[12] For a brief though comprehensive account consult A. W. Ham, "Cartilage and Bone," in Cowdry's "Special Cytology," 2d edition (1932), Vol. II.

[13] The composition of the inorganic phase of bone is remarkably constant for different individuals of a given species, and, as originally shown by Gabriel, is almost the same for different animals. The following values in per cent have been obtained for human bone: CaO, 51.31; MgO, 0.77; K_2O, 0.32; Na_2O, 1.04; water of crystallization, 2.46; P_2O_5, 36.65; CO_2, 5.86; Cl, 0.01; water of constitution, 1.32. In addition very small amounts of fluoride are commonly found both in teeth and bone. *Z. physiol. Chem.*, **18**, 257 (1894); cited by R. Robison, "The Significance of Phosphoric Esters in Metabolism," New York, 1932, p. 42.

According to Taylor and Sheard,[14] the solid inorganic phase of bone consists essentially of small crystals of mineral of the *apatite* group and may therefore be designated by the general formula $3Ca_3(PO_4)_2 \cdot CaX_2$, where X_2 ordinarily represents CO_3, F_2, $(OH)_2$, O, SO_4, etc. To some extent the last may be replaced by Mg. Taylor and Sheard's conclusions are based on the chemical analysis of the inorganic phase of bone and of apatite and the resemblance of their X-ray diffraction patterns and refractive indices. Hastings and associates[15] have likewise concluded that the chief inorganic constituent of bone is probably a crystalline salt of the *apatite* series. They consider its formula to be $CaCO_3 \cdot nCa_3(PO_4)_2$, where n approximates the value 2 in untreated bone. Morgulis,[16] on the other hand, holds the view that the bone salts do not consist merely of $CaCO_3$ and $Ca_3(PO_4)_2$, but very probably also of $Ca(OH)_2$.

The composition of the inorganic phase is essentially the same in pathological calcifications as it is in normal bone, as has been shown by Wells[17] and others.[18]

Several theories have been advanced in the endeavor to explain the mechanism of calcification in bone. These have been recently summarized by Robison,[19] whose own conception is that the enzyme *phosphatase*, which occurs particularly in bone, teeth, kidney, and intestine, and is capable of hydrolyzing organic phosphoric acid esters, plays a significant rôle in the process.

Although the separation of bone salts as a solid phase has occupied the attention of physical chemists,[20] a complete understanding of the process has not yet been attained. The weight of opinion is, however, that the concentrations of Ca^{++} and $PO_4^{\equiv}$ ions in serum are either those of a saturated or somewhat supersaturated solution. Certain experiments described by Robison,[19] as well as the more extensive obser-

[14] *J. Biol. Chem.*, **81**, 479 (1929).

[15] H. H. Roseberry, A. B. Hastings, and J. K. Morse, *ibid.*, **90**, 395 (1931); L. J. Bogert and A. B. Hastings, *ibid.*, **94**, 473 (1931–32).

[16] *Ibid.*, **93**, 455 (1931).

[17] *Arch. Internal Med.*, **7**, 721 (1911); "Calcification and Ossification," Harvey Lectures, 1910–11, p. 102; "Chemical Pathology," Saunders, Philadelphia, 1925, p. 487.

[18] The subject of pathological calcification has been more recently reviewed by D. P. Barr, *Physiol. Rev.*, **12**, 593 (1932). See also B. Kramer and M. J. Shear, *J. Biol. Chem.*, **79**, 147 (1928); **83**, 697 (1929).

[19] Robison, R., "The Significance of Phosphoric Esters in Metabolism," New York Univ. Press, 1932.

[20] L. E. Holt, V. K. La Mer, and H. B. Chown, *J. Biol. Chem.*, **64**, 509, 567 (1925); Holt, *ibid.*, **64**, 579 (1925); A. B. Hastings, C. D. Murray, and J. Sendroy, *ibid.*, **71**, 723 (1926–27); Sendroy and Hastings, *ibid.*, p. 783.

vations of Sendroy and Hastings,[20] suggest that the tendency to deposit the solid salt (calcium phosphate) from aqueous solution, or from serum, is slight until a considerable degree of supersaturation is reached. Once precipitation occurs, however, the concentrations of calcium and phosphorus are brought down considerably below the level at which they ordinarily remain stable in solution.

Robison[21] observed that when bone from a rachitic rat was immersed in a solution of calcium hexosemonophosphate, or calcium glycerophosphate, there eventually resulted (at 37°) a deposition of calcium phosphate in the zone of provisional calcification. He attributed this to the action of phosphatase in liberating $PO_4^{\equiv}$ from the ester, thereby increasing the ion product of $[Ca^{++}] \times [PO_4^{\equiv}]$ at the site of calcification.

Other observers, however, have questioned this conclusion. Shipley[22] had previously demonstrated the *in vitro* calcification of rachitic bone (rat) when immersed in normal serum, and together with Kramer and Howland[23] later showed that this could also be brought about in an inorganic salt solution of proper reaction in which the Ca × P product was 40, or above.[24] These investigators concluded that the process of calcification is not one of simple precipitation of an insoluble calcium salt, but that it depends on the activity of living tissue, inasmuch as protoplasmic poisons were found to exert an inhibiting effect.

In reply Robison and Soames[25] brought out the interesting fact that whereas rachitic bone fails to calcify in salt solutions with a Ca × P product below 40, the addition of a small amount of glycerophosphate leads to definite calcification. Pursuing the problem further, Robison, Macleod, and Rosenheim[26] have recognized two distinct mechanisms by which hypertrophic cartilage undergoes calcification: (1) the phosphatase mechanism which produces in the matrix fluid a condition of

[21] R. Robison and K. M. Soames, *Biochem. J.*, **18**, 740 (1924).

[22] *Bull. Johns Hopkins Hosp.*, **35**, 304 (1924).

[23] *Biochem. J.*, **20**, 379 (1926).

[24] It has been observed that calcification depends, not so much on the individual concentrations of calcium and phosphorus in the serum (practically all the blood calcium is in the plasma or serum), as on the product of these concentrations. Thus if the calcium content is 9 mg. per 100 cc. and phosphorus (i.e., inorganic phosphate P) is 2.8 mg., the product is only 25.2, under which conditions bone formation is not to be expected. Low Ca × P products are characteristic of active rickets and osteomalacia, but just as soon as this product is increased, whether by ultraviolet ray treatment, exposure to sunshine, administration of vitamin D, or improvement in diet, the process of healing of the bones begins immediately. J. Howland and B. Kramer, *Trans. Am. Ped. Soc.*, **34**, 204 (1922).

[25] *Biochem. J.*, **24**, 1922 (1930).

[26] *Ibid.*, **24**, 1927 (1930).

supersaturation with respect to the bone phosphate, and (2) the "inorganic" mechanism which favors deposition of this salt from supersaturated solutions.

Certain evidence indicates the relation of phosphatase to bone formation. The enzyme is absent from the unincubated egg. Its appearance in the embryonic femora and limb buds is coincident with the beginning of ossification. A similar correlation between the advent of phosphatase and the beginning of ossification has been described in the case of the human patella (Martland and Robison).[27] Huggins[28] has shown that when bladder epithelium is transplanted to the rectus sheath, the connective tissue adjacent to the transplant frequently ossifies, forming calcified bone. He has observed that the development of this heterotopic bone coincides with the production of phosphatase, in very high degree. The fact that the blood contains a suitable substrate for bone phosphatase in the form of the acid-soluble phosphoric esters is another point in favor of the view that this enzyme participates in bone metabolism.

On the other hand, it has been shown that the cartilagenous skeleton of the elasmobranch fish contains considerable amounts of phosphatase.[29] This enzyme occurs in the kidney and intestine where normally no calcification takes place.

Phosphatase is a normal constituent of plasma (or serum). Its content is greatly increased in certain diseases of bone, such as clinical hyperparathyroidism (Recklinghausen's disease), Paget's disease, osteomalacia, and notably in active rickets.[30] Although the full significance of these changes is not known at present, they obviously reflect, even more than changes in the concentration of serum calcium and phosphorus, a disturbance in bone metabolism.

Attention has been drawn to the so-called " anti-calcifying " action of cereals. It is not entirely clear whether this effect is due to a low concentration of calcium or phosphorus, as suggested by the work of Steenbock[31] and his associates, or to an unsuitable ratio of the two elements, or, as suggested by E. Mellanby,[32] to some specific anti-calcifying agent such as fatty acids. In her recent review on the influence

[27] Ibid., **18**, 1354 (1924).

[28] Arch. Surgery, **22**, 577 (1931); Biochem. J., **25**, 728 (1931).

[29] O. Bodansky, R. M. and H. Bakwin, J. Biol. Chem., **94**, 551 (1931–32).

[30] H. D. Kay, Brit. J. Exp. Path., **10**, 253 (1929); J. Biol. Chem., **89**, 249 (1931); A. Bodansky, ibid., **101**, 93 (1933).

[31] H. Steenbock, A. Black, and B. H. Thomas, Ind. Eng. Chem., **19**, 906 (1927).

[32] Brit. Med. J., **1**, 831 (1922); **2**, 849 (1922) **1**, 895 (1924); **1**, 515 (1926); H. N. Green and Mellanby, Biochem. J., **22**, 102 (1928).

of diet on the structure of teeth, May Mellanby[33] states that oatmeal and wheat germ, which experimentally produce the worst-calcified teeth, have far more calcium and phosphorus than other cereals which do not exert as marked an effect. Nor does it appear that the ratio of calcium to phosphorus in these cereals is the significant factor. The Ca : P ratio of oatmeal is 1 : 5.7 and of wheat germ 1 : 14.8. Rye flour has a Ca : P ratio of 1 : 16.1, rice 1 : 10.7, and barley 1 : 9.0. None of these is nearly so effective as oatmeal or wheat germ in preventing good tooth calcification.

According to Bruce and Callow,[34] the phosphorus in cereals is present mainly in the form of inositol phosphoric acid, which is not easily absorbed and therefore unavailable for the needs of the body. It may also be observed that cereals leave an acid residue. That this may be a factor contributing to decalcification or faulty bone formation, especially in the young, on diets inadequate with respect to calcium, is a possibility which, however, requires experimental verification. It has been clearly demonstrated that the administration of ammonium chloride, an acid-former, to dogs produces decalcification of bone, this being most conspicuous in young animals kept on a calcium-low diet.[35]

In considering the relation of bone to the organism it should be clearly understood that the mineral deposits of bone are by no means inert masses of material, but are, on the contrary, actively involved in the " swirl " of metabolism. There is a continual interchange of inorganic salts between bone, the circulation, and other tissues and organs, this interchange being subject to certain equilibrium relations. Directly or indirectly, the deposition and depletion of the mineral constituents of bone are under the control of such diverse factors as the concentration of calcium and inorganic phosphorus in the plasma, the acid-base balance of the blood, the effective acidity or alkalinity of the food, the reaction of the intestine, the presence or absence of vitamin D, pregnancy, lactation, and the activity of the parathyroid glands.

The Skin. Of the two principal layers which compose the skin, the lower layer, the *dermis*, or *corium*, is vascular, and the upper layer, or *epidermis*, is avascular. The epidermis, in turn, may be said to consist of four layers or strata, the deepest of which derives considerable nourishment from the blood vessels and lymphatics of the corium. This is the *stratum germinativum*, in which cells are continually formed and are displaced toward the surface of the skin, the cells forming successively the other three layers, the strata *granulosum*, *lucidum*, and *corneum*. These

[33] *Physiol. Rev.*, **8**, 545 (1928).

[34] *Brit. Med. J.*, **2**, 172 (1932).

[35] H. L. Jaffe, A. Bodansky, and J. P. Chandler, *J. Exp. Med.*, **56**, 823 (1932).

cells, by the time they form the stratum corneum, are essentially dead and are eventually lost by desquamation. In these transitions important chemical changes are involved, our knowledge of which is unfortunately far from being complete. The cells of the stratum germinativum are metabolically active, one index of this being the relatively high concentration of a substance, presumably glutathione, which gives the sulfhydryl (SH) group reaction. The water content which is greatest in the lowest layer of the epidermis diminishes in the upper layers, as the surface is approached. Granules of an albuminoid, called *keratohyalin*, are scattered irregularly in the stratum germinativum and are very abundant in the stratum granulosum. These granules fuse together in the stratum lucidum and undergo still more profound change in the stratum corneum, where the characteristic properties of the keratohyalin are lost and keratin is formed.[36]

Keratin is an albuminoid and is the chief constituent not only of the epidermis but of its derivatives, including the hair, nails, hoofs, horns, feathers, tortoise shells, and the shell membrane of bird's eggs. Since the keratins from various sources differ somewhat in composition, it is to be assumed that there is not one keratin but a group of these albuminoids. Indeed, there is a strong probability that even in the same source there may be more than one keratin. A distinction has been made between the so-called keratin " A," which is so resistant that it is even insoluble in fuming nitric acid and in a mixture of sulfuric acid and hydrogen peroxide, and keratin " B," which is soluble in these reagents. The keratins are insoluble in the usual protein solvents and are not acted on by pepsin and trypsin. They give positive xanthoproteic and Millon's reactions. Cystine is the principal amino acid obtained on hydrolysis of keratin (when heated for a long time with strong acid).

A second important constituent of the skin, present especially in the deeper layers of the epidermis, is the pigment melanin, the chemistry of which has been discussed in an earlier chapter (p. 403). In small aggregates melanin appears yellowish brown in color, but more dense masses appear black. It is present in larger amounts in negroes than in Caucasians. Melanin is deposited in the skin when one is sunburned. Besides its occurrence in the skin of man and animals, it is normally present as the pigment of the hair and the choroid of the eye. It is also found in many low forms of life, as in the black secretion of the squid.

The formation of melanin from its precursors is brought about by an enzyme, the existence of which in the epidermal melanoblasts of the skin

[36] For a more detailed account, consult E. V. Cowdry, "The Skin and Its Derivatives," in Cowdry's "Special Cytology," 2d edition (1932), Vol. I.

has been demonstrated by Bloch.[37]   This enzyme has been shown to produce melanin from 3 : 4 dioxyphenylalanine.   The failure of melanin formation in albinos has been associated with the absence of this enzyme.[38]

In addition to melanin, the presence of a lipochrome has been described in skin and hair, to which is attributed the characteristic red coloration which is often seen in hair.

All layers of the epidermis contain fatty substances, approximately one-fifth of which, according to Eckstein's analyses,[39] is free cholesterol. It, as well as the phospholipid fraction, is present in the skin in much greater proportion than in subcutaneous fat.   Associated with cholesterol in the skin, as elsewhere, is ergosterol.   When the body is exposed to direct sunshine, the ergosterol is converted into the antirachitic factor, as has been described in the preceding chapter.   This may be the explanation for the beneficial effect of sunbaths.

The skin contains a wide variety of other organic and inorganic substances, including glucose, glycogen, and mucin, sodium, potassium, calcium, magnesium, iron, silicon, arsenic, in traces, etc.   The sebaceous glands produce a waxy secretion, called sebum.   The perspiration is formed by the sweat glands and contains among its constituents many substances which are also found in the urine.

Muscle.   Skeletal muscle contains approximately 75 per cent water and 25 per cent solids.   Of the latter about 20 per cent is protein, the remaining 5 per cent consisting of lipids, carbohydrate, inorganic salts, and the so-called extractives.   Plain muscle has a somewhat higher water content (80 per cent) than striated muscle and contains more nucleoprotein and less creatine.   The two kinds of muscle are also said to differ in their proportions of sodium to potassium.   Other differences have been described, such as the relative amounts of the various soluble proteins, but these differences are not so well defined.

The most abundant of the muscle proteins exhibits the properties of globulin.   It has been studied by a large number of investigators

---

[37] *Z. physiol. Chem.*, **98**, 226 (1917).   This enzyme was named *dopa* oxidase by Bloch, the term being derived from the initial letters of the name of its substrate, *di-oxy-phenyl-alanine*.   The action of this enzyme is not limited, however, to the conversion of only this substrate into melanin.   Compare with the work of Raper on tyrosinase, *Physiol. Rev.*, **8**, 245 (1928); see also p. 403.

[38] Garrod describes albinism as an inborn error of metabolism.   For a description of the nature of this condition, the student is referred to A. E. Garrod, "Inborn Errors of Metabolism," 2d edition, Oxford Univ. Press (1923).

The pathological occurrence of melanin is discussed by H. G. Wells in his "Chemical Pathology," Saunders, Philadelphia (1925), Chap. XX.

[39] *J. Biol. Chem.*, **69**, 181 (1926).

who applied to it a varied terminology, the most familiar designation
being *myosin*. It has been recently studied anew by Edsall,[40] who
extracted it with a buffered (*p*H 7.8) potassium chloride solution (total
ionic strength 1.2–1.5 *M*). The protein possesses certain distinguishing
characteristics. It may be precipitated by increasing or decreasing the
ionic strength of the filtered extract. In turn, the globulin may be
redissolved and reprecipitated many times without producing any
apparent change in its properties. It also remains unchanged in salt
solution (at *p*H 6.5–7.5) for several months, if kept in the cold and pro-
tected from bacteria. Edsall is of the opinion that this protein either
corresponds to or is identical with the myosin of other investigators
(Danilewsky,[41] von Fürth,[42] Weber[43]), the paramyosinogen of Halliburton,[44] and the protein fraction which Howe[45] extracted from muscle
by moderate salt concentrations. According to Edsall's observations,
the minimum acid- and base-binding capacity occurred at *p*H 6.2 to
6.6. This is somewhat removed from Weber's value of *p*H 5.1–5.5 for
the isoelectric point of myosin. Between *p*H 5 and 6 the protein is
insoluble at all salt concentrations. Among other conspicuous properties are its tendency to form gels, the marked viscosity of its solutions,
and the high degree of hydration. It is stated that even concentrated
precipitates of the protein contain 98 per cent of water, a fact which
probably has a bearing on the ability of living muscle to withstand
dehydration.

Muscle globulin is evidently composed of a mixture of proteins, for
only one of which the term myosin has been reserved by von Muralt
and Edsall.[40] This protein shows double refraction or anisotropism
and possesses other physical properties which suggest its relation to the
rod-like structural elements of the anisotropic disks in muscle. Muscle
globulin is probably the material of which the fibrillae are composed.

Myogen is clearly differentiated from myosin by its solubility in

[40] *J. Biol. Chem.*, **89**, 289 (1930); A. L. von Muralt and J. T. Edsall, *ibid.*, **89**,
315, 351 (1930).

[41] *Z. physiol. Chem.*, **5**, 158 (1881).

[42] *Arch. exp. Path. Pharmakol.*, **36**, 231 (1895); **37**, 389 (1896); *Ergebnisse
Physiol.*, **1**, Abt. I, 110 (1902); **2**, I, 574 (1903).

[43] *Biochem. Z.*, **158**, 443, 473 (1925); **189**, 381, 407 (1927).

[44] *J. Physiol.*, **8**, 133 (1887).

[45] Howe recognized the presence of at least four fractions: (1) *paramyosinogen*,
extracted in 0.225 or 0.525 *M* phosphate (mixture of KH_2PO_4 and K_2HPO_4), but
precipitated at 1.125 *M* phosphate; (2) *myosinogen*, soluble in 1.125 *M* but insoluble
in 1.725 *M* phosphate; (3) *myoglobulin*, soluble in 1.725 *M* but insoluble in 2.025 *M*
phosphate; (4) *albumin*, soluble in 2.025 *M* phosphate but precipitated by trichloracetic acid. *J. Biol. Chem.*, **61**, 493 (1924).

water. It corresponds to the more soluble fractions of Howe. It is supposedly the protein of the sarcoplasm. Presumably the fibril membranes are composed of still another protein.

Muscle hemoglobin (myohemoglobin, myoglobin) has been isolated in crystalline form[46] and has also been characterized with respect to molecular weight (35,000), isoelectric point (pH 6.99), and absorption spectrum. These distinguish it from blood hemoglobin. The iron content, however, is the same in both compounds.

Muscle contains a certain amount of nucleoprotein. Whether a protein comparable to blood fibrinogen is also present is somewhat of an open question. Protein extracted from freshly minced muscle by salt forms a clot on standing. This has been explained as being due to the conversion of " paramyosinogen " and " myosinogen " into "myosin," or muscle fibrin. As has been stated, Edsall's muscle globulin readily forms a gel. In its solubility, the undenatured protein is not, however, identical with blood fibrinogen. The concentrations of neutral salt required to " salt out " muscle globulin are in general greater than those required to precipitate blood fibrinogen and slightly less than those necessary to precipitate euglobulin. This places muscle globulin in a position intermediate between the two plasma proteins.

Boiling water extracts from muscle both inorganic salts and a variety of organic compounds, the latter being termed " extractives." Among the nitrogenous organic extractives are included creatine, creatinephosphate, creatinine, inosinic acid, adenylic acid, adenosine-triphosphoric acid (adenyl-pyrophosphoric acid), glutathione, various purines, such as hypoxanthine, etc. These have been described in other connections. The amount of creatine in human skeletal muscle is about 350 to 400 mg. per 100 grams, and in smooth muscle (such as that of the human uterus) about one-fifth as much. About 5 to 10 mg. of creatinine per 100 grams is present in striated muscle and somewhat smaller quantities in smooth muscle. The nitrogenous base carnosine, $C_9H_{14}N_4O_3$, has been isolated from meat extracts. On hydrolysis it yields histidine and β-alanine. Anserine, first isolated from goose muscle, is methyl carnosine (β-alanyl-methylhistidine). Another base is carnitine, $C_7H_{15}NO_3$, which is a derivative of betaine. The presence of acetyl choline has also been reported. The non-nitrogenous organic extractives include glycogen, glucose, the hexahydric alcohol, inosite, or inositol, $C_6H_6(OH)_6$, the various hexose-phosphates described in

[46] A. H. T. Theorell, *Biochem. Z.* **252**, 1 (1932); see also G. B. Ray and G. H. Paff, *Am. J. Physiol.*, **94**, 521 (1930); M. N. J. Dirken and H. W. Mook, *J. Physiol.*, **69**, 210 (1930).

the discussion of carbohydrate metabolism, a small amount of *l*-lactic acid (absent in resting muscle) and *d*-lactic, or sarcolactic acid.[47]

The inorganic constituents (found in the ash) of striated muscle include potassium (0.25 to 0.4 per cent), sodium (0.06 to 0.16 per cent), magnesium (0.02 to 0.03 per cent), chloride (0.04 to 0.08 per cent), sulfur (0.19 to 0.23 per cent), and phosphorus (0.17 to 0.25 per cent).[48] The calcium content is normally about 70 mg. per 100 grams (0.07 per cent). It is considerably reduced in rickets.[49] The sulfur is practically all present in organic combination in protein. In striated muscle about 80 per cent of the phosphorus is inorganic and the remainder organic. The relation is very different in smooth muscle, where the inorganic phosphorus is frequently 40 per cent or less (as in uterine muscle) and the organic phosphorus about 60 per cent. The buffering power of smooth muscle is said to be less than that of striated muscle.

More sodium chloride and less potassium chloride are present in plain muscle than in striated muscle. The ratio of sodium to potassium in the former is 1 : 1.5, whereas in the latter it is 1 : 5.[49]

Brain and Nerve Tissue. An outstanding difference in the composition of the gray and white matter of the brain is the water content, which in the former varies, on an average, between 83 to 85 per cent and in the latter between 68 to 73 per cent. The white matter, accordingly, contains 27 to 32 per cent solids; these are distributed as follows:

(1) Protein, 7 per cent, including globulin and nucleoprotein, the latter amounting to about 3.7 per cent.

(2) Neurokeratin, an albuminoid, 3 per cent.

(3) Lecithin, 5 per cent.

(4) Kephalin, 3.5 per cent.

(5) Cerebrosides, including phrenosin and kerasin, 5 per cent.

(6) Cholesterol, 5 per cent.

(7) Inorganic matter, 0.8 per cent, as follows: potassium, 0.3 per cent; sodium, 0.02 per cent; chloride, 0.1 per cent; magnesium, 0.02 per cent; calcium, 0.01 per cent; iron, 0.006 per cent.[50]

[47] For a fuller account the reader is referred to D. W. Wilson's review "Nitrogenous Muscle Extractives," *Yale J. Biol. Med.*, **4**, 627 (1932). See also F. Kutscher and D. Ackermann's article on the comparative biochemistry of vertebrates and invertebrates. *Ann. Rev. Biochem.*, **2**, 355 (1933).

[48] E. B. Meigs and L. A. Ryan, *J. Biol. Chem.*, **11**, 401 (1912).

[49] The reader is referred to the following reviews: D. M. Needham, "Red and White Muscle," *Physiol. Rev.*, **6**, 1 (1926); C. L. Evans, "Physiology of Plain Muscle," *ibid.*, p. 358; J. K. Parnas, "The Chemistry of Muscle," *Ann. Rev. Biochem.*, **1**, 431 (1932); **2**, 317 (1933).

[50] These data are based chiefly on those compiled by P. Hari, in his "Kurzes Lehrbuch der physiologischen Chemie," Berlin, 1928, p. 223.

The total solids of the gray matter approximate 15 to 17 per cent and are distributed as follows:

(1) Protein, 8 per cent, of which the nucleoprotein is 3 per cent.
(2) Neurokeratin, 0.4 per cent.
(3) Lecithin, 3 per cent.
(4) Kephalin, 0.7 per cent.
(5) Cerebrosides (phrenosin and kerasin), 3 per cent.
(6) Cholesterol, 0.7 per cent.
(7) Inorganic matter, 0.8 per cent.

Other important constituents are: sphingomyelin, sulfolipids, aminolipids, creatine, creatine-phosphate, inosite, amino acids, and organic acids.

The spinal cord contains a greater proportion of unsaturated phospholipids than any other part of the central nervous system. The water content is 74 per cent, and the total amount of lipids is about 18 per cent. The peripheral nerves, on the other hand, contain only about 60 per cent water. Medullated fibers have more cerebrosides than phospholipids, whereas the reverse relationship is present in the non-medullated fibers. Approximately the same amount of neurokeratin is contained in peripheral nerves as in the gray substance of the brain.

AUTHOR INDEX

A

ABDERHALDEN, E., 62, 100, 104, 105, 107, 147, 395, 396, 407, 420, 478, 483, 540, 554, 560
ABEL, J. J., 471, 472, 473, 474, 487
ABELIN, I., 428
ABOUSHADID, E., 514
ABRAMSON, H. A., 311, 336, 472, 609
ACKERMANN, D., 207, 386, 395, 407, 419, 425
ACKROYD, H., 555, 580
ADAIR, G. S., 228, 229, 231, 234, 248, 249, 261
ADAMS, E. Q., 30
ADAMS, E. T., 524
ADAMS, S. F., 353
ADDIS, T., 448
ADDISON, T., 489
ADLER, F. H., 293
ADOLPH, E. F., 282, 283, 285
AGNEW, M. C., 591
AGNEW, R. G., 591
ALDRICH, T. B., 487
ALLAN, F. N., 475
ALLEN, C. M. VAN, 227
ALLEN, E., 495
ALLEN, E. G., 454
ALLEN, F. M., 475
ALLISON, C. L., 186
ALMEIDA, O., DE, 513
ALSBERG, C. L., 80, 120, 302, 396
ALVAREZ, W. C., 209
AMBERG, S., 437
AMBROSE, A. M., 206, 392, 397
AMIRADZIBI, S., 407
ANDERSON, R. J., 65
ANDERSON, R. S., 151
ANDERSON, W. E., 348, 349, 350, 352, 562, 595
ANDREW, R. H., 130
ANDREWS, J. C., 392

ANGEVINE, M., 203, 230
ANSON, M. L., 117, 118, 235, 238, 242, 243
ARMSTRONG, A. R., 342
ARMSTRONG, E. F., 37, 45, 46
ARNHEIM, F., 146
ARNOLD, A., 425
ARNOLD, R. M., 287
ARNOLD, W., 30
ARRHENIUS, S., 12
ASCHNER, B., 497
ASKANAZY, M., 486
ASKEW, F. A., 590
ATCHLEY, W. O., 290, 414
ATWATER, W. O., 124, 501, 503, 504, 585
AUSTIN, J. H., 186, 218, 236, 262
AUSTIN, W. C., 36
AULT, W. C., 81
AVOGADRO, A., 8, 10

B

BABCOCK, S. M., 531, 534
BABERS, F. H., 65
BABKIN, B. P., 168
BACH, A., 297, 302
BAER, J., 336
BAEYER, A., 28
BAILLY, O., 81
BAKWIN, H., 274, 603
BAKWIN, R. M., 603
BALACAR, J. O., 286
BALDES, K., 398
BALDWIN, M. E., 146
BALL, E. G., 179, 180
BALLOWITZ, K., 400
BALLS, A. K., 184
BALY, E. C. C., 28, 105
BANTING, F. G., 177, 469, 470, 471
BARBIERI, J., 95
BARBOUR, A. D., 319
BARBOUR, H. G., 286
BARCROFT, J., 238, 242, 246, 248, 529

611

GREEN, J. R., 147
GREEN, R. P., 265, 334
GREENBERG, D. M., 26, 27, 271, 272, 292
GREENBERG, M. M., 26, 27
GREENE, C. H., 277, 280, 283, 286, 290, 490
GREENWALD, I., 55, 423, 426
GREGERSON, M. I., 156
GRIFFITH, F. R., 511
GRIFFITH, W. H., 381, 563, 579
GRIFFITHS, W. J., 188
GROLLMAN, A., 26, 27, 246, 292
GROSS, E. J., 419, 567
GROVE, E. W., 204
GRUBER, M., 444
GRÜSSNER, A., 584
GRYNBERG, M. Z., 439
GUDERNATSCH, J. F., 483
GUILLAUMIN, L. O., 219
GULEWITSCH, W., 407, 423
GULICK, M., 367
GUNDERSON, F. L., 575
GUNN, K. B., 512
GUNTHER, L., 271
GÜRBER, A., 261
GUTMAN, A. B., 478, 483
GYÖRGY, P., 276, 577

H

HALDANE, J. B. S., 130, 135, 146, 168, 237, 265, 268, 283
HALDANE, J. S., 237, 250
HALL, H. S., 7
HALLIBURTON, W. D., 607
HALLIDAY, N., 577
HALLOWAY, R. G., 410
HALPERT, B., 191, 192
HALSTED, J. A., 463
HAM, A. W., 600
HÄMÄLÄINEN, J. W., 527
HAMILTON, T. S., 379, 390, 392, 554
HAMMARSTEN, O., 170, 185
HAMMERSBACHER, F., 147
HAMMETT, F. S., 279, 539
HAMSIK, A., 153
HAND, D. B., 132, 303, 410
HANKE, M. E., 162
HANKE, M. T., 205, 207, 405, 587
HANKINS, O. G., 348
HANSEN, C., 349

HANSEN, L. O., 514
HANSON, A. M., 484
HANZAL, R. F., 437
HARDEN, A., 320, 321, 583
HARDING, V. J., 342, 460
HARDY, W. B., 109
HARI, P., 609
HARINGTON, C. R., 97, 471, 477, 478, 541
HÄRLE, R., 84
HARMON, J., 393, 558
HARRIS, L. J., 101, 103, 579, 581, 584, 587, 593
HARRIS, M. M., 394, 420
HARRIS, S., 476
HARRISON, D. C., 301
HARRISON, E. S., 375
HARROP, G. A., 490
HARROW, B., 405, 493, 557
HART, B., 531, 536, 540, 543
HARTMAN, F. A., 489
HARTMAN, W. E., 489, 490
HARTMANN, A. F., 284
HARTRIDGE, H., 245
HARVEY, B. C. H., 161
HARVEY, E. N., 304
HARVEY, R. B., 1, 29
HASSELBACH, K. A., 255, 510
HASTINGS, A. B., 236, 258, 262, 290, 337, 479, 489, 601, 602
HATTERER, C., 356
HAUGAARD, G., 55, 87
HAUROWITZ, F., 146
HAWK, P. B., 455
HAWKINS, J. A., 250
HAWLEY, E., 468
HAWLEY, E. E., 370
HAYMAN, J. M., 463
HEDIN, S. G., 94, 96
HÉDON, E., 468
HEIDELBERGER, M., 65, 258
HEIDENHAIN, R., 159, 164, 198, 447
HEILBRON, I. M., 105, 569
HEILBRUNN, L. V., 3
HEIM, J. W., 288
HEINBECKER, P., 367, 513
HEKTOEN, L., 236, 478
HELFENSTEIN, A., 569
HELFERICH, B., 42
HELLEBRANDT, F. A., 460
HELLSTRÖM, H., 132, 301

SUBJECT INDEX

A

Absorption, 195
  factors in, 195
  from intestine, 196
  from upper alimentary tract, 196
  function of bile in, 198
  function of lymph in, 196
  function of villi in, 196
  mechanism of, 201
  of amino acids, 199
  of carbohydrates, 197, 309
  of fat, 197, 345
  of proteins, 199
Absorption spectra, hemoglobin, 236
  vitamin A, 567, 568
Acalcerosis, 537
Acetaldehyde, conversion into aldol, 338
  relation to glucose metabolism, 325, 328
Acetic acid, physiological occurrence of, 73
Acetoacetic acid, from tyrosine, 402
  origin of, 359, 361, 362
  oxidation of, 361, 362
Acetone, 364
Acetone bodies, 359
  excretion in fasting individuals, 460
  formation of, from amino acids, 366, 386, 402
Acetonuria (ketonuria), 460
  effect of insulin on, 474
Achlorhydria, 174, 175
Achylia, 176
Acid-base balance of the blood, 265, 266, 267
  relation to fat metabolism, 368
Acidosis, 253, 265, 266
  effect of insulin on, 474
  in starvation, 368
  relation to dehydration, 284
  relation to urinary ammonia, 414

Acids, dissociation of, 17
  excretion in urine, 451
  fatty, 73, 74, 75
  neutralization of, by buffers, 252
  reaction with protein, 112
Acromegaly, 499
Actiniohematin, 243
Activators, 168
Addison's disease, 489
Adenase, 136, 437, 438
Adenine, 431, 432, 433, 434
  fate of, in metabolism, 437–439
Adenosine, 437, 439
Adenosine deaminase, 136
Adenosine triphosphoric acid (adenosine triphosphate), 319, 331, 332, 338, 416
Adenylic acid (adenine nucleotide), 331, 433, 608
Adenylpyrophosphoric acid (*see* Adenosine triphosphoric acid)
Adipose tissue, distribution of, in body, 350
Adrenalin (epinephrin), 487
  relation to carbohydrate metabolism, 314, 315, 488
  relation to tyrosine, 404
Adrenals, 487
  hyperfunction of, 491
  hypofunction of, 489
  physiological action of cortical hormone of, 490
  relation to Addison's disease, 489
  vitamin C in, 584, 587
Adsorption, 22
Aetioporphyrin, 239, 240, 241
Agar, galactans in, 34
Age, effect of, on basal metabolism, 510
  on creatine excretion, 427
Agmatine, 209

631

Amylopsin (*see* Amylase), 182, 193, 194
Anaphylaxis, 200
Anemia, nutritional, 540
    relation of copper to, 542
    relation of iron to, 540
Anhydremia, 214
Anions, reaction of with proteins, 110
Anorexia, relation to vitamin B deficiency, 578
Anserine, 407, 608
Anticoagulants, 226
Antienzymes, 176
Antiketogenesis, 365
Antineuritic vitamin (*see* Vitamin B), 573
Antioxidants, 80
    relation to vitamins A and E, 593
Antiprothrombin, 225
Antirachitic vitamin (*see* Vitamin D)
Antiscorbutic vitamin (*see* Vitamin C)
Antithrombin, 225
Antitrypsin, 177
Antiurease, 177
Antixerophthalmic vitamin (*see* Vitamin A), 565
Anuria, 450
Apatite, 601
Aphosphorosis, 537
Appetite, relation to vitamin B, 578
Aqueous humor, composition of, 293, 294
Arabans, 33
Arabinose, 32, 36, 55, 65, 67
    specific rotation of, 62
Araboketose, 32
Arabo-pyranose, 56
Arachidic acid, 74
Arachidonic acid, 81, 82
Area of body, relation to basal metabolism, 510
Arginase, 136, 388, 389
    relation to urea formation, 388, 411, 412
Arginine, amount of, in various proteins, 121
    conversion to glucose, 310, 389
    conversion to putrescine, 208
    formula of, 94
    hydrolysis of, 136
    in urine in cystinuria, 395
    isoelectric point of, 102
    metabolism of, 388

Arginine, relation to creatine, 390, 419
    relation to ornithine, 389, 557
    relation to urea formation, 411
    rôle of, in nutrition, 555, 560, 561
    synthesis of, 390, 557
Arginine phosphate (phosphoarginine), 425
Arsenic, occurrence, in skin, 606
    in tissues, 5
Ascheim-Zondek test, 499
Ascidia, vanadium in, 5
Ascitic fluid, composition of, 290, 291
Ascorbic acid (*see* Vitamin C), 307, 581, 585
Asparaginase, 136
Aspartic acid, amount of, in various proteins, 121
    conversion into glucose, 310, 387
    crystalline form of, 93
    formula of, 93
    metabolism of, 386
    rôle of, in nutrition, 561
    secretion of, by molluscs, 164
Atrophy, 155
Atwater-Rosa-Benedict calorimeter, 501
Autolysis, 154, 155
Auto-oxidation, of cysteine, 306
    of glutathione, 307
Avogadro's hypothesis, 8

B

Bach-Engler theory, 297
Bacon, composition of, 124
Bacteria, action of, on arginine, 208
    on cystine, 209
    on histidine, 207
    on lysine, 208
    on tryptophane, 206
    on tyrosine, 205
    polysaccharides in, 65
    protein synthesis by, 104
Bacterial changes in intestine, 204–209
Bacterial content in feces, 203
Barfoed's test for monosaccharides, 68
Barium, occurrence in tissues, 5
Barley, proteins of, 120
Basal metabolism, 508
    effect of starvation on, 515
    in disorders of the thyroid gland, 516
    influence of age and sex on, 510–512

Corpuscles, red (see Erythrocytes), buffer
 action of, 260
 crenation of, 14
 hemolysis of, 14, 215
 specific gravity of, 218
 water content of, 218
Cortin, 490
Cottonseed oil, constants of, 79
Cream, composition of, 126
Creatine, 418
 excretion, in children, 427
  in eunuchs, 427
  in fasting individuals, 427, 459, 460
  in hyperthyroidism, 428, 429, 483
  in women, 427
 from glycine, 420
 in blood, 217, 279
 in muscle, 428, 608
 in nerve tissue, 610
 metabolism of, 417
 relation to arginine, 389
 relation to carbohydrate metabolism,
  427
 relation to guanidine, 389, 420
 storage of, in tissues, 422
Creatine-phosphate (creatine-phosphoric
 acid; see Phosphocreatine), 423
Creatinine, in blood, 217, 279
 metabolic significance of, 429
 origin of, 418, 421
 relation to guanidine, 389, 420
Creatinine clearance, 463
Creatinine coefficient, 430
Creatinuria, 426 et seq.
Creaton, 423
Cresols, conjugation of, 205
 excretion of, in urine, 205, 455
 formation of, in intestine, 205
Cretinism, 480
 basal metabolism of, 517
Crustacea, copper in, 4, 243, 244
 hexosamines in, 65
 phosphoarginine in, 425
Cryoscopic methods, 13
Crystalloids, 22
Cyanhydrin synthesis, 51
Cyanic acid, relation to urea, 410
Cyanide, effect on oxidations, 297
 relation to goiter, 481
Cyprinine, 88

Cysteic (cysteinic) acid as a precursor of
 taurine, 391
Cysteine, 98
 auto-oxidation of, 306
 conversion into glucose, 392
 oxidation of, 391
Cystine, amounts of, in various proteins,
 121
 conversion into glucose, 310
 conversion into taurine, 391
 crystalline form of, 92
 deposition of, in organs, 395
 formula of, 95
 in glutathione, 306
 in hair, 392
 in keratin, 605
 metabolism of, 391, 394, 443
 occurrence in urine, 393, 462
 putrefaction of, in intestine, 209
 reduction of, 391
 rôle of, in detoxication, 392
 significance of, in nutrition, 392, 402,
  553, 558-561
Cystinuria, 393-395, 462
 cadaverine and putrescine in urine in,
  395
 lysine in urine in, 395
Cytidine, 437, 441
Cytochrome, 244, 245, 304
Cytosine, 431, 432, 435, 440

D

Dairy products, composition of, 126
Dalmatian coach hound, uric acid in, 436
Deaminase (desamidase), 136
Deamination (deaminization) of amino
 acids, 383-385
 by bacteria, 204
Decarboxylation by bacteria, 204
Dehydrase (dehydrogenase), 297, 305
Dehydrogenases, 300
 specificity of, 301
Dehydrogenation, 298
 of fat in liver, 355
Denaturation, of protein, 117
Dental caries, relation to vitamin C, 587
 relation to vitamin D, 591
Dentine, 600
Detoxication, of brombenzene, 396
 of cresols, 204